Fever Pitch

'Whether you are interested in football or not, this is tears-running-down-your-face funny, read-bits-out-loud-to-complete-strangers funny, but also highly perceptive and honest about Hornby's obsession and the state of the game. *Fever Pitch* is not only the best football book ever written, it's the funniest book of the year' Nicholas Lezard, *GQ*

High Fidelity

'Brilliant . . . a very funny and concise explanation of why we men are as we are. If you are male, you should read it and then make your partner read it, so they will no longer hate you but pity you instead' Harry Enfield, *Independent on Sunday*

About a Boy

'A stunner of a novel . . . Utterly read-in-one-day, forget-where-you-are-on-the-tube gripping . . . A brilliant book which tells you more about late-1990s cultural life than any number of flash mags and social treatises ever will – and it's wildly entertaining into the bargain' Carolyn Hart, *Marie Claire*

Nick Hornby was born in 1957 and worked as a teacher before becoming a full-time writer. He lives in north London.

Also by Nick Hornby

Fever Pitch: The Screenplay

My Favourite Year:
A Collection of New Football Writing
edited by Nick Hornby

Nick Hornby

THE OMNIBUS

Fever Pitch
High Fidelity
About a Boy

INDIGO

Fever Pitch first published in Great Britain in 1992
by Victor Gollancz Ltd
High Fidelity first published in Great Britain in 1995
by Victor Gollancz
About a Boy first published in Great Britain in 1998
by Victor Gollancz

An Indigo Paperback
First published in Great Britain by Victor Gollancz in 1999
This paperback edition published in 2000 by Indigo,
an imprint of Orion Books Ltd,
Orion House, 5 Upper St Martin's Lane, London WC2H 9EA

A CIP catalogue record for this book is available
from the British Library

ISBN: 0 575 40255 5

Printed and bound in Great Britain by
Clays Ltd, St Ives plc

CONTENTS

Fever Pitch

I'd like to thank Liz Knights for her tremendous support, encouragement and enthusiasm; Virginia Bovell for her tolerance and understanding; Nick Coleman, Ian Craig, Ian Preece, Caroline Dawnay and Viv Redman.

For my mother, and for my father

INTRODUCTION

SUNDAY, 14TH JULY 1991

It's in there all the time, looking for a way out.

I wake up around ten, make two cups of tea, take them into the bedroom, place one on each side of the bed. We both sip thoughtfully; so soon after waking there are long, dream-filled gaps between the occasional remark – about the rain outside, about last night, about smoking in the bedroom when I have agreed not to. She asks what I'm doing this week, and I think: (1) I'm seeing Matthew on Wednesday. (2) Matthew's still got my *Champions* video. (3) [*Remembering that Matthew, a purely nominal Arsenal fan, has not been to Highbury for a couple of years, and so has had no opportunity to watch the more recent recruits in the flesh*] I wonder what he thought of Anders Limpar.

And in three easy stages, within fifteen, twenty minutes of waking, I'm on my way. I see Limpar running at Gillespie, swaying to his right, going down: PENALTY! DIXON SCORES! 2–0! . . . Merson's back-heel flick and Smith's right-foot shot into the far corner in the same match . . . Merson's little push past Grobbelaar up at Anfield . . . Davis's swivel and smash against Villa . . . (And this, remember, is a morning in July, our month off, when there is no club football of any kind.) Sometimes, when I let this dreamy state take me over completely, I go on and back, through Anfield '89, Wembley '87, Stamford Bridge '78, my whole footballing life flashing before my eyes.

'What are you thinking about?' she asks.

At this point I lie. I wasn't thinking about Martin Amis or Gérard Dépardieu or the Labour Party at all. But then, obsessives have no choice; they have to lie on occasions like this. If we told the truth every time, then we would be unable to maintain relationships with anyone from the real world. We would be left to rot with our Arsenal programmes or our collection of original blue-label Stax records or our King Charles spaniels, and our two-minute daydreams would become longer and longer and longer until we lost our jobs and stopped bathing and shaving and eating, and we would lie on the floor in our own filth rewinding the video again and again in an attempt to memorise by heart the *whole* of the commentary, including David Pleat's expert analysis, for the night of 26th of May 1989. (You think I had to look the date up? Ha!) The truth is this: *for alarmingly large chunks of an average day, I am a moron.*

I would not wish to suggest that the contemplation of football is in itself an improper use of the imagination. David Lacey, the chief football correspondent for the *Guardian*, is a fine writer and an obviously intelligent man, and presumably he must devote even more of his interior life than I do to the game. The difference between Lacey and me is that I rarely *think*. I remember, I fantasise, I try to visualise every one of Alan Smith's goals, I tick off the number of First Division grounds I have visited; once or twice, when I have been unable to sleep, I have tried to count every single Arsenal player I have ever seen. (When I was a kid I knew the names of the wives and girlfriends of the Double-winning team; now, I can only remember that Charlie George's fiancée was called Susan Farge, and that Bob Wilson's wife was called Megs, but even this partial recall is terrifyingly unnecessary.)

None of this is *thought*, in the proper sense of the word. There is no analysis, or self-awareness, or mental rigour going on at all, because obsessives are denied any kind of perspective on their own passion. This, in a sense, is what defines an obsessive (and serves to explain why so few of them recognise themselves as such. A fellow fan who last season went to watch Wimbledon reserves against Luton reserves on a freezing January afternoon on his own – not in a spirit of one-upmanship or some kind of self-mocking, laddish wackiness, but because he was *genuinely interested* – recently strenuously denied to me that he was eccentric in any way).

Fever Pitch is an attempt to gain some kind of an angle on my obsession. Why has the relationship that began as a schoolboy crush endured for nearly a quarter of a century, longer than any other relationship I have made of my own free will? (I love my family dearly, but they were rather foisted on me, and I am no longer in touch with any of the friends I made before I was fourteen – apart from the only other Arsenal fan at school.) And why has this affinity managed to survive my periodic feelings of indifference, sorrow and very real hatred?

The book is also, in part, an exploration of some of the meanings that football seems to contain for many of us. It has become quite clear to me that my devotion says things about my own character and personal history, but the way the game is consumed seems to offer all sorts of information about our society and culture. (I have friends who will regard this as pretentious, self-serving nonsense, the kind of desperate justification one might expect from a man who has spent a huge chunk of his leisure time fretting miserably in the cold. They are particularly resistant to the idea because I tend to overestimate the metaphorical value of football, and therefore introduce it into conversations where it simply does not belong. I now accept that football has no relevance to the Falklands conflict, the Rushdie affair, the Gulf War, childbirth, the ozone layer, the poll tax, etc., etc., and I would like to take this opportunity to apologise to anyone who has had to listen to my pathetically strained analogies.)

Finally, *Fever Pitch* is about being a fan. I have read books written by people who obviously love *football*, but that's a different thing entirely; and I have read books written, for want of a better word, by hooligans, but at least 95 per cent of the millions who watch games every year have never hit anyone in their lives. So this is for the rest of us, and for anyone who has wondered what it might be like to be this way. While the details here are unique to me, I hope that they will strike a chord with anyone who has ever found themselves drifting off, in the middle of a working day or a film or a conversation, towards a left-foot volley into a top right-hand corner ten or fifteen or twenty-five years ago.

1968–1975

HOME DÉBUT

Arsenal v Stoke City

14.9.68

I fell in love with football as I was later to fall in love with women: suddenly, inexplicably, uncritically, giving no thought to the pain or disruption it would bring with it.

In May '68 (a date with connotations, of course, but I am still more likely to think of Jeff Astle than of Paris), just after my eleventh birthday, my father asked me if I'd like to go with him to the FA Cup Final between West Brom and Everton; a colleague had offered him a couple of tickets. I told him that I wasn't interested in football, not even in the Cup Final – true, as far as I was aware, but perversely I watched the whole match on television anyway. A few weeks later I watched the Man Utd–Benfica game, enthralled, with my mum, and at the end of August I got up early to hear how United had got on in the final of the World Club Championship. I loved Bobby Charlton and George Best (I knew nothing about Denis Law, the third of the Holy Trinity, who had missed the Benfica match through injury) with a passion that had taken me completely by surprise; it lasted three weeks, until my dad took me to Highbury for the first time.

My parents were separated by 1968. My father had met someone else and moved out, and I lived with my mother and my sister in a small detached house in the Home Counties. This state of affairs was unremarkable enough in itself (although I cannot recall anyone else in my class with an absent parent – the sixties took another seven or eight years to travel the twenty-odd miles down the M4 from London), but the break-up had wounded all four of us in various ways, as break-ups are wont to do.

There were, inevitably, a number of difficulties that arose from this new phase of family life, although the most crucial in this context was probably the most banal: the commonplace but nevertheless intractable one-parent Saturday-afternoon-at-the-zoo problem. Often Dad was only able to visit us midweek; no one really wanted to stay in and watch TV, for obvious reasons, but on the other hand there wasn't really anywhere else a man could take two children under twelve. Usually the three of us drove to a neighbouring town, or up to one of the airport hotels, where we sat in a cold and early-evening deserted restaurant, and where Gill and I ate steak or chicken, one or the other, in more or less complete silence (children are not great dinner conversationalists, as a rule, and in any case we were used to eating with the TV on), while Dad watched. He must have been desperate to find something else to do with us, but the options in a commuter-belt town between 6.30 and 9.00 on a Monday night were limited.

That summer, Dad and I went to a hotel near Oxford for a week, where in the evenings we sat in a deserted hotel dining room, and where I ate steak or chicken, one or the other, in more or less complete silence. After dinner we went to watch TV with the other guests, and Dad drank too much. Things had to change.

My father tried again with the football that September, and he must have been amazed when I said yes. I had never before said yes to any suggestion of his, although I rarely said no either. I just smiled politely and made a noise intended to express interest but no commitment, a maddening trait I think I invented especially for that time in my life but which has somehow remained with me ever since. For two or three years he had been trying to take me to the theatre; every time he asked I simply shrugged and grinned idiotically, with the result that eventually Dad would get angry and tell me to forget it, which was what I wanted him to say. And it wasn't just Shakespeare, either: I was equally suspicious of rugby matches and cricket matches and boat trips and days out to Silverstone and Longleat. I didn't want to do anything at all. None of this was intended to punish my father for his absence: I really thought that I would be happy to go anywhere with him, apart from every single place he could think of.

1968 was, I suppose, the most traumatic year of my life. After my parents' separation we moved into a smaller house, but for a time, because of some sort of chain, we were homeless and had to stay with our neighbours; I became seriously ill with jaundice; and I started at the local grammar school. I would have to be extraordinarily literal to believe that the Arsenal fever about to grip me had nothing to do with all this mess. (And I wonder how many other fans, if they were to examine the circumstances that led up to their obsession, could find some sort of equivalent Freudian drama? After all, football's a great game and everything, but what is it that separates those who are happy to attend half a dozen games a season – watch the big matches, stay away from the rubbish, surely the sensible way – from those who feel compelled to attend them all? Why travel from London to Plymouth on a Wednesday, using up a precious day's holiday, to see a game whose outcome was effectively decided in the first leg at Highbury? And, if this theory of fandom as therapy is anywhere near the mark, *what the hell is buried in the subconscious of people who go to Leyland DAF Trophy games?* Perhaps it is best not to know.)

There is a short story by the American writer Andre Dubus entitled 'The Winter Father', about a man whose divorce has separated him from his two children. In the winter his relationship with them is tetchy and strained: they move from afternoon jazz club to cinema to restaurant, and stare at each other. But in the summer, when they can go to the beach, they get on fine. 'The long beach and the sea were their lawn; the blanket their home; the ice chest and thermos their kitchen. They lived as a family again.' Sitcoms and films have long recognised this terrible tyranny of place, and depict men traipsing round parks with fractious kids and a frisbee. But 'The Winter Father' means a lot to me because it goes further than that: it manages to isolate what is valuable in the relationship between parents and children, and explains simply and precisely *why* the zoo trips are doomed.

In this country, as far as I know, Bridlington and Minehead are unable to provide the same kind of liberation as the New England beaches in Dubus's story; but my father and I were about to come up with the perfect English equivalent. Saturday afternoons in north London gave us a context in which we could be together. We could talk when we wanted, the football gave us something to talk about (and anyway the silences weren't oppressive), and the days had a structure, a routine. The Arsenal pitch was to be our lawn (and, being an English lawn, we would usually peer at it mournfully through driving rain); the Gunners' Fish Bar on Blackstock Road our kitchen; and the West Stand our home. It was a wonderful set-up, and changed our lives just when they needed changing most, but it was also exclusive: Dad and my sister never really found anywhere to live at all. Maybe now that wouldn't happen; maybe a nine-year-old girl in the nineties would feel that she had just as much right to go to a game as we did. But in 1969 in our town, this was not an idea that had much currency, and my sister had to stay at home with her mum and her dolls.

I don't recall much about the football that first afternoon. One of those tricks of memory enables me to see the only goal clearly: the referee awards a penalty (he runs into the area, points a dramatic finger, there's a roar); a hush as Terry Neill takes it, and a groan as Gordon Banks dives and pushes the ball out; it falls conveniently at Neill's feet and this time he scores. But I am sure this picture has been built up from what I have long known about similar incidents, and actually I was aware of none of this. All I really saw on the day was a bewildering chain of incomprehensible incidents, at the end of which everyone around me stood and shouted. If I did the same, it must have been an embarrassing ten seconds after the rest of the crowd.

But I do have other, more reliable, and probably more meaningful memories. I remember the overwhelming *maleness* of it all – cigar and pipe smoke, foul language (words I had heard before, but not from adults, not at that volume), and only years later did it occur to me that this was bound to have an effect on a boy who lived with his mother and his sister; and I remember looking at the crowd more than at the players. From where I was sitting I could probably have counted twenty thousand heads; only the sports fan (or Mick Jagger or Nelson Mandela) can do that. My father told me that there were nearly as many people in the stadium as lived in my town, and I was suitably awed.

(We have forgotten that football crowds are still astonishingly large, mostly because since the war they have become progressively smaller. Managers frequently complain about local apathy, particularly when their mediocre First or Second Division team has managed to avoid a good hiding for a few weeks; but the fact that, say, Derby County managed to attract an average crowd of nearly seventeen thousand in 1990/91, the year they finished bottom of the First Division, is a miracle. Let's say that three thousand of these are away supporters; that means that among the remaining fourteen thousand from Derby, there were a number of people who went at least *eighteen times* to see the worst football of last or indeed most other seasons. Why, really, should anyone have gone at all?)

It wasn't the size of the crowd that impressed me most, however, or the way that adults were allowed to shout the word 'WANKER!' as loudly as they wanted without attracting any attention. What impressed me most was just how much most of the men around me *hated*, really *hated*, being there. As far as I could tell, nobody seemed to enjoy, in the way that I understood the word, anything that happened during the entire afternoon. Within minutes of the kick-off there was real anger ('You're a DISGRACE, Gould. He's a DISGRACE!' 'A hundred quid a week? A HUNDRED QUID A WEEK! They should give that to me for watching you.'); as the game went on, the anger turned into outrage, and then seemed to curdle into sullen, silent discontent. Yes, yes, I know all the jokes. What else could I have expected at Highbury? But I went to Chelsea and to Tottenham and to Rangers, and saw the same thing: that the natural state of the football fan is bitter disappointment, no matter what the score.

I think we Arsenal fans know, deep down, that the football at Highbury has not often been pretty, and that therefore our reputation as the most boring team in the entire history of the universe is not as mystifying as we pretend: yet when we have a successful side much is forgiven. The Arsenal team I saw on that afternoon had been spectacularly unsuccessful for some time. Indeed they had won nothing since the Coronation and this abject and unambiguous failure was simply rubbing salt into the fans' stigmata. Many of those around us had the look of men who had seen every game of every barren season. The fact that I was intruding on a marriage that had gone disastrously sour lent my afternoon a particularly thrilling prurience (if it had been a real marriage, children would have been barred from the ground): one partner was lumbering around in a pathetic attempt to please, while the other turned his face to the wall, too full of loathing even to watch. Those fans who could not remember the thirties (although at the end of the sixties a good many of them could), when the club won five Championships and two FA Cups, could remember the Comptons and Joe Mercer from just over a decade before; the stadium itself, with its beautiful art deco stands and its Jacob Epstein busts, seemed to disapprove of the current mob even as much as my neighbours did.

I'd been to public entertainments before, of course; I'd been to the cinema and the pantomime and to see my mother sing in the chorus of the *White Horse Inn* at the Town Hall. But that was different. The audiences I had hitherto been a part of had paid to have a good time and, though occasionally one might spot a fidgety child or a yawning adult, I hadn't ever noticed faces contorted by rage or despair or frustration. Entertainment as pain was an idea entirely new to me, and it seemed to be something I'd been waiting for.

It might not be too fanciful to suggest that it was an idea which shaped my life. I have always been accused of taking the things I love – football, of course, but also books and records – much too seriously, and I do feel a kind of anger when I hear a bad record, or when someone is lukewarm about a book that means a lot to me. Perhaps it was these desperate, bitter men in the West Stand at Arsenal who taught me how to get angry in this way; and perhaps it is why I earn some of my living as a critic – maybe it's those voices I can hear when I write. 'You're a WANKER, X.' 'The Booker Prize? THE BOOKER PRIZE? They should give that to me for having to read you.'

Just this one afternoon started the whole thing off – there was no prolonged courtship – and I can see now that if I'd gone to White Hart Lane or Stamford Bridge the same thing would have happened, so overwhelming was the experience the first time. In a desperate and percipient attempt to stop the inevitable, Dad quickly took me to Spurs to see Jimmy Greaves score four against Sunderland in a 5–1 win, but the damage had been done, and the six goals and all the great players left me cold: I'd already fallen for the team that beat Stoke 1–0 from a penalty rebound.

A SPARE JIMMY HUSBAND

Arsenal v West Ham

26.10.68

On this, my third visit to Highbury (a goalless draw – I'd now seen my team score three times in four and a half hours), all the kids were given a free Soccer Stars album. Each page of the album was devoted to one First Division team, and contained fourteen or fifteen spaces in which to glue stickers of the players; we were also given a little packet of the stickers to start our collection off.

Promotional offers aren't often described thus, I know, but the album proved to be the last crucial step in a socialisation process that had begun with the Stoke game. The benefits of liking football at school were simply incalculable (even though the games master was a Welshman who once memorably tried to ban us from kicking a round ball even when we got home): at least half my class, and probably a quarter of the staff, loved the game.

Unsurprisingly, I was the only Arsenal supporter in the first year. QPR, the nearest First Division team, had Rodney Marsh; Chelsea had Peter Osgood, Tottenham had Greaves, West Ham had the three World Cup heroes, Hurst, Moore and Peters. Arsenal's best-known player was probably Ian Ure, famous only for being hilariously useless and for his contributions to the television series *Quiz Ball.* But in that glorious first football-saturated term, it didn't matter that I was on my own. In our dormitory town no club had a monopoly on support and, in any case, my new best friend, a Derby County fan like his father and uncle, was similarly isolated. The main thing was that you were a believer. Before school, at breaktime and at lunchtime, we played football on the tennis courts with a tennis ball, and in between lessons we swapped Soccer Star stickers – Ian Ure for Geoff Hurst (extraordinarily, the stickers were of equal value), Terry Venables for Ian St John, Tony Hately for Andy Lochhead.

And so transferring to secondary school was rendered unimaginably easy. I was probably the smallest boy in the first year, but my size didn't matter, although my friendship with the Derby fan, the tallest by several feet, was pretty handy; and though my performance as a student was undistinguished (I was bunged into the 'B' stream at the end of the year and stayed there throughout my entire grammar school career), the lessons were a breeze. Even the fact that I was one of only three boys wearing shorts wasn't as traumatic as it should have been. As long as you knew the name of the Burnley manager, nobody much cared that you were an eleven-year-old dressed as a six-year-old.

This pattern has repeated itself several times since then. The first and easiest friends I made at college were football fans; a studious examination of a newspaper back page during the lunch hour of the first day in a new job usually provokes some kind of response. And yes, I am aware of the downside of this wonderful facility that men have: they become repressed, they fail in their relationships with women, their conversation is trivial and boorish, they find themselves unable to express their emotional needs, they cannot relate to their children, and they die lonely and miserable. But, you know, what the hell? If you can walk into a school full of eight hundred boys, most of them older, all of them bigger, without feeling intimidated, simply because you have a spare Jimmy Husband in your blazer pocket, then it seems like a trade-off worth making.

DON ROGERS

Swindon Town v Arsenal

(at Wembley) 15.3.69

Dad and I went to Highbury another half a dozen times that season, and by the middle of March 1969, I had gone way beyond fandom. On matchdays I awoke with a nervous churning in the stomach, a feeling that would continue to intensify until Arsenal had taken a two-goal lead, when I would begin to relax: I had only relaxed once, when we beat Everton 3–1 just before Christmas. Such was my Saturday sickness that I insisted on being inside the stadium shortly after one o'clock, some two hours before the kick-off; this quirk my father bore with patience and good humour, even though it was frequently cold and from 2.15 onwards my distraction was such that all communication was impossible.

My pre-match nerves were the same however meaningless the game. That season Arsenal had blown all chance of the Championship by about November, a little later than usual; but this meant that in the wider scheme of things it scarcely mattered whether they won the games I went to see. It mattered desperately to me, however. In these early stages, my relationship with Arsenal was of an entirely personal nature: the team only existed when I was in the stadium (I can't remember feeling especially devastated by their poor results away from home). As far as I was concerned, if they won the games I saw 5–0, and lost the rest 10–0, that would have been a good season, probably to be commemorated by the team travelling down the M4 to see me on an open-topped bus.

I made an exception for the FA Cup-ties; these I wanted Arsenal to win despite my absence, but we got knocked out 1–0 at West Brom. (I had been forced to go to bed before the result came through – the tie was played on a Wednesday night – and my mother wrote the score down on a piece of paper and attached it to my bookcase ready for me to look at in the morning. I looked long and hard: I felt betrayed by what she had written. If she loved me, then surely she could have come up with a better result than this. Just as hurtful as the score was the exclamation mark she had placed after it, as if it were ... well, an exclamation. It seemed as inappropriate as if it had been used to emphasise the death of a relative: 'Gran died peacefully in her sleep!' These disappointments were still entirely new to me, of course, but like all fans, I've come to expect them now. At the time of writing, I have felt the pain of FA Cup defeat twenty-two times, but never as keenly as that first one.)

The League Cup I'd never really heard of, mainly because it was a midweek competition and I hadn't yet been allowed to attend a midweek game. But when Arsenal reached the final, I was prepared to accept it as a consolation for what had seemed to me to be a heartbreakingly poor season, although it had in fact been pretty run-of-the-mill for the sixties.

So Dad paid a tout way over the odds for a pair of tickets (I never found out exactly how much, but later, with justified anger, he led me to understand that they'd been very expensive) and on Saturday, 15th March ('BEWARE THE IDES OF MARCH' was the headline in the *Evening Standard*'s special colour supplement), I went to Wembley for the first time.

Arsenal were playing Swindon Town, a Third Division team, and no one seemed to have any real doubts that Arsenal would win the game, and therefore their first cup for sixteen years. I wasn't so sure. Silent in the car all the way there, I asked Dad on the steps up to the stadium whether he was as confident as everyone else. I tried to make the question conversational – sports chatter between two men on a day out – but it wasn't like that at all: what I really wanted was reassurance from an adult, a parent, my father, that what I was about to witness wasn't going to scar me for life. 'Look,' I should have said to him, 'when they're playing at home, in an ordinary League game, I'm so frightened they'll lose that I can't think or speak or even breathe, sometimes. If you think Swindon have any kind of chance at all, even a chance in a million, it's best if you take me home now, because I don't think I'd be able to cope.'

If I had come out with that, then it would have been unreasonable of my father to make me go inside the stadium. But I simply asked him, in an assumed spirit of idle curiosity, who he thought would win the game, and he said he thought Arsenal would, three or four nothing, the same as everyone else did, and so I got the reassurance I was looking for; but I was scarred for life anyway. Like my mother's exclamation mark, my father's blithe confidence later seemed like a betrayal.

I was so scared that the Wembley experience – a crowd of a hundred thousand, the huge pitch, the noise, the sense of anticipation – passed me by completely. If I noticed anything about the place at all it was that it wasn't Highbury, and my sense of alienation simply added to my unease. I sat shivering until Swindon scored shortly before half-time, and then the fear turned to misery. The goal was one of the most calamitously stupid ever given away by a team of professionals: an inept back-pass (by Ian Ure, naturally), followed by a missed tackle, followed by a goal-keeper (Bob Wilson) slipping over in the mud and allowing the ball to trickle over the line just inside the right-hand post. For the first time, suddenly, I became aware of all the Swindon fans sitting around us, with their awful West Country accents, their absurd innocent glee, their delirious disbelief. I hadn't ever come across opposing fans before, and I loathed them in a way I had never before loathed strangers.

With one minute remaining in the game, Arsenal equalised, unexpectedly and bizarrely, a diving header from a rebound off the goalkeeper's knee. I tried not to weep with relief, but the effort was beyond me; I stood on the seat and yelled at my father, over and over again, 'We'll be all right now, won't we? We'll be all right now!' He patted me on the back, pleased that something had been rescued from the dismal and expensive afternoon, and told me that yes, now, finally, everything would be OK.

It was his second betrayal of the day. Swindon scored twice more in extra time, one a scrappy goal from a corner, the other from Don Rogers after a magnificent sixty-yard run, and it was all too much to bear. When the final whistle went, my father betrayed me for the third time in less than three hours: he rose to his feet to applaud the extraordinary underdogs, and I ran for the exit.

When my father caught up with me he was furious. He delivered his ideas on sportsmanship with great force (what did I care about sportsmanship?), marched me to the car, and we drove home in silence. Football may have provided us with a new medium through which we could communicate, but that was not to say that we used it, or that what we chose to say was necessarily positive.

I don't remember Saturday evening, but I know that on the Sunday, Mother's Day, I elected to go to church rather than stay at home, where there was a danger that I would watch the highlights of the game on *The Big Match* and push myself over the edge into a permanent depressive insanity. And I know that when we got to church, the vicar expressed his pleasure in seeing such a large congregation given the competing temptations of a Cup Final on TV, and that friends and family nudged me and smirked. All this, however, was nothing compared to what I knew I would get at school on Monday morning.

For twelve-year-old boys permanently on the lookout for ways in which to humiliate their peers, opportunities like this were too good to miss. When I pushed open the door to the prefab, I heard somebody shout 'Here he is!', and I was submerged under a mob of screaming, jeering, giggling boys, some of whom, I noted darkly before I was knocked to the floor, didn't even like football.

It may not have mattered much in my first term that I was an Arsenal fan, but in my second it had become more significant. Football was still, in essence, a unifying interest – nothing had changed in that way. But as the months passed, our allegiances had become much more defined, and we were much quicker to tease. This was easily anticipated, I suppose, but on that dreadful Monday morning painful nonetheless. As I lay in the grammar school dirt it occurred to me that I had made a grotesque mistake; it was my fervent wish that I could turn back the clock and insist that my father took me, not to Arsenal *v* Stoke, but to a deserted hotel dining room or the zoo. I didn't want to go through this once a season. I wanted to be with the rest of the class, trampling the hell out of some other poor heartbroken kid – one of the swots or weeds or Indians or Jews who were habitually and horribly bullied. For the first time in my life I was different and on my own, and I hated it.

I have a photograph from the game played on the Saturday after the Swindon tragedy, away at QPR. George Armstrong is just picking himself up, having scored the winner in a 1–0 win; David Court is running towards him, his arms triumphantly aloft. In the background you can see Arsenal fans on the edge of the stand, silhouetted against a block of flats behind the ground, and they too are punching the sky. I couldn't understand anything I saw in the picture at all. How could the players care, after the way they had humiliated themselves (and, of course, me) seven days – *seven days* – before? Why would any fan who had suffered at Wembley the way I had suffered stand up to cheer a nothing goal in a nothing match? I used to stare at this photo for minutes at a time, trying to detect somewhere within it any evidence of the trauma of the previous week, some hint of grief or of mourning, but there was none: apparently everyone had forgotten except me. In my first season as an Arsenal fan I had been betrayed by my mother, my father, the players and my fellow supporters.

ENGLAND!

England v Scotland

May 1969

Although the temptation to plunge into a warm bath containing dissolved essence of Kenneth Wolstenholme is always with me, I know in my heart that in the late sixties and early seventies, some things were better and some things were worse. The England team, of course, was better then: still the world champions, packed with great players, and looking as though they might be able to retain the World Cup in Mexico the following year.

I was proud of England, delighted that my father was taking me to see them play in a big game under floodlights at Wembley (and going back there so soon after the League Cup Final was therapeutic, a successful exorcism of demons that would otherwise have plagued me for years). And though there is no doubt that Colin Bell, Francis Lee and Bobby Moore were better than Geoff Thomas, Dennis Wise and Terry Butcher, it wasn't just the comparative quality that enabled me to feel unambiguous about that England side. The ambiguity came with age: by the time I was sixteen or seventeen, I knew better than the England manager.

A critical faculty is a terrible thing. When I was eleven there were no bad films, just films that I didn't want to see, there was no bad food, just Brussels sprouts and cabbage, and there were no bad books – everything I read was great. Then suddenly, I woke up in the morning and all that had changed. How could my sister not hear that David Cassidy was not in the same *class* as Black Sabbath? Why on *earth* would my English teacher think that *The History of Mr Polly* was better than *Ten Little Indians* by Agatha Christie? And from that moment on, enjoyment has been a much more elusive quality.

But in 1969, as far as I was concerned, there was no such thing as a bad England player. Why would Sir Alf pick someone who wasn't up to the job? What would be the point? I took it on trust that the eleven players who destroyed Scotland that night – two goals each for Hurst and Peters, Colin Stein replying for the Scots – were the best in the country. (Sir Alf had ignored everyone from Arsenal, which simply confirmed that he knew what he was doing.) And anyway the absence of any live football on television meant that we often didn't know who was much good or not: the highlights merely showed good players scoring goals, rather than bad players missing them.

By the early seventies I had become an Englishman – that is to say, I hated England just as much as half my compatriots seemed to do. I was alienated by the manager's ignorance, prejudice and fear, positive that my own choices would destroy any team in the world, and I had a deep antipathy towards players from Tottenham, Leeds, Liverpool and Manchester United. I began to squirm when watching England games on TV, and to feel, as many of us feel, that I had no connection whatsoever with what I saw; I might as well have been Welsh, or Scottish, or Dutch. Is it like this everywhere? I know that in the past the Italians have greeted their boys with rotten tomatoes at the airport when they return from overseas humiliations, but even that sort of commitment is beyond my comprehension. 'I hope they get stuffed,' I have heard Englishmen say on numerous occasions in reference to the England team. Is there an Italian or Brazilian or Spanish version of that sentence? It is difficult to imagine.

Part of this contempt may be related to the fact that we have too many players, all of indistinguishable dingy competence; the Welsh and the Irish have very little choice when it comes to putting out a team, and the fans know that their managers simply have to make do. In those circumstances, occasional poor performances are inevitable and victories are little miracles. Then of course there is the procession of England managers that has treated players of real skill and flair – Waddle and Gascoigne, Hoddle and Marsh, Currie and Bowles, George and Hudson, footballers whose gifts are delicate and difficult to harness, but at the same time much more valuable than a pair of leather lungs – with the kind of disdain the rest of us reserve for child molesters. (Which international squad in the world would be unable to find a place for Chris Waddle, the man who in 1991 ambled through the AC Milan back four whenever he chose?) And finally there are the England fans (discussed at greater length elsewhere), whose activities during the eighties hardly encouraged identification with the team in any of the rest of us.

It wasn't always thus with the fans at international matches. It is impossible not to feel a little ache when one sees replays of games in the 1966 World Cup that did not involve England, for example. In the now-famous game between North Korea and Portugal at Goodison Park (in which the unknown Asian team took a 3–0 lead over one of the best sides in the competition before going out 5–3), you can see a thirty thousand-plus crowd, the vast majority of whom are Scousers, applauding wildly after goals from each team. It is difficult to imagine the same interest now; more likely, you'd get a couple of thousand scallies making slanty eyes at the Asians in one team, and monkey noises at Eusebio in the other. So, yes, of course I feel nostalgic, even if I am longing for a time which never really belonged to us: like I said, some things were better, some were worse, and the only way one can ever learn to understand one's own youth is by accepting both halves of the proposition.

The crowd that night contained none of these Goodison saints, but they were no different from the crowds I had been a part of during the rest of the season, with the exception of an extravagantly emotional Scotsman in the row in front who swayed precariously on his seat for the first half and failed to reappear for the second. And most of us actively *enjoyed* the game, as if for one night only football had become another branch of the entertainment industry. Perhaps, like me, they were enjoying the freedom from the relentless responsibility and pain of club football: I wanted England to win, but they weren't *my* team. What, after all, did my country mean to me, a twelve-year-old from the Home Counties, compared to a north London side thirty miles from where I lived, a side I'd never heard of and never thought about nine months previously?

CAMPING

Arsenal v Everton

7.8.69

For the opening game of my first full season I was at a scout camp in Wales. I hadn't wanted to go. I was never the most ging-gang-gooly gung-ho of scouts at the best of times and, shortly before our departure, I had discovered that my parents were finally getting divorced. Actually, this didn't disturb me unduly, at least consciously: after all, they had been separated for some time now and the legal process seemed to be a simple confirmation of the separation.

From the moment we arrived at the camp, though, I was dreadfully, overwhelmingly homesick. I knew that I was going to find it impossible to get through the ten days away; each morning began with a reverse charge call to my mother, during which I would sob pathetically and embarrassingly down the line back home. I was aware that this sort of behaviour was quite unbelievably feeble, and when an older scout was assigned to talk to me in order to discover what was wrong, I told him about the divorce with a shameless eagerness: it was the only explanation I could come up with that would in any way excuse my cissy longing to see my mother and my sister. It did the trick. For the rest of the holiday I was treated with a reverential pity by the rest of the campers.

I blubbed and dripped through the first week, but it wasn't getting any easier, and on the Saturday my father was dispatched from his Midlands base down to see me. Saturday, of course, was the hardest day of all. I was stuck in some stupid Welsh field for the first home game of the season, and my sense of displacement was all the more acute.

I had missed football in the preceding months. The summer of '69 was the first in my life in which something seemed to be lacking. My dad and I were faced with pre-Arsenal problems; the sports pages no longer held any interest for me (in those days, before Gazza, before cynical and meaningless pre-season tournaments which somehow still offer a methadone alternative to the real competitions to come, before the ludicrous freneticism of the contemporary transfer market, the newspapers went weeks on end without even mentioning football); and we weren't allowed on to the tennis courts at school to kick a ball around. I had longed for and welcomed the previous summers, but this one destroyed so many routines I had come to rely on that it seemed to stifle rather than liberate – as if July and November had swapped places.

Dad arrived at the camp-site in mid-afternoon. We walked over to a rock on the edge of the field and sat down; he talked about how little difference the divorce itself would make to our lives, and how we would be able to go to Highbury much more frequently next season. I knew he was right about the divorce (although to admit as much would have rendered his two hundred-mile round-trip unnecessary), but the football promise seemed hollow. What, in that case, were we doing sitting on a rock in Wales when Arsenal were playing Everton? Quite a way back down the line my self-pity had got the better of me. I really did blame it all – the terrible food, the nightmarish walks, the cramped, uncomfortable tents, the revolting, fly-plagued holes we were supposed to crap into, and, worst of all, the two empty seats in the West Stand – on the fact that I was the child of estranged parents, the product of a broken home; in fact, I was on a scout camp in the middle of Wales because I had joined the scouts. Not for the first time in my life, and certainly not for the last, a self-righteous gloom had edged out all semblance of logic.

Just before five, we went back to my tent to listen to the results. Both of us knew that to a large extent the success of my father's mission depended not on his ability to reassure or persuade but on the news from north London, and I think my father was praying even harder than usual for a home win. I hadn't really been listening to him for the previous twenty minutes anyway. He sat down on somebody else's sleeping bag, an incongruous figure in his immaculate sixties young executive casual gear, and we tuned in to Radio 2. The *Sports Report* theme made my eyes water again (in a different, better world we would be sitting on the hot leather seats of Dad's company car, trying to push through the traffic, and humming along); when it was over, James Alexander Gordon announced a 1–0 home defeat. Dad slumped back against the canvas, tired, knowing now that he'd been wasting his time, and I went back home the next afternoon.

BORING, BORING ARSENAL

Arsenal v Newcastle

27.12.69

'All those terrible nil–nil draws against Newcastle,' my father would complain in years to come. 'All those freezing, boring Saturday afternoons.' In fact, there were only two terrible nil–nil draws against Newcastle, but they occurred in my first two seasons at Highbury, so I knew what he meant, and I felt personally responsible for them.

By now I felt guilty about what I had got my father into. He had developed no real affection for the club, and would rather, I think, have taken me to any other First Division ground. I was acutely aware of this, and so a new source of discomfort emerged: as Arsenal huffed and puffed their way towards 1–0 wins and nil–nil draws I wriggled with embarrassment, waiting for Dad to articulate his dissatisfaction. I had discovered after the Swindon game that loyalty, at least in football terms, was not a moral choice like bravery or kindness; it was more like a wart or a hump, something you were stuck with. Marriages are nowhere near as rigid – you won't catch any Arsenal fans slipping off to Tottenham for a bit of extra-marital slap and tickle, and though divorce is a possibility (you can just stop going if things get too bad), getting hitched again is out of the question. There have been many times over the last twenty-three years when I have pored over the small print of my contract looking for a way out, but there isn't one. Each humiliating defeat (Swindon, Tranmere, York, Walsall, Rotherham, Wrexham) must be borne with patience, fortitude and forbearance; there is simply nothing that can be done, and that is a realisation that can make you simply squirm with frustration.

Of course I hated the fact that Arsenal were boring (I had by now conceded that their reputation, particularly at this stage in their history, was largely deserved). Of course I wanted them to score zillions of goals and play with the verve and thrill of eleven George Bests, but it wasn't going to happen, certainly not in the foreseeable future. I was unable to defend my team's inadequacies to my father – I could see them for myself, and I hated them – and after each feeble attempt at goal and every misplaced pass I would brace myself for the sighs and groans from the seat next to me. I was chained to Arsenal and my dad was chained to me, and there was no way out for any of us.

PELÉ

Brazil v Czechoslovakia

June 1970

Until 1970, people of my age and a good few years older knew more about Ian Ure than they did about the greatest player in the world. We knew that he was supposed to be pretty useful, but we had seen very little evidence of it: he had literally been kicked out of the 1966 tournament by the Portuguese, but he hadn't really been fit anyway, and nobody I knew could remember anything about Chile in 1962. Six years after Marshall McLuhan published *Understanding Media*, a good three-quarters of the population of England had about as clear a picture of Pelé as we'd had of Napoleon one hundred and fifty years before.

Mexico '70 introduced a whole new phase in the consumption of football. It had always been a global game in the sense that the whole world watched it and the whole world played it; but in '62, when Brazil retained the World Cup, television was still a luxury rather than a necessity (and in any case the technology required to relay the games live from Chile didn't exist), and in '66 the South Americans had performed poorly. Brazil were eliminated before the knock-out stage; Argentina went unnoticed until their elimination by England in the quarter-finals, when their captain Rattin was sent off but refused to walk, and Sir Alf referred to them as animals. The only other South American team in the last eight, Uruguay, got thumped 4–0 by Germany. In effect, 1970 was the first major confrontation between Europe and South America that the world had had the opportunity to witness. When Czechoslovakia went one up in Brazil's opening game, David Coleman observed that 'all we ever knew about them has come true'; he was referring to Brazil's sloppy defence, but the words are those of a man whose job it was to introduce one culture to another.

In the next eighty minutes, everything else we knew about them came true too. They equalised with a direct free kick from Rivelino that dipped and spun and swerved in the thin Mexican air (had I ever seen a goal scored direct from a free kick before? I don't remember one), and they went 2–1 up when Pelé took a long pass on his chest and volleyed it into the corner. They won 4–1, and we in 2W, the small but significant centre of the global village, were duly awed.

It wasn't just the quality of the football, though; it was the way they regarded ingenious and outrageous embellishment as though it were as functional and necessary as a corner kick or a throw-in. The only comparison I had at my disposal then was with toy cars: although I had no interest in Dinky or Corgi or Matchbox, I loved Lady Penelope's pink Rolls-Royce and James Bond's Aston Martin, both equipped with elaborate devices such as ejector seats and hidden guns which lifted them out of the boringly ordinary. Pelé's attempt to score from inside his own half with a lob, the dummy he sold to the Peruvian goalkeeper when he went one way round and the ball went the other ... these were football's equivalent of the ejector seat, and made everything else look like so many Vauxhall Vivas. Even the Brazilian way of celebrating a goal – run four strides, jump, punch, run four strides, jump, punch – was alien and funny and enviable, all at the same time.

The strange thing was that it didn't matter, because England could live with it. When we played Brazil in the second match, we were unlucky to lose 1–0; and in a tournament that provided dozens of superlatives – the best team of all time, the best player of all time, even the two best misses of all time (both Pelé's) – we chipped in with a couple of our own, the best save of all time (Banks from Pelé, of course) and the best, most perfectly timed tackle of all time (Moore on Jairzinho). It is significant that our contribution to this superlative jamboree was due to defensive excellence, but never mind – for ninety minutes England were every bit as good as the best team in the world. I still cried after the game, though (mainly because I had misunderstood the way the tournament worked – I thought we were out, and Mum had to explain the vagaries of the group system).

In a way Brazil ruined it for all of us. They had revealed a kind of Platonic ideal that nobody, not even the Brazilians, would ever be able to find again; Pelé retired, and in the five subsequent tournaments they only showed little flashes of their ejector-seat football, as if 1970 was a half-remembered dream they had once had of themselves. At school we were left with our Esso World Cup coin collections and a couple of fancy moves to try out; but we couldn't even get close, and we gave up.

THUMPED

Arsenal v Derby

31.10.70

By 1970 my father had moved abroad and a new Arsenal routine emerged, one which no longer relied on his more infrequent visits. I was introduced to another, older Arsenal fan at school, known as Rat, by the brother of my classmate Frog, and the two of us travelled up to Highbury together. The first three matches we saw were spectacular successes: 6–2 *v* West Brom, 4–0 *v* Forest and 4–0 *v* Everton. These were consecutive home games and it was a golden autumn.

It is stupid and unforgivably fogeyish to contemplate the prices in 1970, but I'm going to anyway: a return to Paddington cost 30p for a child; the return fare from Paddington to Arsenal on the tube was 10p;

and admission to the ground was 15p (25p for adults). Even if you bought a programme it was possible to travel thirty miles and watch a First Division football match for less than 60p.

(Maybe there is a point to this banality after all. If I travel to see my mother on the train now the fare is £2.70 for a day return, a tenfold increase on 1970 adult prices; but in the 91/92 season it now cost £8 to stand on the terraces at Arsenal, a thirty-two-fold increase. For the first time ever, it was cheaper to go to the West End and see the new Woody Allen or Arnold Schwarzenegger – in your own seat – than to stand and watch Barnsley play for a nil–nil draw in the Rumbelows Cup at Highbury. If I were twenty years younger, I wouldn't be an Arsenal supporter in twenty years' time: it is not possible for most kids to find ten or fifteen quid every other Saturday, and if I had been unable to go regularly in my early teens then it is unlikely that my interest would have been sustained.)

The art deco splendour of the West Stand was not possible without Dad's deeper pockets, so Rat and I stood in the Schoolboys' Enclosure, peering at the game through the legs of the linesmen. At the time the club disapproved of perimeter advertising and pre-match DJs, and so we had neither; Chelsea fans may have been listening to the Beatles and the Stones, but at Highbury half-time entertainment was provided by the Metropolitan Police Band and their vocalist, Constable Alex Morgan. Constable Morgan (whose rank never changed throughout his long Highbury career) sang highlights from light operettas and Hollywood musicals: my programme for the Derby game says that he performed Lehár's 'Girls Were Made to Love and Kiss' that afternoon.

It was a bizarre ritual. Just before the kick-off he would hit an extraordinary high note and sustain it as the climax to his performance: in the Lower East Stand, just behind him, the crowd would rise to their feet, while the North Bank would attempt to drown him out by whistling and chanting. The Schoolboys' Enclosure is the kind of quaint title that only Arsenal, with its mock opera, its Old Etonian chairman and its cripplingly heavy history, could have dreamed up, suggesting as it did a safe haven for Jennings and Darbishire, or William Brown, provided he behaved himself: skewiff caps and grubby blazers, frogs in pockets and Sherbet Fountains – an ideal spot, in fact, for two suburban grammar school boys up in town to watch the Big Game.

The reality of the Schoolboys' was somewhat different in 1970, just after number one crops and Doctor Martens had begun to appear on the terraces for the first time. The small, narrow section of terrace was in effect a breeding ground for future hooligans, tough kids from Finsbury Park and Holloway either too small or too poor to watch from the North Bank, where their big brothers stood. Rat and I didn't take any notice of them for the first few weeks; after all, we were all Arsenal fans together, so why should we be worried? Yet something separated us. It wasn't our accents – neither of us was particularly well-spoken. But it may have been our clothes, or our haircuts, or our clean, lovingly folded scarves, or our fervent pre-match scrutiny of the programme, which we kept spotless in an inside pocket or a duffel bag.

We left a couple of minutes before the end of the Derby game, when Arsenal were winning 2–0 (Kelly and Radford, one in each half). A couple of black boys (black boys! Flipping heck!), maybe our age, but yards taller and from a different planet – the planet Real Life, the planet Secondary Modern, the planet Inner City – jostled us as we walked past; my heart skipped a couple of beats and I made for the exit. They followed. We moved a little faster, anxious to get through the maze of alleyways and turnstiles that led out of the ground. Out in the street, I knew the kids wouldn't bother us in the middle of the crowd of grown-ups flooding away from the stadium.

The crowd didn't seem to perturb them in the slightest, however. We broke into a run towards the tube station; so did they. Rat made it, but they caught up with me, pushed me against the wall of the stadium, smacked me in the face a couple of times, stole my red-and-white scarf and left me in a crumpled, traumatised heap on the pavement. People – adults with a reassuring paternal demeanour – stepped over me or around me, just as I have walked around innumerable beatings outside grounds. I had been hit much harder at school (I was not only small but cheeky, a particularly unfortunate combination), but usually by people I knew, which made it somehow acceptable. This was different. This was much scarier: I didn't understand what the limits were – had I been lucky or unlucky? – and though I knew I was obsessed enough with the team to go back and stand in the same place again, the prospect of getting thumped once a fortnight at twenty to five was bleak.

I really don't think that I was aware of class then. A few years later, when I discovered politics, I would have felt that I deserved a smack in the mouth for being a privileged middle-class white male – indeed, in my late teens, when the chief source of my ideological input was the first Clash album, I probably would have delivered it myself – but then I just felt a deep sense of disappointment and shame. Disappointment because I had finally begun to suspect that some people didn't go to football for the Right Reasons (devotion to the Gunners, or at the least a yen for some sparkling wing play); shame because, despite my size and youth, I was still a male and there is something in males, something stupid and unreconstructed but powerful nonetheless, that simply refuses to tolerate anything that might be construed as weakness. (The above version of the afternoon's events is archetypally masculine: there were *two* of them against *one* of me; I was *tiny*, they were *huge*, and so on. It could well have been that I was assaulted by a blind seven-year-old with one arm, but my memory has properly protected me from any suspicion that I might have been a wimp from the sticks.)

Perhaps the worst of it was that I couldn't unburden the experience on to my mum. If I told her, I'd be banned from going to football unaccompanied by my father for years to come; so I kept it to myself, confessed that I'd left the scarf – a present from my gran – on the tube, endured endless complaints about my carelessness and irresponsibility, and was denied my customary Saturday night trip to the chip shop. Any theories about the brutalising experience of urban deprivation would have been wasted on me that night; I was only interested in suburban deprivation, which seemed to me the cruellest deprivation of them all.

CAN YOU SEE ME ON THE BOX?

Southampton v Arsenal

10.4.71

On holiday in Bournemouth, where both my grandmothers lived, and conveniently there is an away match at Southampton. So I book a coach ticket, travel along the coast and squirm through a packed Dell to the far edge of the terrace; and the next day, when Southern show the highlights of the game on TV, there I am on the bottom left of the screen every time a corner is taken (McLintock scored from one of them, the decider in a 2–1 win): a sober lad, seven days short of my fourteenth birthday, unmistakably pre-pubescent . . . but I'm not waving or leering or shoving the boy standing next to me, just standing there, a still point in the middle of all the juvenile hyperactivity around me.

Why was I so serious? I was a *child* everywhere else: at home; at school, where chronic fits of the giggles seized me well into the sixth form; and out with my friends, one or two of whom now had girlfriends, the most side-splittingly, gut-bustingly, snot-dribblingly hilarious development the rest of us had ever seen. (Symbolically, a nickname was altered. Larry, so-called because of his physical and stylistic resemblances to Larry Lloyd, the Liverpool centre-half, became Caz, because of the interest he now shared with Casanova, the Italian striker. We were delighted with the witticism.) But when I was watching Arsenal, I don't think I felt relaxed enough to laugh until I was well into my twenties; if I had been filmed by the corner flag at any time between 1968 and 1981 my expression would have been the same.

The simple truth is that obsessions just aren't funny, and that obsessives don't laugh. But there's a complicated truth here as well: I don't think I was very happy, and the problem with being a thirteen-year-old depressive is that when the rest of life is so uproarious, which it invariably is, there is no suitable context for the gloom. How can you express misery when people keep making you *snigger* all the time? There was no sniggering at Arsenal games, however – not from me, anyway. And even though I had friends who would have been happy to accompany me to matches, significantly my support soon became a solitary activity: the following season I watched around twenty-five games, seventeen or eighteen of them on my own. I just didn't want to have fun at football. I had fun everywhere else, and I was sick of it. What I needed more than anything was a place where unfocused unhappiness could thrive, where I could be still and worry and mope; I had the blues, and when I watched my team I could unwrap them and let them breathe a little.

HOW I WON THE DOUBLE

Arsenal v Newcastle

17.4.71

In a little over a year, things had changed. The team was still short of stars and pretty low on verve, but they suddenly became very hard to beat. In 1970 the dismal seventeen-year hunt for a trophy finally ended when Arsenal won the European Fairs Cup – amazingly, in some style. After thrashing Ajax, Johann Cruyff and all, in the semi, they came from behind to beat Anderlecht of Belgium 4–3 in the final. They won 3–0 at Highbury in the second leg, and grown men danced on the pitch and wept with the relief of it all. I wasn't there. I wasn't allowed to go to a midweek match on a school night on my own.

1971 was Arsenal's *annus mirabilis*. They won the League Championship and the FA Cup in the same season, the famous Double that only three teams this century have managed. In fact, they won the trophies in the same week: on Monday night they won the Championship at Tottenham, and on the Saturday the Cup against Liverpool at Wembley. I wasn't there. I wasn't at Tottenham because I still wasn't allowed to go to a midweek match on a school night on my own; I wasn't at Wembley because Dad didn't come through with a ticket, despite promises to the contrary and, yes, I'm still bitter twenty years on.

So I wasn't there for anything. (I wasn't even there for the parade through Islington on the Sunday after the Cup Final. I had to go to see my Auntie Vi in Dulwich.) I missed it all. And as this book is about the consumption of football, rather than football itself, the Double year – Arsenal's finest season of the century – doesn't really have much place in my story, and how about that for impressionism? Sure, I threw a radio jubilantly against my bedroom wall when the final whistle blew at Tottenham; I literally went dizzy with joy when Charlie George scored the winner in the Cup Final and lay on his back with his arms outstretched; I strutted around school, trying to work out how I could humiliate my classmates in the same way they had humiliated me two years before, settling instead for a beatific smile which was understood by both teachers and boys. As far as they were concerned, I *was* Arsenal, and I was entitled to my triumphant bliss.

But I didn't think so, not really. I'd earned the pain against Swindon, but I hadn't contributed to the Double triumph in the same way, unless you counted a dozen or so League games, a school blazer groaning with lapel badges and a bedroom covered in magazine pictures as a contribution. The others, those who'd got hold of Final tickets and queued for five hours at Tottenham, they've got more to say about the Double than I.

I try now to hang on to the fact that a couple of weeks earlier, before all this glory, I had managed to place myself at the centre of the Double narrative. On my birthday Dad and I went to Arsenal *v* Newcastle (a terrible game, again); I sat clutching a radio that he had given me (the very radio, in fact, that I smashed on 3rd May), pocket-sized for Saturday afternoons. Leeds were top of the First Division, and that afternoon they had a home game against West Brom, fifth from bottom and without an away win all season. There used to be a comic strip called 'Billy's Boots', about a boy whose magic boots transformed their mediocre owner into a superstar; I suddenly seemed to be in possession of a radio which transformed the results of the most useless team into dramatic away victories. When I turned it on shortly after half-time, West Brom scored; when I did it again, they scored a second time. The tannoy at Highbury announced the news and the crowd went berserk; Charlie George scored the only goal and Arsenal went top of the League for the first time that season.

The gift I got that afternoon was priceless, like world peace or an end to Third World poverty, something that couldn't be bought for a million pounds – unless my dad had bought the referee at Leeds for a million pounds, the only possible explanation for some of his decisions that afternoon. One of West Brom's goals was by general consensus hundreds of yards offside, provoking the crowd into invading the pitch, which in turn resulted in Leeds being banned from their ground for the first few games of the following season. 'The crowd has gone mad and they have every right to do so,' Barry Davies pronounced memorably on *Match of the Day* that night; those were the days, when TV commentators actively encouraged riots rather than argued pompously for the return of National Service. If you did slip the ref something, then thanks, Dad. Brilliant idea. Would Leeds have lost at home to West Brom if it hadn't been my birthday? Would the game at Arsenal have finished nil–nil, as Arsenal *v* Newcastle games had always done before? Would we then have gone on to win the League? I doubt it.

ANOTHER CITY

Chelsea v Tottenham

January 1972

It is true to say that while I made a natural Arsenal supporter – I too was often dour, defensive, argumentative, repressed – my father belonged at Stamford Bridge. Chelsea were flamboyant, unpredictable and, it has to be said, not the most reliable of teams; my father had a taste for pink shirts and theatrical ties, and, stern moralist that I was, I think I felt that he could have done with a little more consistency. (Parenthood, George Graham would say, is a marathon, not a sprint.) Whatever the reason, Dad patently enjoyed going to Chelsea more than our trips to Highbury, and it was easy to see why. We once spotted Tommy Steele (or maybe it was John Alderton) coming out of the Gents' in Chelsea's North Stand, and before the games we ate in one of the Italian restaurants on the King's Road. Once we went to look around the Chelsea Drugstore, where I bought the second Led Zeppelin album and sniffed the cigarette smoke in the air suspiciously. (I was as literal-minded as any Arsenal centre-half.)

Chelsea had Osgood and Cooke and Hudson, all flash and flair, and their version of football was bewilderingly different from Arsenal's (this League Cup semi-final, one of the best games I had ever seen, finished 2–2). But more importantly, the Bridge and its environs presented me with a different but still familiar version of *London*: familiar because the middle-class suburban boy has always been aware of it. It was not dissimilar to the London we already knew from trips to see pantomimes and films and museums, a busy, bright-lights-big-city London supremely aware that it was the centre of the world; and the people that I saw at Chelsea in those days were centre-of-the-world people. Football was a fashionable game, and Chelsea were a fashionable team; the models and actors and young executives who were cheering the Blues on were beautiful to look at and made the Bridge (the seats, anyway) an exquisitely exotic place.

But this wasn't what I came to football for. Arsenal and its neighbourhood was for me much more exotic than anything I would ever see around the King's Road, which was full of an old-hat ho-hum glitz; football had gripped me because of its *otherness*. All those quiet terraced streets around Highbury and Finsbury Park, all those embittered but still peculiarly loyal used-car salesmen . . . now that was *real* exoticism; the London that a grammar school boy from the Thames Valley could never have seen for himself no matter how many times he went to the Casino cinema to see films in Cinerama. We wanted different things, my dad and I. Just as he was starting to want a part of what Chelsea was all about (and just as he was, for the first time in his life, able to afford it), I wanted to go tearing off in the other direction.

ISLINGTON BOY

Reading v Arsenal

5.2.72

The white south of England middle-class Englishman or -woman is the most rootless creature on earth; we would rather belong to any other community in the world. Yorkshiremen, Lancastrians, Scots, the Irish, blacks, the rich, the poor, even Americans and Australians have something they can sit in pubs and bars and weep about, songs to sing, things they can grab for and squeeze hard when they feel like it, but we have nothing, or at least nothing we want. Hence the phenomenon of mock-belonging, whereby pasts and backgrounds are manufactured and massaged in order to provide some kind of acceptable cultural identity. Who was it that sang 'I Wanna Be Black'? The title says it all, and everybody has met people who really do: in the mid-seventies, young, intelligent and otherwise self-aware white men and women in London began to adopt a Jamaican patois that frankly didn't suit them at all. How we all wished we came from the Chicago Projects, or the Kingston ghettos, or the mean streets of north London or Glasgow! All those aitch-dropping, vowel-mangling punk rockers with a public school education! All those Hampshire girls with grandparents in Liverpool or Brum! All those Pogues fans from Hertfordshire singing Irish rebel songs! All those Europhiles who will tell you that though their mothers live in Reigate, their sensibilities reside in Rome!

Ever since I have been old enough to understand what it means to be suburban I have wanted to come from somewhere else, preferably north London. I have already dropped as many aitches as I can – the only ones left in my diction have dug themselves too far into definite articles to be winkled out – and I use plural verb forms with singular subjects whenever possible. This was a process that began shortly after my first visits to Highbury, continued throughout my suburban grammar school career, and escalated alarmingly when I arrived at university. My sister, on the other hand, who also has problems with her suburban roots, went the other way when she went to college, and suddenly started to speak like the Duchess of Devonshire; when we introduced each other to our respective sets of friends they found the experience perplexing in the extreme. Which of us, they seemed to be wondering, had been adopted?

Had she fallen on hard times or had I struck lucky? Our mother, born and bred in south-east London but a Home Counties resident for nearly forty years, cuts the accents neatly down the middle.

In a way nobody can blame any of us, the Mockneys or the cod Irish, the black wannabees or the pseudo Sloanes. The 1944 Education Act, the first Labour Government, Elvis, beatniks, the Beatles and the Stones, the sixties . . . we never stood a chance. I blame the eleven-plus. Before the war, maybe, our parents could have scraped the money together to send us to minor public schools, and we would have received our pisspoor cheapskate third-hand classical educations and gone to work in a bank; the eleven-plus, designed to create a meritocracy, made state schools safe for nice families again. Post-war grammar school boys and girls stepped into a void; none of the available cultures seemed to belong to us, and we had to pinch one quick. And what is suburban post-war middle-class English culture anyway? Jeffrey Archer and *Evita*, Flanders and Swann and the Goons, Adrian Mole and Merchant–Ivory, *Francis Durbridge Presents* . . . and John Cleese's silly walk? It's no wonder we all wanted to be Muddy Waters or Charlie George.

The Reading–Arsenal fourth-round Cup-tie in 1972 was the first and most painful of the many exposures to come. Reading was my nearest League team, an unhappy geographical accident that I would have done anything to change; Highbury was thirty-odd miles away, Elm Park a mere eight. Reading fans had Berkshire accents, and incredibly they didn't seem to mind; they didn't even *try* to speak like Londoners. I stood with the home supporters – the match was all-ticket, and it was much easier to go to Reading than to north London to get one – and while I waited my still customary ninety minutes for the game to begin, a whole family (a family!), mother, father and son, all kitted up in blue-and-white scarves and rosettes (rosettes!), started talking to me.

They asked me questions about my team and the stadium, made jokes – peasants! – about Charlie George's hair, offered me biscuits, lent me their programmes and newspapers. I was beginning to enjoy the conversation. My assumed Cockney sounded to my ears flawless against their loathsome burr, and our relationship was beginning to take on a gratifying city-slicker-meets-hicks-from-the-sticks hue.

It was when they asked me about schools that it all went terribly wrong: they had heard about London comprehensives, and wanted to know whether it was all true, and for what seemed like hours I weaved an elaborate fantasy based on the exploits of the half-dozen small-time thugs at the grammar. I can only presume that I had managed to convince myself, and that by this stage my town had, in my head, transmuted into a north London village somewhere between Holloway and Islington; because when the father asked where I lived, I told him the truth.

'Maidenhead?' the father repeated, incredulous. 'Maidenhead? But that's four miles down the road!'

'Nearer ten,' I replied, but he seemed unconvinced that the extra six miles made much difference, and I could see his point. I was blushing.

Then he finished me off. '*You shouldn't be supporting Arsenal this afternoon*,' he said. '*You should be supporting your local team.*'

It was the most humiliating moment of my teenage years. A complete, elaborate and perfectly imagined world came crashing down around me and fell in chunks at my feet. I wanted Arsenal to avenge me, to beat the Third Division team and their pedantic, dull-witted fans into a pulp; but we won 2–1 with a second-half Pat Rice deflection, and at the end of the game the Reading father ruffled my hair and told me that at least it wouldn't take me long to get home.

It didn't stop me, though, and it only took a couple of weeks to rebuild the London Borough of Maidenhead. But I made sure that the next time I went to an away game it was precisely that – far away, where people might believe that my Thames Valley hometown had its own tube station and West Indian community and terrible, insoluble social problems.

HAPPY

Arsenal v Derby

12.2.72

For a match to be really, truly memorable back then, the kind of game that sent me home buzzing inside with the fulfilment of it all, these conditions had to be met: I had to go with my dad; we had to eat lunch in the chip shop (sitting down, no sharing of tables); we had to have seats in the Upper West Stand (the West Stand because you can see down the players' tunnel from there and so can greet the arrival of the team on the pitch before anyone in the ground), between the half-way line and the North Bank; Arsenal had to play well and win by two clear goals; the stadium had to be full, or nearly full, which usually implied an opposing team of some significance; the game had to be filmed, by ITV for *The Big Match* on Sunday afternoon rather than by the BBC for *Match of the Day* (I liked the anticipation, I guess); and Dad had to be wearing warm clothes. He often travelled over from France without an overcoat, forgetting that his Saturday afternoon was likely to be spent in sub-zero temperatures, and his discomfort was so violent that I felt guilty insisting that we stayed right until the final whistle. (I always did insist, however, and when we reached the car he was often so cold that he could hardly speak; I felt bad about it, but not bad enough to risk missing a goal.)

These were enormous demands, and it is hardly surprising that everything came together just the once, as far as I am aware, for this game against Derby in 1972, when an Alan Ball-inspired Arsenal beat the eventual League Champions 2–0 with two Charlie George goals, one a penalty and the other a superb diving header. And because there was a table for us in the chip shop, and because the referee pointed to the spot when Ball was brought down instead of waving play on, and because my dad remembered his coat, I have allowed this game to become something it wasn't: it now represents for me the whole works, the entire fixation, but that's wrong. Arsenal were too good, Charlie's goal was too spectacular, the crowd was too big and too appreciative of the team's performance . . . The 12th of February *did* happen, in just the way I have described it, but only its atypicality is important now. Life isn't, and has never been, a 2–0 home victory against the League leaders after a fish-and-chip lunch.

MY MUM AND CHARLIE GEORGE

Derby County v Arsenal
26.2.72

I begged and pleaded and nagged, and eventually my mother gave in and allowed me to travel to away games. Back then I was jubilant; now I'm indignant. What did she think she was *doing*? Didn't she ever read the papers or watch TV? Hadn't she heard of hooligans? Was she really unaware of what Football Specials, the infamous trains that carried fans all over the country, were *like*? I could have been *killed*.

Now that I think about it, my mother's part in all this was actually quite mysterious. She didn't like me spending my money on Led Zeppelin records, understandably, or on cinema tickets, and she didn't even seem that keen on me buying books. And yet somehow it was OK for me to travel to London or Derby or Southampton on an almost weekly basis and take my chances with any group of nutters that I happened upon. She has never discouraged my mania for football; in fact it was she who bought my ticket for the Reading Cup-tie, driving down a frozen, snow-covered A4 and queuing up while I was at school. And some eight years later I came home to find on our dining table an impossibly elusive ticket for the West Ham–Arsenal Cup Final that she had bought (for twenty quid, money she didn't really have) from a man at work.

Well, yes, of *course* it was something to do with masculinity, but I don't think that her usually tacit, occasionally active football support was supposed to be for my benefit; it was for hers. On Saturdays, it seems to me now, we enacted a weird little parody of a sitcom married couple: she would take me down to the station, I'd go on the train up to London, do my man's stuff and ring her from the forecourt call-box when I got back for a lift home. She would then put my tea on the table and I ate while I talked about my day and, sweetly, she would ask questions about a subject that she didn't know much about, but tried to take an interest in anyway, for my sake. If things had not gone well she would tiptoe around them; on a good day my satisfaction would fill the living room. In Maidenhead, this was exactly what happened from Monday to Friday, every single weekday evening. The only difference was that in our house we didn't get around to it until the weekend.

There is, I know, an argument which says that acting out the role of one's father with one's mother isn't necessarily the best way of ensuring psychic health in later years. But then, we all do it at some time or another, chaps, don't we?

Away games were my equivalent of staying late at the office, and the fifth-round Cup-tie at Derby was the first time I had got to do it properly. In those days there were no restrictions on travelling in the way there are now (British Rail eventually abandoned the Football Specials, and the clubs make their own travel arrangements): we could roll up at St Pancras, buy a dirt-cheap train ticket, and pile on to a dilapidated train, the corridors of which were patrolled by police with guard dogs. Much of the journey took place in darkness – light bulbs were shattered at wearyingly brief intervals – which made reading difficult, although I always, always took a book with me and spent ages finding the carriages which contained middle-aged men who would have no interest in attracting the attention of the alsatians.

At our destination we were met by hundreds and hundreds of police, who then escorted us to the ground by a circuitous route away from the city centre; it was during these walks that my urban hooligan fantasies were given free rein. I was completely safe, protected not only by the law but by my fellow supporters, and I had therefore been liberated to bellow along in my still-unbroken voice with the chanted threats of the others. I didn't look terribly hard, in truth: I was as yet nowhere near as big as I should have been, and wore black-framed Brains-style National Health reading glasses, although these I hid away for the duration of the route marches, presumably to make myself just that little bit more terrifying. But those who mumble about the loss of identity football fans must endure miss the point: this loss of identity can be a paradoxically enriching process. Who wants to be stuck with who they are the whole time? I for one wanted time out from being a jug-eared, bespectacled, suburban twerp once in a while; I loved being able to frighten the shoppers in Derby or Norwich or Southampton (and they *were* frightened – you could see it). My opportunities for intimidating people had been limited hitherto, though I knew it wasn't *me* that made people hurry to the other side of the road, hauling their children after them; it was *us*, and I was a part of us, an organ in the hooligan body. The fact that I was the appendix – small, useless, hidden out of the way somewhere in the middle – didn't matter in the slightest.

If going to the ground was all glory and raw power, standing inside it, and getting back to the station afterwards, was less invigorating. Violence inside the grounds has all but disappeared now, for a variety of reasons: fans are separated properly (back then, if you fancied your chances in the opposition end, you could just walk through the turnstiles), away fans are usually kept back after games until the stadium has cleared, the policing is a lot more sophisticated, and so on. For the first half of the seventies, however, there was a fight at every single Arsenal game I attended. At Highbury they mostly took place on the Clock End, where the opposition's fans stood; usually they were brief flurries, Arsenal fans charging into the enemy, the enemy scattering, the police taking control. These were ritualistic charges, the violence usually contained in the movement itself rather than in fists and boots (it was this 'running' that caused the Heysel tragedy, rather than any real physical attack). But occasionally, particularly against West Ham, Tottenham, Chelsea or Manchester United, the trouble was just as likely to be at the North Bank end of the ground where the noise comes from: when away fans could amass sufficient numbers they would attempt to seize the home fans' territory as if it were an island of strategic military importance.

Consequently it was very difficult to watch football safely at away grounds. Standing in the section 'reserved' for visitors didn't ensure any protection; in fact, it merely informed the opposition of your identity. Standing at the other end was either dangerous (if the Arsenal fans were intending to invade the home end) or pointless – why bother to travel half the length of the country if you then had to pretend to support the opponents? I settled for a place along the side, if possible, where it was quiet; if not, then in the 'away' end, but towards a corner, as far from the more gung-ho members of the Arsenal touring party as possible. But I never enjoyed away games. I felt constantly nervous, often with good reason: at random points throughout the afternoon, fighting would break out, prefaced by the same kind of roar that greeted a goal; but the fact that the roar might occur when the play was nowhere near either end of the pitch was disorienting in the extreme. I have seen players look around, perplexed that their efforts at a throw-in should meet with such vocal enthusiasm.

The afternoon at Derby was worse than most. There had been trouble before the game and at sporadic intervals during it, and though I was way down the terraces, hidden among younger kids and their fathers, I was scared – so scared that in fact I was ambivalent about an Arsenal victory. A draw would have suited me fine, but I could live with defeat and an exit from the Cup if it meant I could get back to Derby station without anything untoward happening to my head. It is at times like this that the players have more responsibilities than they could ever perceive or understand; in any case, this sort of perception was not one of Charlie George's most obvious qualities.

Charlie George is one of the few seventies icons who has so far managed to avoid being deconstructed, possibly because he appears at first glance to be one of the identikit George Best/Rodney Marsh/Stan Bowles long-haired, wayward wasters who were two a new pee twenty years ago. It is true that he was as outrageously gifted as the best of the breed, and that these gifts were appallingly underexploited throughout his career (he only played for England once, and towards the end of his time at Arsenal could not even gain a place in the first team); all this and more – his temper, his problems with managers, the fierce devotion he attracted from younger fans and women – was par for the course, commonplace at a time when football was beginning to resemble pop music in both its presentation and its consumption.

Charlie George differed slightly from the rebel norm on two counts. Firstly, he had actually spent his early teenage years on the terraces of the club for which he later played; and though this is not unusual in itself – plenty of Liverpool and Newcastle players supported these clubs when they were young – George is one of the few genius misfits to have jumped straight over the perimeter fence into a club shirt and shorts. Best was Irish, Bowles and Marsh were itinerant . . . not only was George Arsenal's own, nurtured on the North Bank and in the youth team, but he looked and behaved as if running around on the pitch dressed as a player were the simplest way to avoid ejection from the stadium. Physically, he did not fit the mould: he was powerfully built and over six feet tall, too big to be George Best. On my birthday in 1971, shortly before his goal against Newcastle, one of the frequent red mists that plagued him had descended, and he had grabbed a rugged Newcastle defender by the throat and lifted him from the ground. This was not misfit petulance, this was hard-man menace, and the likely lads on the terraces have never had a more convincing representative.

And secondly, he was not a media rebel. He could not give interviews (his inarticulacy was legendary and genuine); his long, lank hair remained unfeathered and unlayered right up until the time he unwisely decided upon a bubble perm from hell some time in the mid-seventies, and when he first played in the team, at the beginning of the 69/70 season, it looked suspiciously as if he were trying to grow out a number one crop; and he seemed uninterested in womanising – Susan Farge, the fiancée whose name I still remember, is intimidatingly prominent in most of the off-the-pitch photographs. He was a big star, and the media were interested, but they didn't know what to do with him. The Egg Marketing Board tried, but their slogan, 'E for B and Charlie George', was significantly incomprehensible. Somehow, he had made himself unpackageable, media-proof – possibly the very last star of any iconic stature to do so. (For some reason, however, he managed to remain in the otherwise colander-like consciousness of my grandmother for some years after his retirement. 'Charlie George!' she spat disapprovingly and opaquely circa 1983, when I told her that I was off to Highbury to watch a game. What he means to her will, I fear, never properly be understood.)

At Derby he was astonishing on a dreadful, muscle-jellifying winter pitch. (Those pitches! The Baseball Ground at Derby, White Hart Lane, Wembley even . . . was winter grass really an eighties innovation, like the video machine or frozen yoghurt?) He scored twice, two screamers, and to the tune of Andrew Lloyd Webber's then-recent hit, we sang 'Charlie George! Superstar! How many goals have you scored so far?' (To which the Derby fans, like others all over the country had done before them, replied 'Charlie George! Superstar! Walks like a woman and he wears a bra!' It is hard not to laugh when people remember the sixties and seventies as the golden age of terrace wit.) Despite Charlie's double, the game finished 2–2 after a late Derby equaliser, and I therefore got the draw I'd been cravenly hoping for, but not the aggro-free walk back to the station that was supposed to be mine as a consequence.

It was Charlie's fault. A goal, for reasons that would require a book in itself to explain, is a provocative gesture, especially when the terraces are already bathed in a sort of half-light of violence, as they were on that afternoon. I understood that Charlie was a professional footballer, and that if an opportunity to score came his way then our tenuous safety should not in itself be a consideration. This much was clear. But whether it was absolutely essential to celebrate by running over to the Derby fans – in whose snarling, southern-poof-hating, Cockney-baiting, skinheaded, steel-toecapped company we were obliged to spend the remainder of the afternoon, and through whose hostile, alleywayed territory we were obliged to scuttle after the final whistle – and making an unambiguous take-that-you-provincial-fuckers V-sign . . . this was much more opaque. The way I saw it, Charlie's sense of responsibility and duty had momentarily let him down.

He got booed off the pitch and fined by the FA; we got chased all the way on to our train, bottles and cans cascading around our ears. Cheers, Charlie.

SOCIAL HISTORY

Arsenal v Derby

29.2.72

The replay finished nil–nil, a game with no merit whatsoever. But it remains the only first-team game that has taken place at Highbury on a midweek afternoon during my Arsenal time: February 1972 was the time of the power workers' strike. For all of us it meant sporadic electricity, candlelight, occasional cold suppers, but for third-year football fans it meant visits to the Electricity Board showroom, where the cut-off rota was posted, in order to discover which of us were able to offer *The Big Match* on Sunday afternoons. For Arsenal, the power crisis meant no floodlights, hence the Tuesday afternoon replay.

I went to the game, despite school, and though I had imagined that the crowd might consist of me, a few other teenage truants, and a scattering of pensioners, in fact there were more than sixty-three thousand people there, the biggest crowd of the season. I was disgusted. No wonder the country was going to the dogs! My truancy prevented me from sharing my disquiet with my mother (an irony that escaped me at the time), but *what was going on*?

For this thirtysomething, the midweek afternoon Cup-tie (West Ham played giant-killers Hereford on a Tuesday afternoon as well, and got a forty-two thousand-plus crowd) now has that wonderful early seventies sheen, like an episode of *The Fenn Street Gang* or a packet of Number Six cigarettes; maybe it was just that everyone at Upton Park and Highbury, all one hundred and six thousand of us, wanted to walk down one of the millions of tiny alleys of social history.

ME AND BOB McNAB

Stoke City v Arsenal

(Villa Park) 15.4.72

The 71/72 FA Cup was a cracker, an apparently endless source of wonder and tricky trivia questions. Which two teams took eleven hours to settle their fourth-qualifying-round tie? Which player scored nine goals in his team's first-round 11–0 win over Margate? Who did he play for then?

Where was he transferred to later? Who were the two Hereford players who scored in their Southern League side's astonishing 2–1 victory against First Division Newcastle? (A clue: the surnames have special resonance for Arsenal fans.) Oxford City and Alvechurch; Ted Macdougall; Bournemouth; Manchester United; Ronnie Radford and Ricky George: one point for each, seven points and you've won a pair of Malcolm Macdonald sideboards.

And then there were the afternoon Cup replays and Charlie's V-sign, and at Villa Park, in our semi-final against Stoke, our goalkeeper Bob Wilson was carried off in the middle of our 1–1 draw (John Radford had to take over) and I spoke to Bob McNab, the Arsenal left-back, a couple of hours before the kick-off.

I went up to Villa Park with Hislam, a wannabee hooligan from Maidenhead whom I ran into on trains every now and again. I was in awe of him. He wore a white butcher's coat covered in crudely drawn red Arsenal slogans, *de rigueur* for anyone with any terrace pretensions; and on the way home from games he would sit down next to me on the 5.35 from Paddington and ask me the score, explaining that he had been detained in the police cells under the pitch and therefore had no idea of what had been going on above his head. Jenkins, the apparently legendary leader of the North Bank (I'd never heard of him, needless to say), was a personal friend of his.

I was soon to find out, predictably, that this was all rubbish, and that Hislam's relationship with reality was tenuous even on a good day. If there was such a person as Jenkins (the Leader, a scheming hooligan-general responsible for military tactics, probably has its roots in urban, or even suburban, myth) Hislam didn't know him; and even I, desperate to number among my acquaintances a real-life criminal, began to wonder how an ostensibly harmless-looking fourteen-year-old managed to get himself arrested every single Saturday for offences which remained frustratingly vague.

Football culture is so amorphous, so unwieldy, so *big* (when I listened to Hislam talk about incidents in King's Cross and Euston and the back streets of Paddington, the whole of London seemed within the grasp of its tentacles) that it inevitably attracts more than its fair share of fantasists. If you wish to have taken part in a fearsome battle with Tottenham fans, it doesn't have to have happened within the stadium where it could easily be verified. It could have taken place at a station, or on a route to the ground, or in an enemy pub: football rumours of this kind have always been as thick and as impenetrable as smog. Hislam knew this, and was as happy as Larry inventing his gruesome and improbable lies; football was perfectly equipped to feed his ravenous appetite for self-deception, just as it was able to feed mine. For a while, we had a satisfying symbiosis going. He wanted to believe he was a hooligan, and so did I, and for a while he could have told me anything.

Dad had obtained two terrace tickets for the game for me (I hadn't explained to him the full extent of my football solitude) and Hislam had generously agreed to take the spare. When we arrived at Villa Park we had to find the box office to pick them up. It was one-thirty, and a few of the players were there, distributing tickets to wives and family and friends. Bob McNab, the left-back, was one of them; he hadn't played in the first team since January, and I was surprised to see him. I couldn't believe that Bertie Mee was going to give him his first run-out for three months in an FA Cup semi-final. In the end my curiosity overcame my shyness.

'Are you playing, Bob?'

'Yeah.'

Dialogue in works of autobiography is quite naturally viewed with some suspicion. How on earth can the writer remember verbatim conversations that happened fifteen, twenty, fifty years ago? But 'Are you playing, Bob?' is one of only four sentences I have ever uttered to any Arsenal player (for the record the others are 'How's the leg, Bob?' to Bob Wilson, recovering from injury the following season; 'Can I have your autograph, please?' to Charlie George, Pat Rice, Alan Ball and Bertie Mee; and, well, 'How's the leg, Brian?' to Brian Marwood outside the Arsenal club shop when I was old enough to know better) and I can therefore vouch for its absolute authenticity.

I have imagined conversations, of course. Even now I frequently take Alan Smith or David O'Leary to the pub, buy them a low-alcohol lager, sit them down and talk until last-orders and beyond about George Graham's alleged parsimony, Charlie Nicholas's fitness or John Lukic's transfer. But the plain truth is that the club means more to us than it does to them. Where were they twenty years ago? Where will they be in twenty years' time? Where will they be in *two* years' time, a couple of them?

(At Villa Park or Old Trafford, bearing down on the Arsenal goal with the ball at their feet, that's where.)

No, I'm happy with things the way they are, thank you very much. They're players and I'm a fan, and I don't want to blur the boundaries. Men laugh at what they see as the grotesque inadequacy of groupies, but a one-night stand with a star is perfectly understandable, and has its own balance and logic. (If I were a nubile twenty-year-old, I'd probably be down at the training ground throwing my panties at David Rocastle, although this kind of confession from a man, however New he is, is regrettably still not acceptable.) Yet many of us have had opportunities to talk to the players, at boot launches or sports shop openings, in nightclubs or restaurants, and most of us have taken them. ('How's the leg, Bob?' 'Thought you were brilliant Saturday, Tony.' 'Hey, make sure you do Tottenham next week, yeah?') And what are these clumsy, embarrassing, fumbling encounters if they are not passes, beery gropes in the dark? We're not young and desirable nymphettes, we're grown-ups with pot-bellies, and we have nothing to offer at all. Professional footballers are as beautiful and unattainable as models, and I don't want to be a middle-aged bottom-pincher.

I hadn't worked all this out then, when I saw Bob McNab in his pre-match suit. And when I got into the ground, and two blokes in front of me started talking about team changes, I told them that McNab was playing, because he'd told me himself, and they looked at me and then looked at each other and shook their heads (although when the changes were read out over the tannoy they looked at me again). Meanwhile Hislam had taken himself off up to the top of Villa's massive Holte End, to be with The Lads, and was busy telling anyone who would listen how he'd bunked into the ground under the turnstiles (he made this claim to someone he may or may not have known as soon as we walked into the ground). Which of us was the fantasist here? I was, obviously. No one talks to the players before the game, but bunking in without paying . . . what would be the point of lying about that if you had a ticket stub in your pocket?

WEMBLEY II – THE NIGHTMARE CONTINUES

Leeds v Arsenal

5.5.72

A classic anxiety dream, banal in its obviousness. I am attempting to get to Wembley, and I have a ticket for the Final in my pocket. I leave home in plenty of time for the game, but every attempt to travel towards the stadium takes me in the opposite direction. At first this is just an amusing irritation, but eventually it induces panic; at two minutes to three I am in central London, trying to hail a cab and beginning to realise that I'm not going to get to see the match. I like the dream though, in a funny sort of way. I have had it six times now, before every Cup Final that Arsenal have played in since 1972, and so it is a nightmare inextricably linked with success. I wake up sweating, but the sweat serves as the first anticipatory moment of the day.

My Cup Final ticket had come directly from the club, rather than via touts and my dad, and I was ludicrously proud of it. (Even more eccentric was the joy I took in the compliment slip that came with it, which I stored away for years afterwards.) Cup tickets were allocated on the basis of the numbered vouchers that appeared on the back of the programme. If you had all the programmes, as I did, you were more or less assured of a ticket; thus the system was supposed to reward loyal fans, although in effect it rewarded those with enough energy to track down the programmes they needed among the *ad hoc* programme stands outside the ground (a laborious process which constituted a kind of loyalty in itself). I had been to the vast majority of the home games and a few of the aways; I had as much right as any, and probably more right than most, to a spot on the terraces at Wembley, and so my pride came from the feeling of belonging I had lacked in the previous year.

(This sense of belonging is crucial to an understanding of why people travel to the meaningless game in Plymouth on a Wednesday night, and without it football would fail as a business. But where does it end? Those fans who travel the length and breadth of the country every week; does the club 'belong' to them more than it does to me? And the old geezer who only gets along ten times a season, but has been going to Highbury since 1938 . . . doesn't the club belong to him too, and he to the club?

Of course. But it took me another few years to discover that; in the meantime, it was no pain, no gain. Unless I had suffered and shivered, wept into my scarf and paid through the nose, it was simply not possible to take pleasure in or credit for the good times.)

The game itself was as dismal as all the other Arsenal–Leeds games had been: the two teams had developed something of a History, and their meetings were usually violent and low-scoring. My friend Bob McNab was booked in the first two minutes, and from that moment there was a procession of free kicks and squabbles, ankle taps and pointing fingers, and snarls. What made it worse was that this was the Centenary Cup Final; I am sure that if the top brass at the FA had had a free hand in choosing who the two finalists would be, Arsenal and Leeds would have come pretty low down on their list. The pre-match anniversary celebrations (I had found my spot on the terraces a good ninety minutes before the kick-off, as was my custom), which consisted of representatives of all the other Cup finalists marching round the pitch behind banners, suddenly appeared almost satirical in its intent. You remember the Matthews Final in '53? Bert Trautmann playing in goal with a broken neck in '56? Tottenham's Double team in '61? Everton's comeback in '66? Osgood's diving header in '70? Now watch Storey and Bremner attempting to gouge lumps out of each other's thighs. The sourness of the game simply exacerbated the tension in my stomach, every bit as debilitating as it had been during the Swindon game three years earlier. If no one was going to bother with any of the niceties of the game (and there were stretches when it appeared that no one was even going to bother with the ball) then winning the Cup became even more important: there wasn't anything else to think about.

At the beginning of the second half, Mick Jones wriggled to the byline and crossed for Allan Clarke to score for Leeds with a ridiculously effortless nod of the head. Inevitably it was the only goal of the game. We hit the post or the bar or something, and had a shot kicked off the line, but these were token Cup Final moments, not to be taken seriously; you could see that the Arsenal players understood the pointlessness of their effort.

As the end of the game approached I braced myself for the grief that I knew would swallow me whole, as it had done after the Swindon match. I was fifteen, and the option of tears was not available as it had been in 1969; when the final whistle went I can recall my knees buckling slightly.

I didn't feel sorry for the team or for the rest of the fans, but for myself, although now I realise that all football sorrow takes this form. When our teams lose at Wembley we think of the colleagues and classmates we have to face on Monday morning, and of the delirium that has been denied us; it seems inconceivable that we will allow ourselves to be this vulnerable ever again. I felt that I didn't have the *courage* to be a football fan. How could I contemplate going through this again? Was I going to come to Wembley every three or four years for the rest of my life and end up feeling like this?

I felt an arm around my shoulders and realised for the first time that I was standing next to three Leeds fans, an old man, his son, and his grandson. 'Never mind, lad,' said the old man. 'They'll be back.' For a moment it felt as though he was holding me upright, until the first and most intense spasm of misery passed and I regained the strength in my legs. Almost immediately a couple of Arsenal suedeheads with an unmistakable and ominous fury in their eyes pushed their way through the crowd towards the four of us. I stepped back, and they removed the Leeds scarf that was around the little boy's neck. 'Give that back,' his dad said, but only because he knew it would be a weak father who said nothing, not in any expectation of success. There was a brief windmilling of fists and the two older men staggered backwards; I didn't stay around to find out what kind of beating they took. I ran for the gangway and went straight home, frightened and sick. It was the only manner, really, in which the Centenary Cup Final could have ended.

A NEW FAMILY

Arsenal v Wolves

15.8.72

Over the summer of 1972, things changed. Arsenal, the most British (that is to say, the dourest and most aggressive) team you could imagine, went all continental on us, and for half a dozen games at the start of the 72/73 season decided to play Total Football. (This, for the benefit of those with only a sketchy grasp of football tactics, was a Dutch invention which necessitated flexibility from all the players on the pitch. Defenders were required to attack, attackers to play in midfield; it was football's version of post-modernism, and the intellectuals loved it.) That August at Highbury, gentle and appreciative applause was as familiar a sound as sixty thousand shuffling feet had been a couple of years earlier. Imagine Mrs Thatcher coming back from Brussels and lecturing us on the perils of jingoism, and you will have some idea of the improbability of the conversion.

A win at Leicester on the opening Saturday was followed by this destruction of Wolves (5–2, with goals from defenders McNab and Simpson). 'I have never been so excited by an Arsenal performance,' said the man in the *Daily Mail* the next morning. 'They played more good football than in a dozen matches in their Double year.' 'Arsenal have genuinely changed their nature,' said the *Telegraph*. 'The old hardness and obsessive search for the heads of the strikers have disappeared. Instead, as hapless Wolves discovered, there is a new inventiveness and improvisation.'

For the first, but certainly not the last, time, I began to believe that Arsenal's moods and fortunes somehow reflected my own. It wasn't so much that we were both playing brilliantly and winning (although my two recent O-level passes were all the proof I needed that I was a genuine Championship of Life contender); more that during the summer of 1972 my life seemed to me to have become suddenly and bewilderingly exotic, and my team's mysterious adoption of a flamboyant continental style was perfectly and inexplicably analogous. Everything about the Wolves game was disorienting – the five goals, the quality of the passing (Alan Ball was outstanding), the purr of the crowd, the genuine enthusiasm of a normally hostile press. And I watched all this from the Lower East Stand with my father and my stepmother, a woman I had met just a few weeks earlier and whom I had previously always thought of, when I had thought of her at all, simply as the Enemy.

In the four or five years since my parents' separation, I had asked my father almost nothing about his personal life. Part of this was understandable: like most kids I possessed neither the vocabulary nor the nerve to talk about things like this. Another part of it was not quite as easy to explain, and had more to do with the fact that none of us ever referred to what had happened if we could possibly avoid doing so. Even though I was aware that there had been Another Woman when my father left, I never asked him about her; my picture of my father was therefore curiously incomplete. I knew that he worked, and that he lived abroad, but I never attempted to envision any sort of *life* for him: he took me to football, asked me about school and then disappeared for another couple of months into some sort of unimaginable limbo.

It was inevitable that sooner or later I would be made to confront the fact that Dad, like all of us, had another, fuller context. That confrontation eventually occurred in the early summer of 1972, when I discovered that my father and his second wife were the parents of two small children. In July, the amazing news still undigested, I went to visit the undreamed-of family at their home in France. The fact that this set-up had hitherto been concealed from me meant that there had been none of the gradual accumulation of detail that usually occurs in such cases: like Mia Farrow in *The Purple Rose of Cairo*, dragged from the audience through the screen into a film by one of its characters, I was propelled into a world that had been imagined and completed without my participation, entirely alien but still somehow recognisable. My half-brother was small and dark and looked up to and after his little sister, eighteen months younger, blonde and bright and self-confident . . . where had I seen these two before? In our home movies, that's where. But if they were us, Gill and I, why were they speaking half in French and half in English? And what was I supposed to be to them, a brother, or some kind of third parent, or something in between, a trainee intermediary from the adult world? And how come there was a swimming pool and a permanent supply of Coke in the fridge? I loved it and I hated it and I wanted to go home on the next plane and I wanted to stay for the rest of the summer.

When I did get back, I had to invent a *modus vivendi* that would do me for the next few years, a task I thought best accomplished by ensuring that the new world was never ever mentioned in the old, although it wouldn't have achieved much to complain about the absence of a swimming pool in our tiny back garden in any case; thus one huge and important part of my life was kept entirely and pacifically separate from another, an arrangement perfectly designed to produce mendacity, self-delusion and schizophrenia in an already confused teenager.

When my stepmother sat down next to me at Highbury for the Wolves game, it was as if Elsie Tanner had walked into the Crossroads Motel; the appearance of an inhabitant from one world at the centre of the other somehow drained the reality out of both. And then Arsenal started to bang inch-perfect passes along the ground all over the pitch, and our defenders popped up in the opposing penalty area to lob the opposing goalkeeper with Cruyff-like precision and delicacy, and my suspicion that this was a world gone mad was confirmed. I was sitting with the Enemy,

Arsenal thought they were Holland, and if I had looked carefully, I would surely have seen pigs floating serenely over the Clock End.

A couple of months later we got thumped 5–0 at Derby and immediately reverted to our old, dogged and reassuring ways; the fact that the experiment had been so brief seemed to reinforce the impression that it had all been a particularly ingenious metaphor, invented for my benefit and abandoned the moment I had understood it.

A MATTER OF LIFE AND DEATH

Crystal Palace v Liverpool

October 1972

I have learned things from the game. Much of my knowledge of locations in Britain and Europe comes not from school, but from away games or the sports pages, and hooliganism has given me both a taste for sociology and a degree of fieldwork experience. I have learned the value of investing time and emotion in things I cannot control, and of belonging to a community whose aspirations I share completely and uncritically. And on my first visit to Selhurst Park with my friend Frog, I saw a dead body, still my first, and learned a little bit about, well, life itself.

As we walked towards the railway station after the game, we saw the man lying in the road, partially covered by a raincoat, a purple-and-blue Palace scarf around his neck. Another younger man was crouched over him, and the two of us crossed the road and went to have a look.

'Is he all right?' Frog asked.

The man shook his head. 'No. Dead. I was just walking behind him and he keeled over.'

He looked dead. He was grey and, as far as we were concerned, unimaginably motionless. We were impressed.

Frog sensed a story that would interest not only the fourth year but much of the fifth as well. 'Who done him? Scousers?'

At this point the man lost patience. 'No. He's had a heart attack, you little prats. Now fuck off.'

And we did, and that was the end of the incident. But it has never been very far away from me since then, my one and only image of death; it is an image which instructs. The Palace scarf, a banal and homely detail; the timing (after the game, but mid-season); the stranger paying distressed but ultimately detached attention. And, of course, the two idiotic teenagers gawping at a tiny tragedy with unembarrassed fascination, even glee.

It worries me, the prospect of dying in mid-season like that, but of course, in all probability I *will* die sometime between August and May. We have the naive expectation that when we go, we won't be leaving any loose ends lying around: we will have made our peace with our children, left them happy and stable, and we will have achieved more or less everything that we wanted to with our lives. It's all nonsense, of course, and football fans contemplating their own mortality know that it is all nonsense. There will be hundreds of loose ends. Maybe we will die the night before our team appears at Wembley, or the day after a European Cup first-leg match, or in the middle of a promotion campaign or a relegation battle, and there is every prospect, according to many theories about the afterlife, that we will not be able to discover the eventual outcome. The whole *point* about death, metaphorically speaking, is that it is almost bound to occur before the major trophies have been awarded. The man lying on the pavement would not, as Frog observed on the way home, discover whether Palace stayed up or not that season; nor that they would continue to bob up and down between the divisions over the next twenty years, that they would change their colours half a dozen times, that they would eventually reach their first FA Cup Final, or that they would end up running around with the legend 'VIRGIN' plastered all over their shirts. That's life, though.

I do not wish to die in mid-season but, on the other hand, I am one of those who would, I think, be happy to have my ashes scattered over the Highbury pitch (although I understand that there are restrictions: too many widows contact the club, and there are fears that the turf would not respond kindly to the contents of urn after urn). It would be nice to think that I could hang around inside the stadium in some form, and watch the first team one Saturday, the reserves the next; I would like to feel that my children and grandchildren will be Arsenal fans and that I could watch with them. It doesn't seem a bad way to spend eternity, and certainly I'd rather be sprinkled over the East Stand than dumped into the Atlantic or left up some mountain.

I don't want to die immediately after a game, though (like Jock Stein, who died seconds after Scotland beat Wales to qualify for the World

Cup, or like a friend's father, who died at a Celtic–Rangers game a few years ago). It seems *excessive*, somehow, as if football were the only fitting context for the death of a football fan. (And I'm not talking about the deaths of Heysel or Hillsborough or Ibrox or Bradford here, of course; those were tragedies of a different order altogether.) I don't want to be remembered with a shake of the head and a fond smile intended to imply that this is the way I would have chosen to go out if I could; give me gravitas over cheap congruence any time.

So let's get this straight. I don't want to peg out in Gillespie Road after a game because I might be remembered as a crank; and yet, crankily, I want to float around Highbury as a ghost watching reserve games for the rest of time. And in a sense these two desires – at first glance incomprehensibly inconsistent, I would imagine, to those without equivalent fixations – characterise obsessives and encapsulate their dilemma. We hate being patronised (there are some people who know me *only* as a monomaniac, and who ask me slowly and patiently, in words of one syllable, about Arsenal results before turning to someone else to talk about life – as if being a football fan precludes the possibility of possessing a family or a job or an opinion on alternative medicine), but our lunacy makes condescension almost inevitable. I know all this, and I *still* want to lumber my son with the names Liam Charles George Michael Thomas. I get what I deserve, I guess.

GRADUATION DAY

Arsenal v Ipswich

14.10.72

By the time I was fifteen I was no longer quite so small – indeed, there were now a number of boys in my year smaller than me. This was a relief in most ways, but brought with it a problem that gnawed at me constantly for some weeks: I could no longer, if I was to maintain any self-respect, postpone my transfer from the Schoolboys' Enclosure to the North Bank, the covered terrace behind one of the goals where Arsenal's most vocal supporters stood.

I had plotted my début with great care. For much of that season I'd spent more time staring at the alarming lump of noisy humanity to my right than straight ahead at the pitch; I was trying to work out exactly where I would make for and what parts I should avoid. The Ipswich game looked like my ideal opportunity: Ipswich fans were hardly likely to attempt to 'take' the North Bank, and the crowd wouldn't be much more than thirty thousand, about half the capacity. I was ready to leave the Schoolboys behind.

It is difficult to recall now exactly what concerned me. After all, when I travelled up to Derby or Villa I usually stood in the away end, which was simply a displaced North Bank, so it couldn't have been the prospect of trouble (always more likely at away games or at the other end of Arsenal's ground), or fear of the type of people I would be standing with. I rather suspect that I was frightened of being revealed, as I had been at Reading earlier on that year. Supposing the people around me found out I wasn't from Islington? Supposing I was exposed as a suburban interloper who went to a grammar school and was studying for Latin O-level? In the end I had to take the risk. If, as seemed probable, I provoked the entire terrace into a deafening chant of 'HORNBY IS A WANKER' or 'WE ALL HATE SWOTS, HATE SWOTS, HATE SWOTS' to the tune of the 'Dambusters' March', then so be it; at least I would have tried.

I arrived on the terrace shortly after two o'clock. It seemed enormous, bigger even than it had looked from my usual position: a vast expanse of steep grey steps over which had been sprinkled a complex even pattern of metal crush barriers. The position I had decided on – dead centre, half-way down – indicated both a certain amount of gung-ho (the noise at most football grounds begins in the centre of the home terrace and radiates outwards; the sides and the seats only join in at moments of high excitement) and a degree of caution (centre-back was not a place for the faint-hearted débutant).

Rites of passage are more commonly found in literary novels, or mainstream Hollywood films with pretensions, than they are in real life, particularly in real suburban life. All the things that were supposed to change me – first kiss, loss of virginity, first fight, first drink, first drugs – just seemed to *happen*; there was no will involved, and certainly no painful decision-making process (peer-group pressure, bad temper and the comparative sexual precocity of the female teenager made all the decisions for me), and perhaps as a consequence I emerged from all these formative experiences completely unformed. Walking through the North Bank turnstile was the only time I can remember consciously grasping a nettle until I was in my mid-twenties (really – this is not the place to go through all the nettles I should have grasped by then, but I know I didn't bother): I wanted to do it, but at the same time I was, pathetically, a little afraid. My only rite of passage, then, involved standing on one piece of concrete as opposed to another; but the fact that I had made myself do something that I only half-wanted to do, and that it all turned out OK . . . this was important to me.

An hour before the kick-off the view from my spot was spectacular. No corner of the pitch was obscured, and even the far goal, which I had imagined would look tiny, was quite clear. By three o'clock, however, I could see a little strip of the pitch, a narrow grass tunnel running from the near penalty area to the touchline at the far end. The corner flags had disappeared entirely, and the goal beneath me was visible only if I jumped at the crucial moment. Whenever there was a near-miss at our end, the crowd tumbled forward; I was forced seven or eight steps down the terracing and, when I looked round, the carrier bag containing my programme and my *Daily Express* that I had placed at my feet seemed miles away, like a towel on the beach when you're in a rough sea. I did see the one goal of the game, a George Graham volley from about twenty-five yards, but only because it was scored at the Clock End.

I loved it there, of course. I loved the different *categories* of noise: the formal, ritual noise when the players emerged (each player's name called in turn, starting with the favourite, until he responded with a wave); the spontaneous shapeless roar when something exciting was happening on the pitch; the renewed vigour of the chanting after a goal or a sustained period of attacking. (And even here, among younger, less alienated men, that football grumble when things were going badly.) After my initial alarm I grew to love the movement, the way I was thrown towards the pitch and sucked back again. And I loved the anonymity: I was not, after all, going to be found out. I stayed for the next seventeen years.

There is no North Bank now. The Taylor Report recommended that, post-Hillsborough, football stadia should become all-seater, and the football clubs have all decided to act on that recommendation. In March 1973, I was among a crowd of sixty-three thousand at Highbury for an FA Cup replay against Chelsea; crowds of that size are no longer possible, at Highbury or in any other English stadium apart from Wembley. Even in 1988, the year before Hillsborough, Arsenal had two crowds of fifty-five thousand in the same week, and the second of them, the Littlewoods

Cup semi-final against Everton, now looks like the last of the sort of game that comes to represent the football experience in the memory: floodlights, driving rain and an enormous, rolling roar throughout the match. So, yes, of course it is sad; football crowds may yet be able to create a new environment that electrifies, but they will never be able to recreate the old one which required vast numbers and a context in which those numbers could form themselves into one huge reactive body.

Even sadder, though, is the way that Arsenal have chosen to redevelop the stadium. It cost me 25p to watch the Ipswich match; the Arsenal Bond scheme means that from September 1993 entry to the North Bank will cost a minimum £1100 *plus the price of a ticket*, and, even allowing for inflation, that sounds a bit steep to me. A debenture plan makes sound financial sense for the club, but it is inconceivable that football at Highbury will ever be the same again.

The big clubs seem to have tired of their fan-base, and in a way who can blame them? Young working-class and lower-middle-class males bring with them a complicated and occasionally distressing set of problems; directors and chairmen might argue that they had their chance and blew it, and that middle-class families – the new target audience – will not only behave themselves, but pay much more to do so.

This argument ignores central questions about responsibility, fairness, and whether football clubs have a role to play in the local community. But even without these problems, it seems to me that there is a fatal flaw in the reasoning. Part of the pleasure to be had in large football stadia is a mixture of the vicarious and the parasitical, because unless one stands on the North Bank, or the Kop, or the Stretford End, then one is relying on others to provide the atmosphere; and atmosphere is one of the crucial ingredients of the football experience. These huge ends are as vital to the clubs as their players, not only because their inhabitants are vocal in their support, not just because they provide clubs with large sums of money (although these are not unimportant factors) *but because without them nobody else would bother coming.*

Arsenal and Manchester United and the rest are under the impression that people pay to watch Paul Merson and Ryan Giggs, and of course they do. But many of them – the people in the twenty-pound seats, and the guys in the executive boxes – also pay to watch people watching Paul Merson (or to listen to people shouting at him). Who would buy an executive box if the stadium were filled with executives? The club sold the boxes on the understanding that the atmosphere came free, and so the North Bank generated as much income as any of the players ever did. Who'll make the noise now? Will the suburban middle-class kids and their mums and dads still come if they have to generate it themselves? Or will they feel that they have been conned? Because in effect the clubs have sold them tickets to a show in which the principal attraction has been moved to make room for them.

One more thing about the kind of audience that football has decided it wants: the clubs have got to make sure that they're good, that there aren't any lean years, because the new crowd won't tolerate failure. These are not the sort of people who will come to watch you play Wimbledon in March when you're eleventh in the First Division and out of all the cup competitions. Why should they? They've got plenty of other things to do. So, Arsenal . . . no more seventeen-year losing streaks, like the one between 1953 and 1970, right? No flirting with relegation, like in 1975 and 1976, or the odd half-decade where you don't even get to a final, like we had between 1981 and 1987. We mug punters put up with that, and at least twenty thousand of us would turn up no matter how bad you were (and sometimes you were very, very bad indeed); but this new lot . . . I'm not so sure.

THE WHOLE PACKAGE

Arsenal v Coventry

4.11.72

The only trouble with the North Bank was that I bought the whole package. In the second half of my third game there (the middle one against Manchester City was memorable only because our new signing Jeff Blockley, an incompetent to rival Ian Ure, pushed a City corner against the underside of the bar with his hands, the ball bounced down behind the line and the referee wouldn't give them the penalty or the goal – how we laughed!), Coventry City's Tommy Hutchison scored a stunning solo goal. He picked the ball up about forty yards out on the left wing, left a trail of Arsenal defenders in his wake, and curled the ball round Geoff Barnett as he came out right into the far corner. On the North Bank there was a split second of silence as we watched the Coventry fans cavorting around on the Clock End like dolphins, and then came the fierce, unanimous and heartfelt chant, 'You're going to get your fucking heads kicked in.'

I had heard it before, obviously. For a good fifteen years it was the formal response to any goal scored by any away team at any football ground in the country (variations at Highbury were 'You're going home in a London ambulance,' 'We'll see you all outside,' and 'Clock End, do your job,' the Arsenal supporters at the Clock End being nearer to the opposing fans, and thus charged with the responsibility of vengeance). The only difference on this occasion was that I roared along with the imprecation for the first time. I was as outraged by the goal, as offended and as stricken, as anyone on the terrace; it was fortunate that there was an entire football pitch between me and the Coventry fans, or, or . . . or I would have done such things, I knew not what they were, but they would have been the terror of N5.

In many ways, of course, this was funny, in the way that the vast majority of teenage hooligan pretensions are funny, and yet even now I find it difficult to laugh at myself: half my life ago, and I'm still embarrassed. I like to think that there was none of me, the adult man, in that furious fifteen-year-old, but I suspect that this is over-optimistic. A lot of the fifteen-year-old remains, inevitably (as it does in millions of men), which accounts for some of the embarrassment; the rest of it stems from the recognition of the adult in the boy. Either way, it's bad news.

I did learn, in the end. I learned that my threatening anybody was preposterous – I might just as well have promised the Coventry fans to bear their children – and that in any case violence and its attendant culture is uncool (none of the women I have ever wanted to sleep with would have been particularly impressed with me that afternoon). The big lesson, though, the one that tells you football is only a game and that if your team loses there's no need to go berserk . . . I like to think I've learned that one. But I can still feel it in me, sometimes, at away games when we're surrounded by opposing fans and the referee's giving us nothing and we're hanging on and hanging on and then Adams slips and their centre-forward's in and then there's this terrible needling bellow from all around you . . . Then I'm back to remembering just two of the three lessons, which is enough in some ways but not enough in others.

Masculinity has somehow acquired a more specific, less abstract meaning than femininity. Many people seem to regard femininity as a quality; but according to a large number of both men and women, masculinity is a shared set of assumptions and values that men can either accept or reject. You like football? Then you also like soul music, beer, thumping people, grabbing ladies' breasts, and money. You're a rugby or a cricket man? You like Dire Straits or Mozart, wine, pinching ladies' bottoms, and money. You don't fit into either camp? *Macho, nein danke?* In which case it must follow that you're a pacifist vegetarian, studiously oblivious to the charms of Michelle Pfeiffer, who thinks that only leering wideboys listen to Luther Vandross.

It's easy to forget that we can pick and choose. Theoretically it is possible to like football, soul music and beer, for example, but to abhor breast-grabbing and bottom-pinching (or, one has to concede, vice versa); one can admire Muriel Spark *and* Bryan Robson. Interestingly it is men who seem to be more aware than women of the opportunities for mix 'n' match: a feminist colleague of mine literally refused to believe that I watched Arsenal, a disbelief that apparently had its roots in the fact that we had once had a conversation about a feminist novel. How could I possibly have read the book *and* have been to Highbury? Tell a thinking woman that you like football and you're in for a pretty sobering glimpse of the female conception of the male.

And yet I have to accept that my spiteful fury during the Coventry game was the logical conclusion to what had begun four years before. At fifteen I was not capable of picking and choosing, nor of recognising that this culture was not necessarily discrete. If I wanted to spend Saturdays at Highbury watching football, then I also had to wave a spear with as much venom as I could muster. If, as seems probable given my sporadically fatherless state, part of my obsession with Arsenal was that it gave me a quick way to fill a previously empty trolley in the Masculinity Supermarket, then it is perhaps understandable if I didn't sort out until later on what was rubbish and what was worth keeping. I just threw in everything I saw, and stupid, blind, violent rage was certainly in my field of vision.

I was lucky (and it *was* luck, I can take no credit for it) that I nauseated myself pretty quickly; lucky most of all that the women I fancied, and the men I wanted to befriend (at this stage those verbs belonged exactly where I have placed them), would have had nothing to do with me if I hadn't. If I'd met the kind of girl who accepted or even encouraged masculine belligerence then I might not have had to bother. (What was that anti-Vietnam slogan? 'Women say yes to men who say no'?) But there are football fans, thousands of them, who have neither the need nor the desire to get a perspective on their own aggression. I worry for them and I despise them and I'm frightened of them; and some of them, grown men in their mid-thirties with kids, are too old now to go around threatening to kick heads, but they do anyway.

CAROL BLACKBURN

Arsenal v Derby

31.3.73

At this point I feel that I have to defend the accuracy of my memory, and perhaps that of all football fans. I have never kept a football diary, and I have forgotten hundreds and hundreds of games entirely; but I have measured out my life in Arsenal fixtures, and any event of any significance has a footballing shadow. The first time I was best man at a wedding? We lost 1–0 to Spurs in the FA Cup third round, and I listened to the account of Pat Jennings' tragic mistake in a windy Cornish car park. When did my first real love affair end? The day after a disappointing 2–2 draw with Coventry in 1981. That these events are commemorated is perhaps understandable, but what I cannot explain is why I remember some of the other stuff. My sister, for example, recalls coming to Highbury twice, but knows no more than that; I know that she saw a 1–0 win against Birmingham in 1973 (a Ray Kennedy goal, on the afternoon that Liam Brady made his début) and a 2–0 win against Stoke in 1980 (Hollins and Sansom). My half-brother first came in January 1973 to see a 2–2 cup-tie against Leicester, but how come it is I rather than he who knows this? Why, when somebody tells me that he or she came to Highbury in 1976 to see a 5–2 game against Newcastle, do I feel compelled to tell them that the score was actually 5–3? Why can't I smile politely and agree that, yes, that was a great game?

I know how annoying we are, how cranky we must seem, but there is nothing much we can do about it now. (My father is much the same about Bournemouth football and Hampshire cricket in the 1940s.) These scores and scorers and occasions are of a piece: Pat's slip against Tottenham was not, of course, as important as Steve's wedding, but to me the two events have now become intrinsic and complementary parts of some new and different whole. An obsessive's memory is therefore, perhaps, more *creative* than that of an ordinary person; not in the sense that we make things up, but in the sense that we have baroque cinematic recall, full of jump-cuts and split-screen innovation. Who else but a football fan would use a fumble on a muddy field three hundred miles away to recall a wedding? Obsession requires a commendable mental agility.

It is this agility that allows me to date the arrival of my adolescence quite precisely: it arrived on Thursday, 30th November 1972, when Dad took me to London to buy some new clothes. I chose a pair of Oxford bags, a black polo-neck jumper, a black raincoat and a pair of black stack-heeled shoes; I remember the date because on the Saturday, when Arsenal played Leeds United at Highbury and beat them 2–1, I was wearing the entire outfit and feeling better inside myself than I had ever felt. I developed a new hairstyle (supposed to resemble Rod Stewart's, but I never found the courage for the spikes) to go with the clobber; and I developed an interest in girls to go with the haircut. One of these three innovations changed everything.

The Derby game was a really big one. After the indifferent spell that had brought about the end of the Total Football experiment, Arsenal had clawed their way back into the Championship race simply by being what they had always been – mean, fierce, competitive, hard to beat. If they won this game (against the reigning champions), then they stood a chance of going top of the First Division for the first time since the Double year; they were level on points with Liverpool, who were at home to Tottenham that afternoon. And looking at the programme for the Derby game, one is reminded of how extraordinarily balanced football fortunes are. If we had beaten Derby, there would have been every prospect of winning the Championship again; in fact, we lost it by three points, the very gap we allowed to open up that afternoon. The following Saturday we were playing Second Division Sunderland in the FA Cup semi-final, and we lost that too. The two defeats prompted Bertie Mee to break the whole team up, but he never got a new one together again, and three years later he was gone. If we'd won either of the games – and we should and could have won both – then the modern history of the club might have been entirely different.

So the course of the next decade was to be mapped out for Arsenal that afternoon, but I didn't care. The previous evening Carol Blackburn, my girlfriend of some three or four weeks (I can remember watching the TV highlights of the Chelsea–Arsenal FA Cup quarter-final at Stamford Bridge with her – she was a Chelsea fan – at a friend's house a fortnight before) had packed me in. She was, I thought, beautiful, with the long, straight, centre-parted hair and the melting doe eyes of Olivia Newton-John; her beauty had reduced me to nervous and miserable silence for much of the duration of our relationship, and it was no real surprise when she moved on to a boy called Daz, a year older than me and already, incredibly, at work.

I was unhappy during the game (I watched it from the Clock End, although I don't know why; perhaps I felt that the focused energy of the North Bank would be inappropriate), but not because of what was going on in front of me: for the first time in nearly five years of watching Arsenal events on the pitch seemed meaningless, and it hardly registered that we lost 1–0 and blew the chance to go top. I knew instinctively, as Arsenal searched for an equaliser in the later stages of the game, that we would not score, that even if the Derby centre-half caught the ball and threw it at the referee we would miss the resultant penalty. How could we possibly win or draw, with me feeling like this? Football as metaphor, again.

I regretted our defeat against Derby, of course, although not as much as I regretted being dumped by Carol Blackburn. But what I regretted most of all – and this regret came to me much, much later on – was the wedge that had been driven between me and the club. Between 1968 and 1973, Saturdays were the whole point of my entire week, and whatever happened at school or at home was just so much fluff, the adverts in between the two halves of the Big Match. In that time football *was* life, and I am not speaking metaphorically: I experienced the big things – the pain of loss (Wembley '68 and '72), joy (the Double year), thwarted ambition (the European Cup quarter-final against Ajax), love (Charlie George) and ennui (most Saturdays, really) – only at Highbury. I even made new friends, through the youth team or the transfer market. What Carol Blackburn did was to give me another sort of life, the real, untransposed kind in which things happened to me rather than to the club, and as we all know, that is a rum sort of a gift.

GOODBYE TO ALL THAT

Arsenal v Manchester City

4.10.75

I have a few programmes for the 73/74 season, so I must have been to some of the games that year, but I can't remember any of them. I know that the following season I didn't go at all, and that the season after that, 75/76, I only went the once, with my Uncle Brian and my young cousin Michael.

I stopped partly because Arsenal were dire: George, McLintock and Kennedy had gone, and were never properly replaced, Radford and Armstrong were way past their best, Ball couldn't be bothered, a couple of the young players (Brady, Stapleton and O'Leary were all playing) were having understandable difficulties settling in to a struggling side, and some of the new purchases simply weren't up to the mark. (Terry Mancini, for example, a bald, cheerful and uncomplicated centre-half, seemed to have been bought for the Second Division promotion campaign that was beginning to look inevitable.) In seven years Highbury had once again become the unhappy home of a moribund football team, just as it had been when I first fell in love with it.

This time around, though, I didn't want to know (and neither did a good ten thousand others). I'd seen it all before. What I hadn't seen before were the high school and convent girls who worked in the Maidenhead High Street branch of Boots at weekends; and thus it was that some time in 1974, my after-school clearing-up and restocking job (which I had taken on only because I needed to find some football money) became an after-school and Saturday job.

I was still at school in 1975, but only just. I took my A-levels that summer, and scraped by in two of the three subjects; then, with breathtaking cheek, I decided to stay on for an extra term to study for the Cambridge entrance examinations – not, I think, because I wanted to go to Cambridge, but because I didn't want to go to university immediately, and yet neither did I want to travel around the world, or teach handicapped children, or work on a kibbutz, or do anything at all that might make me a more interesting person. So I worked a couple of days a week at Boots, went into school now and again, and hung out with the few people I knew who hadn't yet gone on to college.

I didn't miss football too much. I had swapped one group of friends for another during the sixth form: the football crowd who had got me through the first five years of secondary school, Frog, Larry aka Caz and the rest, had started to seem less interesting than the depressive and exquisitely laconic young men in my English set, and suddenly life was all drink and soft drugs and European literature and Van Morrison. My new group revolved around Henry, a newcomer to the school, who stood as a Raving Maoist in the school election (and won), took all his clothes off in pubs, and eventually ended up in some kind of asylum after stealing mailbags from the local railway station and throwing them up a tree. Kevin Keegan and his astonishing workrate seemed dull, perhaps understandably, by comparison. I watched football on TV, and two or three times went to see QPR in the season they nearly won the Championship with Stan Bowles, Gerry Francis, and the kind of swaggering football that had never really interested Arsenal. I was an intellectual now, and Brian Glanville's pieces in the *Sunday Times* had taught me that intellectuals were obliged to watch football for its art rather than its soul.

My mother has no brothers and sisters – all my relatives come from my father's side – and my parents' divorce isolated my mother and sister and me from the leafier branch of the family, partly through our own choice, partly through our geographical distance. It has been suggested to me that Arsenal substituted for an extended family during my teens, and though this is the kind of excuse I would like to make for myself, it is difficult even for me to explain how football could have performed the same function in my life as boisterous cousins, kindly aunts and avuncular uncles. There was a certain sort of symmetry, then, when my Uncle Brian rang to say that he was taking his Arsenal-loving thirteen-year-old to Highbury and to ask whether I would accompany them: maybe as football was ceasing to be a potent force in my life, the joys of extended family life were about to be revealed to me.

It was strange watching Michael, a younger version of myself, agonising for his team as they went 3–0 down and huffed their way back into the game (Arsenal lost 3–2 without ever really suggesting that they would get so much as a point). I could see the distraction in his face, and began to understand how football could mean so much to boys of that age: what else can we lose ourselves in, when books have started to become hard work and before girls have revealed themselves to be the focus that

I had now discovered they were? As I sat there, I knew it was all over for me, the Highbury scene. I didn't need it any more. And of course it was sad, because these six or seven years had been very important to me, had saved my life in several ways; but it was time to move on, to fulfil my academic and romantic potential, to leave football to those with less sophisticated or less developed tastes. Maybe Michael would take over for a few years, before passing it all on to someone else. It was nice to think that it wouldn't disappear from the family altogether, and maybe one day I would come back, with my own boy.

I didn't mention it to my uncle or to Michael – I didn't want to patronise him by suggesting in any way that football fever was an illness that only afflicted children – but when we were making our way out of the ground I bade it a private and sentimental farewell. I'd read enough poetry to recognise a heightened moment when I saw one. My childhood was dying, cleanly and decently, and if you can't mourn a loss of that resonance properly, then what can you mourn? At eighteen, I had at last grown up. Adulthood could not accommodate the kind of obsession I had been living with, and if I had to sacrifice Terry Mancini and Peter Simpson so that I could understand Camus properly and sleep with lots of nervy, neurotic and rapacious art students, then so be it. Life was about to begin, so Arsenal had to go.

1976–1986

MY SECOND CHILDHOOD

Arsenal v Bristol City

21.8.76

As it turned out, my coolness towards all things Arsenal had had nothing to do with rites of passage, or girls, or Jean-Paul Sartre, or Van Morrison, and quite a lot to do with the ineptitude of the Kidd/Stapleton strikeforce. When Bertie Mee resigned in 1976, and his replacement Terry Neill bought Malcolm Macdonald for £333,333 from Newcastle, my devotion mysteriously resurrected itself, and I was back at Highbury for the start of the new season, as stupidly optimistic for the club and as hungry to see a game as I had ever been in the early seventies, when my obsession had been at fever pitch. If I had been correct in assuming previously that my indifference marked the onset of maturity, then that maturity had lasted just ten months, and by the age of nineteen I was already into my second childhood.

Terry Neill was nobody's idea of a saviour, really. He had come directly from Tottenham, which didn't endear him to some of the Arsenal crowd, and it wasn't even as if he had done a great job there: he had only just avoided taking them into the Second Division (although they were destined for the drop anyway). But he was a new broom, at least, and there were some pretty cobwebbed corners in our team; judging from the size of the crowd for his first game in charge, I was not the only one who had been lured back by the promise of a new dawn.

In fact, Macdonald and Neill and a new era were only partly responsible for my return to the fold. Over the previous few months I had managed to turn myself into a schoolboy again, and I had done it, paradoxically, by leaving school and getting a job. After my university entrance exams I went to work for a huge insurance company in the City; the idea, I think, was to take my fascination with London to some kind of conclusion by becoming a part of the place, but this proved harder to do than I had imagined. I couldn't afford to live there, so I commuted from home (my salary went on the train fares and drinks after work), and I didn't even get to meet that many Londoners (although as I was fixed on the notion that *real* Londoners were people who lived in Gillespie Road, Avenell Road or Highbury Hill, N5, they were always going to be elusive). My workmates were for the most part like me, young commuters from the Home Counties.

So instead of turning myself into a metropolitan adult, I ended up recreating my suburban adolescence. I was bored witless most of the time, just as I had been at school (the company was about to relocate to Bristol, and we were all woefully underemployed); we sat, scores of us, in rows of desks trying to look busy, while embittered supervisors, denied even the minor dignity of the tiny cubicles in which their bosses worked, watched us like hawks and reprimanded us when our time-wasting became too conspicuous or noisy. It is in climates like this that football flourishes: I spent most of the long and lethally hot summer of 1976 talking about Charlie and the Double and Bobby Gould to a colleague, a dedicated and therefore somewhat wry fellow fan who was about to become a policeman just as I was about to become an undergraduate. Before very long I could feel some of my old enthusiasm beginning to re-exert its fierce grip.

Serious fans of the same club always see each other again somewhere – in a queue, or a chip shop, or a motorway service station toilet – and so it was inevitable that I would meet up with Kieran again. I saw him two years later, after the '78 Cup Final: he was sitting on a wall outside Wembley waiting for some friends, his banner drooping miserably in the post-match gloom, and it wasn't the right time to tell him that if it hadn't been for our office conversations that summer, I probably wouldn't even have been there that afternoon, feeling as miserable as he looked.

But that's another story. After my first game back, against Bristol City, I went home feeling as though I'd been tricked. Despite the introduction of Malcolm Macdonald, whose imperious wave to the crowd before the game led one to suspect the worst, Arsenal seemed no better than they had been for the last couple of years; in fact, given that they lost 1–0 at home to a Bristol City side which had crept up from the Second Division to struggle for four years in the First, it could well be argued that they were a good deal worse. I sweated in the August sunshine, and I cursed, and I felt the old screaming frustration that I had been happily living without. Like alcoholics who feel strong enough to pour themselves just one small one, I had made a fatal mistake.

SUPERMAC

Arsenal v Everton

18.9.76

On one of my videos (*George Graham's Greatest Ever Arsenal Team*, if anyone is interested), there is a perfect Malcolm Macdonald moment. Trevor Ross gets hold of the ball on the right, crosses before the Manchester United left-back can put a challenge in, Frank Stapleton leaps, nods and the ball trundles over the line and into the net. Why is this so quintessentially Supermac, given his lack of involvement in any part of the goal? Because there he is, making a desperate lunge for the ball before it crosses the line, apparently failing to make contact, and charging away to the right of the picture with his arms aloft, not to congratulate the goalscorer *but because he is staking a claim to the goal.* (There is an anxious little glance back over his shoulder when he realises that his team-mates seem uninterested in mobbing him.)

That Manchester United match is not the only example of his embarrassing penchant for claiming anything that came anywhere near him. In the FA Cup semi-final against Orient the following season, the record books show that he scored twice. In fact, both shots would have gone off for throw-ins – that is to say, they were not travelling even roughly in the direction of the goal – had they not hit an Orient defender (the same one each time) and looped in a ridiculous arc over the goalkeeper and into the net. Such considerations were beneath Malcolm, however, who celebrated both goals as if he had run the length of the field and beaten every defender before thumping the ball into the bottom left-hand corner. He wasn't much of a one for self-irony.

During this game against Everton, which we won 3–1 (a result which led us all to believe, once more, that a corner had been turned and that Terry Neill was building a team capable of winning the League again), there was another gem. Macdonald is in a chase with the centre-half, who gets a foot in, and lifts the ball agonisingly over his own advancing goalkeeper; but immediately Macdonald's arms are in the air, he is pounding towards us on the North Bank, he turns to acknowledge the joy of the rest of the team. Defenders are famously quick to disclaim an own goal if it is possible, but the Everton centre-half, staggered by his opponent's cheek, told the newspapers that our number nine hadn't got anywhere near the ball. Even so, Macdonald got the credit for it.

In truth, he didn't have much of a career at Arsenal. He retired with a serious knee injury after just three seasons with us, but in that last season he only played four times. He still managed to turn himself into a legend, though. He was a magnificent player, on his day, but there weren't too many of those at Highbury; his best spell was at Newcastle, a habitually poor team, but such was his ambition that he seems to have succeeded in muscling his way into the Arsenal Hall of Fame. (*Arsenal 1886–1986*, by Phil Soar and Martin Tyler, the definitive history of the club, features him prominently on the cover, whereas Wilson and Brady, Drake and Compton are nowhere to be seen.)

So why have we let him take over in this way? Why is a player who played less than a hundred games for Arsenal associated with the club more readily than others who played six or seven times that number? Macdonald was, if nothing else, a *glamorous* player, and we have never been a glamorous team; so at Highbury we pretend that he was more important than he really was, and we hope that when we put him on the cover of our glossy books, nobody will remember that he only played for us for two years, and that therefore we will be mistaken for Manchester United, or Tottenham, or Liverpool. Despite Arsenal's wealth and fame, we've never been in that mould – we have always been too grey, too suspicious of anyone with an ego – but we don't like to admit it. The Supermac myth is a confidence trick that the club plays on itself, and we are happy to indulge it.

A FOURTH DIVISION TOWN

Cambridge United v Darlington

29.1.77

I applied to Cambridge from the right place, at the right time. The university was actively looking for students who had been educated through the state system, and even my poor A-level results, my half-baked answers to the entrance examination and my hopelessly tongue-tied interview did not prevent me from being granted admission. At last my studiously dropped aitches were paying dividends, although not in the way that I had at one stage anticipated. They had not resulted in my acceptance on the North Bank, but they had resulted in my acceptance at Jesus College, Cambridge. It is surely only in our older universities that a Home Counties grammar school education carries with it some kind of street-cred.

It is true that most football fans do not have an Oxbridge degree (football fans are people, whatever the media would have us believe, and most people do not have an Oxbridge degree, either); but then, most football fans do not have a criminal record, or carry knives, or urinate in pockets, or get up to any of the things that they are all supposed to. In a book about football, the temptation to apologise (for Cambridge, and for not having left school at sixteen and gone on the dole, or down the pits, or into a detention centre) is overwhelming, but it would be entirely wrong to do so.

Whose game is it anyway? Some random phrases from Martin Amis's review of *Among the Thugs*, by Bill Buford: 'a love of ugliness'; 'pitbull eyes'; 'the complexion and body scent of a cheese-and-onion crisp'. These phrases are intended to build up a composite picture of the typical fan, and typical fans know this picture is wrong. I am aware that as far as my education and interests and occupation are concerned, I am hardly representative of a good many people on the terraces; but when it comes to my love for and knowledge of the game, the way I can and do talk about it whenever the opportunity presents itself, and my commitment to my team, I'm nothing out of the ordinary.

Football, famously, is the people's game, and as such is prey to all sorts of people who aren't, as it were, the people. Some like it because they are sentimental socialists; some because they went to public school, and regret doing so; some because their occupation – writer or broadcaster or advertising executive – has removed them far away from where they feel they belong, or where they have come from, and football seems to them a quick and painless way of getting back there. It is these people who seem to have the most need to portray football grounds as a bolt-hole for a festering, vicious underclass: after all, it is not in their best interests to tell the truth – that 'pitbull eyes' are few and far between, and often hidden behind specs, and that the stands are full of actors and publicity girls and teachers and accountants and doctors and nurses, as well as salt-of-the-earth working-class men in caps and loud-mouthed thugs. Without football's myriad demonologies, how are those who have been distanced from the modern world supposed to prove that they understand it?

'I would suggest that casting football supporters as "belching sub-humanity" makes it easier for us to be treated as such, and therefore easier for tragedies like Hillsborough to occur,' a wise man called Ed Horton wrote in the fanzine *When Saturday Comes* after reading Amis's review. 'Writers are welcome at football – the game does not have the literature it deserves. But snobs slumming it with "the lads" – there is nothing we need less.' Precisely. So the worst thing I can do for the game is offer atonement for, or deny, or excuse my education; Arsenal came long before Cambridge, and has stayed with me long after, and those three years make no difference to anything, as far as I can see.

In any case, when I arrived at college, it became clear that I was not alone: there were scores of us, boys from Nottingham and Newcastle and Essex, many of whom had been educated through the state system and welcomed by a college anxious to modulate its élitist image; and we all played football, and supported football teams, and within days we had all found each other, and it was like starting at grammar school all over again, except without the Soccer Star stickers.

I went up to Highbury from Maidenhead in the holidays, and travelled down from Cambridge for the big games, but I couldn't afford to do it very often – which is how I fell in love all over again, with Cambridge United. I hadn't intended to – the Us were only supposed to scratch the Saturday afternoon itch, but they ended up competing for attention in a way that nobody else had managed before.

I was not being unfaithful to Arsenal, because the two teams did not inhabit the same universe. If the two objects of my adoration had ever run up against each other at a party, or a wedding, or another of those awkward social situations one tries to avoid whenever possible, they would have been confused: if he loves *us*, whatever does he see in *them*? Arsenal had Highbury and big stars and huge crowds and the whole weight of history on their back; Cambridge had a tiny, ramshackle little ground, the Abbey Stadium (their equivalent of the Clock End was the Allotments End, and occasionally, naughty visiting fans would nip round the back of it and hurl pensioners' cabbages over the wall), less than four thousand watching at most games, and no history at all – they had only been in the Football League for six years. And when they won a game, the tannoy would blast out 'I've Got a Lovely Bunch of Coconuts', an eccentric touch that nobody seemed to be able to explain. It was impossible not to feel a warm, protective fondness for them.

It only took a couple of games before their results started to matter to me a great deal. It helped that they were a first-class Fourth Division team – manager Ron Atkinson had them playing stylish, fast, ball-to-feet football which usually brought them three or four goals at home (they beat Darlington 4–0 on my first visit), and it helped that in goalkeeper Webster and full-back Batson there was an Arsenal connection. I'd seen Webster throw in two goals during one of his few games for Arsenal back in 1969; and Batson, one of the first black players in the Football League in the early seventies, had been converted from a poor midfield player to a classy full-back since his move from Highbury.

What I enjoyed most of all, however, was the way the players revealed themselves, their characters and their flaws, almost immediately. The modern First Division player is for the most part an anonymous young man: he and his colleagues have interchangeable physiques, similar skills, similar pace, similar temperaments. Life in the Fourth Division was different. Cambridge had fat players and thin players, young players and old players, fast players and slow players, players who were on their way out and players who were on their way up. Jim Hall, the centre-forward, looked and moved like a forty-five-year-old; his striking partner Alan Biley, who later played for Everton and Derby, had an absurd Rod Stewart haircut and a greyhound's pace; Steve Spriggs, the midfield dynamo, was small and squat, with little stubby legs. (To my horror I was repeatedly mistaken for him during my time in the city. Once a man pointed me out to his young son as I was leaning against a wall, smoking a Rothmans and eating a meat pie, some ten minutes before a game in which Spriggs was appearing – a misapprehension which says much for the expectations the people of Cambridge had for their team; and once, in a men's toilet in a local pub, I got into an absurd argument with someone who simply refused to accept that I was not who I said I wasn't.) Most memorable of all was Tom Finney, a sly, bellicose winger who, incredibly, was to go on to the 1982 World Cup finals with Northern Ireland, although he only ever sat on the bench, and whose dives and fouls were often followed by outrageous winks to the crowd.

I used to believe, although I don't now, that growing and growing up are analogous, that both are inevitable and uncontrollable processes. Now it seems to me that growing up is governed by the will, that one can *choose* to become an adult, but only at given moments. These moments come along fairly infrequently – during crises in relationships, for example, or when one has been given the chance to start afresh somewhere – and one can ignore them or seize them. At Cambridge I could have reinvented myself if I had been smart enough; I could have shed the little boy whose Arsenal fixation had helped him through a tricky patch in his childhood and early teens, and become somebody else completely, a swaggeringly confident and ambitious young man sure of his route through the world. But I didn't. For some reason, I hung on to my boyhood self for dear life, and I let him guide me through my undergraduate years; and thus football, not for the first or last time, and through no fault of its own, served both as a backbone and as a retardant.

And that was university, really. No Footlights, no writing for *Broadsheet* or *Stop Press*, no Blue, no Presidency of the Union, no student politics, no dining clubs, no scholarships or exhibitions, no nothing. I watched a couple of films a week, I stayed up late and drank beer, I met a lot of nice people whom I still see regularly, I bought and borrowed records by Graham Parker and Television and Patti Smith and Bruce Springsteen and the Clash, I attended one lecture in my entire first year, I played twice a week for the college second or third teams . . . and I waited for home games at the Abbey or cup-ties at Highbury. I managed, in fact, to ensure that any of the privileges a Cambridge education can confer on its beneficiaries would bypass me completely. In truth I was scared of the place, and football, my childhood comforter, my security blanket, was a way of coping with it all.

BOYS AND GIRLS

Arsenal v Leicester City

2.4.77

I did something else in that year, apart from watch football, talk and listen to music: I fell stomach-clenchingly for a smart, pretty and vivacious girl from the teacher-training college. We cleared our desks (she had already attracted the attention of several other suitors in the first few weeks, and I had a girlfriend at home) and spent much of the next three or four years in each other's company.

She is a part of this story, I think, in several ways. For a start, she was the first girlfriend who ever came to Highbury (in the Easter holidays at the end of our second term). The early-season new-broom promise had long since disappeared; in fact, Arsenal had just beaten the club record for the longest losing streak in their history – they had managed to lose, in consecutive games, to Manchester City, Middlesbrough, West Ham, Everton, Ipswich, West Brom and QPR. She charmed the team, however, much as she had charmed me, and we scored three times in the first quarter of the game. Graham Rix got the first on his début and David O'Leary, who went on to score maybe another half a dozen times in the next decade, got two in the space of ten minutes. Once again Arsenal were thoughtful enough to behave so oddly that the match, and not just the occasion, would be memorable for me.

It was strange having her there. In a misguided notion of gallantry – I'm sure she would rather have stood – I insisted that we bought seats in the Lower West Stand; all I remember now is how she responded each time Arsenal scored. Everyone in the row stood up apart from her (in the seats, standing up to acclaim a goal is an involuntary action, like sneezing); three times I looked down to see her shaking with laughter. 'It's so *funny*,' she said by way of explanation, and I could see her point. It had really never occurred to me before that football was, indeed, a funny game, and that like most things which only work if one *believes*, the back view (and because she remained seated she had a back view, right down a line of mostly misshapen male bottoms) is preposterous, like the rear of a Hollywood film set.

Our relationship – the first serious, long-term, stay-the-night, meet-the-family, what-about-kids-one-day sort of thing for either of us – was in part all about discovering for the first time the mysteries of our *counterparts* in the opposite sex. I had had girlfriends before, of course; but she and I had similar backgrounds and similar pretensions, similar interests and attitudes. Our differences, which were enormous, arose mostly because of our genders; if I had been born a girl, she was the sort of girl, I realised and hoped, that I would have been. It was probably for this reason that I was so intrigued by her tastes and whims and fancies, and her belongings induced in me a fascination for girls' rooms that continued for as long as girls had rooms. (Now I am in my thirties they don't have rooms any more – they have flats or houses, and they are often shared with a man anyway. It is a sad loss.)

Her room helped me to understand that girls were much quirkier than boys, a realisation that stung me. She had a collection of Yevtushenko's poems (who the hell was Yevtushenko?) and unfathomable obsessions with Anne Boleyn and the Brontës; she liked all the sensitive singer/songwriters, and was familiar with the ideas of Germaine Greer; she knew a little about paintings and classical music, knowledge gleaned from somewhere outside the A-level syllabus. How had that happened? How come I had to rely on a couple of Chandler paperbacks and the first Ramones album to provide me with some kind of identity? Girls' rooms provided countless clues to their character and background and tastes; boys, by contrast, were as interchangeable and unformed as foetuses, and their rooms, apart from the odd Athena poster here and there (I had a Rod Stewart poster on my wall, which I liked to think was aggressively, authentically and self-consciously down-market) were as blank as the womb.

It is true to say that most of us were defined only by the number and extent of our interests. Some boys had more records than others, and some knew more about football; some were interested in cars, or rugby. We had passions instead of personalities, predictable and uninteresting passions at that, passions which could not reflect and illuminate us in the way that my girlfriend's did . . . and this is one of the most inexplicable differences between men and women.

I have met women who have loved football, and go to watch a number of games a season, but I have not yet met one who would make that Wednesday night trip to Plymouth. And I have met women who love music, and can tell their Mavis Staples from their Shirley Browns, but I have never met a woman with a huge and ever-expanding and neurotically alphabeticised record collection. They always seem to have lost their records, or to have relied on somebody else in the house – a boyfriend, a brother, a flatmate, usually a male – to have provided the physical details of their interests. Men cannot allow that to happen. (I am aware, sometimes, in my group of Arsenal-supporting friends, of an understated but noticeable jockeying: none of us likes to be told something about the club that we didn't know – an injury to one of the reserves, say, or an impending alteration to the shirt design, something crucial like that – by any of the others.) I am not saying that the anally retentive woman does not exist, but she is vastly outnumbered by her masculine equivalent; and while there are women with obsessions, they are usually, I think, obsessive about people, or the focus for their obsession changes frequently.

Remembering my late teens at college, when many of the boys were as colourless as tap water, it is tempting to believe that it all starts around that time, that men have had to develop their facility to store facts and records and football programmes to compensate for their lack of distinguishing wrinkles; but that doesn't explain how it is that one ordinary, bright teenager has already become more interesting than another ordinary, bright teenager, simply by virtue of her sex.

It is perhaps no wonder that my girlfriend wanted to come to Highbury: there wasn't really very much else of me (she'd listened to my Ramones album), or at least nothing that I had yet discovered and extracted. I did have things that were mine – my friends, my relationships with my mum and my dad and my sister, my music, my love for cinema, my sense of humour – but I couldn't see that they amounted to very much that was individual, not in the way that her things were individual; but my solitary and intense devotion to Arsenal, and its attendant necessities (my vowel-mangling was by now at a point of almost inoperable crisis) . . . well, at least it had an edge to it, and gave me a couple of features other than a nose, two eyes and a mouth.

JUST LIKE A WOMAN

Cambridge United v Exeter City

29.4.78

My arrival in Cambridge provoked the two best seasons in United's short history. In my first year they won the Fourth Division by a mile; in my second, they found life a bit tougher in the Third, and had to wait until the final week of the season before clinching promotion. They had two games in a week at the Abbey: one on the Tuesday night against Wrexham, the best team in the division, which they won 1–0, and one on the Saturday against Exeter, which they needed to win to be sure of going up.

With twenty minutes to go, Exeter went into the lead, and my girlfriend (who together with her girlfriend and her girlfriend's boyfriend had wanted to experience at first hand the dizzy glory of promotion) promptly did what I had always presumed women were apt to do at moments of crisis: she fainted. Her girlfriend took her off to see the St John's Ambulancemen; I, meanwhile, did nothing, apart from pray for an equaliser, which came, followed minutes later by a winner. It was only after the players had popped the last champagne cork at the jubilant crowd that I started to feel bad about my earlier indifference.

I had recently read *The Female Eunuch*, a book which made a deep and lasting impression on me. And yet how was I supposed to get excited about the oppression of females if they couldn't be trusted to stay upright during the final minutes of a desperately close promotion campaign? And what was to be done about a male who was more concerned about being a goal down to Exeter City of the Third Division than he was about somebody he loved very much? It all looked hopeless.

Thirteen years later I am still ashamed of my unwillingness, my *inability*, to help, and the reason I feel ashamed is partly to do with the awareness that I haven't changed a bit. I don't want to look after anybody when I'm at a match; I am not *capable* of looking after anybody at a match. I am writing some nine hours before Arsenal play Benfica in the European Cup, the most important match at Highbury for years, and my partner will be with me: what happens if *she* keels over? Would I have the decency, the maturity, the common sense, to make sure that she was properly looked after? Or would I shove her limp body to one side, carry on screaming at the linesman, and hope that she is still breathing at the end of ninety minutes, always presuming, of course, that extra time and penalties are not required?

I know that these worries are prompted by the little boy in me, who is allowed to run riot when it comes to football: this little boy feels that women are *always* going to faint at football matches, that they are weak, that their presence at games will inevitably result in distraction and disaster, even though my present partner has been to Highbury probably forty or fifty times and has shown no signs of fainting whatsoever. (In fact it is I who have come closest to fainting on occasions, when the tension of the last five minutes of a cup-tie constricts my chest and forces all the blood out of my head, if that is biologically possible; and sometimes, when Arsenal score, I see stars, literally – well, little splodges of light, literally – which cannot be a sign of great physical robustness.) But then, that is what football has done to me. It has turned me into someone who would not help if my girlfriend went into labour at an impossible moment (I have often wondered about what would happen if I was due to become a father on an Arsenal Cup Final day); and for the duration of the games I am an eleven-year-old. When I described football as a retardant, I meant it.

WEMBLEY III – THE HORROR RETURNS

Arsenal v Ipswich
6.5.78

It is a truth universally acknowledged that ticket distribution for Cup Finals is a farce: the two clubs involved, as all supporters know, get less than half the tickets, which means that thirty or forty thousand people with no direct interest in the game get the other half. The Football Association's rationale is that the Cup Final is for everybody involved with football, not just the fans, and it's not a bad one: it is, I think, quite reasonable to invite referees and linesmen and amateur players and local league secretaries to the biggest day in football's year. There is more than one way to watch a game, after all, and on this sort of occasion enthusiastic neutrals have their place.

The only flaw in the system is that these enthusiastic neutrals, these unimpeachable servants of the game, invariably decide that their endeavours are best recompensed not by a trip to London to see the big game, but by a phone call to their local tout: a good 90 per cent of them just flog the tickets they are given, and these tickets eventually end up in the hands of the fans who were denied them in the first place. It is a ludicrous process, a typically scandalous slice of Football Association idiocy: everybody knows what is going to happen, and nobody does anything about it.

Dad got me a ticket for the Ipswich Final via work contacts, but there were others available, even at university, because the Blues are customarily sent half a dozen. (The following year, when Arsenal were again in the Final, I ended up with two tickets. One was from my next-door neighbour, who had associations with a very big club in the north-west of England, a club that has been in trouble before with the FA for its cavalier distribution of Cup Final tickets: he simply wrote to them and asked for one, and they sent it to him.) There were, no doubt, many more deserving recipients of a seat than I, people who had spent the season travelling the length of the country watching Arsenal rather than messing around at college, but I was a genuine fan of one of the Cup Final teams, at least, and as such more entitled than many who were there.

My companions for the afternoon were affable, welcoming middle-aged men in their late thirties and early forties who simply had no conception of the import of the afternoon for the rest of us. To them it was an afternoon out, a fun thing to do on a Saturday afternoon; if I were to meet them again, they would, I think, be unable to recall the score that afternoon, or the scorer (at half-time they talked office politics), and in a way I envied them their indifference. Perhaps there is an argument which says that Cup Final tickets are wasted on the fans, in the way that youth is wasted on the young; these men, who knew just enough about football to get them through the afternoon, actively enjoyed the occasion, its drama and its noise and its momentum, whereas I hated every minute of it, as I had hated every Cup Final involving Arsenal.

I had now been an Arsenal supporter for ten seasons – just under half my life. In only two of those ten seasons had Arsenal won trophies; they had reached finals, and failed horribly, in another two. But these triumphs and failures had all occurred in my first four years, and I had gone from the age of fifteen, when I was living one life, to the age of twenty-one, when I was living a completely different one. Like gas lamps and horse-drawn carriages – or perhaps like Spirographs and Sekidens – Wembley and championships were beginning to seem as though they belonged to a previous world.

When we reached, and then won, the FA Cup semi-final in 1978, it felt as though the sun had come out after several years of November afternoons. Arsenal-haters will have forgotten, or will simply refuse to believe, that this Arsenal team was capable of playing delightful, even enthralling football: Rix and Brady, Stapleton and Macdonald, Sunderland and, best of all, for one season only, Alan Hudson . . . for three or four months it looked as if this was a team that could make us happy in all the ways in which it is possible to be made happy at football.

If I were writing a novel, Arsenal would win the '78 Cup Final. A win makes more sense rhythmically and thematically; another Wembley defeat at this point would stretch the reader's patience and sense of justice. The only excuses I can offer for my poor plotting are that Brady was patently unfit and should never have played, and Supermac, who had made some typical and unwise remarks in the press about what he was going to do to the Ipswich back four, was worse than useless. (He had made the same compound error, of boasting loudly and then failing to deliver, four years earlier, when he was playing for Newcastle; some time after the Ipswich fiasco the *Guardian* printed a Cup trivia question: 'What is taken to the Cup Final every year but never used?' The answer they wanted was the ribbons for the losing team, which are never tied on to the handle of the Cup, but some smartass wrote in and suggested Malcolm Macdonald.) It was an overwhelmingly one-sided final, even though Ipswich didn't score until the second half; we never looked like getting the goal back, and lost 1–0.

So I had now lost three out of three at Wembley, and was convinced that I would never, ever see Arsenal running around Wembley with anything at all. Yet '78 is perhaps the least painful of the defeats, because I was with people who were not pained by it at all, not even the man with the red-and-white scarf (suspiciously clean, as if he had bought it outside the stadium). It is a strange paradox that while the grief of football fans (and it is real grief) is private – we each have an individual relationship with our clubs, and I think that we are secretly convinced that none of the other fans understands quite why we have been harder hit than anyone else – we are forced to mourn in public, surrounded by people whose hurt is expressed in forms different from our own.

Many fans express anger, against their own team or the supporters of the opponents – real, foul-mouthed fury that upsets and saddens me. I have never felt the desire to do that; I just want to be on my own to think, to wallow for a little while, and to recover the strength necessary to go back and start all over again. These men, the business types, were sympathetic but unconcerned. They offered me a drink and I declined, so they shook my hand and offered commiserations and I disappeared; to them, it really was only a game, and it probably did me good to spend time with people who behaved for all the world as if football were a diverting entertainment, like rugby or golf or cricket. It's not like that at all, of course, but just for an afternoon it was interesting and instructive to meet people who believed that it was.

SUGAR MICE AND BUZZCOCKS ALBUMS

Cambridge United v Orient

4.11.78

What happened was, Chris Roberts bought a sugar mouse from Jack Reynolds ('The Rock King'), bit its head off, dropped it in the Newmarket Road before he could get started on the body, and it got run over by a car. And that afternoon Cambridge United, who had hitherto been finding life difficult in the Second Division (two wins all season, one home, one away), beat Orient 3–1, and a ritual was born. Before each home game we all of us trooped into the sweet shop, purchased our mice, walked outside, bit the head off as though we were removing the pin from a grenade, and tossed the torsos under the wheels of oncoming cars; Jack Reynolds would stand in the doorway watching us, shaking his head sorrowfully. United, thus protected, remained unbeaten at the Abbey for months.

I know that I am particularly stupid about rituals, and have been ever since I started going to football matches, and I know also that I am not alone. I can remember when I was young having to take with me to Highbury a piece of putty, or Blu-Tack, or some stupid thing, which I pulled on nervously all afternoon (I was a smoker even before I was old enough to smoke); I can also remember having to buy a programme from the same programme seller, and having to enter the stadium through the same turnstile.

There have been hundreds of similar bits of nonsense, all designed to guarantee victories for one or other of my two teams. During Arsenal's protracted and nerve-racking semi-final campaign against Liverpool in 1980, I turned the radio off half-way through the second half of the last game; Arsenal were winning 1–0, and as Liverpool had equalised in the last seconds of the previous game, I couldn't bear to hear it through to the end. I played a Buzzcocks album instead (the *Singles – Going Steady* compilation album), knowing that side one would take me through to the final whistle. We won the match, and I insisted that my flatmate, who worked in a record store, should play the album at twenty past four on Cup Final afternoon, although it did no good. (I have my suspicions that he might have forgotten.)

I have tried 'smoking' goals in (Arsenal once scored as three of us were lighting cigarettes), and eating cheese-and-onion crisps at a certain point in the first half; I have tried not setting the video for live games (the team seems to have suffered badly in the past when I have taped the matches in order to study the performance when I get home); I have tried lucky socks, and lucky shirts, and lucky hats, and lucky friends, and have attempted to exclude others who I feel bring with them nothing but trouble for the team.

Nothing (apart from the sugar mice) has ever been any good. But what else can we do when we're so *weak*? We invest hours each day, months each year, years each lifetime in something over which we have no control; is it any wonder then, that we are reduced to creating ingenious but bizarre liturgies designed to give us the illusion that we are powerful after all, just as every other primitive community has done when faced with a deep and apparently impenetrable mystery?

WEMBLEY IV – THE CATHARSIS

Arsenal v Manchester United

12.5.79

I had no ambitions for myself whatsoever before I was twenty-six or twenty-seven, when I decided that I could and would write for a living, packed my job in and waited around for publishers and/or Hollywood producers to call me up and ask me to do something for them sight unseen. Friends at college must have asked me what I intended to do with my life, particularly because by now I was in my final term; but the future still seemed to me as unimaginable and as uninteresting as it had when I was four or five, so I have no idea what I might have answered. I probably mumbled something about journalism or publishing (the aimless arts undergraduate's exact equivalent of train driving or astronautics), but privately I was beginning to suspect that as I had spent my three years unwisely, these careers would not be possible. I knew people who had spent their entire undergraduate lives writing for university newspapers who were not being offered jobs, so what chance did I stand? I decided that it would be better not to know, and therefore applied for nothing at all.

I may have had no ideas for myself, but I had big ideas for my football teams. Two of these dreams – Cambridge United's promotion from the

Fourth to the Third, and then from the Third to the Second – had been realised already. But the third and most burning ambition, to see Arsenal win the FA Cup at Wembley (and maybe this was, after all, a personal ambition, in that my presence was an essential part of it), still remained unfulfilled.

The team had done remarkably well to return to the Cup Final for a second consecutive season. It took them five games to get past Third Division Sheffield Wednesday (the police have recently decided, in their community-serving way, that the beautiful and strange FA Cup tradition of the multi-game marathon should not be allowed to continue); they then had a tough away draw at Nottingham Forest, the European champions, and another tricky game at Southampton, won after a replay by two brilliant Alan Sunderland goals. The semi-final against Wolves was comparatively straightforward, despite Brady's absence through injury: two second-half goals, from Sunderland and Stapleton, and they were back at Wembley.

Exactly a decade after the Manchester United Cup Final, in May 1989, I was waiting to hear news about a script I had written at the same time as Arsenal's best chance of winning the Championship for eighteen years seemed to be disappearing fast. The script, a pilot for a projected sitcom, had got further than usual; there had been meetings with people from Channel 4, and great enthusiasm, and things looked good. But in despair after a bad result, a home defeat by Derby on the final Saturday of the season, I offered up my work (the acceptance of which would have rescued a career and a self-regard heading for oblivion) on some kind of personal sacrificial altar: if we win the League, I won't mind the rejection slip. The rejection slip duly came, and hurt like hell for months; but the Championship came too, and now, two years later, when the disappointment has long gone but the thrill of Michael Thomas's goal still gives me goose pimples when I think about it, I know that the bargain I made was the right one.

In May 1979 the potential for trade-offs was extensive and complicated. On the Thursday before the Cup Final, Mrs Thatcher was attempting to win her first General Election; on the Thursday after, my finals began. Of the three events, the Cup Final, obviously, was the one that concerned me most, although I was also perturbed, just as obviously, by the prospect of Mrs Thatcher becoming Prime Minister. (Maybe in another, quieter week I would have found time and energy to fret about my examinations, but a mediocre degree was now an inevitability, and in any case at British universities it is as easy to graduate as it is to have a birthday: just hang around for a while and it will happen.) Yet the terrible truth is that I was willing to accept a Conservative government if it guaranteed an Arsenal Cup Final win; I could hardly have been expected to anticipate that Mrs Thatcher would go on to become the longest-serving Prime Minister this century. (Would I have made the same bargain if I had known? Eleven years of Thatcherism for the FA Cup? Of course not. I wouldn't have settled for anything less than another Double.)

The fact that the Tories won comfortably on the Thursday didn't mean that I expected us to win comfortably on the Saturday. I knew that making bargains, like squeezing putty and wearing certain shirts, didn't guarantee success, and in any case the other finalists, Manchester United, were a proper team, not a roll-over-and-die, only-here-for-the-beer shower, like, well, like Ipswich, say, or Swindon. Manchester United were the kind of team who might well unsportingly ignore General Election deals simply by scoring loads of goals and thrashing us.

For most of the game, however, United played as if they knew what my deal had been and were more than happy to fulfil their side of it. Arsenal scored twice in the first half, the opening goal after twelve minutes (the first time in four games I had seen Arsenal take the lead at Wembley), the second goal right before half-time; the interval was a blissfully relaxed fifteen minutes of raucous celebration. Most of the second half passed by in the same way, until with five minutes to go Manchester United scored . . . and with two minutes to go, in traumatising and muddled slow motion, they scored again. We had thrown the game away, players and fans all knew that, and as I watched the United players cavort on the touchline at the far end I was left with the terrible feeling that I'd had as a child – that I hated Arsenal, that the club was a burden I could no longer carry but one that I would never, ever be able to throw off.

I was high up on the terraces with the other Arsenal fans, right behind the goal that Manchester United were defending; I sat down, too dizzy with pain and anger and frustration and self-pity to remain on my feet any longer. There were others who did the same, and behind me a pair of teenage girls were weeping silently, not in the hammy fashion of teenage girls at Bay City Rollers concerts, but in a way that suggested a deep and personal grief.

I was looking after a young American lad for the afternoon, a friend of the family, and his mild sympathy but obvious bafflement threw my distress into embarrassing relief: I *knew* that it was only a game, that worse things happened at sea, that people were starving in Africa, that there might be a nuclear holocaust within the next few months; I knew that the score was still 2–2, for heaven's sake, and that there was a chance that Arsenal could somehow find a way out of the mire (although I also knew that the tide had turned, and that the players were too demoralised to be able to win the game in extra time). But none of this knowledge could help me. I had been but five minutes away from fulfilling the only fully formed ambition I had ever consciously held since the age of eleven; and if people are allowed to grieve when they are passed over for promotion, or when they fail to win an Oscar, or when their novel is rejected by every publisher in London – and our culture allows them to do so, even though these people may only have dreamed these dreams for a couple of years, rather than the decade, the *half-lifetime*, that I had been dreaming mine – then I was bloody well entitled to sit down on a lump of concrete for two minutes and try to blink back tears.

And it really was for only two minutes. When the game restarted, Liam Brady took the ball deep into the United half (afterwards he said that he was knackered, and was only trying to prevent the loss of a third goal) and pushed it out wide to Rix. I was watching this, but not *seeing* it; even when Rix's cross came over and United's goalkeeper Gary Bailey missed it I wasn't paying much attention. But then Alan Sunderland got his foot to the ball, poked it in, right into the goal in front of us, and I was shouting not 'Yes' or 'Goal' or any of the other noises that customarily come to my throat at these times but just a noise, 'AAAARRRRGGGGHHHH', a noise borne of utter joy and stunned disbelief, and suddenly there were people on the concrete terraces again, but they were rolling around on top of each other, bug-eyed and berserk. Brian, the American kid, looked at me, smiled politely and tried to find his hands amidst the mayhem below him so that he could raise them and clap with an enthusiasm I suspected he did not feel.

I floated through my finals as if I had been anaesthetised with a benign, idiocy-inducing drug. Some of my fellow-students, grey with sleeplessness and concern, were perplexed by my mood; others, the football fans, understood and were envious. (At college, just as at school, there were no other Arsenal fans.) I got my mediocre degree without any undue alarm; and some two months later, when I had come down from the Cup Final win and the end-of-year celebrations, I began to face up to the fact that on the afternoon of 12th May I had achieved most of what I had ever wanted to achieve in my life, and that I had no idea what to do with the rest of it. I was twenty-two, and the future suddenly looked blank and scary.

FILLING A HOLE

Arsenal v Liverpool

1.5.80

It is hard for me, and for many of us, to think of years as being self-contained, with a beginning on 1st January and an ending 365 days later. I was going to say that 1980 was a torpid, blank, directionless year for me but that would be wrong; it was *79/80* that was these things. Football fans talk like that: our years, our units of time, run from August to May (June and July don't really happen, especially in years which end with an odd number and which therefore contain no World Cup or European Championship). Ask us for the best or the worst period in our lives and we will often answer with four figures – 66/67 for Manchester United fans, 67/68 for Manchester City fans, 69/70 for Everton fans, and so on – a silent slash in the middle of them the only concession to the calendar used elsewhere in the western world. We get drunk on New Year's Eve, just as everyone else does, but really it is after the Cup Final in May that our mental clock is wound back, and we indulge in all the vows and regrets and renewals that ordinary people allow themselves at the end of the conventional year.

Perhaps we should be given a day off work on Cup Final Eve, so that we can gather together and celebrate. We are, after all, a community within a community; and just as the Chinese have their New Year, when in London the streets around Leicester Square are closed off and the London Chinese have a procession and eat traditional food, and the tourists come to watch them, maybe there is a way in which we can mark the passing of another season of dismal failure, dodgy refereeing decisions, bad back-passes and terrible transfer dealing. We could dress up in our horrible new away shirts, and chant and sing; we could eat

Wagon Wheels – the marshmallow biscuit that only football fans eat, because it is only sold at football grounds – and gangrenous hamburgers, and drink warm and luridly orange fizz from a plastic bottle, a refreshment manufactured especially for the occasion by a company called something like Stavros of Edmonton. And we could get the police to keep us standing in . . . oh, forget it. This terrible litany has made me realise just how awful our lives are for these nine months, and that when they are over I want to live every day of the twelve short weeks available to me as if I were a human being.

For me, 79/80 was a season when football – always hitherto the backbone of life – provided the entire skeleton. For the whole season I did nothing else apart from go to the pub, work (in a garage outside Cambridge, because I could think of nothing better to do), hang out with my girlfriend, whose course lasted a year longer than mine, and wait for Saturdays and Wednesdays. The extraordinary thing was that Arsenal in particular seemed to respond to my need for as much football as possible: they played seventy games that season, twenty-eight of them cup-ties of one kind or another. Every time I gave any indication of becoming more listless than was good for me, Arsenal obliged by providing another match.

By April 1980 I was sick to death of my job, and my indecision, and myself. But just when it began to seem as though the holes in my life were too big to be plugged, even by football, Arsenal's anxiety to distract me became frenzied: between 9th April and 1st May they played six semi-final games, four against Liverpool in the FA Cup and two against Juventus in the Cup-Winners Cup. Only one of these – the first leg of the Juventus tie – was in London, and so everything revolved around the radio. All I can recall about that entire month is that I worked, and slept, and listened to Peter Jones and Bryon Butler live from Villa Park or Hillsborough or Highfield Road.

I'm not a good radio listener, but then very few fans are. The crowd are much quicker than the commentators – the roars and groans precede the descriptions of the action by several seconds – and my inability to see the pitch makes me much more nervous than I would be if I were at the game, or watching on TV. On the radio, every shot at your goal is heading for the top corner, every cross creates panic, every opposition free kick is right on the edge of the area; in those days before televised live games, when Radio 2 was my only link with Arsenal's distant cup exploits, I used to sit playing with the dial, switching between one station and another, desperate to know what was going on, but equally desperate not to have to hear. Radio football is football reduced to its lowest common denominator. Shorn of the game's aesthetic pleasures, or the comfort of a crowd that feels the same way as you, or the sense of security that you get when you see that your defenders and goalkeeper are more or less where they should be, all that is left is naked fear. The bleak, ghostly howl that used to afflict Radio 2 in the evenings was entirely apposite.

The last two of those four semi-finals against Liverpool nearly killed me. In the third match, Arsenal took the lead in the first minute and hung on to it for the next eighty-nine; I sat and stood and smoked and wandered around for the entirety of the second half, unable to read or talk or think, until Liverpool equalised in injury time. The equaliser was like the shot from a gun that had been aimed at my head for an hour, the sickening difference being that it didn't put an end to it all like a bullet would have done – on the contrary, it forced me to go through the whole thing again. In the fourth game, three days later, Arsenal took the lead once more, which was when I became so fearful that I had to turn the radio off and discovered the talismanic properties of the Buzzcocks. This time, Liverpool didn't come back, and Arsenal reached their third FA Cup Final in three years; the trouble was that I was almost too wrung-out and jumpy and nicotine-poisoned to care.

LIAM BRADY

Arsenal v Nottingham Forest

5.5.80

For a year I had lived with the possibility of Liam Brady's transfer to another club in the same way that, in the late fifties and early sixties, American teenagers had lived with the possibility of the impending Apocalypse. I knew it would happen, yet, even so, I allowed myself to hope; I fretted about it daily, read all the papers scrupulously for hints that he might sign a new contract, studied his onfield relationship with the other players at the club carefully in case it revealed signs of bonds too strong to be broken. I had never felt so intensely about an Arsenal player: for five years he was the focus of the team, and therefore the centre of a very important part of myself, and the consciousness of his rumoured desire to leave Arsenal was always with me, a small shadow on any X-ray of my well-being.

Most of this fixation was easy to explain. Brady was a midfield player, a passer, and Arsenal haven't really had one since he left. It might surprise those who have a rudimentary grasp of the rules of the game to learn that a First Division football team can try to play football without a player who can pass the ball, but it no longer surprises the rest of us: passing went out of fashion just after silk scarves and just before inflatable bananas. Managers, coaches and therefore players now favour alternative methods of moving the ball from one part of the field to another, the chief of which is a sort of wall of muscle strung across the half-way line in order to deflect the ball in the general direction of the forwards. Most, indeed all, football fans regret this. I think I can speak for all of us when I say that we used to *like* passing, that we felt that on the whole it was a good thing. It was nice to watch, football's prettiest accessory (a good player could pass to a team-mate we hadn't seen, or find an angle we wouldn't have thought of, so there was a pleasing geometry to it), but managers seemed to feel that it was a lot of trouble, and therefore stopped bothering to produce any players who could do it. There are still a couple of passers in England, but then, there are still a number of blacksmiths.

We overrate the seventies, most of us in our thirties. We look back on it as a golden age, and buy the old shirts, and watch old videos, and talk with awe and regret of Keegan and Toshack, Bell and Summerbee, Hector and Todd. We forget that the England team didn't even qualify for two World Cups, and we overlook the fact that most First Division teams contained at least one player – Storey at Arsenal, Smith at Liverpool, Harris at Chelsea – who simply wasn't very good at football at all. Commentators and journalists complain about the behaviour of today's professionals – Gazza's petulance, Fashanu's elbows, Arsenal's brawling – but they chuckle indulgently when they remember Lee and Hunter scrapping all the way back to the dressing rooms after they had been sent off, or Bremner and Keegan being banished for fighting in a *Charity Shield* game. Players in the seventies weren't as fast or as fit, and probably most of them weren't even as skilful; but every single side had someone who could pass the ball.

Liam Brady was one of the best two or three passers of the last twenty years, and this in itself was why he was revered by every single Arsenal fan, but for me there was more to it than that. I worshipped him because he was great, and I worshipped him because, in the parlance, if you cut him he would bleed Arsenal (like Charlie George he was a product of the youth team); but there was a third thing, too. *He was intelligent.* This intelligence manifested itself primarily in his passing, which was incisive and imaginative and constantly surprising. But it showed off the pitch too: he was articulate, and drily funny, and engaged ('Come on David, put it away' he cried from the commentary box when his friend and old Arsenal colleague David O'Leary was about to take the decisive penalty for Ireland in the 1990 World Cup-tie against Romania); as I progressed through the academic strata, and more and more people seemed to make a distinction between football on the one hand and the life of the mind on the other, Brady seemed to provide a bridge between the two.

Of course, intelligence in a footballer is no bad thing, particularly in a midfield player, a playmaker, although this intelligence is not the same intelligence as that required to enjoy, say, a 'difficult' European novel. Paul Gascoigne has the footballing intelligence by the bucketload (and it is a dazzling intelligence, involving, among other skills, astonishing co-ordination and a lightning-fast exploitation of a situation that will change within a couple of seconds), yet his lack of even the most basic common sense is obvious and legendary. All the best footballers have some kind of wit about them: Lineker's anticipation, Shilton's positioning, Beckenbauer's understanding are products of their brains rather than functions of simple athleticism. Yet it is the classical midfielder whose cerebral attributes receive the most attention, particularly from the sports writers on the quality papers and from the middle-class football fans.

This is not only because the sort of intelligence that Brady and his ilk possess is the most visible, in footballing terms, but because it is analogous to the sort of intelligence that is prized in middle-class culture. Look at the adjectives used to describe playmakers: *elegant, aware, subtle, sophisticated, cunning, visionary* . . . these are words that could equally well describe a poet, or a film-maker, or a painter. It is as if the truly gifted footballer is too good for his milieu, and must be placed on a different, higher plane.

Certainly there was an element of this attitude in my deification of

Brady. Charlie George, the previous idol of the Arsenal North Bank, had never been *mine* in the way Liam was. Brady was different (although of course he wasn't, really – his background was pretty much the same as that of most footballers) because he was languid and mysterious, and though I possessed neither of these qualities, I felt that my education had equipped me to recognise them in others. 'A poet of the left foot,' my sister used to remark drily whenever I mentioned his name, which was often, but there was a truth behind her irony: for a time I wanted footballers to be as unlike themselves as possible and, though this was stupid, other people do it still. Pat Nevin, particularly in his Chelsea days, became a much better player when it was discovered that he knew about art and books and politics.

The Nottingham Forest game, a sleepy nil–nil draw on a sleepy, grey, Bank Holiday Monday, was Brady's last at Highbury; he had decided that his future lay abroad, in Italy, and he was gone for several years. I was there to see him off, and he did a slow, sad lap of honour with the rest of the team. Deep down I think I still hoped that he would change his mind, or that the club would eventually become aware of the irreparable damage it would do to itself if it allowed him to leave. Some said that money was at the heart of it, and that if Arsenal had stumped up more he would have stayed, but I preferred not to believe them. I preferred to believe that it was the promise of Italy itself, its culture and style, that had lured him away, and that the parochial pleasures of Hertfordshire or Essex or wherever he lived had inevitably begun to fill him with an existential ennui. What I knew most of all was that he didn't want to leave us all, that he was torn, that he loved us as much as we loved him and that one day he would come back.

Just seven months after losing Liam to Juventus I lost my girlfriend to another man, slap-bang in the middle of the first dismal post-Brady season. And though I knew which loss hurt the most – Liam's transfer induced regret and sadness, but not, thankfully, the insomnia and nausea and impossible, inconsolable bitterness of a twenty-three-year-old broken heart – I think that in some strange way she and Liam got muddled up in my mind. The two of them, Brady and the Lost Girl, haunted me for a long time, five or six years, maybe, so in a way it was predictable that one ghost should melt into the other. After Brady had gone Arsenal tried out a string of midfield players, some of them competent, some not, all of them doomed by the fact that they weren't the person they were trying to replace: between 1980 and 1986 Talbot, Rix, Hollins, Price, Gatting, Peter Nicholas, Robson, Petrovic, Charlie Nicholas, Davis, Williams and even centre-forward Paul Mariner all played in central midfield.

And I had a string of relationships over the next four or five years, some serious, some not . . . the parallels were endless. Brady's often-rumoured return (he played for four different clubs in his eight years in Italy, and before each transfer the English tabloids were full of unforgivably cruel stories about how Arsenal were on the verge of re-signing him) began to take on a shamanistic quality. I knew, of course, that the bouts of vicious, exhausting depression that afflicted me in the early to mid-eighties were not caused either by Brady or the Lost Girl. They were to do with something else, something much more difficult to comprehend, and something that must have been in me for much longer than either of these two blameless people. But during these terrifying downs, I would think back to times when I had last felt happy, fulfilled, energetic, optimistic; and she and Brady were a part of those times. They weren't entirely responsible for them, but they were very much there during them, and that was enough to turn these two love affairs into the twin supporting pillars of a different, enchanted age.

Some five or six years after he had gone, Brady did come home, to play for Arsenal in Pat Jennings' testimonial game. It was a strange night. We were in even more need of him than ever (a graph of Arsenal's fortunes in the eighties would resemble a U-bend), and before the game I felt nervous, but not in the way that I usually felt nervous before big games – these were the nerves of a former suitor about to embark on an unavoidably painful but long-anticipated reunion. I hoped, I suppose, that an ecstatic and tearful reception would trigger something off in Brady, that he would realise that his absence made him, as well as us, less than whole somehow. But nothing of the kind happened. He played the game, waved at us and flew back to Italy the next morning, and the next time we saw him he was wearing a West Ham shirt and smashing the ball past our goalkeeper John Lukic from the edge of the area.

We never did replace him satisfactorily, but we found different people, with different qualities; it took me a long time to realise that this is as good a way of coping with loss as any.

ARSENALESQUE

West Ham v Arsenal

10.5.80

Everyone knows the song that Millwall fans sing, to the tune of 'Sailing': 'No one likes us/No one likes us/No one likes us/We don't care.' In fact I have always felt that the song is a little melodramatic, and that if anyone should sing it, it is Arsenal.

Every Arsenal fan, the youngest and the oldest, is aware that no one likes us, and every day we hear that dislike reiterated. The average media-attuned football fan – someone who reads a sports page most days, watches TV whenever it is on, reads a fanzine or a football magazine – will come across a slighting reference to Arsenal maybe two or three times a week (about as often as he or she will hear a Lennon and McCartney song, I would guess). I have just finished watching *Saint and Greavsie*, during the course of which Jimmy Greaves thanked the Wrexham manager for 'delighting millions' with the Fourth Division team's victory over us in the FA Cup; the cover of a football magazine kicking around in the flat promises an article entitled 'Why does everyone hate Arsenal?' Last week there was an article in a national newspaper attacking our players for their lack of artistry; one of the players thus abused was eighteen years old and hadn't even played for the first team at the time.

We're boring, and lucky, and dirty, and petulant, and rich, and mean, and have been, as far as I can tell, since the 1930s. That was when the greatest football manager of all time, Herbert Chapman, introduced an extra defender and changed the way football was played, thus founding Arsenal's reputation for negative, unattractive football; yet successive Arsenal teams, notably the Double team in 1971, used an intimidatingly competent defence as a springboard for success. (Thirteen of our league games that year ended nil–nil or 1–0, and it is fair to say that none of them were pretty.) I would guess that 'Lucky Arsenal' was borne out of 'Boring Arsenal', in that sixty years of 1–0 wins tend to test the credulity and patience of opposing fans.

West Ham, on the other hand, like Tottenham, are famous for their poetry and flair and commitment to good, fluent ('progressive', in the current argot, a word which for those of us in our thirties is distressingly reminiscent of Emerson, Lake and Palmer and King Crimson) football.

Everyone has a soft spot for Peters and Moore and Hurst and Brooking and the West Ham 'Academy', just as everyone loathes and despises Storey and Talbot and Adams and the whole idea and purpose of Arsenal. No matter that the wild-eyed Martin Allen and the brutish Julian Dicks currently represent the Hammers, just as Van Den Hauwe and Fenwick and Edinburgh represent Spurs. No matter that the gifted Merson and the dazzling Limpar play for Arsenal. No matter that in 1989 and 1992 we scored more goals than anyone else in the First Division. The Hammers and the Lilleywhites are the Keepers of the Flame, the Only Followers of the True Path; we are the Gunners, the Visigoths, with King Herod and the Sheriff of Nottingham as our twin centre-halves, their arms in the air appealing for offside.

West Ham, Arsenal's opponents in the 1980 Cup Final, were in the Second Division that season, and their lowly status made people drool over them even more. To the nation's delight, Arsenal lost. Saint Trevor of England scored the only goal and slew the odious monster, the Huns were repelled, children could sleep safely in their beds again. So what are we left with, us Arsenal fans, who for most of our lives have allowed ourselves to become identified with the villains? Nothing; and our sense of stoicism and grievance is almost thrilling.

The only things anyone remembers about the game now are Brooking's rare headed goal, and Willie Young's monstrous professional foul on Paul Allen, just as the youngest player to appear in a Cup Final was about to score one of the cutest and most romantic goals ever seen at Wembley. Standing on the Wembley terraces among the silent, embarrassed Arsenal fans, deafened by the boos that came from the West Ham end and the neutrals in the stadium, I was appalled by Young's cynicism.

But that night, watching the highlights on TV, I became aware that a part of me actually enjoyed the foul – not because it stopped Allen from scoring (the game was over, we'd lost, and that hardly mattered), but because it was so comically, parodically *Arsenalesque*. Who else but an Arsenal defender would have clattered a tiny seventeen-year-old member of the Academy? Motson or Davies, I can't remember which, was suitably disgusted and pompous about it all; to me, sick of hearing about how the goodies had put the baddies to flight, his righteousness sounded provocative. There was something about it that reminded me of Bill Grundy winding up the Sex Pistols on television in 1976 and then expressing his outrage about their behaviour afterwards. Arsenal, the first of the true punk rockers: our centre-halves were fulfilling a public need for harmless pantomime deviancy long before Johnny Rotten came along.

LIFE AFTER FOOTBALL

Arsenal v Valencia

14.5.80

Football teams are extraordinarily inventive in the ways they find to cause their supporters sorrow. They lead at Wembley and then throw it away; they go to the top of the First Division and then stop dead; they draw the difficult away game and lose the home replay; they beat Liverpool one week and lose to Scunthorpe the next; they seduce you, half-way through the season, into believing that they are promotion candidates and then go the other way . . . always, when you think you have anticipated the worst that can happen, they come up with something new.

Four days after losing one cup final, Arsenal lost another, to Valencia in the European Cup-Winners Cup, and the seventy-game season came to nothing. We outplayed the Spanish team, but couldn't score, and the game went to penalties; Brady and Rix missed theirs (some say that Rix was never the same again after the trauma of that night, and certainly he never recaptured his form of the late seventies, even though he went on to play for England), and that was that.

As far as I am aware, there isn't another English club that has lost two finals in a week, although in the years to come, when losing in a final was the most that Arsenal supporters dared to hope, I wondered why I felt quite so stricken. But that week also had a beneficially purgative side effect: after six solid weeks of semi-finals and finals, of listening to the radio and looking for Wembley tickets, the football clutter was gone and there was nothing with which to replace it. Finally I had to think about what I was going to do, rather than what the Arsenal manager was going to do. So I applied for teacher training college back in London, and vowed, not for the last time, that I would never allow football to replace life completely, no matter how many games Arsenal played in a year.

PART OF THE GAME

Arsenal v Southampton

19.8.80

The first match of the season, so you're always that bit keener to get along. And over the summer there was an extraordinary bit of transfer business, when we bought Clive Allen for a million pounds, didn't like the look of him in a couple of pre-season friendlies, and swapped him for Kenny Sansom (a striker for a full-back; that's the Arsenal way) before he'd even played a game. So even though Liam had gone, and Southampton were not the most attractive of opponents, there was a forty thousand-plus crowd.

Something went wrong – they hadn't opened enough turnstiles, or the police had made a pig's ear of controlling the crowd flow, whatever – and there was a huge crush outside the North Bank entrances on the Avenell Road. I could pick both my legs up and remain pinioned and, at one stage, I had to put my arms in the air to give myself just that little bit more room and to stop my fists digging into my chest and stomach. It wasn't anything that special, really; fans have all been in situations where for a few moments things have looked bad. But I remember struggling for breath when I approached the front of the queue (I was so constricted that I couldn't fill my lungs properly) which means that it was a little bit worse than usual; when I finally got through the turnstile I sat down on a step for a while, gave myself time to recover, and I noticed that a lot of other people were doing the same.

But the thing was, I trusted the system: I knew that I could not be squashed to death, because that never happened at football matches. The Ibrox thing, well that was different, a freak combination of events; and in any case that was in Scotland during an Old Firm game, and everyone knows that these are especially problematic. No, you see, in England somebody, somewhere, knew what they were doing, and there was this *system*, which nobody ever explained to us, that prevented accidents of this kind. It might *seem* as though the authorities, the club and the police were pushing their luck on occasions, but that was because we didn't understand properly how they were organising things. In the mêlée in Avenell Road that night some people were laughing, making funny strangled faces as the air was pushed out of them; they were laughing because they were only feet away from unconcerned constables and mounted officers, and they knew that this proximity ensured their safety. How could you die when help was that close?

But I thought about that evening nine years later, on the afternoon of the Hillsborough disaster, and I thought about a lot of other afternoons and evenings too, when it seemed as though there were too many people in the ground, or the crowd had been unevenly distributed. It occurred to me that I could have died that night, and that on a few other occasions I have been much closer to death than I care to think about. There was no plan after all; they really had been riding their luck all that time.

MY BROTHER

Arsenal v Tottenham

30.8.80

There must be many fathers around the country who have experienced the cruellest, most crushing rejection of all: their children have ended up supporting the wrong team. When I contemplate parenthood, something I do more and more as my empathetic biological clock ticks nearer to midnight, I am aware that I am genuinely fearful of this kind of treachery. What would I do if my son or daughter decided, at the age of seven or eight, that Dad was a madman, and that Tottenham or West Ham or Manchester United were the team for them? How would I cope? Would I do the decent parental thing, accept that my days at Highbury were over, and buy a couple of season-tickets at White Hart Lane or Upton Park? Hell, no. I am myself too childish about Arsenal to defer to the whims of a child; I would explain to him or her that, although I would respect any decision of this kind, obviously if they wished to see their team then they would have to take themselves, with their own money, under their own steam. That should wake the little sod up.

I have more than once fantasised about Arsenal playing Tottenham in the Cup Final; in this fantasy my son, as rapt and tense and unhappy as I was when I first supported Arsenal, is a Spurs fan, and as we could not get tickets for Wembley we are watching the game at home on TV. In the last minute the old warhorse Kevin Campbell scores the winner . . . and I explode into a frenzy of joy, leaping around the sitting room, punching the air, *jeering at, jostling, tousling the head of my own trauma-*

tised child. I fear that I am capable of this, and therefore the mature, self-knowing thing to do would be to see the vasectomist this afternoon. If my father had been a Swindon Town fan in 1969, on that awful afternoon at Wembley, and had reacted appropriately, we would not have spoken for twenty-two years.

I have already successfully negotiated one hurdle of this kind. In August 1980 my father and his family came back to England after more than ten years abroad in France and America. My half-brother Jonathan was thirteen, and crazy about soccer – partly due to my influence, partly because he had been in the States while the now-defunct North American Soccer League was at its zenith. And so, as quickly as possible, before he had a chance to work out that what was happening at White Hart Lane with Hoddle and Ardiles was infinitely more interesting than what was going on at Highbury with Price and Talbot, I took him to Arsenal.

He'd been once before, in 1973 when, as a six-year-old, he'd shivered uncontrollably through, and stared uncomprehendingly at, a third-round cup match against Leicester, but he'd long forgotten that, so this early-season local derby was a fresh start. It wasn't a bad game, and certainly no indicator of the desperate times ahead: Pat Jennings, the Tottenham reject, kept out Crooks and Archibald for most of the first half, and then whichever of Spurs' terrible post-Pat keepers (Daines? Kendall?) let in a soft one before Stapleton finished them off with a wonderful lob.

But it wasn't the football that captivated Jonathan. It was the violence. All around us, people were fighting – on the North Bank, on the Clock End, in the Lower East Stand, in the Upper West. Every few minutes a huge gash would appear somewhere in the tightly woven fabric of heads on the terraces as the police separated warring factions, and my little brother was beside himself with excitement; he kept turning round to look at me, his face shining with a disbelieving glee. 'This is *incredible*,' he said, over and over again. I had no trouble with him after that: he came to the next game, a drab, quiet League Cup match against Swansea, and to most of the others that season. And now we have season-tickets together, and he drives me to away games, so it's all worked out OK.

Is he an Arsenal fan simply because for a long time he expected to see people attempt to kill each other? Or is it just because he looked up to me, as I know he did for a while, inexplicably, when he was younger, and therefore trusted me and my choice of team? Either way, I probably didn't have the right to inflict Willie Young and John Hawley and the Arsenal offside trap on him for the rest of his days, which is what I have ended up doing. So I feel responsible, but not regretful: if I had not been able to secure his allegiance to the cause, if he had decided to look for his footballing pain elsewhere, then our relationship would have been of an entirely different and possibly much cooler nature.

Here's a funny thing, though: Jonathan and I sit there, at Highbury, week after week, partly because of the distressing circumstances that led to his existence. My father left my mother in order to set up home with his mother, and my half-brother was born, and somehow all this turned me into an Arsenal fan; how odd, then, that my peculiar kink should have been transferred on to him, like a genetic flaw.

CLOWNS

Arsenal v Stoke City

13.9.80

How many games like this did we watch, between Brady's departure and George Graham's arrival? The away team are struggling, unambitious also-rans; their manager (Ron Saunders, or Gordon Lee, or Graham Turner, or, in this case, Alan Durban) wants a draw at Highbury, and plays five defenders, four midfielders who used to be defenders, and a hopeless centre-forward standing on his own up front, ready to challenge for punts from the goalkeeper. Without Liam (and, after this season, without Frank Stapleton), Arsenal didn't have the wit or the imagination to break the opposition down, and maybe we won (with a couple of goals from near-post corners, say, or a deflected long-shot and a penalty), or maybe we drew (nil–nil), or maybe we lost 1–0 to a goal on the break, but it didn't really matter anyway. Arsenal were nowhere near good enough to win the League, yet were much too competent to go down; week after week, year after year, we turned up knowing full well that what we were about to witness would depress us profoundly.

This game against Stoke was very much in the mould – a goalless first half, and then, amid rising discontent, two late goals (ironically, given the towering height of Stoke's several centre-halves, headed in by the two smallest players on the pitch, Sansom and Hollins). Nobody, not even someone like me, would have been able to remember the game had it not been for the post-match press conference, when Alan Durban became angered by the hostility of the journalists towards his team and his tactics. 'If you want entertainment,' he snarled, 'go and watch clowns.'

It became one of the most famous football quotes of the decade. The quality papers in particular loved it for its effortless summary of modern football culture: here was conclusive proof that the game had gone to the dogs, that nobody cared about anything other than results any more, that the Corinthian spirit was dead, that hats were no longer thrown in the air. One could see their point. Why should football be different from every other branch of the leisure industry? You won't find too many Hollywood producers and West End theatre impresarios sneering at the public's desire to be diverted, so why should football managers get away with it?

Over the last few years, however, I have come to believe that Alan Durban was right. It was not his job to provide entertainment. It was his job to look after the interests of the Stoke City fans, which means avoiding defeat away from home, keeping a struggling team in the First Division, and maybe winning a few cup games to alleviate the gloom. The Stoke fans would have been happy with a nil–nil draw, just as Arsenal fans are happy enough with nil–nil draws at Spurs or Liverpool or Manchester United; at home, we expect to beat more or less everyone, and we don't particularly care how it is done.

This commitment to results means, inevitably, that fans and journalists see games in a profoundly different way. In 1969 I saw George Best play, and score, for Manchester United at Highbury. The experience should have been profound, like seeing Nijinsky dance, or Maria Callas sing, and though I do talk about it in that way sometimes, to younger fans, or those who missed out on Best for other reasons, my fond account is essentially phoney: I hated that afternoon. Every time he got the ball he frightened me, and I wished then, as I suppose I wish now, that he had been injured. And I have seen Law and Charlton, Hoddle and Ardiles, Dalglish and Rush, Hurst and Peters, and the same thing happened: I have not enjoyed anything these players have ever done at Highbury (even though I have, on occasions, grudgingly admired things they have done against other teams). Gazza's free kick against Arsenal in the FA Cup semi-final at Wembley was simply astonishing, one of the most remarkable goals I have ever seen . . . but I wish with all my heart that I had not seen it, and that he had not scored it. Indeed, for the previous month I had been praying that Gascoigne would not be playing, which emphasises the separateness of football: who would buy an expensive ticket for the theatre and hope that the star of the show was indisposed?

Neutrals loved the glorious theatre of that Gascoigne moment, of course, but there were very few neutrals in the stadium. There were Arsenal fans, who were as horrified as I was, and Tottenham fans, who were just as thrilled with the second goal, a two-yard Gary Lineker tap-in after a scramble – in fact, they went even more berserk then, because at 2–0 after ten minutes Arsenal were dead and buried. So where is the relationship between the fan and entertainment, when the fan has such a problematic relationship with some of the game's greatest moments?

There *is* such a relationship, but it is far from straightforward. Tottenham, generally regarded as being the better footballing team, are not as well supported as Arsenal, for example; and teams with a reputation for entertaining (West Ham, Chelsea, Norwich) don't get queues around the block. The way our team plays is beside the point for most of us, just as winning cups and championships is beside the point. Few of us have *chosen* our clubs, they have simply been presented to us; and so as they slip from the Second Division to the Third, or sell their best players, or buy players who you know can't play, or bash the ball for the seven hundredth time towards a nine-foot centre-forward, we simply curse, go home, worry for a fortnight and then come back to suffer all over again.

For my own part, I am an Arsenal fan first and a football fan second (and, yes, again, I know all the jokes). I will never be able to enjoy the Gazza goal, and there are countless other similar moments. But I know what entertaining football is, and have loved the relatively few occasions when Arsenal have managed to produce it; and when other teams who are not in competition with Arsenal in any way play with flair and verve, then I can appreciate that, too. Like everyone, I have lamented long and loud the deficiencies of the English game, and the permanently depressing ugliness of the football that our national team plays, but really, deep down, this is pub-speak, and not much more. Complaining about boring football is a little like complaining about the sad ending of *King Lear*: it misses the point somehow, and this is what Alan Durban understood: that football is an alternative universe, as serious and as stressful as work, with the same worries and hopes and disappointments and occasional elations. I go to football for loads of reasons, but I don't go for entertainment, and when I look around me on a Saturday and see those panicky, glum faces, I see that others feel the same. For the committed fan, entertaining football exists in the same way as those trees that fall in the middle of the jungle: you presume it happens, but you're not in a position to appreciate it. Sports journalists and armchair Corinthians are the Amazon Indians who know more than we do – but in another way they know much, much less.

SAME OLD ARSENAL

Arsenal v Brighton

1.11.80

A nothing game, between two nothing teams; I doubt if anyone else who was there remembers anything about it at all, unless it was their first time, or their last time, and doubtless my two companions for the afternoon, my dad and my half-brother, had forgotten the occasion by the following day. I recall it only because (only because!) it was the last time I was at Highbury with my dad, and though we might well go again sometime (he has made a couple of very small noises recently) the game now has an end-of-an-era aura about it.

The team were in much the same state as we had found them twelve years before, and I am sure that he must have complained about the cold, and Arsenal's ineptitude, and I am sure that I felt responsible for both, and wanted to apologise. And I wasn't much different in important ways, either. I was still as gloomy, somehow, as I had been when I was a boy, although because I was now aware of this gloom, understood what it was, it seemed darker and more threatening than it had ever done before. And, of course, the team were still in there, mixed in with it all, leading these lows from the front or trailing them from behind, I don't know which.

But other things had changed, permanently and for the better, particularly in my dealings with my 'other' family. My stepmother had long ceased to be the Enemy – there was a real warmth in our relationship that neither of us could have anticipated years before – and there had never been any problem with the kids; but most important of all, my father and I, almost imperceptibly, had reached the stage where football was no longer the chief method of discourse between us. I lived with him and his family in London for the whole of the 80/81 season, my teacher training year; this was the first time we had had such an arrangement since I was a child, and it was fine. We had other stuff going on by now, as we have done ever since. The failure of his first marriage must still be mixed in there somehow, I suppose, but we have managed to fashion something that works well in its own way; and though there are still frustrations and difficulties, I don't think that these are ruinous, or that the problems we have are any worse than my friends have with their fathers – indeed, we get along much better than most.

I didn't think all that at the time, of course, because as far as I knew, a 2–0 home victory over Brighton had no particular significance, and there would be another last game for us some other time – but then, our début together had been equally inauspicious. It's best just to leave us there, the three of us – Dad topping up his tea with the contents of his hip flask and grumbling about still watching the same old bloody Arsenal, me shifting around uncomfortably in my seat, hoping that somehow things would get better, and Jonathan, still small and pale with cold and, for all I know, wishing that his brother and his father had found a different way to sort out their problems in 1968.

A TRIVIAL PURSUIT

Arsenal v Manchester City

24.2.81

I got lost around this time, and stayed lost for the next few years. Between one home game (against Coventry) and the next (a midweek game against Manchester City), I split up with my girlfriend, all the things that had been rotting away inside me for who knows how many years oozed out for the first time, I started my teaching practice in a difficult west London school, and Arsenal got a draw at Stoke and a beating at Forest. It was strange to see the same players trotting out that evening as they had trotted out three weeks before: I felt that they should have had the decency to reinvent themselves, accept that the faces and physiques and shortcomings they had had in the Coventry game belonged to another period entirely.

If there had been a match every weekday evening and weekend afternoon I would have gone, because the games acted as punctuation marks (if only commas) between bleak periods, when I drank too much and smoked too much and weight fell off me gratifyingly quickly. I remember this one so clearly simply because it was the first of them – they all began to merge into each other a little after this; Lord knows nothing much happened on the pitch, apart from Talbot and Sunderland trundling in a couple of goals.

But football had taken on yet another meaning now, connected with my new career. It had occurred to me – as I think it occurs to many young teachers of a similar ilk – that my interests (football and pop music in particular) would be an advantage in the classroom, that I would be able to 'identify' with 'the kids' because I understood the value of the Jam and Laurie Cunningham. It had not occurred to me that I was as childish as my interests; and that although, yes, I knew what my pupils were talking about most of the time, and that this gave me an entrée of sorts, it didn't help me to teach them any better. In fact the chief problem I had – namely, that on a bad day there was uproarious mayhem in my classroom – was actually exacerbated by my partisanship. 'I'm an Arsenal fan,' I said in my best groovy teacher voice, as a way of introducing myself to some difficult second years. 'Boo!' they replied, noisily and at great length.

On my second or third day, I asked a group of third years to write down on a piece of paper their favourite book, favourite song, favourite film and so on, and went around the class talking to them all in turn. This was how I discovered that the bad boy at the back, the one with the mod haircut and the permanent sneer (and the one, inevitably, with the biggest vocabulary and the best writing style), was completely consumed by all things Arsenal, and I pounced. But when I had made my confession, there was no meeting of minds, or fond, slow-motion embrace; instead, I received a look of utter contempt. 'You?' he said. 'You? What do *you* know about it?'

For a moment I saw myself through his eyes, a pillock in a tie with an ingratiating smile, desperately trying to worm my way into places I had no right to be, and understood. But then something else – a rage born out of thirteen years of Highbury hell, probably, and an unwillingness to abandon one of the most important elements of my self-identity to chalky, tweedy facelessness – took over, and I went mad.

The madness took a strange form. I wanted to grab that kid by his lapels and bang him against the wall, and yell at him, over and over again, 'I know more than you ever will, you snotty little fuckwit!' but I knew that this was not advisable. So I spluttered for a few seconds, and then to my surprise (I watched them as they spewed forth) a torrent of quiz questions gushed out of me. 'Who scored for us in the '69 League Cup Final? Who went in goal when Bob Wilson got carried off in '72 at Villa Park? Who did we get from Spurs in exchange for David Jenkins? Who . . . ?' On and on I went; the boy sat there, the questions bouncing off the top of his head like snowballs, while the rest of the class watched in bemused silence.

It worked, in the end – or at least, I managed to convince the boy that I was not the man he had taken me for. The morning after the Manchester City game, the first home game following my trivia explosion, the two of us talked quietly and cordially about the desperate need for a new midfield player, and I never had any trouble with him for the remainder of my practice. But what worried me was that I hadn't been able to let it go, that football, the great retardant, hadn't let me act like a grown-up in the face of a young lad's jibe. Teaching, it seemed to me, was by definition a job for grown-ups, and I appeared to have got stuck somewhere around my fourteenth birthday – stuck in the third year, in fact.

COACH

My School v Their School

January 1982

I'd seen *Kes*, of course; I'd laughed at Brian Glover dribbling around kids and pushing them over, awarding himself penalties, doing the commentary. And my friend Ray, the deputy head of the school in Cambridge where I was now a Scale 1 English teacher (Cambridge because a job came up there, because I still had friends there, and because my teacher training year in London had taught me that I should avoid London schools if at all possible) had an endless fund of true stories about headmasters who appointed themselves referees for important matches, and sent the fifteen-year-old star striker of the opposing team off in the first two minutes of the match. I was well aware, therefore, of the way school football encouraged teachers to behave in an astonishingly foolish manner.

But what would you do, if your fifth years were 2–0 down at half-time in a local derby (although admittedly school football does tend to throw up a number of local derbies), and you made an astute tactical switch at half-time, and the boys pulled one back, and then, bang on ninety minutes, when your voice is hoarse with frustration and impotence, they equalise? You would probably find yourself, as I did, two feet up in the air, fists punching the sky, letting rip with an undignified and certainly unteacherly howl . . . and just before your feet hit the touchline, you would remember who you were supposed to be, and how old these kids were, and you would start to feel daft.

ON THE PITCH

Arsenal v West Ham

1.5.82

Looking back, it was quite clear that the stuff on the terraces was getting worse and that sooner or later something was going to happen that would change it all, somehow. In my experience there was more violence in the seventies – that is to say, there was fighting more or less every week – but in the first half of the eighties, with Millwall's F-Troop, West Ham's Inter-City Firm (and the calling cards that these factions were reputed to leave on the battered bodies of their victims), the England fans and their alleged National Front agenda – it was less predictable and much nastier. Police confiscated knives and machetes and other weapons I did not recognise, things with spikes coming out of them; and there was that famous photograph of a fan with a dart sticking from his nose.

One beautiful spring morning in 1982 I took Ray's son Mark, then a teenager, down to Highbury to see the West Ham game, and explained to him in an insufferably old-hand way how and where the trouble, if any, would start. I pointed to the top right-hand corner of the North Bank and told him that there were probably West Ham fans up there, without colours, who would either find themselves surrounded by police, and thus rendered harmless, or who would attempt to force their way under the roof and drive out the Arsenal fans gathered there; which was why we were safe on the bottom left-hand side, where I had been standing for a few years now. He was duly grateful, I felt, for my guidance and protection.

In the event I was able, by casting an expert eye over the area, to reassure him that there were no Hammers fans there, and we settled down to watch the game; and about three minutes after the kick-off, there was a huge roar immediately behind us and that terrible, eerily muffled sound of boot on denim. Those behind us pushed forward, and we found ourselves being forced towards the pitch – and then there was another roar, and we looked round and saw billowing clouds of thick yellow smoke. 'Fucking tear gas!' somebody shouted, and, although thankfully it wasn't, the alarm inevitably induced panic. There were now so many people pouring out of the North Bank that we were being driven right down against the low wall which separated us from the pitch, and in the end we had no option: Mark and I, and hundreds of others, jumped over it and on to the holy turf just as West Ham were about to take a corner. We stood there for a few moments, feeling rather self-conscious about standing in the penalty-area during a First Division match, and then the referee blew the whistle and took the players off. And that was more or less the end of our involvement in the incident. We were all escorted the length of the pitch down to the Clock End, from where we watched the rest of the game in fairly subdued silence.

But there is a horrible and frightening irony here. At Highbury there is no perimeter fencing. If there had been, then those of us pushed towards the pitch that afternoon would have been in serious trouble. A couple of years later, during an FA Cup semi-final between Everton and Southampton at Arsenal, a few hundred stupid Everton fans ran on to the pitch after their team scored a late winner, and the FA (although they have changed their minds again now) decided that Highbury should no longer be used as a semi-final venue unless the club fenced the fans in. To their eternal credit, the club refused (leaving aside the safety aspects, it obstructs the view), despite the loss of revenue incurred. Hillsborough, however, had the fences, and thus until 1989 was deemed suitable for these games; and it was in an FA Cup semi-final between Liverpool and Nottingham Forest that all those people died. It was the fencing, the very feature which allowed the game to take place there, that killed them, prevented them from getting out of the crush and on to the pitch.

After the West Ham match, a young Arsenal fan was stabbed in one of the streets near the ground, and died where he lay: a sickening end to a dismal afternoon. When I went back to school on Monday morning I ranted and raved at a class of baffled second years about the whole culture of violence. I tried to argue to them that their hooligan paraphernalia – their Doctor Martens and their green flying jackets and their spiky haircuts – all fed the process, but they were too young, and I was too incoherent. And anyway there was something pretty nauseating, although I didn't appreciate it at the time, about me of all people explaining to a whole load of provincial kids that dressing hard didn't mean you were hard, and that wanting to be hard in the first place was kind of a pathetic ambition.

THE MUNSTERS AND QUENTIN CRISP

Saffron Walden v Tiptree

May 1983

I will watch any football match, any time, any place, in any weather conditions. Between the ages of eleven and twenty-five I was an occasional visitor to York Road, home of Maidenhead United of the Athenian, later the Isthmian League; occasionally I even travelled to see them in away games. (I was there on the great day in '69 when they won the Berks and Bucks Senior Cup, beating Wolverton 3–0 in the final played at, I think, Chesham United's ground. And at Farnborough once, a man came out of the club house and told the travelling fans to keep the noise down.) In Cambridge, when United or Arsenal weren't playing, I went to Milton Road, home of Cambridge City, and when I started teaching I went with my friend Ray to watch his son-in-law Les, whose good looks and impeccable behaviour gave him the air of a non-league Gary Lineker, play for Saffron Walden.

Part of the fascination of non-league football is the rest of the crowd: some, though by no means all, of the people who attend the games are hideously mad, perhaps driven so by the quality of the football they have spent years watching. (There are lunatics on the First Division terraces too – my friends and I spent years on the North Bank trying to avoid one who stood near us every week – but they are less noticeable among all the casual consumers.) At Milton Road there was an old man we called Quentin Crisp, because of the disarming femininity of his white hair and wrinkled face: he wore a crash helmet throughout the entire ninety minutes, and spent his afternoons buzzing round and round the stadium like an ageing greyhound (you could see him on his own at the far end of the ground where there was no terracing, picking his way through mud and over debris, gamely determined to complete his circuit), hurling abuse at the linesmen – 'I'm going to write to the FA about you' – when he got anywhere near them. At York Road there was (and perhaps still is) an entire family, known to everyone as the Munsters due to a somewhat outlandish and unfortunate physical appearance, who had taken it upon themselves to act as stewards to a crowd of two hundred who really had no need of such services; there was also Harry Taylor, a very old and slightly simple man who couldn't stay to see the end of midweek games on a Tuesday because Tuesday was bath night, and whose entrance was greeted by a chant of 'Harry Harry, Harry Harry, Harry Harry, Harry Taylor' to the tune of the old Hare Krishna chant. Non-league football, perhaps by its very nature, attracts these people, and I say this in the full knowledge that I am one of the people attracted.

What I have always wanted is to find a place where I could lose myself in the patterns and rhythms of football without caring about the score. I have this idea that in the right circumstances the game could serve as a kind of New Age therapy, and the frantic movement before me would somehow absorb and then dissolve everything inside me, but it never works that way. First I become diverted by the eccentricities – the fans, the shouts of the players ('Put him in the tea bar!' urged Maidenhead's Micky Chatterton, our hero, to a team-mate faced with a particularly tricky winger one afternoon), the peculiar, ramshackle presentation of the entertainment (Cambridge City took the field to the theme from *Match of the Day*, but frequently the music wound down with a pitiful groan just at the crucial moment). And then once I have been engaged thus, I start to care; and before long Maidenhead and Cambridge City and Walden start to mean more than they should do, and once again I am involved, and then the therapy cannot work.

Saffron Walden's tiny ground is one of the nicest places I have ever watched football, and the people there always seemed startlingly normal. I went because Ray, Mark and Ben their dog went, and I went because Les was playing; and, after a little while, when I got to know the players, I went to watch a gifted, idle striker called, improbably, Alf Ramsey, rumoured to be a heavy smoker, who in classic Greaves style did nothing apart from score once or twice a game.

When Walden beat Tiptree 3–0 and won something or other – the

Essex Senior Cup? – on a mild May evening, there was a warmth to the occasion that professional football will never be able to match. A small, partisan crowd, a good game, a team of players with a genuine affection for their club (Les didn't play for anyone else throughout his career, and like most of his team-mates lived in the town) . . . and when, at the end of the game, the crowd went on to the pitch, it wasn't intended as an act of aggression, or bravado, or scene-stealing, as pitch invasions so frequently are, but to congratulate the team, all of them brothers or sons or husbands of nearly all of the spectators. There is a sourness that is central to the experience of supporting a big team, and you can't do anything about it apart from live with it and accept that professional sport has to be sour if it is to mean anything at all. But sometimes it's nice to have a little holiday from it, and wonder what it would be like if Arsenal players all came from London N4 or N5, and had other jobs, and played only because they loved the game and the team they played for. This is sentimental, but teams like Walden inspire sentiment; sometimes, you feel, it would be nice if the theme from the *A-Team* that marks Arsenal's entrance on to the pitch wound down horribly, as the tapes did at Cambridge City, and the players looked at each other and laughed.

CHARLIE NICHOLAS

Arsenal v Luton

27.8.83

How can you *not* see omens everywhere? In the summer of 1983, after two years, I packed up my teaching job to be a writer; and a couple of weeks later Arsenal signed, against all odds, the hottest property in British football – Charlie Nicholas, the Cannonball Kid, the Celtic player who had scored fifty-something goals in Scotland the previous season. *Now* we were going to see something. And with Charlie around, I felt that there was no way I could fail with my witty yet sensitive plays, the first of which – oh, the unfathomable mysteries of creativity – was about a teacher who becomes a writer.

It is easy to see now that I should not have linked Charlie's career to my own, but at the time I found it irresistible to do so. The optimism of Terry Neill and Don Howe and the press swept me along, and as the Charlie hype became more and more feverish during the summer of '83 (he had, in truth, made a bit of an idiot of himself in the tabloids even before he kicked a ball), it became very easy to believe that the newspapers were talking about me. It was distinctly possible, I felt, that I was on the verge of becoming the Cannonball Kid of television drama, and then of the West End theatre (even though I knew nothing about either, and indeed had frequently expressed my contempt for the stage).

The neat and obvious synchronism of it all still baffles me. The last new dawn, back in '76 when Terry Neill took over and Malcolm Macdonald came to the club, I was about to depart for university. And the one after Charlie's arrival, just a year later (when we were top of the First Division for a couple of months, and playing as well as anyone could remember), came right after I walked out of various terrible messes I had made in Cambridge and moved back to London to start a new life. Maybe football teams and people are always having fresh starts; maybe Arsenal and I have more than most, and therefore we are suited to each other.

In the event, Charlie proved to be a pretty accurate indicator of my fortunes. I was there for this, his first game, of course, along with a good forty thousand others, and he was OK: he didn't score, but he played his part, and we won 2–1. And though he got two in the next game, away at Wolves, that was it in the League until after Christmas (he got one League Cup goal at Tottenham in November). The next game at home, against Manchester United, he looked slow and out of touch, and the team were outclassed – we lost 3–2, but we were never really in the game. (In fact he didn't score at all at Highbury until 27th December, with a penalty against Birmingham which we greeted with the fervour of a hat-trick against Tottenham.) His first season was, in short, a disaster, as it was for the whole team, and the manager, Terry Neill, got the sack after a dismal run of results in November and early December.

The other Cannonball Kid, the literary version, finished his imaginative play and got a kind and encouraging rejection letter back; then started another, which was also rejected, a little less kindly. And he was doing the most dismal sorts of work – private tuition, proof reading and supply teaching – to pay the rent. He showed no signs of scoring before Christmas either, or for a few more Christmases to come; if he had supported Liverpool, and tied his fortunes to Ian Rush, he would have won a Booker Prize by May.

*

I was twenty-six in 1983, and Charlie Nicholas was just twenty-one; it suddenly occurred to me over the next few weeks, as I looked at the hundreds of Charlie haircuts and earrings on the terraces and regretted that my already thinning hair would not allow me to participate, that my heroes were not going to age as I did. I will reach thirty-five, forty, fifty, but the players never will: Paul Merson, Rocky, Kevin Campbell . . . I am more than a decade older than the people I love in the current Arsenal team. I am even a year older than David O'Leary, the veteran, the Old Man, whose pace is patently no longer what it was, whose first-team outings are limited to protect his creaking joints and his waning stamina. It doesn't make any difference, however. To all intents and purposes, I am still twenty years younger than O'Leary, and ten years younger than all the twenty-four-year-olds. In one important sense, I really am: they have done things that I never will, and sometimes I feel that if I could just score once into the North Bank end and run behind the goal to the fans, then I could at last leave behind all childish things.

A SEVEN-MONTH HICCUP

Cambridge United v Oldham Athletic

1.10.83

It was the beginning of another typical Cambridge season. They'd won one, drawn a couple, lost a couple, but they always started like this; at the beginning of October my friends and I watched them beat Oldham (whose team, incidentally, included Andy Goram, Mark Ward, Roger Palmer and Martin Buchan) 2–1; they moved into comfortable mid-table obscurity, their natural habitat, and we went home fully and happily prepared for another season of nothingness.

And that was it. Between 1st October and 28th April they failed to beat Palace at home, Leeds away, Huddersfield at home, Portsmouth away, Brighton and Derby at home, Cardiff away, Middlesbrough at home, Newcastle away, Fulham at home, Shrewsbury away, Manchester City at home, Barnsley away, Grimsby at home, Blackburn away, Swansea and Carlisle at home, Charlton and Oldham away, Chelsea at home, Brighton away, Portsmouth at home, Derby away, Cardiff and Wednesday at home, Huddersfield and Palace away, Leeds at home, Middlesbrough away, Barnsley at home and Grimsby away. Thirty-one games without a win, a Football League record (you can look it up), seventeen of them at home . . . and I saw all seventeen, as well as a fair few games at Highbury. I missed only United's home defeat by Derby in the FA Cup third round – the girl I was living with took me to Paris for the weekend as a Christmas present. (When I saw the date on the tickets, I was unable, shamingly, to hide my disappointment, and she was understandably hurt.) My friend Simon managed only sixteen of the seventeen League games – he smashed his head on a bookshelf in London a few hours before the Grimsby game on the 28th of December; his girlfriend had to take his car keys away from him because he kept making dazed attempts to drive from Fulham up to the Abbey.

It would, however, be absurd to pretend that my allegiance was sorely tested: I never once thought of abandoning the team simply because they were incapable of beating anyone at all. In fact this long losing run (which resulted, inevitably, in relegation) became charged with a drama all of its own, a drama which would have been entirely absent in the normal course of events. After a while, when winning a game appeared to be an option that had somehow become impossible, we began to adjust to a different order, and look for things that would replace the satisfaction of winning: goals, draws, a brave performance in the face of overwhelmingly hostile fortune (and the team were terribly, terribly unlucky on occasions, as a team that does not win for six whole months would have to be) . . . these all became causes for quiet, if occasionally self-mocking, celebration. And in any case Cambridge developed a certain infamy over the course of the year. Whereas previously their results had been deemed unworthy of note, they now always got a mention on *Sports Report*; telling people that I was there for the duration, even seven years later, has a certain social cachet in some quarters.

In the end I learned, from this period more than any other in my footballing history, that it simply doesn't matter to me how bad things get, that results have nothing to do with anything. As I have implied before, I would like to be one of those people who treat their local team like their local restaurant, and thus withdraw their patronage if they are being served up noxious rubbish. But unfortunately (and this is one reason why football has got itself into so many messes without having to clear any of them up) there are many fans like me. For us, the consumption is all; the quality of the product is immaterial.

COCONUTS

Cambridge United v Newcastle United

28.4.84

At the end of April, Newcastle, with Keegan and Beardsley and Waddle, came to the Abbey. They were near the top of the Second Division, and they needed a win badly if they were going to make sure of promotion, and Cambridge were already long down by then. Cambridge were awarded a penalty in the first few minutes and scored, though given their recent history this was not in itself enthralling – as we had learned over the previous months that there were countless ways to convert a lead into a defeat. But there were no further goals in the game; in the last five minutes, with Cambridge thumping the ball as far into the allotments as possible, you would have thought that they were about to win the European Cup. At the final whistle the players (most of whom, bought or pulled out of the reserves to stop the rot, had never played in a winning team) embraced each other and waved happily to the ecstatic home fans; and for the first time since October the club DJ was able to play 'I've Got a Lovely Bunch of Coconuts'. It didn't mean a thing in the long run, and the next season they got relegated again, but after that long, bleak winter it was a memorable couple of hours.

This was the last time I went to the Abbey; that summer I decided to run away from Cambridge and United, and back to London and Arsenal. But the afternoon – eccentric, funny, joyful from one perspective and heartbreaking from another, private in a way that football usually isn't (there were probably less than three thousand Cambridge fans in the crowd for the Newcastle game) – was a perfect end to my relationship with the club. And sometimes, when it seems to me that supporting a First Division team is a thankless and indefensible chore, I miss them a lot.

PETE

Arsenal v Stoke City

22.9.84

'You must meet my friend,' I am always being told. 'He's a big Arsenal fan.' And I meet the friend, and it turns out that, at best, he looks up the Arsenal score in the paper on Sunday morning or, at worst, he is unable to name a single player since Denis Compton. None of these blind dates ever worked; I was too demanding, and my partners simply weren't interested in commitment.

So I wasn't really expecting very much when I was introduced to Pete in the Seven Sisters Road before the Stoke game; but it was a perfect, life-changing match. He was (and still is) as stupid as I am about it all – he has the same ludicrous memory, the same propensity to allow his life to be dominated for nine months of the year by fixture lists and TV schedules. He is gripped by the same stomach-fizzing fear before big games, and the same dreadful glooms after bad defeats. Interestingly, I think he has had the same tendency to let his life drift along a little, the same confusions about what he wants to do with it, and I think that, like me, he has allowed Arsenal to fill gaps that should have been occupied by something else, but then we all do that.

I was twenty-seven when I met him, and without his influence I suppose I might have drifted away from the club over the next few years. I was approaching the age at which drifting sometimes begins (although the things that one is supposed to drift towards – domesticity, children, a job I really cared about – just weren't there), but with Pete the reverse happened. Our desire for all things football sharpened, and Arsenal began to creep back deep into both of us.

Maybe the timing helped: at the beginning of the 84/85 season Arsenal led the First Division for a few weeks. Nicholas was playing with breath-taking skill in midfield, Mariner and Woodcock looked like the striking partnership we'd been lacking for years, the defence was solid, and yet another of those little sparks of optimism lit me up and led me to believe once again that if things could change for the team then they could change for me. (By Christmas, after a disappointing string of results for me and the team, we were all back in the Slough of Despond.) Maybe if Pete and I had met at the beginning of the following dismal season, things would not have turned out the same way – maybe we would not have had the same incentive to make the partnership work during those crucial first few games.

I suspect, though, that the quality of Arsenal's early-season football had very little to do with anything. There was another agenda altogether, involving our shared inability to get on with things away from Highbury and our shared need to carve out a little igloo for ourselves to protect us from the icy winds of the mid-eighties and our late twenties. Since I met Pete in 1984, I have missed fewer than half a dozen games at Arsenal in seven years (four in that first year, all connected with the continuing upheaval in my personal life, and none at all for four seasons), and travelled to more away games than I had ever done before. And though there are fans who haven't missed any games, home or away, for decades, I would have been amazed by my current attendance record if I had known about it in, say, 1975, when I grew up for a few months and stopped going, or even in 1983, when my relationship with the club was polite and cordial but distant. Pete pushed me over the edge, and sometimes I don't know whether to thank him for that or not.

HEYSEL

Liverpool v Juventus

29.5.85

When I ran away from Cambridge and came to London in the summer of 1984, I found work teaching English as a foreign language at a school in Soho, a temporary post that somehow lasted four years, in the same way that everything I fell into through lethargy or chance or panic seemed to last much longer than it should have done. But I loved the work and loved the students (mostly young western Europeans taking time out from degree courses); and though the teaching left me plenty of time to write, I didn't do any, and spent long afternoons in coffee bars in Old Compton Street with other members of staff, or a crowd of charming young Italians. It was a wonderful way to waste my time.

They knew, of course, about the football (the topic somehow seemed to crop up in more than one conversation class). So when the Italian students started to complain, on the afternoon of the 29th of May, that they had no access to a television, and therefore could not watch Juve beat Liverpool in the European Cup Final that night, I offered to come down to the school with the keys so that we could watch the match together.

There were scores of them when I arrived, and I was the only non-Italian in the place; I was pushed, by their cheerful antagonism and my own vague patriotism, into becoming an honorary Liverpool fan for the night. When I turned the TV on, Jimmy Hill and Terry Venables were still talking, and I left the sound down so that the students and I could talk about the game, and I put a little bit of technical vocabulary up on the board while we were still waiting. But after a while, when conversation started to flag, they wanted to know why the game hadn't started and what the Englishmen were saying, and it wasn't until then that I understood what was going on.

So I had to explain to a group of beautiful young Italian boys and girls that in Belgium, the English hooligans had caused the deaths of thirty-eight people, most of them Juventus supporters. I don't know how I would have felt watching the game at home. I would have felt the same rage that I felt that night in the school, and the same despair, and the same terrible sick shame; I doubt if I would have had the same urge to apologise, again and again and again, although perhaps I should have done. I would certainly have cried, in the privacy of my own front room, at the sheer stupidity of it all but in the school I wasn't able to. Maybe I thought it would be a bit rich, an Englishman weeping in front of Italians on the night of Heysel.

All through 1985, our football had been heading unstoppably for something like this. There was the astonishing Millwall riot at Luton, where the police were routed, and things seemed to go further than they ever have done at an English football ground (it was then that Mrs Thatcher conceived her absurd ID-card scheme); there was the Chelsea *v* Sunderland riot, too, where Chelsea fans invaded the pitch and attacked players. These incidents took place within weeks of each other, and they were just the pick of the bunch. Heysel was coming, as inevitably as Christmas.

In the end, the surprise was that these deaths were caused by something as innocuous as running, the practice that half the juvenile fans in the country had indulged in, and which was intended to do nothing more than frighten the opposition and amuse the runners. The Juventus fans – many of them chic, middle-class men and women – weren't to know that, though, and why should they have done? They didn't have the intricate knowledge of English crowd behaviour that the rest of us had absorbed almost without noticing. When they saw a crowd of screaming English hooligans running towards them, they panicked, and ran to the edge of their compound. A wall collapsed and, in the chaos that ensued, people were crushed to death. It was a horrible way to die and we probably watched people do it: we all remember the large bearded man, the one who looked a little like Pavarotti, imploring with his hand for a way out that nobody could provide.

Some of the Liverpool fans who were later arrested must have felt genuinely bewildered. In a sense, their crime was simply being English: it was just that the practices of their culture, taken out of its own context and transferred to somewhere that simply didn't understand them, killed people. 'Murderers! Murderers!' the Arsenal fans chanted at the Liverpool fans the December after Heysel, but I suspect that if exactly the same circumstances were to be recreated with any group of English fans – and these circumstances would include a hopelessly inadequate local police force (Brian Glanville, in his book *Champions of Europe*, reports that the Belgian police were amazed that the violence began before the game started, when a simple phone call to any metropolitan constabulary in England could have put them right), a ludicrously decrepit stadium, a vicious set of opposing fans, and pitifully poor planning on the part of the relevant football authorities – then the same thing would surely happen.

I think this is why I felt quite so ashamed by the events of that night. I knew that Arsenal fans might have done the same, and that if Arsenal had been playing in the Heysel that night then I would certainly have been there – not fighting, or running at people, but very much a part of the community that spawned this sort of behaviour. And anyone who has ever used football in the ways that it has been used on countless occasions, for the great smell of brute it invariably confers on the user, must have felt ashamed too. Because the real point of the tragedy was this: it was possible for football fans to look at TV coverage of, say, the Luton–Millwall riot, or the Arsenal–West Ham stabbing, and feel a sense of sick horror but no real sense of connection or involvement. The perpetrators were not the kind of people that the rest of us understood, or identified with. But the kids' stuff that proved murderous in Brussels belonged firmly and clearly on a continuum of apparently harmless but obviously threatening acts – violent chants, wanker signs, the whole petty hard-act works – in which a very large minority of fans had been indulging for nearly twenty years. In short, Heysel was an organic part of a culture that many of us, myself included, had contributed towards. You couldn't look at those Liverpool fans and ask yourself, as you had been able to do with the Millwall fans at Luton, or the Chelsea fans in their League Cup match, 'Who *are* these people?'; you already knew.

I am still embarrassed by the fact that I watched the game; I should have turned the TV off, told everyone to go home, made a unilateral decision that football no longer mattered, and wouldn't for quite a while. But everyone I know, more or less, wherever they were watching, stuck with it; in my school room, nobody really cared who won the European Cup any more, but there was still a last, indelible trace of obsession left in us that made us want to talk about the dubious penalty decision which gave Juventus their 1–0 win. I like to think I have an answer for most irrationalities connected with football, but this one seems to defy all explanation.

DYING ON ITS FEET

Arsenal v Leicester

31.8.85

The season following Heysel was the worst I can remember – not just because of Arsenal's poor form, although that didn't help (and I regret to say that if we had won the League or the Cup, then I'm sure I would have been able to put all those deaths into some kind of *perspective*), but because everything seemed poisoned by what had gone on in May. Gates, which had been falling imperceptibly for years, were down even further, and the whacking great holes in the terraces were suddenly noticeable; the atmosphere at games was subdued; without the European competitions, second, third or fourth place in the League was useless (a high position had previously guaranteed a team a place in the UEFA Cup), and as a consequence, most First Division fixtures in the second half of the season were even more meaningless than usual.

One of my Italian students, a young woman with a Juventus season-ticket, found out that I was a football fan and asked if she could come with me to Highbury for the Leicester game. And though she was good company, and the chance of talking to a female European obsessive about the difference between her obsession and mine doesn't come along too frequently, I was hesitant about it. It definitely wasn't because I couldn't take a young lady to stand on the North Bank among the thugs (even an Italian, a Juventus fan, three and a half months after Heysel): as we had seen in May, the people she spent her time with on Sunday afternoons were familiar with the symptoms of the English disease, and she had already waved away my clumsy and pious apologies on behalf of the Liverpool fans. It was more because I was ashamed of the whole thing – the desperate quality of Arsenal's football, the half-empty stadium, the quiet, uninterested crowd. In the event, she said she enjoyed herself, and even claimed that Juventus were just as bad early-season (Arsenal scored after quarter of an hour and spent the rest of the match trying to keep out a dismal Leicester team). I didn't bother to tell her that this was as good as we ever got.

In my previous seventeen years of fandom, going to football had always held something above and beyond its complicated and distorted personal meanings. Even if we weren't winning, there had always been Charlie George or Liam Brady, big, noisy crowds or fascinating sociopathic disturbances, Cambridge United's gripping losing runs or Arsenal's endless cup replays. But looking at it all through the Italian girl's eyes, I could see that post-Heysel there was simply nothing going on at all; for the first time, football seemed to have been stripped right down to its subtext, and without it I would surely have been able to give it all up, as thousands of others seemed to be doing.

DRINKING AGAIN

Arsenal v Hereford

8.10.85

There is, I think, a distinction to be made between the type of hooliganism that takes place in this country, and the type involving English fans that takes place abroad. Most fans I have talked to argue that drink hasn't ever had a very large influence on the domestic violence (there has been trouble even at games with morning kick-offs, a scheme designed to stop people going to the pub before the match); travelling abroad, however, with the duty-free ferry crossings, the long, boring train journeys, the twelve hours to kill in a foreign city . . . this is a different problem altogether. There were eyewitness reports of widespread drunkenness among the Liverpool fans before Heysel (although one must bear in mind that the Yorkshire police tried, shamefully, to argue that drink had been a factor at Hillsborough), and there is a suspicion that many of the England riots of the early eighties, in Berne and Luxembourg and Italy, were alcohol-fuelled (although probably not alcohol-induced) too.

There was a lot of anguished and long-overdue self-flagellation after Heysel; drink, inevitably, was the focus for a great deal of it, and before the start of the new season its sale was banned inside our stadia. This angered some fans, who argued that as drink had only a tenuous connection with hooliganism, the real purpose of this move was to obviate the need for any radical action. Everything was wrong, people said – the relationship between clubs and fans, the state of the grounds and the lack of facilities therein, the lack of fan representation in any decision-making process, the works – and banning the sale of alcohol when everybody did their drinking in pubs (it is, as many fans have pointed out, impossible to get drunk inside a stadium anyway, given the number of people waiting to be served) wasn't going to help a bit.

I agree, as anybody would, with all of this, but it is still difficult to claim that, even with a few more toilets and a supporters' representative on the board of directors at every club, Heysel wouldn't have happened. The point was that banning the sale of alcohol didn't, couldn't possibly, do any harm: it wasn't going to cause any violence, and may even have stopped one or two fights. And, if nothing else, it showed that we were serious about our repentance. The ban could have been taken as a small but heartfelt token towards those in Italy who might have lost loved ones because a few silly boys had had too much to drink.

And what happened? The clubs whined because it affected their relationship with their more affluent fans, and the ban was lifted. On 8th October, seventeen weeks after Heysel, Pete and I and a couple of others decided to buy ourselves a seat in the Lower West Stand for a League Cup game on a miserable night, and to our astonishment were able to buy a round of shorts to keep the cold out: the rule had been changed from 'No alcohol' to 'No alcohol within sight of the pitch', as if it were the heady combination of grass and whisky that enraged us all and turned us into lunatics. So where had all the hair-shirt penitence gone? What, practically, were the clubs doing to prove that we were capable of getting a grip on ourselves, and that one day we would be able to play other European teams without wiping out half their supporters? The police were doing things, and the fans were doing things (it was this post-Heysel climate of despair that produced the lifesaving *When Saturday Comes* and all the club fanzines, and the Football Supporters' Association, whose Rogan Taylor was such an accomplished, impassioned and intelligent spokesman in the weeks after Hillsborough, four years later); but the clubs, I'm afraid to say, did nothing; this one poignant little gesture would have cost them a few bob, so they scrapped it.

THE PITS

Aston Villa v Arsenal

22.1.86

Arsenal v Aston Villa

4.2.86

Away at Villa in the quarter-final of the League Cup in January '86 was one of the best nights I can remember: fantastic away support in a magnificent stadium I hadn't visited since I was a kid, a good game and a reasonable result (1–1 after a first-half Charlie Nicholas goal and an early second-half period of domination when Rix and Quinn missed unmissable chances). There was also an interesting historical element to the evening: the freezing January air, near us at least, was thick with marijuana smoke, the first time I had really noticed that there was some sort of different terrace culture emerging.

Over Christmas there had been a mini-revival of sorts: we beat Liverpool at home and Manchester United away on consecutive Saturdays, just when things were beginning to look really bad. (In the run-up to the Liverpool game we lost 6–1 at Everton, and then went three consecutive Saturdays without even scoring. On the middle Saturday we drew nil–nil at home to Birmingham, who were relegated, in what must surely have been the worst game ever played in the history of First Division football.) We began to allow ourselves to hope a little – always a foolish thing to do – but from February through to the end of the season everything fell apart.

Home to Villa in the League Cup quarter-final replay was probably my worst-ever night, a new low in a relationship already studded with them. It wasn't just the manner of the defeat (this was the night that Don Howe played Mariner in midfield and left Woodcock on the bench); it wasn't just that there was really nobody left in the League Cup, and we should at least have gone on to Wembley (if we had beaten Villa then it was Oxford in the semis); it wasn't even that we weren't going to win anything, for the sixth year in succession. It was more than all these things, although they were in themselves bleak enough.

Part of it was my own latent depression, permanently looking for a way out and liking what it saw at Highbury that night; but even more than that, I was as usual looking to Arsenal to show me that things did not stay bad for ever, that it *was* possible to change patterns, that losing streaks did not last. Arsenal, however, had other ideas: they seemed to want to show me that troughs could indeed be permanent, that some people, like some clubs, just couldn't ever find ways out of the rooms they had locked themselves into. It seemed to me that night and for the next few days that we had both of us made too many wrong choices, and had let things slide for far too long, for anything ever to come right; I was back with the feeling, much deeper and much more frightening this time, that I was chained to the club, and thus to this miserable half-life, for ever.

I was stunned and exhausted by the defeat (2–1, although the one came in the last minute, and we were well beaten by then): the next morning a girlfriend phoned me at work, and, hearing the tired dejection in my voice, asked me what was wrong. 'Haven't you heard?' I asked her pitifully. She sounded worried and then, when I told her what had happened, I could hear, just for a second, relief – so it wasn't, after all, the things she had momentarily feared for me – before she remembered who she was talking to, and the relief was replaced by all the sympathy she could muster. I knew she didn't really understand this sort of pain, and I wouldn't have had the courage to explain it to her; because this idea, that there was this log-jam, this impasse, and that until Arsenal sorted themselves out then neither could I . . . this idea was stupid and reprehensible (it gave a whole new meaning to relegation) and, worse than that, I knew now that I really did believe it.

FREEING THE LOG-JAM

Arsenal v Watford

31.3.86

It wasn't just the few results after the Villa game, I suspect, that enabled the Arsenal board to see that something had to be done, even though they were bad enough: the particularly pathetic 3–0 FA Cup defeat at Luton has been cited (on the *History of Arsenal 1886–1986* video, for example) as the game that provoked manager Don Howe's resignation, but everyone knows that's not true. Howe actually resigned after a 3–0 victory over Coventry, because he found out that chairman Peter Hill-Wood had approached Terry Venables behind his back.

We had heard a few 'Howe Out' chants on the North Bank, in between the Villa game and his resignation; when he did resign, however, the managerless team fell apart, and the chants then became directed against the chairman, although I couldn't join in. I know the board went about things in a pretty underhand way, but something had to be done. That Arsenal team – full of cliques and overpaid, over-the-hill stars – would never be bad enough to go down, but never good enough to win anything, and the stasis made you want to scream with frustration.

The girlfriend who had tried, and failed, to get any sense out of me on the morning after the Villa match came with me to the Watford game, her first experience of live football. In a way it was a ludicrous introduction: there were less than twenty thousand in the ground, and most of those that were there had come simply to register their disapproval with everything that had taken place. (I belonged to the other category: those that were there because they were always there.)

After the players had bumbled around for an hour or so, and had gone two down, something strange happened: the North Bank switched allegiance. Each Watford attack was greeted by a roar of encouragement, each near miss (and there were hundreds of them) given an 'Oooh!' of commiseration. It was funny, in a way, but it was also desperate. Here were fans who had been completely disenfranchised, who could think of no more hurtful way to express their disgust than to turn their back on the team; it was, in effect, a form of self-mutilation. It was obvious, now, that the bottom had been reached, and it was a relief. We knew that whoever the manager was (Venables quickly made it clear that he didn't want to get involved in this sort of mess), things could not get any worse.

After the game there was a demonstration outside the main entrance, although it was difficult to ascertain precisely what people wanted; some were chanting for the reinstatement of Howe, others simply giving vent to a vague but real anger. We wandered along to have a look, but none of my crowd could muster the requisite rage needed to participate. From my own point of view, I could still remember my childish, melodramatic behaviour on the telephone the morning after the Villa game, and the demonstration was oddly comforting – the girl who had had to tolerate my sulk could see that I was not the only one, that there was this whole community who cared about what was happening to their Arsenal more than they cared about anything else. The things that I have often tried to explain to people about football – that it is not an escape, or a form of entertainment, but a different version of the world – were clear for her to see; I felt vindicated, somehow.

1986–1992

GEORGE

Arsenal v Manchester United

23.8.86

My mother has two cats, one called O'Leary and the other called Chippy, Liam Brady's nickname; the walls of her garage still bear the graffiti I chalked up there twenty years ago: 'RADFORD FOR ENGLAND!' 'CHARLIE GEORGE!' My sister Gill can still, when pushed, name most of the Double team.

Some time in May 1986 Gill called me at the language school during my midmorning break. She was then working at the BBC, and the Corporation announces big news as it comes in over the tannoy for the benefit of all staff.

'George Graham,' she said, and I thanked her and put the phone down.

This is how things have always worked in my family. I feel bad that Arsenal has intruded into their lives, too.

It wasn't a very imaginative appointment, and it was obvious that George was second or even third choice for the job, whatever the chairman says now. It is possible that if he hadn't played for the club, with great distinction, around the time that I started going then he wouldn't even have been considered for the position. He came from Millwall, whom he had rescued from relegation and then led to promotion, but I can't remember him setting the world on fire there; I worried that his lack of experience would lead to him treating Arsenal as another Second Division team, and that he would think small, buy small, concentrate on keeping his job rather than attacking the other big teams and, at first, these fears seemed well founded – the only new player he bought in his first year was Perry Groves from Colchester for £50,000, yet he sold Martin Keown immediately, and Stewart Robson not long after, and these were young players we knew and liked. So the squad got smaller and smaller: Woodcock and Mariner had gone, Caton went, and nobody replaced them.

He won his first game, at home against Manchester United, with a late Charlie Nicholas goal, and we went home cautiously positive. But he lost the next two, and by the middle of October he was in a little trouble. There was a nil–nil draw at home to Oxford which was as poor as anything we had seen in the previous six years, and already the people around me were yelling abuse at him, outraged at his perceived parsimony. In mid-November, however, after thumping Southampton 4–0 (admittedly all four of our goals were scored after the Southampton goalkeeper had been carried off), we went top of the League, and stayed there for a couple of months, and there was more, lots more, to come on top of that. He turned Arsenal into something that anyone under the age of fifty could never have seen before at Highbury, and he saved, in all the ways the word implies, every single Arsenal fan. And goals ... where we had come to expect 1–0 wins at Highbury, suddenly fours and fives, even sixes, became commonplace; I have seen five hat-tricks, by three different players, in the last seven months.

The Manchester United game was significant for another reason: it was my first as a season-ticket holder. Pete and I bought terrace tickets that summer, not because we expected the new manager to change anything, really, but because we had come to terms with the hopelessness of our addiction. It was no use pretending any longer that football was a passing fancy, or that we were going to be selective with our games, so I flogged a pile of old punk singles that had somehow acquired value, and used the money to tie myself to the fortunes of George, and have often bitterly regretted it, but never for very long.

The most intense of all footballing relationships is, of course, between fan and club. But the relationship between fan and manager can be just as powerful. Players can rarely alter the whole tone of our lives like managers can, and each time a new one is appointed it is possible to dream bigger dreams than the previous one ever allowed. When an Arsenal manager resigns or is sacked, the occasion is as sombre as the death of a monarch: Bertie Mee quit around the same time as Harold Wilson, but there is no question that the former resignation signified more to me than the latter. Prime Ministers, however manic or unjust or wicked, simply do not have the power to do to me what an Arsenal manager can, and it is no wonder that when I think about the four I have lived with and through, I think about them as relatives.

Bertie Mee was a grandfather, kindly, slightly otherworldly, a member of a generation I didn't understand; Terry Neill was a new stepfather, matey, jocular, dislikeable however hard he tried; Don Howe was an uncle by marriage, dour and stolid yet probably and unpredictably good for a couple of card tricks at Christmas. But George . . . George is my dad, less complicated but much more frightening than the real one. (Disconcertingly, he even looks a little bit like my dad – an upright, immaculately groomed, handsome man with an obvious taste for expensive, well-cut formal clothes.)

I dream about George quite regularly, perhaps as often as I dream about my other father. In dreams, as in life, he is hard, driven, determined, indecipherable; usually he is expressing disappointment in me for some perceived lapse, quite often of a sexual nature, and I feel guilty as all hell. Sometimes, however, it is the other way around, and I catch him stealing or beating someone up, and I wake up feeling diminished. I do not like to think about these dreams or their meanings for too long.

George ended his fifth year with Arsenal just as he had begun his first, with a home game against Manchester United, but this time Highbury was awash with self-congratulation rather than sceptical anticipation: we had won the 1991 Championship some forty-five minutes before the kick-off, and the stadium was replete with noise and colour and smiles. There was a large banner draped over the edge of the West Stand Upper Tier which read, simply, 'George Knows', and which in a peculiar way isolated and defined my filial relationship with the man. He *did* know, in a way that fathers very rarely do, and on that enchanted evening every one of his mystifying decisions (the sale of Lukic, the purchase of Linighan, even the persistence with Groves) began to look unfathomably wise. Perhaps little boys want fathers to be this way, to act but never to explain the actions, to triumph on our behalf and then to be able to say, 'You doubted me but I was right, and now you must trust me'; it is one of football's charms that it can fulfil this kind of impossible dream.

A MALE FANTASY

Arsenal v Charlton Athletic

18.11.86

Typically, I remember her first game and she doesn't: a moment ago I poked my head round the bedroom door and asked her the name of the opponents, score and scorers, but all she could tell me was that Arsenal won and Niall Quinn got one. (2–0, and the other goal came courtesy of a Charlton defender.)

It is fair to say that back then, in the first few months of our relationship, we were having trouble (trouble caused by me), and I don't think either of us thought that we were going to last much longer. The way she tells it now, she thought that the end was coming sooner rather than later, and chose Charlton on a wet and cold November night because she thought she wasn't going to get too many more opportunities to come to Highbury with me. It wasn't a great game, but it was a good time to come, because Arsenal were slap-bang in the middle of a tremendous twenty-two-game unbeaten run, and crowds were up, spirits were up, young players (Rocky, Niall, Adams, Hayes, who later became her inexplicable favourite) were in the team and playing well, and the previous Saturday we'd all been down to Southampton to see the new League leaders.

She craned her neck and watched what she could see, and after the game we went to the pub and she said that she'd like to come again. This is what women always say and it usually means that they would like to come again in another life, and not even the next life but the one after that. I said, of course, that she would be welcome whenever; immediately she asked whether there was another home game on the Saturday. There was, and she came to that too, and to most home games for the rest of the season. She has travelled to Villa Park and Carrow Road and other London grounds, and one year she bought a season-ticket. She still comes regularly, and can recognise every member of the Arsenal squad without any difficulty, although there is no doubt that her enthusiasm is on the wane now, and that my perpetual intensity irritates her more as we both get older.

I wouldn't like to think that it was all this that saved the relationship – in fact, I know it wasn't. But it certainly had a lubricious effect, initially, and her sudden interest complicated things that were already confused. On New Year's Day 1987, when she and I went to watch a 3–1 win over Wimbledon, I began to realise why the woman who not only tolerates but actively participates in the football ritual has become for many men something of a fantasy figure: some men I knew, who had wrecked the previous night's jollities and the bank holiday's traditional familial calm by dragging themselves off to Goodison or somewhere to watch a morning kick-off, would return home to tensions and baleful glances all of their own making, whereas I was in the fortunate position of being at Highbury because it was an organic part of our day.

Later, however, I began to wonder whether this Arsenal-sharing really was what I wanted. Once, during the height of her sudden passion, we were watching a father struggling into the stadium with a very young child, and I remarked in passing that I wouldn't take a child of mine to a game until he or she was old enough to want to go; this led on to a conversation about future child-care arrangements on Saturday afternoons, a conversation that haunted me for weeks, months, afterwards. 'Alternate home games, I suppose,' she said, and for a while I presumed she meant that she would try to get along to every other match at Highbury, that our children could be left somewhere once a month but no more frequently than that, and that she would come when she could. But what she meant was that we would *take it in turns* to go, that for half the home games every year I would be at home listening to *Sport on Five* or Capital Gold (Capital Gold is less authoritative, somehow, but keeps you bang up-to-date with all the London clubs) while she sat in *my seat* watching *my team*, the team to which I had introduced her just a few years before. So now where is the advantage? Friends with partners who loathe football get to go to every game; meanwhile I – who have an apparently ideal relationship with a woman who knows why Arsenal aren't the same without Smithy leading the line – I'm looking at a future sitting in my living room with a pile of *Postman Pat* videos and the window open, mournfully hoping that a gust of wind will blow a roar my way. It wasn't what I had anticipated, that evening against Charlton when she said she wanted to go again.

There's more. All my footballing life I have lived with people – my mum, my dad, my sister, girlfriends, flatmates – who have had to learn to tolerate football-induced moods, and they have all of them, more or less, done so with good humour and tact. Suddenly I found myself living with someone who was attempting to claim moods for herself, and I didn't like it. Her elation after the 1987 Littlewoods Cup Final . . . that was her *first season.* What right did she have to swagger into the pub that Sunday evening with an Arsenal hat on? No right at all. For Pete and me, this was the first trophy since 1979, and how could she, who had only been going for the previous four months, understand what that felt like? 'They don't win things every season, you know,' I kept telling her, with all the pointless and bilious envy of a parent whose Mars Bar-munching child has never experienced the deprivations of wartime rationing.

I soon found that the only way to claim all the emotional territory for myself was to go on a sort of sulk war, confident in the knowledge that when it came to football I could pout and grump any pretender to the Football Pain throne right off the terraces, and eventually I beat her, as I knew I would. It happened at the end of the 88/89 season when, after a home defeat by Derby, it looked as though we were going to miss out on the Championship after having led the First Division for most of the season. And though I was genuinely inconsolable (that evening we went to see Eric Porter in *King Lear* at the Old Vic, and the play didn't engage me because I couldn't see what Lear's problem was), I nurtured every bit of the misery until it grew to monstrous, terrifying proportions, I behaved badly in order to prove a point, and inevitably we had an argument (about going to see some friends for a cup of tea), and once it had started I knew that Arsenal was all mine once again: she was left with no alternative but to say that it was only a game (she didn't use those words, thankfully, but the implication was, I felt, clear), that there was always next year, that even this year all hope was not lost, and I leaped on these words triumphantly.

'*You don't understand,*' I shouted, as I had wanted to shout for months, and it was true – she didn't, not really. And I think that once I had been given this opportunity, once I had uttered the words that most football fans carry around with them like a kidney donor card, it was all over. What was she left with? She could attempt, or pretend, to behave even worse than I had done; or she could withdraw, yield ground, leave the agony and the ecstasy more or less entirely to me and use her own distress merely to buttress mine. She is much too gentle a person to attempt to out-tantrum me, so she chose the latter course, and I can safely and smugly say that I am top Arsenal dog in this house, and that when and if we have children it will be my bottom exclusively that fills our season-ticket seat. I'm ashamed, of course I'm ashamed, that I have had to play dirty like this, but for a while back then I was beginning to worry.

FROM NW3 TO N17

Tottenham v Arsenal

4.3.87

If this book has a centre, then it is here, on the Wednesday night in March 1987 that I travelled from a psychiatrist's office in Hampstead to White Hart Lane in Tottenham to see a Littlewoods Cup semi-final replay. I didn't plan it that way, of course: the trip to Hampstead had been arranged well before a replay became necessary. But now, when I am attempting to explain why football has managed to slow me down and speed me up, and how Arsenal and I got all mixed up together in my head, this particular conjunction looks implausibly neat.

It is easier to explain why Arsenal and Spurs needed a replay than it is to explain why I needed a psychiatrist, so I shall begin there. The two legs of the semi-final had produced an aggregate score of 2–2, and even extra time on the Sunday at White Hart Lane had failed to push one of the teams over the edge and out of the competition, although four measly goals in three and a half hours of football is an inadequate indicator of the draining drama of the two games. In the first one, at Highbury, Clive Allen celebrated his typically predatory piece of finishing in the first half by leaping into the air and landing flat on his back from a height of about five feet, one of the most eccentric expressions of joy I have ever seen; and Paul Davis missed an open goal from less than six inches, and Hoddle hit the bar with a brilliant curling free kick, and poor Gus Caesar (Arsenal's thin squad was being stretched to the point of disaster), tormented beyond all dignity by Waddle, had to be replaced by the only other player we had available, a young man called Michael Thomas, who had never played in the first team before.

In the second game Allen scored again early on, so Spurs were 2–0 up on aggregate, and had four other one-on-ones with Lukic as Arsenal pushed forward, and missed them all; and at half-time the Spurs announcer told the Spurs fans how they could apply for tickets for the

Final at Wembley, a misguided and provocative moment of extreme smugness that served to awaken and enrage the subdued Arsenal fans (and, we heard later, the team, who heard the tannoy message in the dressing room) to the extent that when our players came out for the second half, they were met with a proud and defiant roar; thus inspired, the team bravely inched their way back into the game and, even though on paper Adams, Quinn, Hayes, Thomas and Rocastle were no match for Waddle, Hoddle, Ardiles, Gough and Allen, first Viv Anderson, scrappily, and then Niall, refulgently, scored to push the game into extra time. We should have won in the extra thirty minutes – Tottenham were in pieces, and both Hayes and Nicholas could have finished them off – but given the number of chances Tottenham had had over the two games, and our two-goal deficit with three-quarters of the tie gone, a replay was better than anything we had dared hope for. After the game George came on to the pitch and tossed a coin to settle the venue for the deciding match, and when he looked over towards us and pointed straight down at the White Hart Lane mud to indicate that he had lost the call, the Arsenal fans roared again: we'd beaten Spurs twice at their place in the space of a few weeks (the League game at the beginning of January finished 2–1) and had only managed a draw and a defeat against them at Highbury. We would all be back on Wednesday.

This, then, is how the replay came about – football is easy like that. And if you want to know how we came to be in the Littlewoods Cup semi-final, then that's easy too: we'd beaten Forest at Highbury in the quarter-final, and before that Manchester City, Charlton and Huddersfield over two legs in the second round, and before Huddersfield there was nothing at all. The contrast between the strong, clean, straight lines of a cup run and the messy, tangled, overgrown paths of a life is plangent: I wish I could draw one of those big knock-out trophy diagrams to show how I'd ended up playing on the unfamiliar turf of a Hampstead psychiatrist's carpet.

The best I can do is as follows. In the spring of 1986, I had become frustrated beyond patience by my inability to find, even seven years after leaving college, a job I wanted to do, and by my failure, six years after losing the Lost Girl, to hold down any kind of permanent, healthy relationship, although temporary and sickly relationships, usually involving some kind of third party, were a dime-a-dozen. And as I had spent a lot of time talking to the principal of my language school, a man who was then training to become a Jungian therapist, and had become interested in what he had to say about the value of therapy, I somehow ended up going to see a lady in Bounds Green once a week.

Huge parts of me didn't like going. Had Willie Young ever bothered with therapy? Or Peter Storey? Or Tony Adams? Yet every Thursday I sat in a big armchair, flicking the leaves of the rubber plant that dangled over my head, trying to talk about my family and my jobs and my relationships and, as often as not, Arsenal; after a few months of this leaf-flicking, some sort of lid blew off, and I lost the last few pieces of the spurious muddle-through optimism that had been sustaining me for the previous few years. Like most depressions that plague people who have been more fortunate than most, I was ashamed of mine because there appeared to be no convincing cause for it; I just felt as though I had come off the rails somewhere.

I had no idea at what point this might have happened. Indeed, I wasn't even sure which rails these were. I had loads of friends, including girlfriends, I was in work, I was in regular contact with all the members of my immediate family, I had suffered no bereavements, I had somewhere to live . . . I was still on all the tracks that I could think of; so what, precisely, was the nature of the derailment? All I know is that I felt, inexplicably, *unlucky*, *cursed* in some way that would not be immediately apparent to anyone without a job or a lover or a family. I knew myself to be doomed to a life of dissatisfactions: my talents, whatever they were, would go permanently unrecognised, my relationships wrecked by circumstances entirely beyond my control. And because I knew this beyond any doubt, then there was simply no point in attempting to rectify the situation by looking for work that would stimulate me, or for a personal life that would make me happy. So I stopped writing (because if you are born under a bad sign, as I had been, there is simply no point in persisting with something that will inevitably bring with it only the humiliation of perpetual rejection), and involved myself in as many miserable and debilitating triangular relationships as I possibly could, and settled down to the remainder of my allotted three-score years and ten of unrelieved and terrible nothingness.

It wasn't, in truth, a future I could regard with a great deal of enthusiasm, and even though it was the therapy that seemed to have brought most of this bleakness on, or out, it seemed to me that I needed more of it: the last shred of common sense I had left suggested that many of these problems were in me rather than in the world, that they were of a psychological rather than an actual nature, that I hadn't been born under a bad sign at all but that I was some sort of self-destructive nutcase, that I literally needed my head seeing to. Except I was flat broke and couldn't afford to see any more of my lady in Bounds Green, so she sent me to see the man in Hampstead, who had the power to refer me back to her at a preferential rate if he was convinced that I was sick enough. And so it came to pass – and there are a number of Arsenal-loathing football fans all over the country who might find the episode gloriously and hilariously significant – that this Arsenal fan was obliged to preface his attendance at the Littlewoods Cup semi-final replay by visiting a psychiatrist, in order to persuade him that I was round the twist. I got the referral I needed, and I didn't even have to produce my season-ticket.

I travelled from Hampstead down to Baker Street, from Baker Street to King's Cross, from King's Cross to Seven Sisters, and got a bus the rest of the way up the Tottenham High Road; and from Baker Street onwards, the point at which my return journey from the psychiatrist became an outward journey to a football match, I felt better, less isolated, more purposeful (although on the final stage of the journey I felt bad again, but this was a comforting pre-match bad, my stomach churning and my body weary at the thought of the emotional effort to come); I no longer had to try to explain to myself where I was going or where I had been, and I was back in the mainstream. The value of the herd instinct, again: I was only too happy to experience the loss of identity that crowds demand. It was then that it occurred to me that I would never really be able to explain or even remember precisely how the evening had started as it had, and that in some ways, football isn't a very good metaphor for life at all.

I usually hate games between Arsenal and Tottenham, especially the away games, when the hostile territory brings out the very worst in the Arsenal fans, and I have stopped going to White Hart Lane now. 'I hope your wife dies of cancer, Roberts,' a man behind me shouted a few years back. And in September 1987, just before David Pleat was forced to resign his position as Tottenham manager, but just after unsavoury allegations about his personal life had appeared in the tabloids, I sat among several thousand people roaring 'Sex case! Sex case! HANG HIM HANG HIM

HANG HIM!', and felt, perhaps understandably, that I was much too delicate a soul for this sort of entertainment; the blow-up dolls being tossed around merrily at our end, and the hundreds of pairs of amusing breast spectacles that were *de rigueur* for the committed Arsenal fan that afternoon, hardly helped to make the sensitive liberal feel any more at ease. And in 1989, when Spurs beat us at White Hart Lane for the first time for four years, there was an awful and disturbing ugliness in the Arsenal end after the final whistle, and seats were broken, and that was enough for me. The anti-Semitic chanting, even though Arsenal have just as many Jewish fans as Tottenham, is obscene and unforgivable, and over the last few years the rivalry between the two sets of fans has become intolerably hateful.

A cup-tie is different, however. The older season-ticket holders, those who hate Tottenham, but not with the drooling and violent rage of some of the twenty and thirtysomethings, are sufficiently motivated to travel, and so some of the bile is diluted. And the result, and the football, matters more than it does in many of the League games between Arsenal and Spurs, who for most seasons over the last twenty or thirty years have found themselves in mid-table, and consequently there is some sort of a focus for the aggression. Paradoxically, when the game means something then the identity of the opponents signifies less.

Anyway, I know that my middle-class sensibilities were not unduly disturbed, and that there were no chanted sex-case or cancer references to sour my memory of the evening. The game was fast and open, just as it had been on the Sunday, and once again we seemed to spend the whole of the first half watching Clive Allen bear down on the unprotected goal in front of us, but the longer it went on the more I feared for Arsenal. The team was getting younger and younger with each match (Thomas, a full-back replacement for Caesar in the first leg, was playing his first full match, in midfield) and though it was nil–nil at half-time, Allen finally scored, right at the beginning of the second half; shortly afterwards Nicholas was stretchered off, and Ian Allinson, a trier but hardly the man to save the match, had to come on, and it was all up.

A couple of rows in front of me, a line of middle-aged men and women, blankets over their legs, soup flasks twinkling, started singing the Irish song that the older fans in the seats – I have never heard a North Bank rendition – often used to sing on big nights, and everyone who knew the words ('And then he got up and he sang it again/Over and over and over again') joined in. So I thought, with, what, six or seven minutes left, that at least I would remember the occasion with some fondness, even though it was to have a bitter and dismal conclusion; and then Allinson, jinking unconvincingly down the left, put in a feeble shot on the turn that totally deceived Clemence and snuck in guiltily at the near post, and there was this enormous explosion of relief and unhinged joy. And Tottenham fell apart, just as they had on Sunday: over the next two minutes Hayes intercepted a bad back-pass and shot into the side netting, Thomas grooved his way through to the edge of the area, with the sort of insouciance we later came to love and hate, and shot just past the post. On my video, you can see, as Anderson goes to take a throw-in, the Arsenal fans literally bouncing with excitement. And there was more to come. As Tottenham's digital clock stopped on ninety minutes, Rocky picked up a loose cross, chested it down, and hit it through Clemence and into the net; and almost immediately the referee blew the final whistle, and the rows of people disappeared and were replaced by one shuddering heap of ecstatic humanity.

It was the second of three or four lifetime football moments where my delirium was such that I had no idea what I was doing, where everything went blank for a few moments. I know that an old man behind me grabbed me around the neck and wouldn't let go, and that when I returned to a state approaching normal consciousness the rest of the stadium was empty save for a few Tottenham fans who stood watching us, too stunned and sick to move (in my mind I see white faces, but we were too far away to be able to detect shock-induced pallor), and the Arsenal players were cavorting beneath us, as overjoyed and probably as baffled by their win as we were.

We were all still in the stadium twenty minutes after the final whistle, and then we roared out on to the street, and Pete and I drove back to the Arsenal Tavern, where we were locked in after closing time so that we could watch the highlights of the game on their big TV screen, and so that I could drink much too much.

The depression that I had been living with for the best part of the 1980s packed up and started to leave that night, and within a month I was better. Inevitably part of me wishes that it had been something else that effected the cure – the love of a good woman, or a minor literary triumph, or a transcendent realisation during something like Live Aid that my life was blessed and worth living – something worthy and real and meaningful. It embarrasses me to confess that a decade-long downer lifted because Arsenal won at Spurs in the Littlewoods Cup (I would be slightly less embarrassed if it had been an FA Cup win, but the *Littlewoods*!), and I have often tried to work out why it happened like this. The win meant a lot to all Arsenal fans, of course: for seven years our team hadn't even come very close to winning a semi-final, and the decline had begun to look terminal. And there might even be a medical explanation. It could be that the monstrous surge of adrenalin released by a last-minute winner at Tottenham in a semi-final when you were one down with seven minutes left, all hope abandoned, maybe this surge corrects some kind of chemical imbalance in the brain or something.

The only convincing explanation I can come up with, however, is that I stopped feeling unlucky that night, and that the log-jam that had provoked such despair just over a year before had been sorted, not by me, predictably, but by Arsenal; and so I jumped on to the shoulders of the team and they carried me into the light that had suddenly shone down on all of us. And the lift they gave me enabled me to part company from them, in some ways: though I am still one of Arsenal's most devoted fans, and though I still go to every home game, and feel the same tensions and elations and glooms that I have always felt, I now understand them to have an entirely separate identity whose success and failure has no relationship with my own. That night, I stopped being an Arsenal lunatic and relearned how to be a fan, still cranky, and still dangerously obsessive, but only a fan nonetheless.

JUST ANOTHER SATURDAY

Chelsea v Arsenal

7.3.87

Everyone went to Chelsea on the Saturday to continue the party, and it lasted for about another fifteen minutes, until something – a Hayes miss, or a Caesar back-pass, I can't remember now – provoked the howls of frustration and irritation that you could have heard on any Saturday of the previous few years. The average football fan is notoriously, almost savagely unsentimental.

It has to be said, however, that Stamford Bridge is not a place where moist-eyed affection or indulgent forgiveness will ever thrive. Games at Chelsea are inevitably dismal – it is no coincidence that the only League fixture Arsenal lost during their otherwise all-conquering '91 Championship season was this one. The track around the outside of the pitch distances the fans from the players, and affects the atmosphere; and as most supporters on the terraces at both ends are completely in the open (and thus liable for a good soaking if there's one in the offing) there is no noise anyway. In my experience the home fans' reputation for vicious thuggery and for witless and ugly racism, although there has been a little less of both over the last couple of years, is well deserved, and everyone knows that you're safer standing, thus receiving the benefit of well-organised and thorough police protection, than you are sitting, and leaving yourself prone to isolation, recognition and ultimately demolition, the very process that did for a friend a few years back.

And the game went on, and the sky darkened, and Arsenal got worse, eventually conceding a goal, which in their hangover listlessness was one goal too many. And you stand there on the huge crumbling terrace, your feet stiffening and then actually burning in the cold, with the Chelsea fans jeering and gesturing at you, and you wonder why you bothered, when you knew, not only in your heart of hearts but with your head as well, that the game would be dull, and the players would be inept, that the feelings engendered on the Wednesday would have dribbled away to a flat nothingness before twenty minutes of the Saturday game had passed when, if you had stayed at home or gone record shopping, you could have kept the embers glowing for another week longer. But then, these are the games, the 1–0 defeats at Chelsea on a miserable March afternoon, that give meaning to the rest, and it is precisely because you have seen so many of them that there is real joy to be had from those others that come once every six, seven, ten years.

At the end of the game the away fans managed a respectful and muted gratitude for their team, a recognition of recent past achievements, but it had been a dismal afternoon, a piece of dues-paying, spadework, absolutely nothing more than that. And yet as we were waiting to be let out (another thing about Chelsea: you are kept behind for a good thirty minutes while the streets outside are cleared of their menace) the sheer awfulness of it all deepened and thus the experience was lent a perverse kind of glory, so that those of us there became entitled to award themselves a campaign medal.

Two things happened. First, it began to snow and the discomfort was such that you wanted to laugh at yourself for tolerating this fan's life any longer; and secondly, a man came out with a rolling machine and proceeded to drive up and down the pitch with it. He was not the irascible old git of football club legend, but an enormous young man with a monstrous skinhead haircut, and he obviously hated Arsenal with all the passion of his employers' followers. As he drove towards us on his machine, he gave us the finger, a delighted and maniacal smile on his face; and on his return visit he gave us the finger again, and so it went on – up, back and the finger. Up, back and the finger. And we had to stand and watch him do it, over and over again, in the dark and the freezing cold, while the snow fell on us in our concrete compound. It was a proper, thorough restoration of normal service.

GOLDEN

Arsenal v Liverpool

(at Wembley) 11.4.87

And on the other hand, some days are just golden. My depression had gone completely now; all I could feel was the place where the ache had been, and that was a pleasurable sensation, just as when you are recovering from food poisoning and eating again, the soreness of the stomach muscles is pleasurable. I was six days off my thirtieth birthday, and I had the idea that everything had pulled round for me just in time; that thirty was the falls at the end of the river and if I had still been down when I got there I would have gone right over the edge. So I felt good about that, and Arsenal back at Wembley felt good, because with a young team and a new manager the Littlewoods Cup seemed like an unimaginably delicious hors d'oeuvre, rather than a meal in itself. I had just turned twenty-three when we were last all there together, and for me and the team, the seven intervening years had been unpredictably horrible; but now we had come out of the dark and into the light.

There *was* light, too, a glorious and gloriously apposite April sunshine. And though you are always aware of how it feels when the winter is over, however long that winter might have been, there is nothing like a football stadium, especially Wembley, to remind you, because you stand there in the shadowed dark looking down into the light, on to the brilliant lush green and it's as if you are in a cinema watching a film about another and more exotic country. It was as sunny outside the stadium as in it, of course, but it didn't seem that way, because of this trick football grounds have of using just a rectangle of the sunshine so that you can see it and understand it.

So there was all that already, even before the game started. And though we were playing Liverpool (admittedly Liverpool in one of their less mighty guises, pre-Beardsley and Barnes, but post-Dalglish, although he was their sub that day), and thus could only be expected to lose, I really had convinced myself that it wouldn't matter, and that me being back, and the team being back, was enough. So when Craig Johnston put Rush through, and he paused for a moment, took his time, and smashed the ball neatly and authoritatively past our goalkeeper Lukic's groping left hand, I was stung but not surprised, and determined not to let the goal and the defeat that was bound to follow spoil my recuperation or my new, springy optimism.

But Charlie equalised before half-time, after he had hit the post and caused a massive scramble in the Liverpool penalty area; and in a wonderful second half of football, when both teams played with grace and skill and desire, our substitute, the poor, maligned Perry Groves, skipped past Gillespie, crossed, Charlie swung, the ball hit a defender and rolled gently past the deceived Grobbelaar and into the goal. It all seemed so languid, and the ball trundled in so slowly, that I feared that it would not have the strength to cross the line completely, or it would be cleared before the referee had spotted that it had indeed gone over, but in the end it found just enough puff to touch the net. Nicholas and Groves, one of whom had come from Celtic for nearly three-quarters of a million pounds, the other of whom had come from Colchester United for about one-fifteenth of that sum, ran behind the goal and did a little dance of joy, just the two of them, in front of us; they could not ever have imagined dancing together before, and they never would again, but there they were, yoked just for one tiny moment in the one-hundred-and-one-year history of the club by their unrepeatable and frankly fortuitous collaboration. And that is how Arsenal came to win the Littlewoods Cup, not the most prestigious trophy I know, but much more than Pete and I and the rest of us could have dared hope for two years previously. It was some kind of reward for blind persistence.

*

One thing I know for sure about being a fan is this: it is not a vicarious pleasure, despite all appearances to the contrary, and those who say that they would rather do than watch are missing the point. Football is a context where watching *becomes* doing – not in the aerobic sense, because watching a game, smoking your head off while doing so, drinking after it has finished and eating chips on the way home is unlikely to do you a whole lot of Jane Fonda good, in the way that chuffing up and down a pitch is supposed to. But when there is some kind of triumph, the pleasure does not radiate from the players outwards until it reaches the likes of us at the back of the terraces in a pale and diminished form; our fun is not a watery version of the team's fun, even though they are the ones that get to score the goals and climb the steps at Wembley to meet Princess Diana. The joy we feel on occasions like this is not a celebration of others' good fortune, but a celebration of our own; and when there is a disastrous defeat the sorrow that engulfs us is, in effect, self-pity, and anyone who wishes to understand how football is consumed must realise this above all things. The players are merely our representatives, chosen by the manager rather than elected by us, but our representatives nonetheless, and sometimes if you look hard you can see the little poles that join them together, and the handles at the side that enable us to move them. I am a part of the club, just as the club is a part of me; and I say this fully aware that the club exploits me, disregards my views, and treats me shoddily on occasions, so my feeling of organic connection is not built on a muddle-headed and sentimental misunderstanding of how professional football works. This Wembley win belonged to me every bit as much as it belonged to Charlie Nicholas or George Graham (does Nicholas, who was dropped by Graham right at the start of the following season, and then sold, remember the afternoon as fondly?), and I worked every bit as hard for it as they did. The only difference between me and them is that I have put in more hours, more years, more decades than them, and so had a better understanding of the afternoon, a sweeter appreciation of why the sun still shines when I remember it.

BANANAS

Arsenal v Liverpool

15.8.87

Because my partner is small, and therefore disadvantaged when it comes to watching football from the terraces, I gave my season-ticket away for the afternoon and bought seats high up in the West Stand for the first game of the new season. It was the afternoon that Smith made his début for Arsenal, and Barnes and Beardsley theirs for Liverpool, and it was hot, and Highbury was heaving.

We were level with the penalty spot at the Clock End of the ground, so we had a perfect view of the Davis diving header that equalised Aldridge's opening goal, and a perfect view of the astonishing twenty-five-yard header from Nicol that gave Liverpool their winner in the very last minute; we could also see, with terrible clarity, the extraordinary behaviour of the Liverpool fans beneath us and to our right.

In his book on Barnes and race issues in Liverpool, *Out of His Skin*, Dave Hill only mentions that first game in passing ('Liverpool's travelling supporters went home delighted, any doubts about the wisdom of the manager's summer shopping spree already on the retreat'). He pays more attention to Liverpool's game a few weeks later against Everton at Anfield in the Littlewoods Cup, during which the away supporters chanted 'Niggerpool! Niggerpool', and 'Everton are white!' (Everton, mysteriously, still haven't managed to find a black player good enough for their team.)

Yet Barnes's first game did throw up information that Hill could have used, because we could see quite clearly, as the teams warmed up before the kick-off, that banana after banana was being hurled from the away supporters' enclosure. The bananas were designed to announce, for the benefit of those unversed in codified terrace abuse, that there was a monkey on the pitch; and as the Liverpool fans have never bothered to bring bananas to previous Arsenal matches, even though we have always had at least one black player in the side since the turn of the decade, one can only presume that John Barnes was the monkey to whom they were referring.

Those who have seen John Barnes, this beautiful, elegant man, play football, or give an interview, or even simply walk out on to a pitch, and have also stood next to the grunting, overweight orang-utans who do things like throw bananas and make monkey noises, will appreciate the dazzling irony of all this. (There may well be attractive, articulate and elegant racists, but they certainly never come to football matches.) And maybe the bananas were not intended as an expression of racial hatred, but as a grotesque form of welcome – maybe these Liverpudlians, with their famous quick and ready wit, merely wanted to welcome Barnes in a way that they thought he could understand, just as the Spurs supporters gave Ardiles and Villa an Argentinian tickertape welcome in '78. (This latter theory is hard to believe, but it is no harder than believing that so many fans could be so poisonously angry about the arrival at their club of one of the best players in the world.) Yet however hysterically ironic the scene might have been, and whatever the Liverpool fans might have meant, it was a revolting, nauseating sight.

Arsenal, by and large, have no problems with this kind of filth any more, although they have problems with other kinds, particularly anti-Semitism. There are black fans, on the terraces and in the seats, and our best players – Rocastle, Campbell, Wright – are black, and enormously popular. You can still, even now, occasionally hear idiots who jeer the black players on opposing teams. (One night I turned round angrily to confront an Arsenal fan making monkey noises at Manchester United's Paul Ince, and found that I was abusing a blind man. A blind racist!) And sometimes, when an opposing black player commits a foul, or misses a good chance, or doesn't miss a good chance, or argues with the referee, you sit quivering in a panic of liberal foreboding. 'Please don't say anything, anybody,' you sit muttering to yourself. 'Please don't ruin it all for me.' (For *me*, please note, not for the poor bastard who has to play just feet away from some evil fascist stormtrooper – such is the indulgent self-pity of the modern free-thinker.) Then some Neanderthal rises to his feet, points at Ince, or Wallace, or Barnes, or Walker, and you hold your breath . . . and he calls him a cunt, or a wanker, or something else obscene, and you are filled with an absurd sense of metropolitan sophisticate pride, because the adjectival epithet is missing; you know that this would not be the case if you were watching a game on Merseyside or in the West Country or in the North-East, or anywhere that has no real multiracial community. It's not much to be grateful for, really, the fact that a man calls another man a cunt but not a black cunt.

*

It seems lame to say that I loathe the baiting of black players that takes place as a matter of routine inside some football grounds, and if I had had any guts I would have either (a) confronted some of the worst perpetrators or (b) stopped going to games. Before remonstrating with the blind racist I was making some frantic calculations – how hard is he? How hard are his mates? How hard are my mates? – until I heard something, a certain whininess in his voice, maybe, that led me to conclude that I wasn't about to get a pasting, and acted accordingly, but this is rare. More usually I take the view that these people, like the people who smoke on tube trains, know what they're doing, and their abuse is intended to intimidate anyone, black or white, who feels like doing something about it. And as for not going . . . what I'm supposed to say is that football grounds are for everyone, not just for racist thugs, and when decent people stop going then the game is in trouble. And part of me believes that (Leeds fans have done amazing things to conquer the foul atmosphere that used to engulf their ground); part of me, however, knows that I can't stop because of the strength of my obsession.

I wish all the things that other fans like me wish: I wish that football commentators would express outrage more than they do; I wish Arsenal really did insist on the ejection of fans who sing songs about Hitler gassing Jews, instead of forever threatening to do so; I wish all players, black and white, would do more to make their disgust known. (If, say, Everton's goalkeeper Neville Southall simply walked off the pitch in protest every time his own fans made these noises, then the problems at Goodison Park would stop almost overnight, but I know that things are not done this way.) But most of all, I wish I were enormous and of a violent disposition, so that I could deal with any problem that arises near me in a fashion commensurate with the anger I feel.

THE KING OF KENILWORTH ROAD

Luton v Arsenal

31.8.87

Non-footballing friends and family have never met anyone madder than I; indeed, they are convinced that I am as obsessed as it is possible to be. But I know that there are people who would regard the level of my commitment – every home game, a handful of away games, and one or two reserve or youth games each season – as inadequate. People like Neil Kaas, a Luton fan who took me and my half-brother to watch Arsenal at Kenilworth Road as his guest in the days when Luton's ban on away fans was in operation, are obsessives with all traces of timidity or self-doubt removed; they make me look like the faint-hearted dilettante they suspect me of being.

Eight things you didn't know about Neil Kaas:

(1) He would, of course, travel to Plymouth on a Wednesday night, thus using up a precious day's holiday. (He has travelled to Wigan, and Doncaster, and everywhere else; and on the way back from a midweek game in Hartlepool, the coach broke down, and he and his party watched *Police Academy 3* seven times.)

(2) When I first met him, he had just returned from a kibbutz, although when I got to know him better I was amazed that he had managed to tear himself away from the Hatters for any length of time. He explained that he had gone because the Luton fans were about to organise a boycott of all home games in protest against a planned move to Milton Keynes; Neil knew that even though he had given the boycott his sincere backing, he would be unable to maintain it unless he took himself off to the other side of the world.

(3) After a bizarre chain of circumstances too complicated to relate here, he watched a game against QPR from the directors' box, having been introduced by David Evans to the rest of the Luton board as 'the next Chairman of Luton Town'.

(4) He has single-handedly driven Mike Newell and a number of other players away from the club, by ensuring that he is always positioned near the players' tunnel to abuse viciously and incessantly anybody he believes is not good enough to tread the Kenilworth Road turf.

(5) A report in the *Independent* once made some reference to a loud-mouth with a foghorn voice who sits in the main stand at Luton, said loudmouth precluding enjoyment for anyone in his immediate vicinity; having watched with Neil I can only conclude, regretfully, that he is the man.

(6) He attends every open evening at Luton, occasions which enable the fans to talk to the manager and the directors, although recently he has begun to suspect that they will no longer allow him to ask questions. He is mystified by this, although some of the questions I know him to

have asked are not really questions at all, but slanderous and noisy allegations of impropriety and incompetence.

(7) He has written to Luton Council proposing that they commission a statue commemorating Raddy Antic, whose last-minute goal at Maine Road prevented Luton dropping into Division Two.

(8) On Sunday mornings, just a few hours after he has returned from wherever he has been on the Saturday afternoon, he plays for Bushey 'B' (a team which suffered the misfortune of having two points deducted when the goalkeeper's dog stopped a shot on the line) in the Maccabi League, although he has had disciplinary problems of late, both with his manager and with referees, and at the time of writing is sidelined.

This litany contains *a* truth about Neil, but not *the* truth, which is that he has a cheerful and ironic perspective on his own excesses, and talks about them as if they were the property of someone else – his younger brother, maybe. And away from Kenilworth Road he is charming, interested, and unflaggingly polite, at least to strangers, so the rage that invariably afflicts him on Saturdays is induced exclusively by Luton.

Luton are not a big club, and they don't have many fans – their home crowds are between a third and a quarter the size of Arsenal's. What was memorable about watching this game with him was not the football, which ended up a drab 1–1 draw after Davis had put us into the lead, but the sense of proprietorship that emanates from someone who has to his own satisfaction taken the club over. It seemed, as we walked to our seats, that Neil knew maybe one in three of the crowd, and stopped for a chat with half of those. And when he travels to away games, it is not as a mote in some huge invading army, but as a visible and recognisable face in a ragged crowd of a couple of hundred, maybe even less than that for some of the more problematic midweek fixtures.

Yet this is part of the attraction for him: he is the Lord of Luton, the King of Kenilworth Road. So when his friends hear the results on a Saturday, on national radio and television, or on the tannoys of other League grounds, they think, simply, 'Neil Kaas' when they hear the Luton score. Neil Kaas 0 Liverpool 2, Neil Kaas saved from relegation with last-minute goal, Neil Kaas wins Littlewoods Cup . . .

And this too is an appeal that football has for me, although I could never claim to be a definition of Arsenal in the way that Neil and Luton define each other. This appeal is one that has emerged slowly over the years, but it is a powerful attraction nevertheless: *I like the thought of people remembering me on a regular basis.*

I know that this happens. On the night of the 26th of May 1989 I came back to my flat after carousing deep into the night to find fourteen or fifteen phone messages from friends all over Britain and Europe, some of whom I hadn't spoken to for months; often, on the day after an Arsenal calamity or triumph, I receive phone calls from friends, even non-footballing friends, who have been reminded to contact me by a newspaper or a chance idle glance at a sports round-up at the end of a news bulletin. (To prove the point: I just went downstairs to pick up the mail, and there was a postcard, a thank-you note from a friend whom I assisted in a banal and unspectacular way some weeks ago, and whom I haven't heard from since. At first I was puzzled as to why she should thank me now, long after the event in question – I wasn't expecting her to do so – but the PS at the end, 'Sorry about the Arse', serves as an explanation.)

Even though you know that anything – Mickey Rourke or Brussels sprouts or Warren Street underground station or toothache, the associations that people might have for you are endless and private – can set somebody off on a train of thought which will end up with you sitting in one of its carriages, you have no idea when this might happen. It is unpredictable and haphazard. With football, there is none of this randomness: you know that on nights like the '89 Championship night, or on afternoons like the afternoon of the 1992 Wrexham disaster, you are in the thoughts of scores, maybe even hundreds, of people. And I love that, the fact that old girlfriends and other people you have lost touch with and will probably never see again are sitting in front of their TV sets and thinking, momentarily but *all at the same time*, Nick, just that, and are happy or sad for me. Nobody else gets that, only us.

MY ANKLE

Arsenal v Wimbledon

19.9.87

I can't remember how it happened – probably I trod on the ball or something equally graceless. And I didn't realise the implication of it straight away. I just knew, when I hobbled off the five-a-side court, that my ankle hurt like hell and was swelling like a bastard in front of my eyes. But when I was sitting in my flatmate's car on the way back to our flat, I began to panic: it was a quarter to one, I couldn't walk, and I had to be at Highbury by three.

At home, I sat with a bag of frozen peas balanced on the end of my leg while I contemplated the options. My flatmate, his girlfriend and my girlfriend suggested that, since I was completely immobile and in obvious pain, I should sit at home listening to the radio, but obviously that wasn't possible; and once I realised that I was going to the game somehow, that there were taxis and seats in the Lower West Stand and friends' shoulders to lean on if necessary, the panic subsided and it became a simple matter of logistics.

It wasn't so bad, in the end. We got the tube to Arsenal instead of Finsbury Park – not as far to walk – and we all stood outside, not in our usual spot under the North Bank roof, even though it pelted down for the whole of a goalless second half, so that I could lean against a crush barrier and avoid any tumbles down the North Bank when Arsenal scored. But still. Getting soaked to the skin (and insisting that everyone else got soaked to the skin with me), shivering with the pain and trebling my journey time to and from the ground didn't seem like too bad a price to pay. Not when you consider the cataclysmic alternative, anyway.

THE MATCH

Coventry v Arsenal

13.12.87

Pete and I left around twelve, I guess, for a 3 p.m., Sunday afternoon kick-off, and got there just in time. It was an awful game, unspeakable, a nil–nil draw in freezing conditions . . . and it was live on television, so we could have stayed at home. My powers of self-analysis fail me completely here: I don't know why we went. We just did.

I didn't see a live League game on television until 1983, and neither did anyone else of my generation. When I was a kid there wasn't so much football on TV: an hour on Saturday night, an hour on Sunday afternoon, sometimes an hour midweek, when our clubs had European games. We got to see an entire ninety minutes only very rarely. Occasional England games were shown live; then there was the FA Cup Final, and maybe the European Cup Final . . . two or three live club games a year, maximum.

That was obviously ridiculous. Even Cup semi-finals, or Championship deciders, weren't televised live; sometimes the stations weren't even allowed to show us highlights. (When Liverpool just pipped QPR for the Championship in 1976, we got to see the goals on the news, but that was all; there was a whole set of incomprehensible rules about TV coverage that no one understood.) So despite satellite technology, and colour televisions, and 24-inch screens, we had to sit with our ears pressed against transistor radios. Eventually the clubs realised that there was big money to be made, and the TV companies were happy to give it to them; the behaviour of the Football League thereafter has resembled that of the mythical convent girl. The League will let anybody do anything they want – change the time of the kick-off, or the day of the game, or the teams, or the shirts, it doesn't matter; nothing is too much trouble for them. Meanwhile the fans, the paying customers, are regarded as amenable and gullible idiots. The date advertised on your ticket is meaningless: if ITV or BBC want to change the fixture to a time more convenient to them, they will do so. In 1991, Arsenal fans intending to travel to the crucial match at Sunderland found that after a little television interference (kick-off was changed from three to five), the last train to London left before the game finished. Who cared? Just us, nobody important.

I will continue to attend televised games at Highbury, mostly because I've already paid for my ticket. But, sod it, I'm not going to travel to Coventry or Sunderland or anywhere else if I can sit at home and watch the match, and I hope lots of other people do the same. Television will notice our absence, one day. In the end, however much they mike up the crowd, they will be unable to create any atmosphere whatsoever, because there will be nobody there: we'll all be at home, watching the box. And when that happens, I hope that the managers and the chairmen spare us the pompous and embittered column in the programme complaining about our fickleness.

NO APOLOGY NECESSARY

Arsenal v Everton

24.2.88

I know that I have apologised a great deal during the course of these pages. Football has meant too much to me, and come to represent too many things, and I feel that I have been to watch far too many games, and spent too much money, and fretted about Arsenal when I should have been fretting about something else, and asked for too much indulgence from friends and family. Yet there are occasions when going to watch a game is the most valid and rewarding leisure pursuit I can think of, and Arsenal against Everton, another second-leg Littlewoods Cup semi-final, was one of those times.

It came four days after another huge game, against Manchester United in the FA Cup, a game which Arsenal won 2–1 but only after McClair had sent a penalty high over the bar and into an ecstatic North Bank with the last kick of the game (and Nigel Winterburn pursued him relentlessly and unpleasantly back to the half-way line after he had done so, one of the first hints of this Arsenal team's embarrassing indiscipline); so it was an enormous week, with gigantic crowds – fifty-three thousand on the Saturday, fifty-one thousand on the Wednesday.

We beat Everton 3–1 that night, 4–1 on aggregate, a comfortable enough win which Arsenal fully deserved, but we had to wait for it. Four minutes before half-time Rocastle beat Everton's offside trap, went round Southall, and stroked the ball well wide of a completely empty goal; and then three minutes later Hayes was through too, only this time Southall brought him down six inches from the goal-line. Hayes took the penalty himself, and, like McClair, booted it well over the bar. And the crowd is going spare with frustration and worry; you look around and you see faces working, completely absorbed, and the susurration that spreads around the ground after particularly dramatic incidents lasts all the way through half-time because there is so much to talk about but, at the beginning of the second half, Thomas chips Southall and scores, and you want to burst with relief, and the noise that greets the goal has a special depth to it, a bottom that you only get when everyone in the stadium except for the away supporters gives the roar everything they've got, even people right up the top in the fifteen-quid seats. And though Heath equalises soon after, Rocky then makes up for his earlier miss, and Smith gets another one, and the whole of Highbury, all four sides of the ground, is alive, yelling and hugging itself with delight at the prospect of another Wembley final, and the manner in which it has been achieved. It's extraordinary, knowing that you have a role to play in all this, that the evening wouldn't have been the same without you and thousands like you.

Absurdly, I haven't yet got around to saying that football is a wonderful sport, but of course it is. Goals have a rarity value that points and runs and sets do not, and so there will always be that thrill, the thrill of seeing someone do something that can only be done three or four times in a whole game if you are lucky, not at all if you are not. And I love the pace of it, its lack of formula; and I love the way that small men can destroy big men (watch Beardsley against Adams) in a way that they can't in other contact sports, and the way that the best team does not necessarily win. And there's the athleticism (with all due respect to Ian Botham and the England front row, there are very few good fat footballers), and the way that strength and intelligence have to combine. It allows players to look beautiful and balletic in a way that some sports do not: a perfectly timed diving header or a perfectly struck volley allows the body to achieve a poise and grace that some sportsmen can never exhibit.

But there's even more to it than all that. During matches like the Everton semi-final, although nights like that are inevitably rare, there is this powerful sensation of being exactly in the right place at the right time; when I am at Highbury on a big night, or, of course, Wembley on an even bigger afternoon, I feel as though I am at the centre of the whole world. When else does this happen in life? Maybe you've got a hot ticket for the first night of an Andrew Lloyd Webber show, but you know that the show is going to run for years and years, so you'd actually have to tell people afterwards that you saw it before they did, which is kind of uncool and in any case completely ruins the effect. Or maybe you saw the Stones at Wembley, but then even something like that is repeated for night after night nowadays, and consequently doesn't have the same one-off impact of a football match. It's not *news*, in the same way that an Arsenal *v* Everton semi-final is news: when you look at your newspaper the next day, whichever one you read, there will be extensive space given over to an account of *your* evening, the evening to which you contributed simply by turning up and shouting.

You just can't find this outside a football ground; there is nowhere else you can be in the entire country that will make you feel as though you are at the heart of things. Because whichever nightclub you go to, or play, or film, or whichever concert you see, or restaurant you eat at, life will have been going on elsewhere in your absence, as it always does; but when I am at Highbury for games like these, I feel that the rest of the world has stopped and is gathered outside the gates, waiting to hear the final score.

WELCOME TO ENGLAND

England v Holland

March 1988

In 1988 I began working for a Far Eastern trading company. I started out as a teacher, but it soon became clear that my middle-management pupils were more perplexed by the bizarre requests they received from their head office than they were by the English language. So the teaching vanished, and instead I did what I can only describe as Other Things, since a generic description of my duties is beyond me. I wrote countless letters to solicitors, and a long essay on Jonathan Swift which was translated and faxed back to base; I ascertained to my employers' satisfaction what constituted drinking water; I pored over the landscape plans for Hampton Court and took photographs of Beaulieu Motor Museum; I went to see Directors of Social Services to talk about orphanages; I became involved in protracted negotiations for equestrian centres in Warwickshire and pedigree dogs in Scotland. It was varied work.

The managers worked astonishingly hard: their contracted hours were from 8 a.m. to 8 p.m. on Monday to Friday, and from 8 a.m. to 2 p.m. on Saturday, but these were nominal – a twelve-hour day, like Gordon Gekko's lunch, was for wimps. But when I told three of my students that Gullit and Van Basten were coming to town to pit their wits against Lineker and Shilton, the temptation was too much even for them, and I was instructed to buy tickets and act as their chaperon and inductor for the evening.

Every couple of years I forget what a miserable experience it is to go to Wembley to watch England play, and give it another try. In '85 I went to watch a World Cup qualifier a couple of weeks after Scotland's Jock

Stein had died, and listened to the most mind-bogglingly obscene celebratory songs; four years later I went to another one, and sat among people who gave drunken Nazi salutes during the National Anthem. Why I thought that things would be any different for a friendly against Holland I can't remember, but it turned out to be an embarrassing misapprehension.

Our timing was just right. We were walking down Wembley Way about fifteen minutes before kick-off, with reserved-seat tickets in our pockets, and I was feeling pleased with my expert organisation. As we approached our entrance, however, we were met by a determined and indiscriminate mounted police charge, and we were forced back down the road with hundreds of other ticket holders, and my colleagues began to panic. We regrouped and started again; this time our £12.00 tickets were regarded, reluctantly, as certificates of legitimate interest, and we were allowed to approach the stadium. As we did so, the game kicked off and England scored almost immediately, but we missed all that – we were still negotiating admission. One of the entrance doors was hanging off its hinges, and an official told us that large numbers of people had forced their way into the ground.

Once inside, it was obvious that our seats had gone. The gangways were packed with people like us, all clutching now-worthless ticket stubs, all too afraid to confront the crop-headed, thick-necked people sitting in our seats. There wasn't a steward in sight. 'Here come the fucking Wongs,' remarked one of a group of young men, as I led my charges down the steps to find a position from which we could see at least a square of the pitch. I didn't bother translating. We stood and watched for about half an hour, during which time Holland took a 2–1 lead; the dreadlocked Gullit, the main reason why the game had sold out in the first place, provoked monkey noises every time he touched the ball. Just before half-time we gave up and went home. I got back to my flat just in time to watch the highlights on TV.

People have told me that they're beginning to turn things round at Wembley now, and post-Italia '90, what with Gazzamania and Lineker charm, the composition of the average England crowd is changing. This often happens when a team is doing well, and in itself it doesn't offer much cause for hope, because when they play badly again you lose that lot. It seems to me, and this is not a theory that I can support with any hard evidence, but never mind, that bad teams attract an ugly following.

Only boneheads entertain serious doubts nowadays about the link between social and economic conditions and football violence, but why is it that, say, Birmingham City fans have a markedly worse reputation than Sunderland fans? Even if we accept, for the sake of argument, that the West Midlands suffers from the same kind of social and economic deprivation that plagues the North-East, then how does one explain the impeccable behaviour of the Villa supporters? Two teams from the same city; but one plays in the First Division, and the other languishes in the Third. When Leeds, Chelsea and Manchester United were in the Second Division their fans terrified everybody; when Millwall came up to the First their reputation for monstrous, evil violence evaporated a little. And I don't think that poor football actually changes the way people behave; it's not that, although there is an element of compensatory pride involved ('We might not be much good at football, but we can give you a good kicking'); it's more that – how can I put this tactfully? – there is a higher proportion of nutters among the never-say-die, we'll-support-you-evermore hardcore than among the sod-that-for-a-lark floating punter.

So among crowds of twenty-five thousand, you'll find a few hundred troublemakers; when you're getting crowds of five or six thousand, the same few hundred will still be turning up, and suddenly the tiny minority have become much more significant, and the club are landed with a reputation. And once you've got a reputation, you start to appeal to those who are attracted by the promise of violence inherent in that reputation. That, I think, is what happened with Chelsea and Millwall in the late seventies and early eighties; it is also what happened with England between elimination from the World Cup in 1974 and qualification for Italy in 1990. For most of that time they were a desperate side, and they attracted a pretty desperate crowd.

The problem here is that unless a team is playing well, winning things, filling their stadia, clubs simply cannot afford to alienate the very people they are supposed to be purging. I can think of at least one club chairman who has in the past been conspicuously ambivalent about some of the unpleasant characters that keep his club afloat, and I have not been aware of any particularly strident campaigning on the part of the England authorities to drive out one crowd and bring in another (any campaigning of that kind has been done by the fans themselves); they know, deep down, which side their bread is buttered on.

I tried to compensate for the evening by offering to take my new workmates to Highbury, where I knew that we would be left undisturbed whether we stood on the terraces or sat in the seats. But every time I suggested it, they just looked at me and smiled, as if the invitation was an extreme example of the famously incomprehensible English sense of humour. I guess they still think I spend every Saturday afternoon being charged by police horses and then cowering in a gangway somewhere, too frightened to claim the seat I have paid for, and on the evidence of the Holland game it would be an obvious assumption to make; in their position, I would have been on the phone back to Head Office first thing on Thursday morning, begging and pleading for a posting somewhere, anywhere, else in the world.

GUS CAESAR

Arsenal v Luton

(at Wembley) 24.4.88

The Littlewoods Cup Final that year was a disaster, and sometimes I still find myself drifting back to it: 2–1 up with ten minutes left, and at the end of one of the most one-sided periods of football I have ever seen (Hayes hits the post, Smith hits the bar, Smith one-on-one with Dibble but doesn't beat him), the ball is on the penalty spot after Rocky has been brought down and Winterburn is about to . . .

No. He's missed it again, for the fortieth or fiftieth time since that April afternoon. My daydreams are so vivid that I really do find it hard to believe that he won't get another chance some time, and my re-emergence back into my underground journey, or the book I am reading, is ludicrously slow, only achievable once I have forced myself to recognise, sometimes by saying the words under my breath, that the game is over, finished, and will never be played again. But you see, if Winterburn had scored (and why did none of the others volunteer to take it? A Wembley final isn't the place to take your first one), we would have won 3–1, no question, and retained the cup we had won the year before; but he didn't, and Luton went up the other end and scored twice in the last seven minutes and won 3–2. Fairly or unfairly, the Arsenal fans I have spoken to blame one man: Augustus Caesar.

There have been so many players that the crowd have rubbished over the years, and not all of them were bad: Ure, Sammels, Blockley, Rix, Chapman, Hayes, Groves, even Michael Thomas for the second half of the first Championship season and a good chunk of the following year. But Gus was different. There was no debate whatsoever about his talents. Hayes, Groves, Thomas and Rix all had their defenders among the fans, but Gus had none, or none that I ever came across; the nadir of his Arsenal career was probably during a horrible 1–0 defeat at Wimbledon in January 1990, when every back-pass or clearance he accomplished without disaster was greeted with ironic cheers and applause for the entire game. I can't begin to imagine how anyone could ever cope with that kind of public humiliation.

Soon after I had stopped teaching and begun to try to write, I read a book called *The Hustler* by Walter Tevis. I was much taken by Fast Eddie, the character played by Paul Newman in the film, just as I had been much taken with the notion that I was the Cannonball Kid when Charlie Nicholas moved down from Celtic. And as the book seemed to be about anything you wanted to do that was difficult – writing, becoming a footballer, whatever – I paid it extra-special attention. At one point (oh God oh God oh God) I typed these words out on a piece of paper and pinned it above my desk:

> 'That's what the whole goddamned thing is: you got to commit yourself to the life you picked. And you picked it – most people don't even do that. You're smart and you're young and you've got, like I said before, talent.'

As the rejection slips piled up, these words comforted me; and as I began to panic about the way things that everybody else had, like careers and nice flats and a bit of cash for the weekend, seemed to be slipping out of arm's reach, friends and family began to try to reassure me. 'You know you're good,' they said. 'You'll be OK. Just be patient.' And I *did* know I was good, and I *had* committed myself to the life I had picked, and my friends, and Fast Eddie's friends, couldn't all be wrong, so I sat back and waited. I know now that I was wrong, stupid, to do so, and I know because Gus Caesar told me so.

Gus is living proof that this self-belief, this driven sense of vocation (and I am not talking about arrogance here, but the simple healthy self-confidence that is absolutely necessary for survival), can be viciously misleading. Did Gus commit himself to the life he had picked? Of course he did. You don't get anywhere near the first team of a major First Division football club without commitment. And did he know he was good? He must have done, and justifiably so. Think about it. At school he must have been much, much better than his peers, so he gets picked for the school team, and then some representative side, South London Boys or what have you; and he's still better than anyone else in the team, by miles, so the scouts come to watch, and he's offered an apprenticeship not with Fulham or Brentford or even West Ham but with the mighty Arsenal. And it's still not over, even then, because if you look at any First Division youth team of five years ago you won't recognise most of the names, because most of them have disappeared. (Here's the Arsenal youth team of April 1987, from a randomly plucked programme: Miller, Hannigan, McGregor, Hillier, Scully, Carstairs, Connelly, Rivero, Cagigao, S. Ball, Esqulant. Of those, only Hillier has come through, although Miller is still with us as a highly rated reserve goalkeeper; Scully is still playing professional football somewhere, though not for Arsenal or any other First Division team. The rest have gone, and gone from a club famous for giving its own players a fair crack.)

But Gus survives, and goes on to play for the reserves. And suddenly, it's all on for him: Don Howe is in trouble, and flooding the first team with young players – Niall Quinn, Hayes, Rocastle, Adams, Martin Keown. And when Viv Anderson is suspended over Christmas 1985 Gus makes his début, as a right-back, at of all places Old Trafford, and we win 1–0 up there, so he's part of a back four that's kept a clean sheet away at Manchester United.

Howe gets the sack, and George Graham keeps him on, and he's used as a sub in quite a few games over George's first season, so things are still going well for him – not as well as they are for Rocky and Hayes and Adams and Quinn, but then these players are having an exceptional first full season, and when the squad for the England Under-21s is announced it's full of Arsenal players, *and Gus Caesar is one of them.* The England selectors, like the Arsenal fans, are beginning to trust

Arsenal's youth policy implicitly, and Gus gets a call-up even though he isn't in the first team regularly. But never mind why, he's in, he's recognised as one of the best twenty or so young players in the whole country.

Now at this point Gus could be forgiven for relaxing his guard a little. He's young, he's got talent, he's committed to the life he's picked, and at least some of the self-doubt that plagues everyone with long-shot dreams must have vanished by now. At this stage you have to rely on the judgement of others (I was relying on the judgements of friends and agents and anyone I could find who would read my stuff and tell me it was OK); and when those others include two Arsenal managers and an England coach then you probably reckon that there isn't much to worry about.

But as it turns out, they are all wrong. So far he has leaped over every hurdle in his path comfortably, but even at this late stage it is possible to be tripped up. Probably the first time we notice that things aren't right is in January 1987, in that first-leg semi-final against Tottenham: Caesar is painfully, obviously, out of his depth against those Spurs forwards. In truth he looks like a rabbit caught in headlights, frozen to the spot until Waddle or Allen or somebody runs him over, and then he starts to thrash about, horribly and pitifully, and finally George and Theo Foley put him out of his misery by substituting him. He doesn't get another chance for a while. The next time I remember him turning out is against Chelsea at Stamford Bridge in a 1–1 draw, a week or two before the Luton final, but again there is a moment in the first half where Dixon runs at him, turns him one way, then the other, then back again, like your dad used to do to you when you were a really little kid in the back garden, and eventually strolls past him and puts the ball just the wrong side of the post. We knew that there was going to be trouble at Wembley, when O'Leary was out injured and Gus was the only candidate to replace him. Caesar leaves it late, but when the ball is knocked into the box seven minutes from time, he miskicks so violently that he falls over; at this point he looks like somebody off the street who has won a competition to appear as a centre-half in a Wembley final, and not like a professional footballer at all, and in the ensuing chaos Danny Wilson stoops to head the ball over the line for Luton's equalising goal.

That's it. End of story. He's at the club for another three or four years, but he's very much the last-resort centre-back, and he must have known, when George bought Bould and then Linighan and then Pates, with

Adams and O'Leary already at the club, that he didn't have much of a future – he was the sixth in line for two positions. He was given a free transfer at the end of the 90/91 season, to Cambridge United; but within another couple of months they let him go too, to Bristol City, and a couple of months after that Bristol City let him go to Airdrie. To get where he did, Gus Caesar clearly had more talent than nearly everyone of his generation (the rest of us can only dream about having his kind of skill) and it still wasn't quite enough.

Sport and life, especially the arty life, are not exactly analogous. One of the great things about sport is its cruel clarity: there is no such thing, for example, as a bad one hundred-metre runner, or a hopeless centre-half who got lucky; in sport, you get found out. Nor is there such a thing as an unknown genius striker starving in a garret somewhere, because the scouting system is foolproof. (*Everyone* gets watched.) There are, however, plenty of bad actors or musicians or writers making a decent living, people who happened to be in the right place at the right time, or knew the right people, or whose talents have been misunderstood or overestimated. Even so, I think there is a real resonance in the Gus Caesar story: it contains a terrifying lesson for any aspirants who think that their own unshakeable sense of destiny (and again, this sense of destiny is not to be confused with arrogance – Gus Caesar was not an arrogant footballer) is significant. Gus must have known he was good, just as any pop band who has ever played the Marquee know they are destined for Madison Square Garden and an *NME* front cover, and just as any writer who has sent off a completed manuscript to Faber and Faber knows that he is two years away from the Booker. You trust that feeling with your life, you feel the strength and determination it gives you coursing through your veins like heroin . . . and it doesn't mean anything at all.

WALKING DISTANCE

Arsenal v Sheffield Wednesday

21.1.89

It made sense to move into the area, for other reasons too: your money goes a lot further in decrepit areas of north London than it does in Shepherd's Bush or Notting Hill, and the public transport up here is good (five minutes from King's Cross, two tube lines, millions of buses). But really, living within walking distance of the ground was the fulfilment of a pitiful twenty-year ambition, and it's no use trying to dress it up in logic.

It was fun looking. One flat I saw had a roof terrace which overlooked a section of the front of the stadium, and you could see these huge letters, 'RSEN', no more than that but just enough to get the blood pumping. And the place we got gazumped on was on the route that the open-top bus takes when we win something. The rooms were smaller and darker than the ones we have now, but the living-room window framed the entire West Stand; I would have been able to pause, during the writing of this book, look out, and return to the Amstrad refreshed.

In the end we had to settle for somewhere a little less spiritual overlooking Finsbury Park, and even if you stand on a stool and stick your head out of the window you can't see anything, not even the Barclays League pennant which at the time of writing (although not, I fear, for much longer) is still ours to flutter. But still! People park their cars in our road before the game! And on a windy day the tannoy is clearly audible, even from inside the flat, if the windows are open! (I don't know about the audibility of roars, obviously, because I am never at home when the team are, but I would like to think that the noisier celebrations make it this far. Maybe one day I will borrow my brother-in-law's smart Sony recorder, place it on the chair by the TV under the window and let it run, just out of interest.) And best of all, just a few days after moving in, I was walking down the road – *this really happened* – and I found, just lying there, filthy dirty and somewhat torn but there nonetheless, a twenty-year-old Peter Marinello bubblegum card. You cannot imagine how happy this made me, to know that I was living in an area so rich in archaeological interest, so steeped in my own past.

As we turned the corner into our new street, the rental-van radio brought us news of a Kevin Richardson goal at Goodison Park, the third in an eventual 3–1 win (*and* Everton's goal never crossed the line), which seemed like a pretty good omen. But I was waiting for the following Saturday, my first ever *home* home game against Sheffield Wednesday, when finally, at the age of thirty-one, I would walk down Avenell Road, through the turnstiles and on to the North Bank as a north Londoner.

*

What was I expecting to find, when I opened the front door on to the street at twenty to three (twenty to three!) that Saturday afternoon and turned right towards the ground? I imagine I thought it was going to be like one of those sitcom depictions of suburbia, with all the identical front doors opening at precisely the same time, and identically dressed men marching down the street together, clutching identical briefcases, brollies and newspapers. In my street, of course, it would be Arsenal supporters, rather than commuters, who emerged, and they would all be wearing flat caps and faded bar-type red-and-white scarves. And they would see me and smile and wave, and I would immediately become a much-loved and valued member of a happy, working-class Arsenal community.

But no doors opened. Nobody supports Arsenal in my street. Some of my neighbours are what used to be known, years ago, as yuppies, and they have no interest in football; others are transients, squatters or short-lease tenants, never around for long enough to acquire the taste for it. The rest of them . . . I don't know. You can't come up with a theory for everyone, and there's no accounting for taste. All I know is that there used to be one other fan in our street, a young lad who wandered around in an away shirt, but he moved soon after we got here; and apart from him I could have been back in Maidenhead, were it not for the cars cruising up and down, looking for a matchday parking space.

I suspect that I moved here a good twenty years too late, and that for the last couple of decades the local support has dwindled away steadily. According to the club's information, a huge percentage of fans live in the Home Counties (when I travelled down from Cambridge, the trains were packed with Arsenal supporters by the time we got to Hatfield). Football in London – at Spurs, Chelsea, Highbury and, to a lesser extent, West Ham – has become a suburban afternoon out. The demographics have changed now, and all those people who used to walk to the game from Islington and Finsbury Park and Stoke Newington have gone: they're either dead or they've sold up, moved out to Essex or Hertfordshire or Middlesex. And though you see a fair few people walking around with club shirts on, and some of the shopkeepers take an interest in the results (one of the guys who runs the news-stand inside the station is a committed and knowledgeable fan, although his brother supports Chelsea), I'm more alone here than I ever thought I would be at the end of the sixties, all those years ago, when I used to pester my dad to buy a house on Avenell Road, and he said I'd get fed up with it.

TYRANNY

Arsenal v Charlton

21.3.89

I'm writing about me, now. The boy who fretted his way through the first part of this book has gone; the young man who spent most of his twenties twisted in on himself isn't around either. I can no longer use age, or rather youth, to explain myself in the way I have been able to do elsewhere.

As I get older, the tyranny that football exerts over my life, and therefore over the lives of people around me, is less reasonable and less attractive. Family and friends know, after long years of wearying experience, that the fixture list always has the last word in any arrangement; they understand, or at least accept, that christenings or weddings or any gatherings, which in other families would take unquestioned precedence, can only be plotted after consultation. So football is regarded as a given disability that has to be worked around. If I were wheelchair-bound, nobody close to me would organise anything in a top-floor flat, so why would they plan anything for a winter Saturday afternoon?

Like everyone, I have a peripheral role to play in the lives of most of the people I know, however, and these people are often uninterested in the forthcoming First Division programme. So there have been wedding invitations that I have reluctantly but unavoidably had to turn down, although I am always careful to provide a socially acceptable excuse involving family problems or work difficulties; 'Home to Sheffield United' is deemed an inadequate explanation in situations like these.

And then there are the unpredictable Cup replays, the rearranged midweek fixtures, the games transferred from Saturday to Sunday at short notice in order to accommodate the television schedules, so I have to refuse invitations that clash with potential fixtures, as well as those which clash with actual fixtures. (Or I do arrange something, but warn the parties involved that I might have to pull out at the last moment, which sometimes doesn't go down too well.)

But it gets harder and harder, and sometimes hurting someone is unavoidable. The Charlton game was rearranged for the same night as a very close friend's birthday party, a party to which only five people had been invited. Once I realised that there was a conflict of interest, there was the usual brief panic as I contemplated a home game taking place without me; and then I phoned her with a heavy heart and told her what had happened. I was hoping for a laugh and absolution, but I got neither, and from the sound of her voice, from the disappointment and tired impatience it contained, I understood that I wasn't going to. Instead, she said one of those awful things, 'You must do what you think is right', or 'You must do what you want to do', something like that; one of those chilling deliverances designed to find you out, and I said that I'd have to think about it, but we both knew that I wasn't going to think about it at all, that I had been exposed as the worthless, shallow worm I was, and I went to the game. I was glad I went, too. Paul Davis scored one of the best goals I have ever seen at Highbury, a diving header after he'd sprinted the length of the pitch following a Charlton attack.

There are two points that arise from incidents like this. Firstly, I have begun to suspect that my relationship is with Highbury, rather than with the team: if the match had taken place at the Valley or Selhurst Park or Upton Park, none of them inaccessible, you might have thought, to a man as obsessive as this one, then I wouldn't have gone. So what's this all about? Why am I hell-bent on seeing a match involving Arsenal in one part of London, but not another? What, in the jargon of the therapist, is the fantasy here? What do I imagine would happen to me if I didn't go to Highbury just for one evening, and missed a game that might have been crucial to the eventual outcome of the Championship race but hardly promised unmissable entertainment? The answer, I think, is this: I am frightened that in the next game, the one after the one I have missed, I won't understand something that's going on, a chant or the crowd's antipathy to one of the players; and so the place I know best in the world, the one spot outside my own home where I feel I belong absolutely and unquestionably, will have become alien to me. I missed the game against Coventry in 1991, and the game against Charlton in 1989, but I was abroad at the time. And though the first of those absences felt odd, the fact that I was several hundred miles from the stadium assuaged the panic and made it tolerable; the only time I have ever been somewhere else in London while Arsenal were at home (I was at Victoria, queuing for a ticket on Freddie Laker's Skytrain, while we were beating QPR 5–1 in September 1978, and my recall of both score and opponents signifies something), I felt squirmingly uncomfortable.

But one day, soon, it's going to have to happen again, I know that. Illness (but I've been to Highbury with flu and sprained ankles and more or less anything that didn't require access to a toilet), a future child's first football match or school play (surely I'd go to the school play . . . but I fear that I'm daft enough to pass it over and thus ensure that the child spends hours on some Hampstead couch in the year 2025 explaining to a disbelieving shrink that throughout his or her childhood I always put Arsenal first), family bereavement, work . . .

Which brings me to the second point arising from these rearranged game problems: work. My brother now has a job which demands more than a nine-to-five routine, and though I can't recall him missing a game through work hitherto, it is only a matter of time. One day soon, this season or next, someone will call an impromptu meeting that won't end until half past eight or nine o'clock, and he will be sitting staring at a memo while three or four miles away the Merse is humiliating an opposing full-back. And he won't like it, but he won't have much choice, so he'll shrug and get on with it.

I don't think I could do that kind of job, for the reasons outlined above. But if I did, I hope I'd be able to shrug. I hope I wouldn't kick out, in my panic, and pout, and plead, and generally reveal myself as someone who has yet to come to terms with the demands of adult life. Writers are luckier than most, but one day, I suppose, I will have to do something at a time disastrously inconvenient to me – I'll have a one-off chance to interview somebody who can only fit me in on a Saturday afternoon, or there will be some impossible deadline which requires a Wednesday evening in front of the word-processor. Proper writers go on author tours, and appear as guests on *Wogan*, and all sorts of things fraught with perils, so maybe one day there will be all that to contend with. Not yet, though. The publishers of this book cannot reasonably expect me to write about this kind of neurosis and then ask me to miss a few games to help them publicise it. 'I'm mad, remember?' I will tell them. 'That's what this whole thing is about! No way can I do a reading in Waterstone's on a Wednesday night!' And so I survive a little longer.

Is it really a coincidence, blind luck, that I have not yet found myself in an unavoidable match-missing position in over a decade as a wage-earner?

(Even my superiors at the Far Eastern company, usually completely mystified by the compulsion of a social life, were in no doubt that Arsenal came first.) Or has my obsession shaped and guided my ambition? I would prefer to think not, of course, because if it has then the implications are alarming: all those options that I thought were still mine during my teenage years have in that case never existed, and the Stoke game in 1968 effectively prevented me from becoming an entrepreneur or a doctor or a real journalist. (Like many fans, I have never even contemplated becoming a sportswriter. How could I report on Liverpool versus Barcelona when I would rather be at Highbury to watch Arsenal against Wimbledon? Being paid a lot of money to write about the game I love is one of my darkest, clammiest fears.) I prefer to think of my freedom to go to Highbury whenever there is a game as a fortuitous side-effect of my chosen path, and leave it at that.

HILLSBOROUGH

Arsenal v Newcastle

15.4.89

There were rumours emanating from those with radios, but we didn't really know anything about it until half-time, when there was no score given for the Liverpool–Forest semi-final, and even then nobody had any real idea of the sickening scale of it all. By the end of our game, a dull, distracted 1–0 win, everyone knew there had been deaths. And a few people, those who had been to Hillsborough for the big occasions, were able to guess whereabouts in the ground the tragedy had occurred; but then, nobody who runs the game has ever been interested in the forebodings of fans.

By the time we got home it was clear that this wasn't just another football accident, the sort that happens once every few years, kills one or two unlucky people, and is generally and casually regarded by all the relevant authorities as one of the hazards of our chosen diversion. The numbers of dead rose by the minute – seven, then a score, then fifty-something and eventually ninety-five – and you realised that if anybody had even a shred of common sense left available to them, nothing would ever be the same again.

*

It is easy to understand why bereaved families wish to see officers from the South Yorkshire police brought to trial: their error of judgement was catastrophic. Yet, though it is clear that the police messed up badly that afternoon, it would be terribly vengeful to accuse them of anything more than incompetence. Very few of us are unfortunate enough to be in a position where our professional mistakes kill people. The police at Hillsborough were never able to guarantee safety, however many gates they did or didn't open; no police force at any football ground in the country could do that. It could have happened anywhere. It could have happened at Highbury – on the concrete steps leading out of the North Bank down to the street, maybe (and it doesn't require a very elaborate fantasy to imagine that); or it could have happened at Loftus Road, where thousands of fans can only gain access to the away end through a *coffee bar*. And there would have been an inquiry, and newspaper reports, and blame attached to the police, or stewards, or drunken fans, or somebody. But that wouldn't have been right, not when the whole thing was based on such a ludicrous premise.

The premise was this: that football stadia built in most cases around a hundred years ago (Norwich City's ground, fifty-eight years old, is the youngest in the First Division) could accommodate between fifteen and sixty-three thousand people without those people coming to any harm. Imagine the entire population of a small town (my own home town has a population of around fifty thousand) trying to get into a large department store, and you will have some idea of the hopefulness of this. These people stood, in blocks of ten or twelve thousand, on steeply banked and in some cases crumbling concrete terracing, modified but essentially unchanged over several decades. Even in the days when the only missiles hurled into the air were flat hats, this patently wasn't safe: thirty-three people were killed at Burnden Park, Bolton, in 1946 when crush barriers collapsed, and the Ibrox disaster in 1971 was the second to take place there. By the time football became a forum for gang warfare, and containment rather than safety become a priority (those perimeter fences again), a major tragedy became an inevitability. How could anyone have hoped to get away with it? With sixty thousand-plus crowds, all you can do is shut the gates, tell everyone to squash up, and then pray, very hard. The Ibrox disaster in 1971 was an awful warning that wasn't heeded: there were specific causes for it, but ultimately what was responsible was the way we watch football, among crowds that are way too big, in grounds that are far too old.

These grounds had been built for a generation of fans that didn't drive, or even rely on public transport overly much, and so they were placed carefully in the middle of residential areas full of narrow streets and terraced houses. Twenty or thirty years after the catchment areas began to expand dramatically, and people started travelling from ten or twenty or fifty miles away, nothing has changed. This was the time to build new stadia, out of town, with parking facilities and improved safety provisions; the rest of Europe did, and as a consequence the grounds in Italy, Spain, Portugal and France are bigger, better and safer, but typically, in a country whose infrastructure is finally beginning to fall apart, we didn't bother. Here, tens of thousands of fans walk up narrow, winding underground tunnels, or double-park their cars in tiny, quiet, local streets, while the relevant football authorities seem content to carry on as if nothing at all – behaviour, the fan base, methods of transport, even the state of the grounds themselves, which like the rest of us start to look a bit tatty after the first half-century or so – had changed. There was so much that could and should have been done, and nothing ever was, and everyone trundled along for year after year after year, for a hundred years, until Hillsborough. Hillsborough was the fourth post-war British football disaster, the third in which large numbers of people were crushed to death following some kind of failure in crowd control; it was the first which was attributed to something more than bad luck. So you can blame the police for opening the wrong gate at the wrong time if you like, but in my opinion to do so would be to miss the point.

The Taylor Report, famously and I think rightly, recommended that every football ground should become all-seater. Of course this brings with it new dangers – a possible repeat of the Bradford fire disaster, for example, where people died because highly flammable rubbish had been allowed to accumulate under the stands. And seats in themselves are not going to eliminate hooliganism, and could, if the clubs are very stupid, exacerbate it. Seats can be used as weapons, and long rows of people can obstruct police intervention if trouble does break out, although all-seaters should give clubs greater control over who occupies which part of the ground. The real point is that the likelihood of dying in the way that people at Ibrox and Hillsborough died will be minimised if the clubs implement Lord Justice Taylor's recommendations properly, and that, as far as I can see, is all that matters.

At the time of writing, the Taylor Report is prompting noisy dissent among fans and among some clubs. The problems are manifold. Changing the stadia to make them safe will prove expensive, and many clubs haven't got the money. In order to raise the money, some of them will be charging much higher entrance fees, or introducing schemes like the Arsenal and West Ham bonds, which may mean that many young working-class males, the traditional core of support, will be excluded. Some fans want to continue standing. (Not, I think, because standing is an inherently superior way of watching a game – it isn't. It's uncomfortable, and anyone under six feet two has a restricted view. Fans worry that the end of terrace culture will mean the end of noise and atmosphere and all the things that make football memorable, but the all-seated ends at Ibrox make more noise than the Clock End and the North Bank put together; seats in themselves do not turn football grounds into churches.) All ground capacities will be reduced, some to below current average attendance figures. And some clubs will have to close down altogether.

I have listened to and read the arguments of hundreds of fans who disagree with the Taylor Report, and who see the future of football as a modified version of the past, with safer terraces and better facilities, rather than as anything radically different. And what has struck me most is the conservative and almost neurotic sentimental attachments these arguments evince – in a sense, the same kind of neurotic sentimental attachment that informs this book. Every time a club mentions a new stadium, there is an outcry; when Arsenal and Tottenham mooted ground-sharing a few years back, at a projected site near, I think, Alexandra Palace, the protests were loud and long ('Tradition!'), and as a consequence we now find ourselves with an assortment of the tiniest stadia in the world. The Stadium of Light in Lisbon holds 120,000, the Bernabeu in Madrid 95,000, Bayern Munich's ground 75,000; but Arsenal, the biggest team in the biggest city in Europe, will be able to squeeze in less than forty thousand when their development is completed.

We didn't want new grounds, and now we don't want the old ones, not if they have to be modified to ensure our safety and the clubs have to charge more as a consequence. 'What if I want to take my kids to a game? I won't be able to afford it.' But neither can we afford to take our kids to Barbados, or to Le Manoir aux Quat' Saisons, or to the opera. Come the Revolution, of course, we will be able to do all those things as often as we like, but until then this seems a particularly poor argument, a whinge rather than a cogent objection.

'What about the little clubs who might go to the wall?' It will be very sad for Chester's couple of thousand fans if their team goes under – I would be devastated if I were one of them – but that in itself is absolutely no reason why clubs should be allowed to endanger the lives of their fans. If clubs have to close down because they do not have the money for the changes deemed necessary to avoid another Hillsborough, then so be it. Tough. If, like Chester and Wimbledon and scores of other teams, they are poor, it is in part because not enough people care whether they survive or go under (Wimbledon, a First Division team in a densely populated area, attracted tiny crowds even before they were forced to move to the other side of London), and that tells a story of its own. However, the converse of this is that there is absolutely no chance of being crushed on a terrace at these grounds; forcing clubs to install seating for fans who have their own back-garden-sized patch of concrete to stand on is ludicrous.

'What about the supporters who have followed the club through thick and thin, paid the players' wages? How can clubs really contemplate selling them up the river?' This is an argument that goes right to the heart of football consumption. I have explained elsewhere that if clubs erode their traditional fan base, they could find themselves in serious difficulties, and in my opinion they would be misguided to do so. Obviously the ground improvements have to be paid for somehow, and increased admission prices are inevitable; most of us accept that we will have to pay another couple of quid to watch our team. The bond schemes at Arsenal and West Ham go way beyond that, however: using these price increases to swap one crowd for another, to get rid of the old set of fans and to bring in a new, more affluent group, is a mistake.

Even so, it is a mistake that clubs are perfectly at liberty to make. Football clubs are not hospitals or schools, with a duty to admit us regardless of our financial wherewithal. It is interesting and revealing that opposition to these bond schemes has taken on the tone of a crusade, as if the clubs had a moral obligation to their supporters. What do the clubs *owe* us, any of us, really? I have stumped up thousands of pounds to watch Arsenal over the last twenty years; but each time money has changed hands, I have received something in return: admission to a game, a train ticket, a programme. Why is football any different from the cinema, say, or a record shop? The difference is that all of us feel these astonishingly deep allegiances, and that until recently we had all anticipated being able to go to watch every game that our team plays for the rest of our lives; now it is beginning to appear as though that will not be possible for some of us. But that won't be the end of the world. It could even be that increased admission prices will improve the quality of the football we watch; perhaps clubs will be able to play fewer games, the players will become injured less frequently, and there will be no need to play in rubbishy tournaments like the ZDS Cup in order simply to earn a few quid. Again, one must look to Europe: the Italians, the Portuguese and the Spanish have high ticket prices, but they can afford to pay for the best players in Europe and South America. (They are also less obsessed with lower-league football than we are. There *are* third- and fourth-division clubs, but they are semi-professional, and do not influence the way the game is structured. The First Division takes precedence and the football climate is all the healthier for it.)

Over the years we have come to confuse football with something else, something more *necessary*, which is why these cries of outrage are so heartfelt and so indignant. We view everything from the top of this mountain of partisan passion; it is no wonder that all our perspectives are wrong. Perhaps it was time to climb down, and see what everyone else in the outside world sees.

For the most part, what the outside world saw made a lot of cold, harsh, practical sense. The cover of *The Economist* that week carried a picture of the extraordinary shrine of flowers, flags and banners that Liverpool and Everton fans and hundreds of others had created in the goalmouth beneath the Kop at Anfield; the headline, neatly placed just above the crossbar, was 'The game that died'. I bought the magazine, for the first and only time, and was shocked to realise how much I found myself agreeing with it. Perhaps it was predictable that a magazine entitled *The Economist* should be best equipped to penetrate the muddle that football had got itself into; here, after all, is a multi-million-pound industry which doesn't have two pennies to rub together.

The Economist on the inevitability of the disaster: 'Hillsborough was not just a calamitous accident. It was a brutal demonstration of systematic failure.' On the state of the grounds: 'Britain's football grounds now resemble maximum-security prisons, but only the feebleness of the regulations has allowed the clubs to go on pretending that crowd safety is compatible with prison architecture.' On the football authorities: 'For complacency and incompetence, there's nothing like a cartel; and of Britain's surviving cartels, the Football League is one of the smuggest and slackest.' On the people who own football clubs: 'Like old-fashioned newspaper magnates, they are willing to pay for prestige – which they see in terms of owning star players, rather than comfortable modern stadiums.' And on what needs to be done: 'Having fewer clubs, operating out of smarter stadiums, ought to revive the interest of those who have been driven away from football during the past ten years.'

These views and others in the same issue – well informed, well argued, devoid of the football authorities' dilatory self-interest, the Government's loathing for the game (if Hillsborough did nothing else, it wrecked Thatcher's ludicrously misbegotten ID-card scheme) and the distorting obsession of the fans – helped one to begin looking at the whole football débâcle with something approaching clarity. It was only after Hillsborough, when outsiders began to take an interest in the way football conducts itself, that it became clear just how deeply entrenched in the football way of looking at things we had all become. And that way, as parts of this book demonstrate, is not always the wisest.

On 1st May, two weeks and two days later, Arsenal played Norwich at Highbury, our first game since the disaster. It was a glorious bank holiday afternoon, and Arsenal played wonderfully well, and won 5–0; as far as everyone there that day, myself included, was concerned, everything seemed more or less all right with the world again. The mourning period was over, the TV cameras were there, the sun was out, Arsenal were scoring goals galore . . . after the bleakness of the previous fortnight, the match took on a celebratory air. It was a tired and muted celebration, but it was a celebration nonetheless, and from this distance that looks particularly bizarre now.

What were we all thinking of that afternoon? How on earth did the Forest–Liverpool game ever get replayed? It's all a part of the same thing, in a way. I went to the Arsenal–Norwich game, and loved it, for the same reasons I had watched the Liverpool–Juventus final after the Heysel disaster, and for the same reasons that football hasn't really changed that much in over a hundred years: because the passions the game induces consume everything, including tact and common sense. If it is possible to attend and enjoy a football match sixteen days after nearly a hundred people died at one – and it is possible, I did it, despite my new post-Hillsborough realism – then perhaps it is a little easier to understand the culture and circumstances that allowed these deaths to happen. Nothing ever matters, apart from football.

THE GREATEST MOMENT EVER

Liverpool v Arsenal

26.5.89

In all the time I have been watching football, twenty-three seasons, only seven teams have won the First Division Championship: Leeds United, Everton, Arsenal, Derby County, Nottingham Forest, Aston Villa and, a staggering eleven times, Liverpool. Five different teams came top in my first five years, so it seemed to me then that the League was something that came your way every once in a while, even though you might have to wait for it; but as the seventies came and went, and then the eighties, it began to dawn on me that Arsenal might never win the League again in my lifetime. That isn't as melodramatic as it sounds. Wolves fans celebrating their third Championship in six years in 1959 could hardly have anticipated that their team would spend much of the next thirty years in the Second and Third Divisions; Manchester City supporters in their mid-forties when the Blues last won the League in 1968 are in their early seventies now.

Like all fans, the overwhelming majority of the games I have seen have been League games. And as most of the time Arsenal have had no real interest in the First Division title after Christmas, nor ever really come close to going down, I would estimate that around half of these games are meaningless, at least in the way that sportswriters talk about meaningless games. There are no chewed nails and chewed knuckles and screwed-up faces; your ear doesn't become sore from being pressed up hard against a radio, trying to hear how Liverpool are getting on; you are not, in truth, thrown into agonies of despair or eye-popping fits of ecstasy by the result. Any meanings such games throw up are the ones that you, rather than the First Division table, bring to them.

And after maybe ten years of this, the Championship becomes something you either believe in or you don't, like God. You concede that it's possible, of course, and you try to respect the views of those who have managed to remain credulous. Between approximately 1975 and 1989 I didn't believe. I hoped, at the beginning of each season; and a couple of times – the middle of the 86/87 season, for example, when we were top for eight or nine weeks – I was almost lured out of my agnostic's cave. But in my heart of hearts I knew that it would never happen, just as I knew that they were not, as I used to think when I was young, going to find a cure for death before I got old.

In 1989, eighteen years after the last time Arsenal had won the League, I reluctantly and foolishly allowed myself to believe it was indeed possible that Arsenal could win the Championship. They were top of the First Division between January and May; on the last full weekend of the Hillsborough-elongated season they were five points clear of Liverpool with three games left to play. Liverpool had a game in hand, but the accepted wisdom was that Hillsborough and its attendant strains would make it impossible for them to keep winning, and two of Arsenal's three games were at home to weaker teams. The other was against Liverpool, away, a game that would conclude the First Division season.

No sooner had I become a born-again member of the Church of the Latterday Championship Believers, however, than Arsenal ground to a catastrophic halt. They lost, dismally, at home to Derby; and in the final game at Highbury, against Wimbledon, they twice threw away the lead to draw 2–2 against a team they had destroyed 5–1 on the opening day of the season. It was after the Derby game that I raged into an argument with my partner about a cup of tea, but after the Wimbledon game I had no rage left, just a numbing disappointment. For the first time I understood the women in soap operas who have been crushed by love affairs before, and can't *allow* themselves to fall for somebody again: I had never before seen all that as a matter of choice, but now I too had left myself nakedly exposed when I could have remained hard and cynical. I wouldn't allow it to happen again, never, ever, and I had been a fool, I knew that now, just as I knew it would take me years to recover from the terrible disappointment of getting so close and failing.

It wasn't quite all over. Liverpool had two games left, against West Ham and against us, both at Anfield. Because the two teams were so close, the mathematics of it all were peculiarly complicated: whatever score Liverpool beat West Ham by, Arsenal had to halve. If Liverpool won 2–0, we would have to win 1–0, and so on. In the event Liverpool won 5–1, which meant that we needed a two-goal victory; 'YOU HAVEN'T GOT A PRAYER, ARSENAL', was the back-page headline of the *Daily Mirror*.

I didn't go to Anfield. The fixture was originally scheduled for earlier in the season, when the result wouldn't have been so crucial, and by the time it was clear that this game would decide the Championship, the tickets had long gone. In the morning I walked down to Highbury to buy a new team shirt, just because I felt I had to do something, and though admittedly wearing a shirt in front of a television set would not, on the face of it, appear to offer the team an awful lot of encouragement, I knew it would make me feel better. Even at noon, some eight hours before the evening kick-off, there were already scores of coaches and cars around the ground, and on the way home I wished everyone I passed good luck; their positiveness ('Three–one', 'Two–nil, no trouble', even a breezy 'Four–one') on this beautiful May morning made me sad for them, as if these chirpy and bravely confident young men and women were off to the Somme to lose their lives, rather than to Anfield to lose, at worst, their faith.

I went to work in the afternoon, and felt sick with nerves despite myself; afterwards I went straight round to an Arsenal-supporting friend's house, just a street away from the North Bank, to watch the game. Everything about the night was memorable, right from the moment when the teams came on to the pitch and the Arsenal players ran over to the Kop and presented individuals in the crowd with bunches of flowers. And as the game progressed, and it became obvious that Arsenal were going to go down fighting, it occurred to me just how well I knew my team, their faces and their mannerisms, and how fond I was of each individual member of it. Merson's gap-toothed smile and tatty soul-boy haircut, Adams's manful and endearing attempts to come to terms with his own inadequacies, Rocastle's pumped-up elegance, Smith's lovable diligence . . . I could find it in me to forgive them for coming so close and blowing it: they were young, and they'd had a fantastic season and as a supporter you cannot really ask for more than that.

I got excited when we scored right at the beginning of the second half, and I got excited again about ten minutes from time, when Thomas had a clear chance and hit it straight at Grobbelaar, but Liverpool seemed to be growing stronger and to be creating chances at the end, and finally, with the clock in the corner of the TV screen showing that the ninety minutes had passed, I got ready to muster a brave smile for a brave team. 'If Arsenal are to lose the Championship, having had such a lead at one time, it's somewhat poetic justice that they have got a result on the last day, even though they're not to win it,' said co-commentator David Pleat as Kevin Richardson received treatment for an injury with the Kop already celebrating. 'They will see that as scant consolation, I should think, David,' replied Brian Moore. Scant consolation indeed, for all of us.

Richardson finally got up, ninety-two minutes gone now, and even managed a penalty-area tackle on John Barnes; then Lukic bowled the ball out to Dixon, Dixon on, inevitably, to Smith, a brilliant Smith flick-on . . . and suddenly, in the last minute of the last game of the season, Thomas was through, on his own, with a chance to win the Championship for Arsenal. 'It's up for grabs now!' Brian Moore yelled; and even then I found that I was reining myself in, learning from recent lapses in hardened scepticism, thinking, well, at least we came close at the end there, instead of thinking, please Michael, please Michael, please put it in, please God let him score. And then he was turning a somersault, and I was flat out on the floor, and everybody in the living room jumped on top of me. Eighteen years, all forgotten in a second.

What is the correct analogy for a moment like that? In Pete Davies's brilliant book about the 1990 World Cup, *All Played Out*, he notices that the players use sexual imagery when trying to explain what it feels like to score a goal. I can see that sometimes, for some of the more workaday transcendent moments. Smith's third goal in our 3–0 win against Liverpool in December 1990, for example, four days after we'd been beaten 6–2 at home by Manchester United – that felt pretty good, a perfect release to an hour of mounting excitement. And four or five years back, at Norwich, Arsenal scored four times in sixteen minutes after trailing for most of the game, a quarter of an hour which also had a kind of sexual otherworldliness to it.

The trouble with the orgasm as metaphor here is that the orgasm, though obviously pleasurable, is familiar, repeatable (within a couple of hours if you've been eating your greens), and predictable, particularly for a man – if you're having sex then you know what's coming, as it were. Maybe if I hadn't made love for eighteen years, and had given up hope of doing so for another eighteen, and then suddenly, out of the blue, an opportunity presented itself . . . maybe in these circumstances it would be possible to recreate an approximation of that Anfield moment. Even though there is no question that sex is a nicer activity than watching football (no nil–nil draws, no offside trap, no cup upsets, *and* you're warm), in the normal run of things, the feelings it engenders are simply not as intense as those brought about by a once-in-a-lifetime last-minute Championship winner.

None of the moments that people describe as the best in their lives seem analogous to me. Childbirth must be extraordinarily moving, but it doesn't really have the crucial surprise element, and in any case lasts too long; the fulfilment of personal ambition – promotions, awards, what have you – doesn't have the last-minute time factor, nor the element of powerlessness that I felt that night. And what else is there that can possibly provide the *suddenness*? A huge pools win, maybe, but the gaining of large sums of money affects a different part of the psyche altogether, and has none of the *communal* ecstasy of football.

There is then, literally, nothing to describe it. I have exhausted all the available options. I can recall nothing else that I have coveted for two decades (what else *is* there that can reasonably be coveted for that long?), nor can I recall anything else that I have desired as both man and boy. So please, be tolerant of those who describe a sporting moment as their best ever. We do not lack imagination, nor have we had sad and barren lives; it is just that real life is paler, duller, and contains less potential for unexpected delirium.

When the final whistle blew (just one more heart-stopping moment, when Thomas turned and knocked a terrifyingly casual back-pass to Lukic, perfectly safely but with a coolness that I didn't feel) I ran straight out of the door to the off-licence on Blackstock Road; I had my arms outstretched, like a little boy playing aeroplanes, and as I flew down the street, old ladies came to the door and applauded my progress, as if I were Michael Thomas himself; then I was grievously ripped off for a bottle of cheap champagne, I realised later, by a shopkeeper who could see that the light of intelligence had gone from my eyes altogether. I could hear whoops and screams from pubs and shops and houses all around me; and as fans began to congregate at the stadium, some draped in banners, some sitting on top of tooting cars, everyone embracing strangers at every opportunity, and TV cameras arrived to film the party for the late news, and club officials leaned out of windows to wave at the bouncing crowd, it occurred to me that I was glad I hadn't been up to Anfield, and missed out on this joyful, almost Latin explosion on my doorstep. After twenty-one years I no longer felt, as I had done during the Double year, that if I hadn't been to the games I had no right to partake in the celebrations; I'd done the work, years and years and years of it, and I belonged.

SEATS

Arsenal v Coventry

22.8.89

These are some of the things that have happened to me in my thirties: I have become a mortgage holder; I have stopped buying *New Musical Express* and the *Face*, and, inexplicably, I have started keeping back copies of Q magazine under a shelf in my living room; I have become an uncle; I have bought a CD player; I have registered with an accountant; I have noticed that certain types of music – hip-hop, indie guitar pop, thrash metal – all sound the same, and have no tune; I have come to prefer restaurants to clubs, and dinners with friends to parties; I have developed an aversion to the feeling that a bellyful of beer gives you, even though I still enjoy a pint; I have started to covet items of furniture; I have bought one of those cork boards you put up in the kitchen; I have started to develop certain views – on the squatters who live in my street, for example, and about unreasonably loud parties – which are not altogether consistent with the attitudes I held when I was younger. And, in 1989, I bought a season-ticket for the seats, after standing on the North Bank for over fifteen years. These details do not tell the whole story of how I got old, but they tell some of it.

You just get tired. I got tired of the queues, and the squash, and tumbling half-way down the terrace every time Arsenal scored, and the fact that my view of the near goal was always partially obscured at big games, and it seemed to me that being able to arrive at the ground two minutes before kick-off without being disadvantaged in any way had much to recommend it. I didn't miss the terraces, really, and in fact I enjoyed them, the backdrop they provided, their noise and colour, more than I ever had when I stood on them. This Coventry game was our first in the seats, and Thomas and Marwood scored directly in front of us, at our end, and from our side.

There are five of us: Pete, of course, and my brother, and my girlfriend, although her place is usually taken by someone else nowadays, and me, and Andy, who used to be Rat when we were kids in the Schoolboys' Enclosure – I bumped into him on the North Bank in George's second season, a decade or so after I had lost touch with him, and he too was ready to leave the terraces behind.

What you're really doing, when you buy a seat season-ticket, is upping the belonging a notch. I'd had my own spot on the terraces, but I had no proprietorial rights over it and if some bloody big-game casual fan stood in it, all I could do was raise my eyebrows. Now I really do have my own home in the stadium, complete with flatmates, and neighbours with whom I am on cordial terms, and with whom I converse on topics of shared interest, namely the need for a new midfielder/striker/way of playing. So I correspond to the stereotype of the ageing football fan, but I don't regret it. After a while, you stop wanting to live from hand to mouth, day to day, game to game, and you begin wanting to ensure that the remainder of your days are secure.

SMOKING

Arsenal v Liverpool

25.10.89

I remember the game for conventional reasons, for substitute Smith's late winner and thus a handy Cup win over the old enemy. But most of all I remember it as the only time in the 1980s and, hitherto, the 1990s, that I had no nicotine in my bloodstream for the entire ninety minutes. I have gone through games without smoking in that time: during the first half of the 83/84 season I was on nicotine chewing gum, but never managed to kick that, and in the end went back to the cigarettes. But in October '89, after a visit to Allen Carr the anti-smoking guru, I went cold turkey for ten days, and this game came right in the middle of that unhappy period.

I want to stop smoking and, like many people who wish to do the same, I firmly believe that abstinence is just around the corner. I won't buy a carton of duty-frees, or a lighter, or even a household-sized box of matches because, given the imminence of my cessation, it would be a waste of money. What stops me from doing so now, today, this minute, are the things that have always stopped me: a difficult period of work up ahead, requiring the kind of concentration that only a Silk Cut can facilitate; the fear of the overwhelming domestic tension that would doubtless accompany screaming desperation; and, inevitably and pathetically, the Arsenal.

They do give me some leeway. There's the first half of the season, before the FA Cup begins, and before the Championship has warmed up. And there are times like now, when with my team out of everything by the end of January I am looking at almost five months of dull but tension-free afternoons. (But I've got this book to write, and deadlines, and . . .) And yet some seasons – the 88/89 Championship year, for example, or the chase for the Double in 90/91 where every game between January and May was crucial – I cannot contemplate what it would be like to sit there without a smoke. Two down against Tottenham in a Cup semi-final at Wembley with eleven minutes gone and no fag? Inconceivable.

Am I going to hide behind Arsenal for ever? Will they always serve as an excuse for smoking, and never having to go away at weekends, and not taking on work that might clash with a home fixture? The Liverpool game was, I think, their way of telling me that it's not their fault, that it is I who control my actions, and not they; and though actually I do remember that I survived the evening without running on to the pitch and shaking the players silly, I have forgotten it all when the forthcoming fixtures convince me that now is not the right time to tackle my nicotine addiction. I have argued before that having Arsenal on my back, like a hump, year after year after year, is a real disability. But I use that disability too, I milk it for all it is worth.

SEVEN GOALS AND A PUNCH-UP

Arsenal v Norwich

4.11.89

For a match to be really, truly memorable, the kind of game that sends you home buzzing inside with the fulfilment of it all, you require as many of the following features as possible:

(1) *Goals:* As many as possible. There is an argument which says that goals begin to lose their value in particularly easy victories, but I have never found this to be a problem. (I enjoyed the last goal in Arsenal's 7–1 win over Sheffield Wednesday as much as I enjoyed the first.) If the goals are to be shared, then it is best if the other team get theirs first: I have a particular penchant for the 3–2 home victory, with a late winner after losing 2–0 at half-time.

(2) *Outrageously bad refereeing decisions:* I prefer Arsenal to be the victim, rather than the recipient, of these, as long as they don't cost us the match. Indignation is a crucial ingredient of the perfect footballing experience; I cannot therefore agree with match commentators who argue that a referee has had a good game if he isn't noticed (although like everybody else, I don't like the game stopped every few seconds). I prefer to notice them, and howl at them, and feel cheated by them.

(3) *A noisy crowd:* In my experience, crowds are at their best when their team is losing but playing well, which is one of the reasons why coming back for a 3–2 win is my favourite kind of score.

(4) *Rain, a greasy surface, etc.:* Football in August, on a perfect grassy-green pitch, is aesthetically more appealing, although I do like a bit of slithery chaos in the goalmouth. Too much mud and the teams can't play at all, but you can't beat the sight of players sliding ten or fifteen yards for a tackle or in an attempt to get a touch to a cross. There's something intensifying about peering through driving rain, too.

(5) *Opposition misses a penalty:* Arsenal's goalkeeper John Lukic was the penalty king, so I have seen a fair few of these; Brian McClair's last-minute horror in the fifth-round FA Cup-tie in 1988 – so wild that it nearly cleared the North Bank roof – remains my favourite. However, I retain a residual fondness for Nigel Clough's efforts, also in the last minute, during a League game in 1990, when he missed; the referee ordered the kick to be retaken, and he missed again.

(6) *Member of opposition team receives a red card:* 'It's disappointing to hear the reaction of the crowd,' remarked Barry Davies during the Portsmouth–Forest FA Cup quarter-final in 1992, when Forest's Brian Laws was sent off and the Portsmouth supporters went mad; but what does he expect? For fans, a sending-off is always a magic moment, although it is crucial that this doesn't happen too early. First-half dismissals frequently result either in boringly easy victories for the team with eleven men (c.f., Forest *v* West Ham, FA Cup semi-final, 1991), or

in an impenetrable defensive reorganisation which kills the game dead; second-half sendings-off in a tight game are impossibly gratifying. If I had to plump for just one dismissal to take on to a desert island with me, it would have to be Bob Hazell of Wolves, sent off in the last minute of a fourth-round Cup-tie at Highbury in 1978, when the score was 1–1. As I remember it, he took a swing at Rix, who was trying to get the ball off him so that we could take a corner quickly; from said corner, Macdonald, freed of his disgraced marker for the first time in the game and thus completely unmarked, headed us into a winning lead. I also enjoyed, enormously, Tony Coton's long and lonely march at Highbury in 1986 – there is something special about seeing a goalkeeper go – and Massing's murderous assault on Caniggia, followed by his valedictory wave to the crowd, during the opening game of the 1990 World Cup.

(7) *Some kind of 'disgraceful incident' (aka 'silliness', aka 'nonsense', aka 'unpleasantness'):* We are entering doubtful moral territory here – obviously players have a responsibility not to provoke a highly flammable crowd. A brawl between Coventry and Wimbledon on a wet November afternoon in front of a stupefied crowd of ten thousand is one thing, but a brawl between Celtic and Rangers players, given the barely controllable sectarian bitterness on the terraces, is quite another. Yet one has to conclude, regretfully and with a not inconsiderable degree of Corinthian sadness, that there is nothing like a punch-up to enliven an otherwise dull game. The side-effects are invariably beneficent – the players and the crowd become more committed, the plot thickens, the pulse quickens – and as long as the match doesn't degenerate as a consequence into some kind of sour grudge-match, brawls strike me as being a pretty desirable feature, like a roof terrace or a fireplace. If I were a sportswriter or a representative of the football authorities, then no doubt I would purse my lips, make disapproving noises, insist that the transgressors be brought to justice – argy-bargy, like soft drugs, would be no fun if it were officially sanctioned. Luckily, however, I have no such responsibility: I am a fan, with no duty to toe the moral line whatsoever.

The Arsenal–Norwich game at the end of 1989 had seven goals, and Arsenal came back from 2–0 down and then 3–2 down to win 4–3. It had two penalties, one in the last minute with the score at 3–3 (both, incidentally, terrible decisions on the part of the referee) . . . and Norwich's Gunn saved it, the ball rolled back to Dixon, who scuffed it, and it trickled, very gently, into the empty net. And then, all hell broke loose, with more or less everyone bar the Arsenal keeper involved in a bout of fisticuffs which seemed to last for ever but which was probably over in a matter of seconds. Nobody was sent off, but never mind: how was it not possible to enjoy a game like that?

The two teams were fined heavily, which was only right, of course. In situations like this, the FA could hardly send them a letter thanking the players for giving the fans what they want. And given Arsenal's later problems, discussed elsewhere, the fight has in retrospect lost some of its gloss. But it's this centre of the world thing again: after the game we went home knowing that what we had seen, live, was the most significant sporting moment of the afternoon, a moment which would be talked about for weeks, months, which would make the news, which everyone would be asking you about at work on Monday morning. So, in the end, one has to conclude that it was a privilege to be there, to see all those grown men make fools of themselves in front of thirty-five thousand people; I wouldn't have missed it for the world.

SADDAM HUSSEIN AND WARREN BARTON

Arsenal v Everton

19.1.91

A little-known fact: football fans knew before anybody else that the Gulf War had started. We were sat in front of the TV, waiting for the highlights of the Chelsea–Tottenham Rumbelows Cup-tie just before midnight, when Nick Owen looked at his monitor, announced a newsflash, and expressed the hope that we would be able to go to Stamford Bridge shortly. (The report of the game in the *Daily Mirror* made peculiar reading the next morning, incidentally, given the circumstances: 'Wave after wave of attacks left Tottenham hanging on for grim life', that kind of thing.) ITV beat the BBC to the news by several minutes.

Like most people, I was frightened: by the possibility of nuclear and chemical weapons being used; of Israel's involvement; of hundreds of thousands of people dying. By three o'clock on the Saturday afternoon, sixty-three hours after the start of the conflict, I was more discombobulated than I can recall being at the start of a football match: I'd watched too much late-night television, and dreamed too many strange dreams.

There was a different buzz in the crowd, too. The North Bank chanted 'Saddam Hussein is a homosexual' and 'Saddam run from Arsenal'. (The first message is scarcely in need of decoding; in the second, 'Arsenal' refers to the fans rather than the players. Which makes the chant self-aggrandising, rather than ridiculing, and which paradoxically reveals a respect for the Iraqi leader absent in the speculation about his sexual preferences. A consistent ideology is probably too much to ask for.)

It was an interesting experience, watching a football match with the world at war; one I had never had before. How was Highbury to become the centre of the universe, with a million men preparing to kill each other a thousand miles away? Easy. Merse's goal just after half-time earned us a 1–0 win, which would not in itself have been enough to distract attention away from Baghdad; but when Warren Barton's free-kick got Wimbledon a result up at Anfield, and we went top of the League for the first time that season, everything became focused again. Eight points behind in December and one point clear in January . . . By a quarter to five, Saddam was forgotten, and Highbury was humming.

TYPICAL ARSENAL

Arsenal v Manchester United

6.5.91

In May 1991 we won the League again, for the second time in three years and the third time in my whole life. In the end there was none of the drama of 1989: Liverpool collapsed ignominiously, and we were allowed to run away with it. On the evening of the 6th May, Liverpool lost at Forest before our home game against Manchester United, and the United game was thus transformed into a riotous, raucous celebration.

If ever a season has exemplified Arsenal, it was that one. It wasn't just that we lost only one League game all season, and conceded an astonishingly miserly eighteen goals, although these statistics are in themselves indicative of the team's traditional tenacity. It was that the Championship was achieved despite almost comical antagonism and adversity. We had two points deducted after becoming involved, in retrospect unwisely, in another brawl, less than a year after the exciting Norwich fracas; soon afterwards, our captain was imprisoned after a stupendously idiotic piece of drunken driving. And these incidents came on top of heaps of others, on and off the pitch – fights, tabloid reports of obnoxious drunken behaviour, mass displays of petulance and indiscipline (most notably at Aston Villa at the end of 1989, when most of the team surrounded an unhelpful linesman long after the final whistle, gesturing and shouting to the extent that those of us who had travelled to support them couldn't help but feel embarrassed), and so on and on and on. Each of these transgressions isolated the club and its devotees further and further from the lip-pursing, right-thinking, Arsenal-hating mainland; Highbury became a Devil's Island in the middle of north London, the home of no-goods and miscreants.

'You can stick your fucking two points up your arse,' the crowd sang gleefully, over and over again, throughout the Manchester United game, and it began to seem like the quintessential Arsenal song: take our points, imprison our captain, hate our football, sod the lot of you. It was our night, a show of solidarity and defiance that had no grey areas of vicarious pleasure for anyone else, an acclamation of the virtues of all things unvirtuous. Arsenal aren't a Nottingham Forest or a West Ham or even a Liverpool, a team that inspires affection or admiration in other football fans; we share our pleasures with nobody but ourselves.

I don't like the fact that for the last couple of years Arsenal have brawled and bitched their way through their seasons, of course I don't. And I would rather that Tony Adams hadn't skidded his way down a residential street after a bucketful of lager, that the club hadn't paid all of his wages while he was inside, that Ian Wright hadn't spat at Oldham fans, that Nigel Winterburn hadn't involved himself in a bizarre row with a supporter on the touchline at Highbury. These are, on the whole, Bad Things. But in a sense my feelings are beside the point. It is part of the essential Arsenal experience that they are loathed, and in an era in which more or less everybody plays with an offside trap and an extra defender, perhaps these distasteful incidents are the Arsenal way of upping the ante in order to stake sole claim to the territory.

So in the end, the question of why Arsenal behave like this is not a very interesting one. I suspect that the answer is that they behave like this because they are Arsenal, and they understand their allotted role in the football scheme of things. A more interesting question is this: what does it do to the fans? How is your psyche affected, when you commit yourself for a lifetime to the team that everybody loves to hate?

Are football fans like the dogs that come to resemble their masters?

Emphatically, yes. The West Ham fans I know have an innate sense of underdog moral authority, the Tottenham fans give off an air of smug, ersatz sophistication, the Manchester United fans are imbued with a frustrated grandeur, Liverpool fans are simply grand. And as for Arsenal fans . . . It is impossible to believe that we have remained unaffected by loving what the rest of the world regards as fundamentally unlovable. Ever since 15th March 1969, I have been aware of the isolation my team induces, maybe even demands. My partner believes that my tendency to adopt an attitude of beleaguered defiance at each minor setback or perceived act of disloyalty has been learned from Arsenal, and she may be right. Like the club, I am not equipped with a particularly thick skin; my oversensitivity to criticism means that I am more likely to pull up the drawbridge and bitterly bemoan my lot than I am to offer a quick handshake and get on with the game. In true Arsenal style, I can dish it out but I can't take it.

So that second Championship win, though less enthralling than the first, was far more satisfying, and more truly indicative of the Arsenal way: the club and the fans closed ranks and overcame, with a magnificently single-minded sense of purpose, almost insurmountable difficulties all of their own making. It was a triumph not only for the team, but for what the team has come to represent, and by extension for what all Arsenal fans have become. The 6th of May was our night, and everybody else could go hang.

PLAYING

Friends v Other Friends

every Wednesday night

I started playing football seriously – that is to say, I started to care about what I was doing, rather than simply going through the motions to appease a schoolteacher – at the same time as I started watching. There were the games at school with the tennis ball, and the games in the street with a punctured plastic ball, two- or three-a-side; there were the games with my sister in the back garden, games up to ten in which she received a nine-goal start and threatened to go indoors if I scored; there were games with the local aspirant goalkeeper in the nearby playing fields after *The Big Match* on a Sunday afternoon, where we would re-enact high-scoring League games and I would provide live commentary at the same time. I played five-a-side in the local sports centre before I went to university, and second- or third-team football at college. I played for the staff team when I was teaching in Cambridge, and a mixed game twice a week with friends during the summer, and for the last six or seven years, all the football enthusiasts I know have been gathering on a five-a-side court in west London once a week. So I have been playing for two-thirds of my life, and I would like to play throughout as many of the three or four decades remaining to me as possible.

I'm a striker; or rather, I am not a goalkeeper, defender or midfield player, and not only can I remember without difficulty some of the goals I scored five or ten or fifteen years ago, I still, privately, take great pleasure in doing so, although I am sure that this sort of indulgence will result in my eventual blindness. I'm no good at football, needless to say, although happily that is also true of the friends I play with. We are just good enough to make it worthwhile: every week one of us scores a blinding goal, a scorching right-foot volley or a side-foot into a corner that caps a mazy run through a bewildered opposition defence, and we think about it secretly and guiltily (this is not what grown men should dream about) until the next time. Some of us have no hair on the tops of our heads, although this, we remind each other, has never been a handicap to Ray Wilkins, or that brilliant Sampdoria winger whose name escapes me; many of us are a few pounds overweight; most of us are in our mid-thirties. And even though there is an unspoken agreement that we don't tackle very hard, a relief for those of us who never could, I have noticed in the last couple of years that I wake up on Thursday mornings almost paralysed by stiffening joints, pulled hamstrings and sore Achilles tendons; my knee is swollen and puffy for the next two days, a legacy of the medial ligament torn in a game ten years ago (the subsequent exploratory operation was the closest I ever got to being a real footballer); whatever pace I had has been eroded by my advancing years and my self-abusive lifestyle. By the end of our sixty minutes I am bright red with exertion, and my Arsenal replica away shirt (old model) and shorts are sopping wet.

This is how close I came to becoming a professional: at college, one or two of the first team (I was in the third team in my final year) played for the Blues, a team consisting of the eleven best players in the whole of the University. To my knowledge, two Blues players in my time went on to play at a professional level. The best one, the university god, a blond striker who seemed to glow with talent in the way stars do, played as sub a few times for Torquay United in the Fourth Division – he may even have scored for them once. Another played for Cambridge City – City, Quentin Crisp's team, the team with the wonky *Match of the Day* tape and a crowd of two hundred, not United – as a full-back; we went to see him, and he was way off the pace.

So ... if I had ranked number one in my college, as opposed to number twenty-five or thirty, then I might have been able, if I had been lucky, to look bad in a very poor semi-professional team. Sport doesn't allow you to dream in the way that writing or acting or painting or middle-management does: I knew when I was eleven that I would never play for Arsenal. Eleven is too young to know something as awful as that.

Luckily, it is possible to be a professional footballer without walking on to a League pitch, and without being blessed with a footballer's physique or pace or stamina or talent. There are the grimaces and gestures – the screwed-up eyes and slumped shoulders when you miss a good chance, the high-fives when you score, the clenched fists and hand-claps when your team-mates require encouragement, the open arms and upturned palms indicating your superior positioning and your team-mate's greed, the finger pointing to where you would like a pass delivered, and, after the pass has been delivered just right and you have messed up anyway, the raised hand acknowledging both facts. And sometimes, when you receive the ball with your back to goal and knock a short pass out wide, you know you have done it just right, just so, and that were it not for your paunch (but then, look at Molby) and your lack of hair (Wilkins, that Sampdoria winger – Lombardo? – again), and your lack of height (Hillier, Limpar), were it not for all those *peripherals*, you would have looked just like Alan Smith.

A SIXTIES REVIVAL

Arsenal v Aston Villa

11.1.92

There was a part of me that was afraid to write all this down in a book, just as a part of me was afraid to explain to a therapist precisely what it had all come to mean: I was worried that by so doing it would all go, and I'd be left with this great big hole where football used to be. It hasn't happened, not yet, anyway. What has happened is more disturbing: I have begun to relish the misery that football provides. I am looking forward to more Championships, and days out at Wembley, and last-minute victories over Tottenham at White Hart Lane, of course I am, and when they come I will go as berserk as anyone. I don't want them yet, though. I want to defer the pleasure. I have been cold and bored and unhappy for so long that when Arsenal are good, I feel slightly but unmistakably disoriented, but I shouldn't have worried. What goes around, comes around.

I started this book in the summer of 1991. Arsenal were the runaway First Division champions, about to enter the European Cup for the first time in exactly twenty years. They had the biggest squad, the brightest prospects, the strongest defence, the deadliest attack, the most astute manager; after their final match of the 90/91 season, in which they crushed poor Coventry 6–1 with four goals in the last twenty-odd minutes, the papers were full of us. 'READY TO RULE EUROPE'; 'THEY'RE GUNNER RULE FOR FIVE YEARS'; 'WE'RE THE BEST EVER'; 'CHAMPIONS SET SIGHTS ON THE BIGGEST PRIZE OF ALL'. There had been nothing in my time to compare with this sort of rich optimism. Even Arsenal-haters among my friends were predicting a triumphant and stately procession through to the European Cup Final, as well as another League title for sure, no trouble.

There was a little hiccup at the beginning of the season, but the team had found their form by the time the European Cup started in the middle of September: they crushed the Austrian champions 6–1, a magnificent performance which we believed would scare the rest of the continent rigid. We drew Benfica of Portugal in the next round, and I travelled on one of the two supporters' club planes to Lisbon, where we hung on for a creditable 1–1 draw in front of eighty thousand Portuguese in the intimidating Stadium of Light. In the return at Highbury, however, we got stuffed, overrun, outplayed, and it was all over, maybe for another twenty years. Then we dropped out of the running for the Championship, after a string of terrible results over Christmas; and then, unbelievably and cataclysmically, we were knocked out of the FA Cup by Wrexham, who had the previous season finished bottom of the Fourth Division as Arsenal finished top of the First.

It was strange, trying to write about how miserable most of my footballing life has been in the midst of all that post-Championship hope and glory. So as the season crumbled to dust, and Highbury became a place for discontented players and unhappy fans once more, and the future began to look so dismal that it was impossible to remember why we thought it bright in the first place, I began to feel comfortable again. The Great Collapse of 1992 had a sort of sympathetic magic to it. Wrexham was a quite brilliant and entirely authentic recreation of Swindon, humiliating enough to enable me to relive childhood trauma; at the same time as I was trying to recall the old boring, boring Arsenal of the sixties, and seventies, and, yes, the eighties, Wright and Campbell and Smith and the rest obligingly stopped scoring, and began to look as inept as their historical counterparts had ever done.

Against Aston Villa, one week after Wrexham, my whole life flashed before my eyes. A nil–nil draw, against a nothing team, in a meaningless game, in front of a restive, occasionally angry but for the most part wearily tolerant crowd, in the freezing January cold . . . All that was missing was Ian Ure falling over his feet, and my dad, grumbling away in the seat next to me.

High Fidelity

For Virginia

then...

My desert-island, all-time, top five most memorable split-ups, in chronological order:

1) Alison Ashworth
2) Penny Hardwick
3) Jackie Allen
4) Charlie Nicholson
5) Sarah Kendrew.

These were the ones that really hurt. Can you see your name in that lot, Laura? I reckon you'd sneak into the top *ten*, but there's no place for you in the top five; those places are reserved for the kind of humiliations and heartbreaks that you're just not capable of delivering. That probably sounds crueller than it is meant to, but the fact is that we're too old to make each other miserable, and that's a good thing, not a bad thing, so don't take your failure to make the list personally. Those days are gone, and good fucking riddance to them; unhappiness really meant something back then. Now it's just a drag, like a cold or having no money. If you really wanted to mess me up, you should have got to me earlier.

1. Alison Ashworth (1972)

Most nights we used to mess around in the park around the corner from my house. I lived in Hertfordshire, but I might just as well have lived in any suburb in England: it was that sort of suburb, and that sort of park – three minutes away from home, right across the road from a little row of shops (a VG supermarket, a newsagent, an off-licence). There was nothing around that could help you get your geographical bearings; if the shops were open (and they closed at five-thirty, and one o'clock on Thursdays, and all day Sunday), you could go into the newsagent's and look for a local newspaper, but even that might not give you much of a clue.

We were twelve or thirteen, and had recently discovered irony – or at least, what I later understood to be irony: we only allowed ourselves to play on the swings and the roundabout and the other kids' stuff rusting away in there if we could do it with a sort of self-conscious ironic detachment. This involved either an imitation of absent-mindedness (whistling, or chatting, or fiddling with a cigarette stub or a box of matches usually did the trick) or a flirtation with danger, so we jumped off the swings when they could go no higher, jumped on to the roundabout when it would go no faster, hung on to the end of the swingboat until it reached an almost vertical position. If you could somehow prove that these childish entertainments had the potential to dash your brains out, then playing on them became OK somehow.

We had no irony when it came to girls, though. There was just no time to develop it. One moment they weren't there, not in any form that interested us, anyway, and the next you couldn't miss them; they were everywhere, all over the place. One moment you wanted to clonk them on the head for being your sister, or someone else's sister, and the next you wanted to . . . actually, we didn't know what we wanted the next, but it was something, something. Almost overnight, all these sisters (there was no other kind of girl, not yet) had become interesting, *disturbing*, even.

See, what did we have that was any different from what we'd had before? Squeaky voices, but a squeaky voice doesn't do much for you, really – it makes you preposterous, not desirable. And the sprouting pubic hairs were our secret, strictly between us and our Y-fronts, and it would be years before a member of the opposite sex could verify that they were where they should be. Girls, on the other hand, quite clearly had breasts, and, to accompany them, a new way of walking: arms folded over the chest, a posture which simultaneously disguised and drew attention to what had just happened. And then there was make-up and perfume, invariably cheap, and inexpertly, sometimes even comically, applied, but still a quite terrifying sign that things had progressed without us, beyond us, behind our backs.

I started going out with one of them . . . no, that's not right, because I had absolutely no input into the decision-making process. And I can't say that she started going out with me, either: it's that phrase 'going out with' that's the problem, because it suggests some sort of parity and equality. What happened was that David Ashworth's sister Alison peeled off from the female pack that gathered every night by the bench and adopted me, tucked me under her arm and led me away from the swingboat.

I can't remember now how she did this. I don't think I was even aware of it at the time, because halfway through our first kiss, my first kiss, I can recall feeling utterly bewildered, totally unable to explain how Alison Ashworth and I had become so intimate. I wasn't even sure how I'd ended up on her side of the park, away from her brother and Mark Godfrey and the rest, nor how we had separated from her crowd, nor why she tipped her face towards me so that I knew I was supposed to put my mouth on hers. The whole episode defies any rational explanation. But all these things happened, and they happened again, most of them, the following evening, and the evening after that.

What did I think I was doing? What did she think she was doing? When I want to kiss people in that way now, with mouths and tongues and all that, it's because I want other things too: sex, Friday nights at the cinema, company and conversation, fused networks of family and friends, Lemsips brought to me in bed when I am ill, a new pair of ears for my records and CDs, maybe a little boy called Jack and a little girl called Holly or Maisie, I haven't decided yet. But I didn't want any of those things from Alison Ashworth. Not children, because we were children, and not Friday nights at the pictures, because we went Saturday mornings, and not Lemsips, because my mum did that, not even sex, especially not sex, please God not sex, the filthiest and most terrifying invention of the early seventies.

So what was the significance of the snog? The truth is that there was no significance; we were just lost in the dark. One part imitation (people I had seen kissing by 1972: James Bond, Simon Templar, Napoleon Solo, Barbara Windsor and Sid James or maybe Jim Dale, Elsie Tanner, Omar Sharif and Julie Christie, Elvis, and lots of black-and-white people my mum wanted to watch, although they never waggled their heads from side to side) to one part hormonal slavery to one part peer-group pressure (Kevin Bannister and Elizabeth Barnes had been at it for a couple of weeks) to one part blind panic . . . there was no consciousness, no desire and no pleasure, beyond an unfamiliar and moderately pleasant warmth in the gut. We were little animals, which is not to imply that by the end of the week we were tearing our tank tops off; just that, metaphorically speaking, we had begun to sniff each other's bottom, and we did not find the odour entirely repellent.

But listen, Laura. On the fourth night of our relationship I turned up in the park and Alison was sitting on the bench with her arm around

Kevin Bannister, with Elizabeth Barnes nowhere in sight. Nobody – not Alison, or Kevin, or me, or the sexually uninitiated retards hanging off the end of the swingboat said anything at all. I stung, and I blushed, and I suddenly forgot how to walk without being aware of every single part of my body. What to do? Where to go? I didn't want to fight; I didn't want to sit there with the two of them; I didn't want to go home. So, concentrating very hard on the empty No. 6 packets that marked out the path between the girls and the boys, and not looking up or behind me or to either side, I headed back towards the massed ranks of the single males hanging off the swingboat. Halfway home, I made my only error of judgement: I stopped and looked at my watch, although for the life of me I don't know what I was attempting to convey, or who I was trying to kid. What sort of time, after all, could make a thirteen-year-old boy spin away from a girl and towards a playground, palms sweating, heart racing, trying desperately not to cry? Certainly not four o'clock on a late September afternoon.

I scrounged a fag off Mark Godfrey and went and sat on my own on the roundabout.

'Scrubber,' spat Alison's brother David, and I smiled gratefully at him.

And that was that. Where had I gone wrong? First night: park, fag, snog. Second night: ditto. Third night: ditto. Fourth night: chucked. OK, OK. Maybe I should have seen the signs. Maybe I was asking for it. Round about that second ditto I should have spotted that we were in a rut, that I had allowed things to fester to the extent that she was on the lookout for someone else. But she could have tried to tell me! She could at least have given me another couple of days to put things right!

My relationship with Alison Ashworth had lasted six hours (the two-hour gap between school and *Nationwide*, times three), so I could hardly claim that I'd got used to having her around, that I didn't know what to do with myself. In fact, I can hardly recall anything about her at all, now. Long black hair? Maybe. Small? Smaller than me, certainly. Slanted, almost oriental eyes and a dark complexion? That could have been her, or it could have been someone else. Whatever. But if we were doing this list in grief order, rather than chronological order, I'd put it right up there at number two. It would be nice to think that as I've got older times have changed, relationships have become more sophisticated, females less cruel, skins thicker, reactions sharper, instincts more developed. But there still seems to be an element of that evening in everything that has happened to me since; all my other romantic stories seem to be a scrambled version of that first one. Of course, I have never had to take that long walk again, and my ears have not burned with quite the same fury, and I have never had to count the No. 6 packets in order to avoid mocking eyes and floods of tears . . . not really, not actually, not as such. It just feels that way, sometimes.

2. Penny Hardwick (1973)

Penny Hardwick was a nice girl, and, nowadays, I'm all for nice girls, although then I wasn't so sure. She had a nice mum and dad, and a nice house, detached, with a garden and a tree and a fishpond, and a nice girl's haircut (she was blonde, and she kept her hair a sort of sporty, clean, wholesome, form-captain mid-length), and nice, smiling eyes, and a nice younger sister, who smiled politely when I rang on the doorbell and kept out of the way when we wanted her to. She had nice manners – my mum loved her – and she always got nice school reports. Penny was nice-looking, and her top five recording artistes were Carly Simon, Carole King, James Taylor, Cat Stevens and Elton John. Lots of people liked her. She was so nice, in fact, that she wouldn't let me put my hand underneath or even on top of her bra, and so I finished with her, although obviously I didn't tell her why. She cried, and I hated her for it, because she made me feel bad.

I can imagine what sort of person Penny Hardwick became: a nice person. I know that she went to college, did well, and landed a job as a radio producer for the BBC. I would guess that she is bright, and serious-minded, maybe too much so, sometimes, and ambitious, but not in a way that makes you want to vomit; she was a version of all these things when we went out, and at another stage in my life I would have found all these virtues attractive. Then, however, I wasn't interested in qualities, just breasts, and she was therefore no good to me.

I would like to be able to tell you that we had long, interesting conversations, and that we remained firm friends throughout our teenage years – she would have made someone a lovely friend – but I don't think we ever talked. We went to the pictures, to parties and to discos, and we wrestled. We wrestled in her bedroom, and my bedroom, and her living room, and my living room, and in bedrooms at parties, and in living rooms at parties, and in the summer we wrestled on various plots of grass. We were wrestling over the same old issue. Sometimes I got so bored of trying to touch her breasts that I would try to touch her between her legs, a gesture that had a sort of self-parodying wit about it: it was like trying to borrow a fiver, getting turned down, and asking to borrow fifty quid instead.

These were the questions boys asked other boys at my school (a school which contained only boys): 'Are you getting any?'; 'Does she let you have any?'; 'How much does she let you have?' and so on. Sometimes the questions were derisory, and expected the answer 'No': 'You're not getting anything, are you?'; 'You haven't even had a bit of tit, have you?' Girls, meanwhile, had to be content with the passive voice. Penny used the expression 'broken into': 'I don't want to be broken into yet,' she would explain patiently and maybe a little sadly (she seemed to understand that one day – but not now – she would have to give in, and when it happened she wouldn't like it) when she removed my hand from her chest for the one hundred thousandth time. Attack and defence, invasion and repulsion . . . it was as if breasts were little pieces of property that had been unlawfully annexed by the opposite sex – they were rightfully ours and we wanted them back.

Luckily, however, there were traitors, fifth columnists, in the opposing camp. Some boys knew of other boys whose girlfriends would 'let' them do anything; sometimes these girls were supposed to have actively assisted in their own molestation. Nobody had ever heard of a girl who had gone as far as undressing, or even removing or loosening undergarments, of course. That would have been taking collaboration too far. As I understood it, these girls had simply positioned themselves in a way that encouraged access. 'She tucks her stomach in and everything,' Clive Stevens remarked approvingly of his brother's girlfriend; it took me nearly a year to work out the import of this manoeuvre. No wonder I still remember the stomach-tucker's first name (Judith); there's a part of me that still wants to meet her.

Read any woman's magazine and you'll see the same complaint over and over again: men – those little boys ten or twenty or thirty years on – are hopeless in bed. They are not interested in 'foreplay'; they have no desire to stimulate the erogenous zones of the opposite sex; they are selfish, greedy, clumsy, unsophisticated. These complaints, you can't help feeling, are kind of ironic. Back then, all we wanted was foreplay, and girls weren't interested. They didn't want to be touched, caressed, stimulated, aroused;

in fact, they used to thump us if we tried. It's not really very surprising, then, that we're not much good at all that. We spent two or three long and extremely formative years being told very forcibly not even to think about it. Between the ages of fourteen and twenty-four, foreplay changes from being something that boys want to do and girls don't, to something that women want and men can't be bothered with. (Or so they say. Me, I like foreplay – mostly because the times when all I wanted to do was touch are alarmingly fresh in my mind.) The perfect match, if you ask me, is between the *Cosmo* woman and the fourteen-year-old boy.

If somebody had asked me why I was so hell-bent on grabbing a piece of Penny Hardwick's chest, I wouldn't have known what to say. And if somebody were to ask Penny why she was so hell-bent on stopping me, I'll bet she'd be stumped for an answer too. What was in it for me? I wasn't asking for any sort of reciprocation, after all. Why didn't she want her erogenous zones stimulated? I have no idea. All I know is that you could, if you wanted to, find the answers to all sorts of difficult questions buried in that terrible war-torn interregnum between the first pubic hair and the first soiled Durex.

And in any case, maybe I didn't want to put my hand under Penny's bra as much as I thought. Maybe other people wanted me to touch her more than I did. After a couple of months of fighting on sofas all over town with Penny, I'd had enough: I had admitted, unwisely in retrospect, to a friend that I wasn't getting anywhere, and my friend had told some other friends, and I was the butt of a number of cruel and unpleasant jokes. I gave Penny one last try, in my bedroom while my mum and dad were at the town hall watching a local dramatic society interpretation of *Toad of Toad Hall*; I used a degree of force that would have outraged and terrified an adult female, but got nowhere, and when I walked her home we hardly spoke.

I was offhand with her the next time we went out, and when she went to kiss me at the end of the evening I shrugged her off. 'What's the point?' I asked her. 'It never goes anywhere.' The time after that she asked whether I still wanted to see her, and I looked the other way. We had been going out for three months, which was as near to a permanent relationship as you could get in the fourth year. (Her mum and dad had even met my mum and dad. They liked each other.) She cried, then, and I loathed her for making me feel guilty, and for making me finish with her.

I went out with a girl called Kim, who I knew for a fact had already been invaded, and who (I was correct in assuming) wouldn't object to being invaded again; Penny went out with Chris Thomson from my class, a boy who had had more girlfriends than all the rest of us put together. I was out of my depth, and so was she. One morning, maybe three weeks after my last grapple with Penny, Thomson came roaring into our form room. 'Oi, Fleming, you spastic. Guess who I knobbed last night?'

I felt the room spin round.

'You never got so much as a bit of tit in three months, and I shagged her first week!'

I believed him; everyone knew that he got whatever he wanted from whoever he saw. I had been humiliated, beaten, out-performed; I felt stupid, and small, and much, much younger than this unpleasant, oversized, big-mouthed moron. It shouldn't have mattered so much. Thomson was in a league of his own when it came to matters of the lower body, and there were plenty of little jerky creeps in 4b who had never so much as put their arm around a girl. Even my side of the debate, inaudible though it was, must have appeared impossibly sophisticated to them. I wasn't losing that much face. But I still couldn't understand what had happened. How had this transformation in Penny been effected? How had Penny gone from being a girl who wouldn't do anything to a girl who would do everything there was to do? Maybe it was best not to think about it too hard; I didn't want to feel sorry for anybody else except me.

I expect Penny turned out all right, and I know I turned out all right, and I would suspect that even Chris Thomson isn't the world's worst person. At least, it's hard to imagine him skidding into his place of work, his bank or his insurance office or car showroom, chucking his briefcase down and informing a colleague with raucous glee that he has 'knobbed' said colleague's wife. (It is easy enough to imagine him knobbing the wife, however. He looked like a wife-knobber, even then.) Women who disapprove of men – and there's plenty to disapprove of – should remember how we started out, and how far we have had to travel.

3. Jackie Allen (1975)

Jackie Allen was my friend Phil's girlfriend, and I pinched her off him, slowly, patiently, over a period of months. It wasn't easy. It required a great deal of time, application and deception. Phil and Jackie started going out together around the same time as Penny and I did, except they went on and on: through the giggly, hormonal fourth form, and the end-of-the-world 'O'-level and school-leaving fifth, and on into the mock-adult sobriety of the lower sixth. They were our golden couple, our Paul and Linda, our Newman and Woodward, living proof that in a faithless, fickle world it was possible to grow old, or at least older, without chopping and changing every few weeks.

I'm not too sure why I wanted to fuck it all up for them, and for everyone who needed them to go out together. You know when you see T-shirts piled up in a clothes shop, beautifully folded and colour-coded, and you buy one? It never looks the same when you take it home. It only looked good in the shop, you realize too late, because it had its mates around it. Well, it was kind of like that. I had hoped that if I went out with Jackie, then some of that elder-stateswoman dignity would rub off on me, but of course without Phil she didn't have any. (If that's what I wanted, I should perhaps have looked for a way to go out with both of them, but that sort of thing is hard enough to pull off when you're an adult; at seventeen it could be enough to get you stoned to death.)

Phil started working in a men's boutique on Saturdays, and I moved in. Those of us who didn't work, or who, like me, worked after school but not at weekends, met on Saturday afternoons to walk up and down the High Street, spend too much time and too much money in Harlequin Records, and 'treat ourselves' (we had somehow picked up our mothers' vocabulary of post-war abstention) to a filter coffee, which we regarded as the last word in French cool. Sometimes we called in to see Phil; sometimes he let me use his staff discount. It didn't stop me from screwing his girlfriend behind his back.

I knew, because both Alison and Penny had taught me, that busting up with someone could be miserable, but I didn't know that getting off with someone could be miserable too. But Jackie and I were miserable in a thrilling, grown-up way. We met in secret and phoned each other in secret and had sex in secret and said things like 'What are we going to do?' in secret and talked about how nice it would be when we didn't have to do things in secret any more. I never really thought about whether that was true or not. There wasn't time.

I tried not to run Phil down too much – I felt bad enough as it was, what with screwing his girlfriend and all. But it became unavoidable, because when Jackie expressed doubts about him, I had to nurture those doubts as if they were tiny, sickly kittens, until eventually they became sturdy, healthy grievances, with their own cat-flaps which allowed them to wander in and out of our conversation at will.

And then one night at a party I saw Phil and Jackie huddled together in a corner, and Phil was obviously distressed, pale and near to tears, and then he went home, and the next morning she phoned up and asked if I wanted to go out for a walk, and we were away, and we weren't doing things in secret any more; and we lasted about three weeks.

You'd say that this was childish, Laura. You'd say that it is stupid of me to compare Rob and Jackie with Rob and Laura, who are in their mid-thirties, established, living together. You'd say that adult adultery beats teenage adultery hands down, but you'd be wrong. I have been one point of a triangle several times since then, but that first point was the sharpest. Phil never spoke to me again; our Saturday shopping crowd wouldn't have much to do with us either. My mum had a phone call from Phil's mum. School was, for a few weeks, uncomfortable.

Compare and contrast with what happens if I make that sort of mess now: I can go to different pubs and clubs, leave the ansaphone on, go out more, stay in more, fiddle around with my social compasses and draw a new circle of friends (and anyway, my friends are never her friends, whoever she might be), avoid all contact with disapproving parents. That sort of anonymity was unavailable then, though. You had to stand there and take it, whatever it was.

What perplexed me most of all was the feeling of flat disappointment that overtook me when Jackie called me that Sunday morning. I couldn't understand it. I had been plotting this capture for months, and when capitulation came I felt nothing – less than nothing, even. I couldn't tell Jackie this, obviously, but on the other hand I was quite unable to show the enthusiasm I felt she needed, so I decided to have her name tattooed down my right arm.

I don't know. Scarring myself for life seemed much easier than having to tell Jackie that it had all been a grotesque mistake, that I'd just been messing about; if I could show her the tattoo, my peculiar logic ran, I wouldn't have to bother straining after words that were beyond me. I should explain that I am not a tattoo kind of guy; I am, and was, neither rock'n'roll go-to-hell decadent or lager-squaddy muscular. But there was a disastrous fashion for them at our school around that time, and I know for a fact that several men now in their mid-thirties, accountants and schoolteachers, personnel managers and computer programmers, have terrible messages ('MUFC KICK TO KILL', 'LYNYRD SKYNYRD') from that era burned into their flesh.

I was just going to have a discreet 'J ♡ R' done on my upper arm, but Victor the tattooist wasn't having any of it.

'Which one is she? "J" or "R"?'

'"J".'

'And how long have you been seeing this "J" bird, then?'

I was frightened by the aggressive masculinity of the parlour – the other customers (who were all firmly in the lager-squaddy muscular team, and seemed inexplicably amused to see me), the nude women on the walls, the lurid examples of services offered, most of which were conveniently located on Victor's forearms, even Victor's mildly offensive language.

'Long enough.'

'I'll fucking be the judge of that, not you.'

This struck me as an odd way to do business, but I decided to save this observation for another time.

'A couple of months.'

'And you're going to marry her, are you? Or have you knocked her up?'

'No. Neither.'

'So you're just going out? You're not lumbered?'

'Yeah.'

'And how did you meet her?'

'She used to go out with a friend of mine.'

'Did she now. And when did they break up?'

'Saturday.'

'Saturday.' He laughed like a drain. 'I don't want your mum in here moaning at me. Fuck off out of it.'

I fucked off out of it.

Victor was spot on, of course; in fact, I have often been tempted to seek him out when I have been plagued by diseases of the heart. He'd be able to tell me in ten seconds whether someone was worth a tattoo or not. But even after Phil and Jackie were ecstatically and tearfully reunited, things didn't go back to the way they had been. Some of the girls at her school, and some of the boys at ours, presumed that Jackie had been using me to renegotiate the terms of her relationship with Phil, and the Saturday shopping afternoons were never the same again. And we no longer admired people who had gone out together for a long time; we were sarcastic about them, and they were even sarcastic about themselves. In a few short weeks, mock-marital status had ceased to be something to aspire to, and had become a cause for scorn. At seventeen, we were becoming as embittered and as unromantic as our parents.

See, Laura? You won't change everything around like Jackie could. It's happened too many times, to both of us; we'll just go back to the friends and the pubs and the life we had before, and leave it at that, and nobody will notice the difference, probably.

4. Charlie Nicholson (1977–1979)

I met Charlie at tech: I was doing a media studies course, and she was studying design, and when I first saw her I realized she was the sort of girl I had wanted to meet ever since I'd been old enough to want to meet girls. She was tall, with blond cropped hair (she said she knew some people who were at St Martin's with some friends of Johnny Rotten, but I was never introduced to them), and she looked different and dramatic and exotic. Even her name seemed to me dramatic and different and exotic, because up until then I had lived in a world where girls had girls' names, and not very interesting ones at that. She talked a lot, so that you didn't have those terrible, strained silences that seemed to characterize most of my sixth-form dates, and when she talked she said remarkably interesting things – about her course, about my course, about music, about films and books and politics.

And she liked me. She liked *me. She* liked me. She *liked* me. Or at least, I think she did. I *think* she did. Etc. I have never been entirely sure what it is women like about me, but I know that ardour helps (even I know how difficult it is to resist someone who finds you irresistible) and I was certainly ardent: I didn't make a nuisance of myself, not until the end, anyway, and I never outstayed my welcome, not while there was still a welcome to be outstayed, but I was kind and sincere and thoughtful and devoted and I remembered things about her and I told her she was beautiful and bought her little presents that usually referred to a conversation we had had recently. None of this was an effort, of course, and none of it was done with any sense of calculation: I found it easy to remember things about her, because I didn't think about anything else, and I really did think she was beautiful, and I would not have been able to prevent myself from buying her little presents, and I did not have to feign devotion. There was no effort involved. So when one of Charlie's friends, a girl called Kate, said wistfully one lunchtime that she wished she could find somebody like me, I was surprised and thrilled. Thrilled because Charlie was listening, and it didn't do me any harm, but surprised because all I had done was act out of self-interest. And yet this was enough, it seemed, to turn me into someone desirable. Weird.

And, anyway, by moving to London I had made it easier to be liked by girls. At home, most people had known me, or my mum and dad – or had known somebody who knew me, or my mum and dad – when I was little, and consequently I'd always had the uncomfortable feeling that my boyhood was about to be exposed to the world. How could you take a girl out for an underage drink in a pub when you knew you had a scout uniform still hanging in your closet? Why would a girl want to kiss you if she knew (or knew somebody who knew) that just a few years before, you had insisted on sewing souvenir patches from the Norfolk Broads and Exmoor on your anorak? There were pictures all over my parents' house of me with big ears and disastrous clothes, sitting on tractors, clapping with glee as miniature trains drew into miniature stations; and though later on, distressingly, girlfriends found these pictures cute, it all seemed too close for comfort then. It had only taken me six years to change from a ten-year-old to a sixteen-year-old; surely six years wasn't long enough for a transformation of that magnitude? When I was sixteen, that anorak with the patches on was just a couple of sizes too small.

Charlie hadn't known me as a ten-year-old, however, and she didn't know anybody who knew me, either. She knew me only as a young adult. I was already old enough to vote when I met her; I was old enough to spend the night with her, the whole night, in her hall of residence, and have opinions, and buy her a drink in a pub, secure in the knowledge that my driving licence with its scrambled proof of age was in my pocket . . . and I was old enough to have a history. At home I didn't have a history, just stuff that everybody already knew, and that therefore wasn't worth repeating.

But I still felt a fraud. I was like all those people who suddenly shaved their heads and said they'd *always* been punks, they'd been punks before punk was even thought of: I felt as though I was going to be found out at any moment, that somebody was going to burst into the college bar brandishing one of the anorak photos and yelling, 'Rob used to be a *boy*! A little *lad*!', and Charlie would see it and pack me in. It never occurred to me that she probably had a whole pile of pony books and some ridiculous party dresses hidden away at her parents' place in St Albans. As far as I was concerned, she had been born with enormous earrings, drainpipe jeans and an incredibly sophisticated enthusiasm for the works of some guy who used to splodge orange paint around.

We went out for two years, and for every single minute I felt as though I was standing on a dangerously narrow ledge. I couldn't ever get comfortable, if you know what I mean; there was no room to stretch out and relax. I was depressed by the lack of flamboyance in my wardrobe. I was fretful about my abilities as a lover. I couldn't understand what she saw in the orange paint guy, however many times she explained. I worried that I was never ever going to be able to say anything interesting or amusing to her about anything at all. I was intimidated by the other men on her design course, and became convinced that she was going to go off with one of them. She went off with one of them.

I lost the plot for a while then. And I lost the subplot, the script, the soundtrack, the intermission, my popcorn, the credits and the exit sign. I hung around Charlie's hall of residence until some friends of hers caught me and threatened to give me a good kicking. I decided to kill Marco (Marco!), the guy she went off with, and spent long hours in the middle of the night working out how to do it, although whenever I bumped into him I just muttered a greeting and sloped off. I did a spot of shoplifting, the precise motivation for which escapes me now. I took an overdose of Valium, and stuck a finger down my throat within a minute. I wrote endless letters to her, some of which I posted, and scripted endless conversations, none of which we had. And when I came round, after a couple of months of darkness, I found to my surprise that I had jacked in my course and was working in Record and Tape Exchange in Camden.

Everything happened so fast. I had kind of hoped that my adulthood would be long and meaty and instructive, but it all took place in those two years; sometimes it seems as though everything and everyone that has happened to me since were just minor distractions. Some people never got over the sixties, or the war, or the night their band supported Dr Feelgood at the Hope and Anchor, and spend the rest of their days walking backwards; I never really got over Charlie. That was when the important stuff, the stuff that defines me, went on.

Some of my favourite songs: 'Only Love Can Break Your Heart' by Neil Young; 'Last Night I Dreamed That Somebody Loved Me' by the Smiths; 'Call Me' by Aretha Franklin; 'I Don't Want To Talk About It' by anybody. And then there's 'Love Hurts' and 'When Love Breaks Down' and 'How Can You Mend A Broken Heart' and 'The Speed Of The Sound Of Loneliness' and 'She's Gone' and 'I Just Don't Know What to Do With Myself' and . . . some of these songs I have listened to around once a week, on average (three hundred times in the first month, every now and again thereafter), since I was sixteen or nineteen or twenty-one. How can that not leave you bruised somewhere? How can that not turn you into the sort of person liable to break into little bits when your first love goes all wrong? What came first, the music or the misery? Did I listen to music because I was miserable? Or was I miserable because I listened to music? Do all those records turn you into a melancholy person?

People worry about kids playing with guns, and teenagers watching violent videos; we are scared that some sort of culture of violence will take them over. Nobody worries about kids listening to thousands – literally thousands – of songs about broken hearts and rejection and pain and misery and loss. The unhappiest people I know, romantically speaking, are the ones who like pop music the most; and I don't know whether pop music has caused this unhappiness, but I do know that they've been listening to the sad songs longer than they've been living the unhappy lives.

Anyway. Here's how not to plan a career: a) split up with girlfriend; b) junk college; c) go to work in record shop; d) stay in record shops for rest of life. You see those pictures of people in Pompeii and you think, how weird: one quick game of dice after your tea and you're frozen, and that's how people remember you for the next few thousand years. Suppose it was the first game of dice you've ever played? Suppose you were only doing it to keep your friend Augustus company? Suppose you'd just at that moment finished a brilliant poem or something? Wouldn't it be annoying to be commemorated as a dice player? Sometimes I look at my shop (because I haven't let the grass grow under my feet the last fourteen years! About ten years ago I borrowed the money to start my own!), and at my regular Saturday punters, and I know exactly how those inhabitants of Pompeii must feel, if they could feel anything (although the fact that they can't is kind of the point of them). I'm stuck in this pose, this shop-managing pose, for ever, because of a few short weeks in 1979 when I went a bit potty for a while. It could be worse, I guess; I could have walked into an army recruiting office, or the nearest abattoir. But even so, I feel as though I made a face and the wind changed, and now I have to go through life grimacing in this horrible way.

Eventually I stopped posting the letters; a few months after that I stopped writing them too. I still fantasized about killing Marco, although the imagined deaths became swifter (I allow him a brief moment to register, and then BLAM!) – I didn't go in quite so much for the sicko slow stuff. I started sleeping with people again, although every one of these affairs I regarded as a fluke, a one-off, nothing likely to alter my dismal self-perception. (And, like James Stewart in *Vertigo*, I had developed a 'type': cropped blond hair, arty, dizzy, garrulous, which led to some disastrous mistakes.) I stopped drinking so much, I stopped listening to song lyrics with quite the same morbid fascination. (For a while, I regarded just about any song in which somebody had lost somebody else as spookily relevant, which, as that covers the whole of pop music, and as I worked in a record shop, meant I felt pretty spooked more or less the whole time.) I stopped constructing the killer one-liners that left Charlie writhing on the floor with regret and self-loathing.

I made sure, however, that I was never in anything, work or relationships, too deep: I convinced myself that I might get the call from Charlie at any moment, and would therefore have to leap into action. I was even unsure about opening my own shop, just in case Charlie wanted me to go abroad with her and I wasn't able to move quickly enough; marriage, mortgages and fatherhood were out of the question. I was realistic too: every now and again I updated Charlie's life, imagining a whole series of disastrous events (She's living with Marco! They've bought a place together! She's married him! She's pregnant! She's had a little girl!), just to keep myself on my toes, events which required a whole series of readjustments and conversions to keep my fantasies alive. (She'll have nowhere to go when they split! She'll *really* have nowhere to go when they split, and I'll have to support her financially! Marriage'll wake her up! Taking on another man's kid will show her what a great guy I am!) There was no news I couldn't handle; there was nothing she and Marco could do that would convince me that it wasn't all just a stage we were going through. They are together still, for all I know, and, as of today, I am unattached again.

5. Sarah Kendrew (1984–1986)

The lesson I learned from the Charlie débâcle is that you've got to punch your weight. Charlie was out of my class: too pretty, too smart, too witty, too much. What am I? Average. A middleweight. Not the brightest bloke in the world, but certainly not the dimmest: I have read books like *The Unbearable Lightness of Being* and *Love in the Time of Cholera*, and understood them, I think (they were about girls, right?), but I don't like them very much; my all-time top five favourite books are *The Big Sleep* by Raymond Chandler, *Red Dragon* by Thomas Harris, *Sweet Soul Music* by Peter Guralnick, *The Hitchhiker's Guide to the Galaxy* by Douglas Adams and, I don't know, something by William Gibson, or Kurt Vonnegut. I read the *Guardian* and the *Observer*, as well as the *NME* and music glossies; I am not averse to going down to Camden to watch subtitled films (top five subtitled films: *Betty Blue*, *Subway*, *Tie Me Up! Tie Me Down!*, *The Vanishing*, *Diva*), although on the whole I prefer American films. (Top five American films, and therefore the best films ever made: *The Godfather*, *Godfather Part II*, *Taxi Driver*, *Goodfellas* and *Reservoir Dogs*.)

I'm OK looking; in fact, if you put, say, Mel Gibson on one end of the looks spectrum and, say, Berky Edmonds from school, whose grotesque ugliness was legendary, on the other, then I reckon I'd be on Mel's side, just. A girlfriend once told me that I looked a bit like Peter Gabriel, and he's not too bad, is he? I'm average height, not slim, not fat, no unsightly facial hair, I keep myself clean, wear jeans and T-shirts and a leather jacket more or less all the time apart from in the summer, when I leave the leather jacket at home. I vote Labour. I have a pile of classic comedy videos – *Python*, *Fawlty Towers*, *Cheers* and so on. I can see what feminists are on about, most of the time, but not the radical ones.

My genius, if I can call it that, is to combine a whole load of averageness into one compact frame. I'd say that there were millions like me, but there aren't, really: lots of blokes have impeccable music taste but don't read, lots of blokes read but are really fat, lots of blokes are sympathetic to feminism but have stupid beards, lots of blokes have a Woody Allen sense of humour but look like Woody Allen. Lots of blokes drink too much, lots of blokes behave stupidly when they drive cars, lots of blokes get into fights, or show off about money, or take drugs. I don't do any of these things, really; if I do OK with women it's not because of the virtues I have, but because of the shadows I don't have.

Even so, you've got to know when you're out of your depth. I was out of my depth with Charlie; after her, I was determined never to get out of my depth again, and so for five years, until I met Sarah, I just paddled around in the shallow end. Charlie and I didn't *match.* Marco and Charlie matched; Sarah and I matched. Sarah was average-attractive (smallish, slim, nice big brown eyes, crooked teeth, shoulder-length dark hair that always seemed to need a cut no matter how often she went to the hairdresser's), and she wore clothes that were the same as mine, more or less. All-time top five favourite recording artists: Madness, Eurythmics, Bob Dylan, Joni Mitchell, Bob Marley. All-time top five favourite films: *National Velvet, Diva* (hey!), *Gandhi, Missing, Wuthering Heights.*

And she was sad, in the original sense of the word. She had been dumped a couple of years before by a sort of male equivalent to Charlie, a guy called Michael who wanted to be something at the BBC. (He never made it, the wanker, and each day we never saw him on TV or heard him on the radio, something inside us rejoiced.) He was her moment, just as Charlie was mine, and when they split, Sarah had sworn off men for a while, just as I had sworn off women. It made sense to swear off together, to pool our loathing of the opposite sex and get to share a bed with someone at the same time. Our friends were all paired off, our careers seemed to have hardened into permanence, we were frightened of being left alone for the rest of our lives. Only people of a certain disposition are frightened of being alone for the rest of their lives at twenty-six; we were of that disposition. Everything seemed much later than it was, and after a few months she moved in with me.

We couldn't fill a room. I don't mean that we didn't have enough stuff: she had loads of books (she was an English teacher), and I had hundreds of records, and the flat is pretty poky anyway – I've lived here for over ten years and most days I feel like a cartoon dog in a kennel. I mean that neither of us seemed loud enough, or powerful enough, so that when we were together I was conscious of how the only space we occupied was that taken up by our bodies. We couldn't *project* like some couples can.

Sometimes we tried, when we were out with people even quieter than us; we never talked about why we suddenly became shriller and louder, but I'm sure we both knew that it happened. We did it to compensate for the fact that life was going on elsewhere, that somewhere Michael and Charlie were together, having a better time than us with people more glamorous than us, and making a noise was a sort of defiant gesture, a futile but necessary last stand. (You can see this everywhere you go: young middle-class people whose lives are beginning to disappoint them making too much noise in restaurants and clubs and wine bars. 'Look at me! I'm not as boring as you think I am! I know how to have fun!' Tragic. I'm glad I learned to stay home and sulk.) Ours was a marriage of convenience as cynical and as mutually advantageous as any, and I really thought that I might spend my life with her. I wouldn't have minded. She was OK.

There's a joke I saw in a sitcom once – *Man About the House*, maybe? – a terribly unsound joke, wherein a guy takes a really fat girl with specs out for the evening, gets her drunk, and makes a move on her when he takes her home. 'I'm not that kind of girl!' she shrieks. He looks at her aghast. 'But . . . but you *must* be,' the bloke says. It made me laugh when I was sixteen, but I didn't think about it again until Sarah told me she had met someone else. 'But . . . but you *can't* have,' I wanted to splutter. I don't mean that Sarah was unfanciable – she wasn't, by any means, and anyway this other guy must have fancied her. I just mean that her meeting someone else was contrary to the whole spirit of our arrangement. All we really had in common (our shared admiration of *Diva* did not, if truth be told, last us much beyond the first few months) was that we had been dumped by people, and that on the whole we were against dumping – we were fervent anti-dumpers. So how come I got dumped?

I was being unrealistic, of course. You run the risk of losing anyone who is worth spending time with, unless you are so paranoid about loss that you choose someone unlosable, somebody who could not possibly appeal to anybody else at all. If you're going to go in for this stuff at all, you have to live with the possibility that it won't work out, that somebody called Marco, say, or in this case Tom, is going to come along and upset you. But I didn't see it like that at the time. All I saw then was that I'd moved down a division and that it still hadn't worked out, and this seemed a cause for a great deal of misery and self-pity.

And then I met you, Laura, and we lived together, and now you've moved out. But, you know, you're not offering me anything *new* here; if you want to force your way on to the list, you'll have to do better than this. I'm not as vulnerable as I was when Alison or Charlie dumped me, you haven't changed the whole structure of my daily life like Jackie did, you haven't made me feel bad about myself like Penny did (and there's no way you can humiliate me, like Chris Thomson did), and I'm more robust than I was when Sarah went – I know, despite all the gloom and self-doubt that bubbles up from the deep when you get dumped, that you did not represent my last and best chance of a relationship. So, you know. Nice try. Close, but no cigar. See you around.

now...

ONE

Laura leaves first thing Monday morning with a hold-all and a carrier bag. It's sobering, really, to see how little she is taking with her, this woman who loves her things, her teapots and her books and her prints and the little sculpture she bought in India: I look at the bag and think, Jesus, this is how much she doesn't want to live with me.

We hug at the front door, and she's crying a little.

'I don't really know what I'm doing,' she says.

'I can see that,' I say, which is sort of a joke and sort of not. 'You don't have to go now. You can stay until whenever.'

'Thanks. But we've done the hard part now. I might as well, you know . . .'

'Well, stay for tonight then.'

But she just grimaces, and reaches for the door handle.

It's a clumsy exit. She hasn't got a free hand, but she tries to open the door anyway and can't, so I do it for her, but I'm in the way, so I have to go through on to the landing to let her out, and she has to prop the door open because I haven't got a key, and I have to squeeze back past her to catch the door before it shuts behind her. And that's it.

I regret to say that this great feeling, part liberation and part nervous excitement, enters me somewhere around my toes and sweeps through me in a great wave. I have felt this before, and I know it doesn't mean that much – confusingly, for example, it doesn't mean that I'm going to feel ecstatically happy for the next few weeks. But I do know that I should work with it, enjoy it while it lasts.

This is how I commemorate my return to the Kingdom of the Single: I sit down in my chair, the one that will stay here with me, and pick bits of the stuffing out of the arm; I light a cigarette, even though it is still early and I don't really feel like one, simply because I am now free to smoke in the flat whenever I want, without rows; I wonder whether I have already met the next person I will sleep with, or whether it will be someone currently unknown to me; I wonder what she looks like, and whether we'll do it here, or at her place, and what that place will be like; I decide to have a Chess Records logo painted on the sitting-room wall. (There was a shop in Camden that had them all – Chess, Stax, Motown, Trojan – stencilled in the brickwork beside the entrance, and it looked brilliant. Maybe I could get hold of the guy who did that and ask him to do smaller versions here.) I feel OK. I feel good. I go to work.

My shop is called Championship Vinyl. I sell punk, blues, soul and R&B, a bit of ska, some indie stuff, some sixties pop – everything for the serious record collector, as the ironically old-fashioned writing in the window says. We're in a quiet street in Holloway, carefully placed to attract the bare minimum of walk-past punters; there's no reason to come here at all, unless you live here, and the people that live here don't seem terribly interested in my Stiff Little Fingers white label (twenty-five quid to you – I paid seventeen for it in 1986) or my mono copy of *Blonde On Blonde.*

I get by because of the people who make a special effort to shop here Saturdays – young men, always young men, with John Lennon specs and leather jackets and armfuls of square carrier bags – and because of the mail order: I advertise in the back of the glossy rock magazines, and get letters from young men, always young men, in Manchester and Glasgow and Ottawa, young men who seem to spend a disproportionate amount of their time looking for deleted Smiths singles and 'ORIGINAL NOT RE-RELEASED' underlined Frank Zappa albums. They're as close to being mad as makes no difference.

I'm late to work, and when I get there Dick is already leaning against the door reading a book. He's thirty-one years old, with long, greasy black hair; he's wearing a Sonic Youth T-shirt, a black leather jacket that is trying manfully to suggest that it has seen better days, even though he only bought it a year ago, and a Walkman with a pair of ludicrously large headphones which obscure not only his ears but half his face. The book is a paperback biography of Lou Reed. The carrier bag by his feet – which really has seen better days – advertises a violently fashionable American independent record label; he went to a great deal of trouble to get hold of it, and he gets very nervous when we go anywhere near it. He uses it to carry tapes around; he has heard most of the music in the shop, and would rather bring new stuff to work – tapes from friends, bootlegs he has ordered through the post – than waste his time listening to anything for a second time. ('Want to come to the pub for lunch, Dick?' Barry or I ask him a couple of times a week. He looks mournfully at his little stack of cassettes and sighs. 'I'd love to, but I've got all these to get through.')

'Good morning, Richard.'

He fumbles nervously with the giant headphones, gets one side stuck round his ear, and the other side falls over one eye.

'Oh, hi. Hi, Rob.'

'Sorry I'm late.'

'No, no problem.'

'Good weekend?'

I unlock the shop as he scrabbles around for his stuff.

'All right, yeah, OK. I found the first Liquorice Comfits album in Camden. The one on Testament of Youth. It was never released here. Japanese import only.'

'Great.' I don't know what the fuck he's talking about.

'I'll tape it for you.'

'Thanks.'

''Cos you liked their second one, you said. *Pop, Girls, Etc.* The one with Hattie Jacques on the cover. You didn't see the cover, though. You just had the tape I did for you.'

I'm sure he did tape a Liquorice Comfits album for me, and I'm sure I said I liked it, too. My flat is full of tapes Dick has made me, most of which I've never played.

'How about you, anyway? Your weekend? Any good? No good?'

I cannot imagine what kind of conversation we'd have if I were to tell Dick about my weekend. He'd probably just crumble to dust if I explained that Laura had left. Dick's not big on that sort of thing; in fact, if I were ever to confess anything of a remotely personal nature – that I had a mother and father, say, or that I'd been to school when I was younger – I reckon he'd just blush, and stammer, and ask if I'd heard the new Lemonheads album.

'Somewhere in between. Good bits and bad bits.'

He nods. This is obviously the right answer.

The shop smells of stale smoke, damp, and plastic dust-covers, and it's narrow and dingy and dirty and overcrowded, partly because that's what I wanted – this is what record shops should look like, and only Phil Collins fans bother with those that look as clean and wholesome as a suburban Habitat – and partly because I can't get it together to clean or redecorate it.

There are browser racks on each side, and a couple more in the window, and CDs and cassettes on the walls in glass cases, and that's more or less the size of it; it's just about big enough, provided we don't get any customers, so most days it's just about big enough. The stockroom at the back is bigger than the shop part in the front, but we have no stock, really, just a few piles of second-hand records that nobody can be bothered to price up, so the stockroom is mostly for messing about in. I'm sick of the sight of the place, to be honest. Some days I'm afraid I'll go berserk, rip the Elvis Costello mobile down from the ceiling, throw the 'Country Artists (Male) A–K' rack out into the street, go off to work in a Virgin Megastore and never come back.

Dick puts a record on, some West Coast psychedelic thing, and makes us some coffee while I go through the post; and then we drink the coffee; and then he tries to stuff some records into the bulging, creaking browser racks while I parcel up a couple of mail orders; and then I have a look at the *Guardian* quick crossword while he reads some American import rock magazine; then he has a look at the *Guardian* quick crossword while I read the American import magazine; and before we know it, it's my turn to make the coffee.

At about half-past eleven, an Irish drunk called Johnny stumbles in. He comes to see us about three times a week, and his visits have become choreographed and scripted routines that neither he nor I would want to change. In a hostile and unpredictable world, we rely on each other to provide something to count on.

'Fuck off, Johnny,' I tell him.

'So my money's no good to you?' he says.

'You haven't got any money. And we haven't got anything that you want to buy.'

This is his cue to launch into an enthusiastic rendition of Dana's 'All Kinds Of Everything', which is my cue to come out from behind the counter and lead him back towards the door, which is his cue to hurl himself at one of the browser racks, which is my cue to open the door with one hand, loosen his grip on the rack with the other, and push him out. We devised these moves a couple of years ago, so we've got them off pat now.

Johnny is our only pre-lunch customer. This isn't a job for the wildly ambitious.

*

Barry doesn't show up until after lunch, which isn't unusual. Both Dick and Barry were employed to work part-time, three days each, but shortly after I'd taken them on they both started turning up every day, including Saturdays. I didn't know what to do about it – if they really had nowhere else to go and nothing else to do, I didn't want to, you know, draw attention to it, in case it prompted some sort of spiritual crisis – so I upped their money a bit and left it at that. Barry interpreted the pay rise as a signal to cut his hours back, so I haven't given him one since. That was four years ago, and he's never said anything about it.

He comes into the shop humming a Clash riff. Actually, 'humming' is the wrong word: he's making that guitar noise that all little boys make, the one where you stick your lips out, clench your teeth and go 'DA-DA!' Barry is thirty-three years old.

'Awlright boys? Hey, Dick, what's this music, man? It stinks.' He makes a face and holds his nose. 'Phwooar.'

Barry intimidates Dick, to the extent that Dick rarely says a word when Barry is in the shop. I only get involved when Barry is being really offensive, so I just watch Dick reach for the hi-fi on the shelf above the counter and turn the cassette off.

'Thank fuck for that. You're like a child, Dick. You need watching all the time. I don't know why I should have to do it all, though. Rob, didn't you notice what he was putting on? What are you playing at, man?'

He talks relentlessly, and more or less everything he says is gibberish. He talks a lot about music, but also a lot about books (Terry Pratchett and anything else which features monsters, planets and so on), and films, and women. Pop, girls, etc., like the Liquorice Comfits said. But his conversation is simply enumeration: if he has seen a good film, he will not describe the plot, or how it made him feel, but where it ranks in his best-of-year list, his best-of-all-time list, his best-of-decade list – he thinks and talks in tens and fives, and as a consequence Dick and I do too. And he makes us write lists as well, all the time: 'OK, guys. Top five Dustin Hoffman films.' Or guitar solos, or records made by blind musicians, or Gerry and Sylvia Anderson shows ('I don't believe you've got *Captain Scarlet* at number one, Dick. The guy was immortal! What's fun about that?'), or sweets that come in jars ('If either of you have got Rhubarb and Custard in the top five, I'm resigning now.').

Barry puts his hand into his leather-jacket pocket, produces a tape, puts it in the machine and jacks up the volume. Within seconds the shop is shaking to the bass line of 'Walking On Sunshine', by Katrina and the Waves. It's February. It's cold. It's wet. Laura has gone. I don't want to hear 'Walking On Sunshine'. Somehow it doesn't fit my mood.

'Turn it off, Barry.' I have to shout, like a lifeboat captain in a gale.

'It won't go up any more.'

'I didn't say "up", you fuckwit. I said "off".'

He laughs, and walks through into the stockroom, shouting out the horn parts: 'Da DA! da da da da da-da da-da-da-da.' I turn it off myself, and Barry comes back into the shop.

'What are you doing?'

'I don't want to hear "Walking On Sunshine"!'

'That's my new tape. My Monday morning tape. I made it last night, specially.'

'Yeah, well it's fucking Monday afternoon. You should get out of bed earlier.'

'And you'd have let me play it this morning, would you?'

'No. But at least this way I've got an excuse.'

'Don't you want something to cheer you up? Bring a bit of warmth to your miserable middle-aged bones?'

'Nope.'

'What do you want to hear when you're pissed off then?'

'I don't know. Not "Walking On Sunshine", for a start.'

'OK, I'll wind it on.'

'What's next?'

'"Little Latin Lupe Lu".'

I groan.

'Mitch Ryder and the Detroit Wheels?' Dick asks.

'No. The Righteous Brothers.' You can hear the defensiveness in Barry's voice. He has obviously never heard the Mitch Ryder version.

'Oh. Oh well. Never mind.' Dick would never go so far as to tell Barry that he's messed up, but the implication is clear.

'What?' says Barry, bristling.

'Nothing.'

'No, come on. What's wrong with the Righteous Brothers?'

'Nothing. I just prefer the other one,' says Dick mildly.

'Bollocks.'

'How can it be bollocks to state a preference?' I ask.

'If it's the wrong preference, it's bollocks.'

Dick shrugs and smiles.

'What? What? What's that smug smile for?'

'Leave him alone, Barry. It doesn't matter. We're not listening to fucking "Little Latin Lupe Lu" anyway, so give it a rest.'

'Since when did this shop become a fascist regime?'

'Since you brought that terrible tape in.'

'All I'm trying to do is cheer us up. That's all. Very sorry. Go and put some old sad bastard music on, see if I care.'

'I don't want old sad bastard music on either. I just want something I can ignore.'

'Great. That's the fun thing about working in a record shop, isn't it? Playing things that you don't want to listen to. I thought this tape was going to be, you know, a talking point. I was going to ask you for your top five records to play on a wet Monday morning and all that, and you've gone and ruined it.'

'We'll do it next Monday.'

'What's the point of that?'

And so on, and on, probably for the rest of my working life.

I'd like to do a top five records that make you feel nothing at all; that way, Dick and Barry would be doing me a favour. Me, I'll be playing the Beatles when I get home. *Abbey Road*, probably, although I'll programme the CD to skip out 'Something'. The Beatles were bubblegum cards and *Help* at the Saturday morning cinema and toy plastic guitars and singing 'Yellow Submarine' at the top of my voice in the back row of the coach on school trips. They belong to me, not to me and Laura, or me and Charlie, or me and Alison Ashworth, and though they'll make me feel something, they won't make me feel anything bad.

TWO

I was worried about what it would be like, coming back to the flat tonight, but it's fine: the unreliable sense of well-being I've had since this morning is still with me. And, anyway, it won't always be like this, with all her things around. She'll clear it out soon, and the Marie Celestial air about the place – the half-read Julian Barnes paperback on the bedside table and the knickers in the dirty clothes basket – will vanish. (Women's knickers were a terrible disappointment to me when I embarked on my co-habiting career. I never really recovered from the shock of discovering that women do what we do: they save their best pairs for the nights when they know they are going to sleep with somebody. When you live with a woman, these faded, shrunken tatty M&S scraps suddenly appear on radiators all over the house; your lascivious schoolboy dreams of adulthood as a time when you are surrounded by exotic lingerie for ever and ever amen . . . those dreams crumble to dust.)

I clear away the evidence of last night's traumas – the spare duvet on the sofa, the balled-up paper hankies, the coffee mugs with dog-ends floating in the cold, oily-looking dregs, and then I put the Beatles on, and then when I've listened to *Abbey Road* and the first few tracks of *Revolver*, I open the bottle of white wine that Laura brought home last week, sit down and watch the *Brookside* omnibus that I taped.

In the same way that nuns end up having their periods at the same time, Laura's mum and my mum have mysteriously ended up synchronizing their weekly phone calls. Mine rings first.

'Hello, love, it's me.'

'Hi.'

'Everything all right?'

'Not bad.'

'What sort of week have you had?'

'Oh, you know.'

'How's the shop doing?'

'So-so. Up and down.' Up and down would be great. Up and down would imply that some days are better than others, that customers came and went. This has not been the case, frankly.

'Your dad and I are very worried about this recession.'

'Yeah. You said.'

'You're lucky Laura's doing so well. If it wasn't for her I don't think either of us would ever get off to sleep.'

She's gone, Mum. She's thrown me to the wolves. The bitch has fucked off and left me . . . Nope. Can't do it. This does not seem to be the right time for bad news.

'Heaven knows she's got enough on her plate without having to worry about a shop full of bloomin' old pop records . . .'

How can one describe the way people born before 1940 say the word 'pop'? I have been listening to my parents' sneering one-syllable explosion – heads forward, idiotic look on their faces (because pop fans are idiots) for the time it takes them to spit the word out – for well over two decades.

. . . 'I'm surprised she doesn't make you sell up and get a proper job. It's a wonder she's hung on as long as she has. I would have left you to get on with it years ago.'

Hold on, Rob. Don't let her get to you. Don't rise to the bait. Don't . . . ah, fuck it.

'Well, she has left me to get on with it now, so that should cheer you up.'

'Where's she gone?'

'I don't bloody know. Just . . . gone. Moved out. Disappeared.'

There is a long, long silence. The silence is so long, in fact, that I can watch the whole of a row between Jimmy and Jackie Corkhill without hearing so much as a long-suffering sigh down the receiver.

'Hullo? Anybody there?'

And now I *can* hear something – the sound of my mother crying softly. What is it with mothers? What's happening here? As an adult, you know that as life goes on, you're going to spend more and more time looking after the person who started out looking after you, that's par for the course; but my mum and I swapped roles when I was about nine. Anything bad that has happened to me in the last couple of decades – detentions, bad exam marks, getting thumped, getting bunged from college, splitting up with girlfriends – has ended up like this, with Mum visibly or audibly upset. It would have been better for both of us if I had moved to Australia when I was fifteen, phoned home once a week and reported a sequence of fictitious major triumphs. Most fifteen-year-olds would find it tough, living on their own, on the other side of the world, with no money and no friends and no family and no job and no qualifications, but not me. It would have been a piece of piss compared to listening to this stuff week after week.

It's . . . well, it's *not fair*. 'Snot fair. It's never been fair. Since I left home, all she's done is moan, worry and send cuttings from the local newspaper describing the minor successes of old school friends. Is that good parenting? Not in my book. I want sympathy, understanding, advice and money, and not necessarily in that order, but these are alien concepts in Canning Close.

'I'm all right, if that's what's upsetting you.'

I know that's not what's upsetting her.

'You know that's not what's upsetting me.'

'Well, it bloody well should be, shouldn't it? Shouldn't it? Mum, I've just been dumped. I'm not feeling so good.' And not so bad, either – the Beatles, half a bottle of Chardonnay and *Brookside* have all done their stuff – but I'm not telling her that. 'I can't deal with me, let alone you.'

'I knew this would happen.'

'Well, if you knew it would happen, what are you so cut up about?'

'What are you going to *do*, Rob?'

'I'm going to drink the rest of a bottle of wine in front of the box. Then I'm going to bed. Then I'll get up and go to work.'

'And after that?'

'Meet a nice girl, and have children.'

This is the right answer.

'If only it was that easy.'

'It is, I promise. Next time I speak to you, I'll have it sorted.'

She's almost smiling. I can hear it. I'm beginning to see some light at the end of the long, dark telephonic tunnel.

'But what did Laura say? Do you know why she's gone?'

'Not really.'

'Well, I do.'

This is momentarily alarming until I understand what she's on about.

'It's nothing to do with marriage, Mum, if that's what you mean.'

'So *you* say. I'd like to hear her side of it.'

Cool it. Don't let her . . . Don't rise . . . ah, fuck it.

'Mum, how many more times, for Christ's sake? Laura didn't *want* to get married. She's not that sort of girl. To coin a phrase. That's not what happens now.'

'I don't know what does happen now. Apart from you meet someone, you move in together, she goes. You meet someone, you move in together, she goes.'

Fair point, I guess.

'Shut up, Mum.'

Mrs Lydon rings a few minutes later.

'Hello, Rob. It's Janet.'

'Hello, Mrs L.'

'How are you?'

'Fine. You?'

'Fine, thanks.'

'And Ken?'

Laura's dad isn't too clever – he has angina, and had to retire from work early.

'Not too bad. Up and down. You know. Is Laura there?'

Interesting. She hasn't phoned home. Some indication of guilt, maybe?

'She's not, I'm afraid. She's round at Liz's. Shall I get her to give you a ring?'

'If she's not too late back.'

'No problem.'

And that's the last time we will ever speak, probably. 'No problem': the last words I ever say to somebody I have been reasonably close to before our lives take different directions. Weird, eh? You spend Christmas at somebody's house, you worry about their operations, you give them hugs and kisses and flowers, you see them in their dressing gown . . . and then, bang, that's it. Gone for ever. And sooner or later there will be another mum, another Christmas, more varicose veins. They're all the same. Only the addresses, and the colours of the dressing gown, change.

THREE

I'm in the back of the shop, trying to tidy it up a bit, when I overhear a conversation between Barry and a customer – male, middle-aged, from the sound of him, and certainly not hip in any way whatsoever.

'I'm looking for a record for my daughter. For her birthday. "I Just Called To Say I Love You". Have you got it?'

'Oh, yeah,' says Barry. ''Course we've got it.'

I know for a fact that the only Stevie Wonder single we have at the moment is 'Don't Drive Drunk'; we've had it for donkey's years and have never managed to get rid of it, even at sixty pence. What's he playing at?

I go out the front to see what's going on. Barry is standing there, smiling at him; the guy looks a bit flustered.

'Could I have it then?' He half-smiles with relief, as if he were a little boy who has remembered to say 'please' at the very last minute.

'No, I'm sorry, but you can't.'

The customer, older than I first thought and wearing a cloth cap and a dirty beige raincoat, stands rooted to the spot; I didn't want to come into this noisy dark hell-hole in the first place, you can see him thinking, and now I'm being messed about.

'Why not?'

'Sorry?' Barry's playing Neil Young, and Neil has just this second gone electric.

'Why not?'

'Because it's sentimental, tacky crap, that's why not. Do we look like the sort of shop that sells fucking "I Just Called To Say I Love You", eh? Now, be off with you, and don't waste our time.'

The old guy turns round and walks out, and Barry chuckles merrily.

'Thanks a lot, Barry.'

'What's up?'

'You just drove a fucking customer away, that's what's up.'

'We didn't have what he wanted. I was just having some fun, and I never cost you a penny.'

'That's not the point.'

'Oh, so what's the point, then?'

'The point is, I don't want you talking to anyone who comes in here like that ever again.'

'Why not? You think that silly old duffer was going to become a regular?'

'No, but . . . listen Barry, the shop isn't doing so well. I know we used to take the piss out of anyone who asked for anything we didn't like, but it's got to stop.'

'Bollocks. If we'd had the record, I would have sold it to him, and you'd be fifty pee or a quid better off, and you'd never have seen him again. Big fucking deal.'

'What harm has he ever done you?'

'You know what harm he's done me. He offended me with his terrible taste.'

'It wasn't even his terrible taste. It was his daughter's.'

'You're going soft in your old age, Rob. There was a time when you'd have chased him out the shop and up the road.'

He's right; there was. It feels like a long time ago now. I just can't muster that sort of anger any more.

Tuesday night I reorganize my record collection; I often do this at periods of emotional stress. There are some people who would find this a pretty dull way to spend an evening, but I'm not one of them. This is my life, and it's nice to be able to wade in it, immerse your arms in it, touch it.

When Laura was here I had the records arranged alphabetically; before that I had them filed in chronological order, beginning with Robert Johnson, and ending with, I don't know, Wham!, or somebody African, or whatever else I was listening to when Laura and I met. Tonight, though, I fancy something different, so I try to remember the order I bought them in: that way I hope to write my own autobiography, without having to do anything like pick up a pen. I pull the records off the shelves, put them in piles all over the sitting-room floor, look for *Revolver*, and go on from there, and when I've finished I'm flushed with a sense of self, because this, after all, is who I am. I like being able to see how I got from Deep Purple to Howling Wolf in twenty-five moves; I am no longer pained by the memory of listening to 'Sexual Healing' all the way through a period of enforced celibacy, or embarrassed by the reminder of forming a rock club at school, so that I and my fellow fifth-formers could get together and talk about Ziggy Stardust and *Tommy*.

But what I really like is the feeling of security I get from my new filing system; I have made myself more complicated than I really am. I have a couple of thousand records, and you have to be me – or, at the very least, a doctor of Flemingology – to know how to find any of them. If I want to play, say, *Blue* by Joni Mitchell, I have to remember that I bought it for someone in the autumn of 1983, and thought better of giving it to her, for reasons I don't really want to go into. Well, you don't know any of that, so you're knackered, really, aren't you? You'd have to ask me to dig it out for you, and for some reason I find this enormously comforting.

A weird thing happens on Wednesday. Johnny comes in, sings 'All Kinds Of Everything', tries to grab a handful of album covers. And we're doing our little dance out of the shop when he twists away from me, looks up and says, 'Are you married?'

'I'm not, Johnny, no. You?'

He laughs into my armpit, a terrifying, maniacal chuckle that smells

of drink and tobacco and vomit and ends in an explosion of phlegm.
'You think I'd be in this fucking state if I had a wife?'

I don't say anything – I just concentrate on tangoing him towards the door – but Johnny's blunt, sad self-appraisal has attracted Barry's attention – maybe he's still cross because I told him off yesterday – and he leans over the counter. 'It doesn't help, Johnny. Rob's got a lovely woman at home, and look at him. He's in a terrible way. Bad haircut. Spots. Terrible jumper. Awful socks. The only difference between you and him, Johnny, is that you don't have to pay rent on a shop every week.'

I get this sort of stuff from Barry all the time. Today, though, I can't take it and I give him a look that is supposed to shut him up, but which he interprets as an invitation to abuse me further.

'Rob, I'm doing this for your own good. That's the worst jumper I've ever seen. I have never seen a jumper that bad worn by anybody I'm on speaking terms with. It's a disgrace to the human race. David Coleman wouldn't wear that on *A Question of Sport*. John Noakes would have had it arrested for fashion crimes. Val Doonican would take one look at that and . . .'

I hurl Johnny out on to the pavement, slam the door shut, race across the shop floor, pick Barry up by the lapels of his brown suede jacket, and tell him that if I have to listen to one more word of his useless, pathetic, meaningless babble again in my entire life I will kill him. When I let him go I'm shaking with anger.

Dick comes out from the stockroom and hops up and down.

'Hey, guys,' he whispers. 'Hey.'

'What are you, some kind of fucking idiot?' Barry asks me. 'If this jacket's torn, pal, you're gonna pay big.' That's what he says, 'pay big'. Jesus. And then he stomps out of the shop.

I go and sit down on the stepladder in the stockroom, and Dick hovers in the doorway.

'Are you all right?'

'Yeah. I'm sorry.' I take the easy way out. 'Look, Dick, I haven't got a lovely woman at home. She's gone. And if we ever see Barry again, perhaps you could tell him that.'

'Of course I will, Rob. No problem. No problem at all. I'll tell him next time I see him,' Dick says.

I don't say anything. I just nod.

'I've . . . I've got some other stuff to tell him anyway, so it's no problem.

I'll just tell him about, you know, Laura, when I tell him the other stuff,' Dick says.

'Fine.'

'I'll start with your news before I tell him mine, obviously. Mine isn't much, really, just about someone playing at the Harry Lauder tomorrow night. So I'll tell him before that. Good news and bad news, kind of thing,' Dick says.

He laughs nervously. 'Or rather, bad news and good news, because he likes this person playing at the Harry Lauder.' A look of horror crosses his face. 'I mean, he liked Laura too, I didn't mean that. And he likes you. It's just that . . .'

I tell him that I know what he meant, and ask him to make me a cup of coffee.

'Sure. Course. Rob, look. Do you want to . . . have a chat about it, kind of thing?'

For a moment, I'm almost tempted: a heart-to-heart with Dick would be a once-in-a-lifetime experience. But I tell him there's nothing to say, and for a moment I thought he was going to hug me.

FOUR

The three of us go to the Harry Lauder. Things are cool with Barry now; Dick filled him in when he came back to the shop, and the two of them are doing their best to look after me. Barry has made me an elaborately annotated compilation tape, and Dick now rephrases his questions four or five times instead of the usual two or three. And they more or less insisted that I came to this gig with them.

It's an enormous pub, the Lauder, with ceilings so high that the cigarette smoke gathers above your head like a cartoon cloud. It's tatty, and draughty, and the benches have had the stuffing slashed out of them, and the staff are surly, and the regular clientele are either terrifying or unconscious, and the toilets are wet and smelly, and there's nothing to eat in the evening, and the wine is hilariously bad, and the bitter is fizzy and much too cold; in other words, it's a run-of-the-mill north London pub. We don't come here that often, even though it's only up the road, because the bands that usually play here are the kind of abysmal second-division punk group you'd pay half your wages not to listen to. Occasionally, though, like tonight, they stick on some obscure American folk/country artist, someone with a cult following which could arrive together in the same car. The pub's nearly a third full, which is pretty good, and when we walk in Barry points out Andy Kershaw and a guy who writes for *Time Out*. This is as buzzy as the Lauder ever gets.

The woman we have come to see is called Marie LaSalle; she's got a couple of solo records out on an independent label, and once had one of her songs covered by Nanci Griffith. Dick says she lives here now; he read somewhere that she finds England more open to the kind of music she makes, which means, presumably, that we're cheerfully indifferent rather than actively hostile. There are a lot of single men here – not single as in unmarried, but single as in no friends. In this sort of company the three of us – me morose and monosyllabic, Dick nervy and shy, Barry solicitously self-censoring – constitute a wild and massive office outing.

There's no support, just a crappy PA system squelching out tasteful country-rock, and people stand around cradling their pints and reading the handbills that were thrust at them on the way in. Marie LaSalle comes on stage (as it were – there is a little platform and a couple of microphones a few yards in front of us) at nine; by five past nine, to my intense irritation and embarrassment, I'm in tears, and the feel-nothing world that I've been living in for the last few days has vanished.

There are many songs that I've been trying to avoid since Laura went, but the song that Marie LaSalle opens with, the song that makes me cry, is not one of them. The song that makes me cry has never made me cry before; in fact, the song that makes me cry used to make me puke. When it was a hit, I was at college, and Charlie and I used to roll our eyes and stick our fingers down our throats when somebody – invariably a geography student, or a girl training to be a primary school teacher (and I don't see how you can be accused of snobbishness if all you are doing is stating the plain, simple truth) put it on the jukebox in the bar. The song that makes me cry is Marie LaSalle's version of Peter Frampton's 'Baby, I Love Your Way'.

Imagine standing with Barry, and Dick, in his Lemonheads T-shirt, and listening to a cover version of a Peter Frampton song, and blubbing! Peter Frampton! 'Show Me The Way'! That perm! That stupid bag thing he used to blow into, which made his guitar sound like Donald Duck! *Frampton Comes Alive*, top of the American rock charts for something like seven hundred and twenty years, and bought, presumably, by every brain-dead, coke-addled airhead in LA! I understand that I was in dire need of symptoms to help me understand that I have been deeply traumatized by recent events, but did they have to be this extreme? Couldn't God have settled for something just mildly awful – an old Diana Ross hit, say, or an Elton John original?

And it doesn't stop there. As a result of Marie LaSalle's cover version of 'Baby, I Love Your Way' ('I know I'm not supposed to like that song, but I do,' she says with a cheeky smile when she's finished), I find myself in two apparently contradictory states: a) I suddenly miss Laura with a passion that has been entirely absent for the last four days, and b) I fall in love with Marie LaSalle.

These things happen. They happen to men, at any rate. Or to this particular man. Sometimes. It's difficult to explain why or how you can find yourself pulled in two different directions at once, and obviously a certain amount of dreamy irrationality is a prerequisite. But there's a logic to it, too. Marie is pretty, in that nearly cross-eyed American way – she looks like a slightly plumper, post-*Partridge Family*, pre-*LA Law* Susan Dey – and if you were going to develop a spontaneous and pointless crush on somebody, you could do a lot worse. (One Saturday morning, I woke up, switched on the TV and found myself smitten with Sarah Greene from *Going Live*, a devotion I kept very quiet about at the time.) And she's charming, as far as I can tell, and not without talent: once she has got Peter Frampton out of her system, she sticks to her own songs, and they're good, affecting and funny and delicate. All my life I have wanted to go to bed with – no, have a relationship with – a musician: I'd want her to write songs at home, and ask me what I thought of them, and maybe include one of our private jokes in the lyrics, and thank me in the sleeve notes, maybe even include a picture of me on the inside cover, in the background somewhere, and I could watch her play live from the back, in the wings (although I'd look a bit of a berk at the Lauder, where there are no wings: I'd be standing on my own, in full view of everybody).

The Marie bit is easy enough to understand, then. The Laura thing takes a bit more explaining, but what it is, I think, is this: sentimental music has this great way of taking you back somewhere at the same time that it takes you forward, so you feel nostalgic and hopeful all at the same time. Marie's the hopeful, forward part of it – maybe not her, necessarily, but somebody like her, somebody who can turn things around for me. (Exactly that: I always think that women are going to save me, lead me through to a better life, that they can change and redeem me.) And Laura's the backward part, the last person I loved, and when I hear those sweet, sticky acoustic guitar chords I reinvent our time together, and, before I know it, we're in the car trying to sing the harmonies on 'Sloop John B' and getting it wrong and laughing. We never did that in real life. We never sang in the car, and we certainly never laughed when we got something wrong. This is why I shouldn't be listening to pop music at the moment.

Tonight, it really doesn't matter either way. Marie could come up to me as I was leaving and ask if I wanted to go for something to eat; or I could get home, and Laura would be sitting there, sipping tea and waiting nervously for absolution. Both of these daydreams sound equally attractive, and either would make me very happy.

Marie takes a break after an hour or so. She sits on the stage and swigs from a bottle of Budweiser, and some guy comes out with a box of cassettes and puts them on the stage beside her. They're £5.99, but they haven't got any pennies, so really they're six quid. We all buy one from her, and to our horror she speaks to us.

'You enjoying yourselves?'

We nod.

'Good, 'cos I'm enjoying myself.'

'Good,' I say, and that seems to be the best I can do for the moment.

I've only got a tenner, so I stand there like a prawn while the guy fishes around for four pound coins.

'You live in London now, is that right?' I ask her.

'Yup. Not far from here, actually.'

'You like it?' Barry asks. Good one. I wouldn't have thought of that.

'It's OK. Hey, you guys might be the sort to know. Are there any good record shops up around here, or do I have to go into the West End?'

What's the use of taking offence? We are the sort of guys who would know about record shops. That's what we look like, and that's what we are.

Barry and Dick almost fall over in their haste to explain.

'He's got one!'

'He's got one!'

'In Holloway!'

'Just up the Seven Sisters Road!'

'Championship Vinyl!'

'We work there!'

'You'd love it!'

'Come in!'

She laughs at the onslaught of enthusiasm.

'What d'you sell?'

'Bit of everything good. Blues, country, vintage soul, new wave . . .'

'Sounds great.'

Somebody else wants to talk to her, so she smiles nicely at us and turns round. We go back to where we were standing.

'What did you tell her about the shop for?' I ask the others.

'I didn't know it was classified information,' says Barry. 'I mean, I know we don't have any customers, but I thought that was a bad thing, not, like, a business strategy.'

'She won't spend any money.'

'No, course not. That's why she was asking if we knew any good record shops. She just wants to come in and waste our time.'

I know I'm being stupid, but I don't want her coming to my shop. If she came into my shop, I might really get to like her, and then I'd be waiting for her to come in all the time, and then when she did come in I'd be nervous and stupid, and probably end up asking her out for a drink in some cack-handed roundabout way, and either she wouldn't catch my drift, and I'd feel an idiot, or she'd turn me down flat, and I'd feel an idiot. And on the way home after the gig, I'm already wondering whether she'll come tomorrow, and whether it will mean anything if she does, and if it does mean something, then which one of us it will mean something to, although Barry is probably a non-starter.

Fuck. I hate all this stuff. How old do you have to get before it stops?

When I get home there are two ansaphone messages, one from Laura's friend Liz and one from Laura. They go like this:

1) Rob, it's Liz. Just phoning up to see, well, to see if you're OK. Give us a ring sometime. Um . . . I'm not taking sides. Yet. Lots of love, bye.

2) Hi, it's me. There are a couple of things I need. Can you call me at work in the morning? Thanks.

Mad people could read all sorts of things into either of these calls; sane people would come to the conclusion that the first caller is warm and affectionate, and that the second doesn't give a shit. I'm not mad.

FIVE

I call Laura first thing. I feel sick, dialling the number, and even sicker when the receptionist puts me through. She used to know who I am, but now there's nothing in her voice at all. Laura wants to come round on Saturday afternoon, when I'm at work, to pick up some more underwear, and that's fine by me; we should have stopped there, but I try to have a different sort of conversation, and she doesn't like it because she's at work, but I persist, and she hangs up on me in tears. And I feel like a pillock, but I couldn't stop myself. I never can.

I wonder what she'd say, if she knew that I was simultaneously uptight about Marie coming into the shop? We have just had a phone call in which I suggested that she'd fucked up my life and, for the duration of the call, I believed it. But now – and I can do this with no trace of bemusement or self-dissatisfaction – I'm worrying about what to wear, and whether I look better stubbly or clean-shaven, and about what music I should play in the shop today.

Sometimes it seems as though the only way a man can judge his own niceness, his own *decency*, is by looking at his relationships with women – or rather, with prospective or current sexual partners. It's easy enough to be nice to your mates. You can buy them a drink, make them a tape, ring them up to see if they're OK . . . there are any number of quick and painless methods of turning yourself into a Good Bloke. When it comes to girlfriends, though, it's much trickier to be consistently honourable. One moment you're ticking along, cleaning the toilet bowl and expressing your feelings and doing all the other things that a modern chap is supposed to do; the next, you're manipulating and sulking and double-dealing and fibbing with the best of them. I can't work it out.

I phone Liz early afternoon. She's nice to me. She says how sorry she is, what a good couple she thought we made, that I have done Laura good, given her a centre, brought her out of herself, allowed her to have fun, turned her into a nicer, calmer, more relaxed person, given her an interest in something other than work. Liz doesn't use these words, as such – I'm interpreting. But this is what she means, I think, when she says we made a good couple. She asks how I am, and whether I'm looking after myself; she tells me that she doesn't think much of this Ian guy. We arrange to meet for a drink some time next week. I hang up.

Which fucking Ian guy?

Marie comes into the shop shortly afterwards. All three of us are there. I'm playing her tape, and when I see her walk in I try to turn it off before she notices, but I'm not quick enough, so I end up turning it off just as she begins to say something about it, and then turning it back on again, then blushing. She laughs. I go to the stockroom and don't come out. Barry and Dick sell her seventy quid's worth of cassettes.

Which fucking Ian guy?

Barry explodes into the stockroom. 'We're only on the guest list for Marie's gig at the White Lion, that's all. All three of us.'

In the last half-hour, I have humiliated myself in front of somebody I'm interested in, and found out, I think, that my ex was having an affair. I don't want to know about the guest list at the White Lion.

'That's really, really great, Barry. The guest list at the White Lion! All we've got to do is get to Putney and back and we've saved ourselves a fiver each. What it is to have influential friends, eh?'

'We can go in your car.'

'It's not my car, is it? It's Laura's. Laura's got it. So we're two hours on the tube, or we get a minicab, which'll cost us, ooh, a fiver each. Fucking great.'

Barry gives a what-can-you-do-with-this-guy shrug and walks out. I feel bad, but I don't say anything to him.

I don't know anybody called Ian. Laura doesn't know anybody called Ian. We've been together three years and I've never heard her mention an Ian. There's no Ian at her office. She hasn't got any friends called Ian, and she hasn't got any girlfriends with boyfriends called Ian. I won't say that she has never met anyone called Ian in the whole of her life – there must have been one at college, although she went to an all-girls school – but I am almost certain that since 1989 she has been living in an Ianless universe.

And this certitude, this Ian-atheism, lasts until I get home. On the windowsill where we put the post, just inside the communal front door, there are three letters amidst the takeaway menus and the minicab cards: a bill for me, a bank statement for Laura . . . and a TV licence reminder for Mr I. Raymond (Ray to his friends and, more pertinently, to his neighbours), the guy who until about six weeks ago lived upstairs.

I'm shaking when I get into the flat, and I feel sick. I know it's him; I knew it was him the moment I saw the letter. I remember Laura going up to see him a couple of times; I remember Laura . . . not *flirting*, exactly, but certainly flicking her hair more often, and grinning more inanely, than seemed to be strictly necessary when he came down for a drink last Christmas. He would be just her type – little-boy-lost, right-on, caring, just enough melancholy in his soul to make him appear interesting. I never liked him much then, and I fucking hate him now.

How long? How often? The last time I spoke to Ray – Ian – the night before he moved . . . was something going on then? Did she sneak upstairs on nights when I was out? Do John and Melanie, the couple in the ground-floor flat, know anything about this? I spend a long time looking for the change-of-address card he gave us, but it's gone, ominously and significantly – unless I chucked it, in which case strike the ominous significance. (What would I do if I found it? Give him a ring? Drop round, and see if he's got company?)

I'm starting to remember things now: his dungarees; his music (African, Latin, Bulgarian, whatever fucking world music fad was trendy that week); his hysterical, nervous, nerve-jangling laugh; the terrible cooking smells that used to pollute the stairway; the visitors that used to stay too late and drink too much and leave too noisily. I can't remember anything good about him at all.

I manage to block out the worst, most painful, most disturbing memory until I go to bed, when I hear the woman who lives up there now stomping around and banging wardrobe doors. This is the very worst thing, the thing that would bring anybody (any man?) in my position out in the coldest and clammiest of sweats: *we used to listen to him having sex.* We could hear the noises he made; we could hear the noises she made (and there were two or three different partners in the time the three of us – the four of us, if you count whoever was in Ray's bed – were separated by a few square metres of creaking floorboard and flaking plaster).

'He goes on long enough,' I said one night, when we were both lying awake, staring at the ceiling. 'I should be so lucky,' said Laura. This was a joke. We laughed. Ha, ha, we went. Ha, ha, ha. I'm not laughing now. Never has a joke filled me with such nausea and paranoia and insecurity and self-pity and dread and doubt.

When a woman leaves a man, and the man is unhappy (and yes, finally, after all the numbness and the silly optimism and the who-cares shrug of the shoulders, I am unhappy – although I would still like to be included somewhere in the cover shot of Marie's next album) . . . is this what it's all about? Sometimes I think so, and sometimes I don't. I went through this period, after the Charlie and Marco thing, of imagining them together, *at it*, and Charlie's face contorted with a passion that I was never able to provoke.

I should say, even though I do not feel like saying it (I want to run myself down, feel sorry for myself, celebrate my inadequacies – that's what you do at times like these), that I think things were OK in That Department. I think. But in my fearful imaginings Charlie was as abandoned and as noisy as any character in a porn film. She was Marco's plaything, she responded to his every touch with shrieks of orgasmic delight. No woman in the history of the world had better sex than the sex Charlie had with Marco in my head.

But that was nothing. That had no basis in reality at all. For all I know, Marco and Charlie never even consummated their relationship and Charlie has spent the intervening decade trying – but failing miserably – to recapture the quiet, undemonstrative ecstasy of the nights that we spent together. I know, however, that Ian was something of a demon lover; so does Laura. I could hear it all; so could Laura. In truth, it pissed me off; I thought it pissed her off, too. Now I'm not so sure. Is this why she went? Because she wanted a bit of what was happening upstairs?

I don't really know why it matters so much. Ian could be better at talking than me, or cooking, or working, or housework, or saving money, or earning money, or spending money, or understanding books or films; he could be nicer than me, better-looking, more intelligent, cleaner, more generous-spirited, more helpful, a better human being in any way you care to mention . . . and I wouldn't mind. Really. I accept and understand that you can't be good at everything, and I am tragically unskilled in some very important areas. But sex is different; knowing that a successor is better in bed is impossible to take, and I don't know why.

I know enough to know that this is daft. I know, for example, that the best sex I have ever had was not important; the best sex I have ever had was with a girl called Rosie, whom I slept with just four times. It wasn't enough (the good sex, I mean, not the four times, which were more than enough). She drove me mad, and I drove her mad and the fact that we had the knack of being able to come at the same time (and this, it seems to me, is what people mean when they talk about good sex, no matter what Dr Ruth tells you about sharing and consideration and pillow talk and variety and positions and handcuffs) counted for nothing.

So what is it that sickens me so much about 'Ian' and Laura? Why do I care so much about how long he can go on for and how long I could go on for and what noises she made with me and what noises she makes with him? Just, I guess, this in the end: that I still hear Chris Thomson, the Neanderthal, testosterone-crazed, fourth-year adulterer, calling me a spastic and telling me he has knobbed my girlfriend. And that voice still makes me feel bad.

During the night, I have one of those dreams that aren't really dreams at all, just stuff about Laura fucking Ray, and Marco fucking Charlie, and I'm pleased to wake up in the middle of the night, because it means stopping the dream. But the pleasure only lasts a few seconds and then everything sinks in: that somewhere Laura really is fucking Ray (maybe not exactly now, because it's 3.56 a.m., although with his stamina – his *inability to climax*, ha ha – you never know), and I'm here, in this stupid little flat, on my own, and I'm thirty-five years old, and I own a tiny failing business, and my friends don't seem to be friends at all but people whose phone numbers I haven't lost. And if I went back to sleep and slept for forty years and woke up without any teeth to the sound of Melody Radio in an old people's home, I wouldn't worry that much, because the worst of life, i.e. the rest of it, would be over. And I wouldn't even have had to kill myself.

It's only just beginning to occur to me that it's important to have something going on somewhere, at work or at home, otherwise you're just clinging on. If I lived in Bosnia, then not having a girlfriend wouldn't seem like the most important thing in the world, but here in Crouch End it does. You need as much ballast as possible to stop you floating away; you need people around you, things going on, otherwise life is like some film where the money ran out, and there are no sets, or locations, or supporting actors, and it's just one bloke on his own staring into the camera with nothing to do and nobody to speak to, and who'd believe in this character then? I've got to get more stuff, more clutter, more *detail* in here, because at the moment I'm in danger of falling off the edge.

'Have you got any soul?' a woman asks the next afternoon. That depends, I feel like saying; some days yes, some days no. A few days ago I was right out; now I've got loads, too much, more than I can handle. I wish I could spread it a bit more evenly, I want to tell her, get a better balance, but I can't seem to get it sorted. I can see she wouldn't be interested in my internal stock control problems though, so I simply point to where I keep the soul I have, right by the exit, just next to the blues.

SIX

Exactly one week after Laura has gone I get a call from a woman in Wood Green who has some singles she thinks I might be interested in. I normally don't bother with house clearance, but this woman seems to know what she's talking about: she mutters about white labels and picture sleeves and all sorts of other things that suggest we're not just talking about half a dozen scratched Electric Light Orchestra records that her son left behind when he moved out.

Her house is enormous, the sort of place which seems to have meandered to Wood Green from another part of London, and she's not very nice. She's mid-to-late forties, with a dodgy tan and a suspiciously taut-looking face; and though she's wearing jeans and a T-shirt, the jeans have the name of an Italian where the name of Mr Wrangler or Mr Levi should be, and the T-shirt has a lot of jewellery stuck to the front of it, arranged in the shape of the CND sign.

She doesn't smile, or offer me a cup of coffee, or ask me whether I found the place OK despite the freezing, driving rain that prevented me from seeing my *A–Z* in front of my face. She just shows me into a study off the hall, turns the light on, and points out the singles – there are hundreds of them, all in custom-made wooden boxes – on the top shelf, and leaves me to get on with it.

There are no books on the shelves that line the walls, just albums, CDs, cassettes and hi-fi equipment; the cassettes have little numbered stickers on them, always a sign of a serious person. There are a couple of guitars leaning against the walls, and some sort of computer that looks as though it might be able to do something musical if you were that way inclined.

I climb up on a chair and start pulling the singles boxes down. There are seven or eight in all, and, though I try not to look at what's in them as I put them on the floor, I catch a glimpse of the first one in the last box: it's a James Brown single on King, thirty years old, and I begin to prickle with anticipation.

When I start going through them properly, I can see straight away that it's the haul I've always dreamed of finding, ever since I began collecting records. There are fan club-only Beatles singles, and the first half-dozen Who singles, and Elvis originals from the early sixties, and loads of rare blues and soul singles, and . . . *there's a copy of 'God Save The Queen' by the Sex Pistols on A&M!* I have never even seen one of these! I have never even seen anyone who's seen one! And oh no oh no oh God – 'You Left The Water Running' by Otis Redding, released seven years after his death, withdrawn immediately by his widow because she didn't . . .

'What d'you reckon?' She's leaning against the door frame, arms folded, half-smiling at whatever ridiculous face I'm making.

'It's the best collection I've ever seen.' I have no idea what to offer her. This lot must be worth at least six or seven grand, and she knows it. Where am I going to get that kind of money from?

'Give me fifty quid and you can take every one away with you today.'

I look at her. We're now officially in Joke Fantasy Land, where little old ladies pay good money to persuade you to cart off their Chippendale furniture. Except I am not dealing with a little old lady, and she knows perfectly well that what she has here is worth a lot more than fifty quid. What's going on?

'Are these stolen?'

She laughs. 'Wouldn't really be worth my while, would it, lugging all this lot through someone's window for fifty quid? No, they belong to my husband.'

'And you're not getting on too well with him at the moment?'

'He's in Spain with a twenty-three-year-old. A friend of my daughter's. He had the *fucking* cheek to phone up and ask to borrow some money and I refused, so he asked me to sell his singles collection and send him a cheque for whatever I got, minus ten per cent commission. Which reminds me. Can you make sure you give me a five-pound note? I want to frame it and put it on the wall.'

'They must have taken him a long time to get together.'

'Years. This collection is as close as he has ever come to an achievement.'

'Does he work?'

'He calls himself a musician, but . . .' she scowls her disbelief and contempt. 'He just sponges off me and sits around on his fat arse staring at record labels.'

Imagine coming home and finding your Elvis singles and your James Brown singles and your Chuck Berry singles flogged off for nothing out of sheer spite. What would you do? What would you say?

'Look, can't I pay you properly? You don't have to tell him what you got. You could send the forty-five quid anyway, and blow the rest. Or give it to charity. Or something.'

'That wasn't part of the deal. I want to be poisonous but fair.'

'I'm sorry, but it's just . . . I don't want any part of this.'

'Suit yourself. There are plenty of others who will.'

'Yeah, I know. That's why I'm trying to find a compromise. What about fifteen hundred? They're probably worth four times that.'

'Sixty.'

'Thirteen.'

'Seventy-five.'

'Eleven. That's my lowest offer.'

'And I won't take a penny more than ninety.' We're both smiling now. It's hard to imagine another set of circumstances that could result in this kind of negotiation.

'He could afford to come home then, you see, and that's the last thing I want.'

'I'm sorry, but I think you'd better talk to someone else.' When I get back to the shop I'm going to burst into tears and cry like a baby for a month, but I can't bring myself to do it to this guy.

'Fine.'

I stand up to go, and then get back on my knees: I just want one last, lingering look.

'Can I buy this Otis Redding single off you?'

'Sure. Ten pee.'

'Oh, come on. Let me give you a tenner for this, and you can give the rest away for all I care.'

'OK. Because you took the trouble to come up here. And because you've got principles. But that's it. I'm not selling them to you one by one.'

So I go to Wood Green and I come back with a mint-condition 'You Left The Water Running', which I pick up for a tenner. That's not a bad morning's work. Barry and Dick will be impressed. But if they ever find out about Elvis and James Brown and Jerry Lee Lewis and the Pistols and the Beatles and the rest, they will suffer immediate and possibly dangerous traumatic shock, and I will have to counsel them, and . . .

How come I ended up siding with the bad guy, the man who's left his wife and taken himself off to Spain with some nymphette? Why can't I bring myself to feel whatever it is his wife is feeling? Maybe I should go home and flog Laura's sculpture to someone who wants to smash it to pieces and use it for scrap; maybe that would do me some good. But I know I won't. All I can see is that guy's face when he gets his pathetic cheque through the mail, and I can't help but feel desperately, painfully sorry for him.

It would be nice to report that life is full of exotic incidents like this, but it isn't. Dick tapes me the first Liquorice Comfits album, as promised; Jimmy and Jackie Corkhill stop arguing, temporarily; Laura's mum doesn't ring, but my mum does. She thinks Laura might be more interested in me if I did some evening classes. We agree to differ or, at any rate, I hang up on her. And Dick, Barry and I go by minicab to the White Lion to see Marie, and our names are indeed on the guest list. The ride costs exactly fifteen quid, but that doesn't include the tip, and bitter is two pounds a pint. The White Lion is smaller than the Lauder, so it's half-full rather than two-thirds empty, and it's much nicer, too, and there's even a support act, some terrible local singer-songwriter for whom the world ended just after 'Tea For The Tillerman' by Cat Stevens, not with a bang but a wimp.

The good news: 1) I don't cry during 'Baby, I Love Your Way', although I do feel slightly sick. 2) We get a mention: 'Is that Barry and Dick and Rob I see down there? Nice to see you, fellas.' And then she says to the audience, 'Have you ever been to their shop? Championship Vinyl in north London? You really should.' And people turn round to look at us, and we look at each other sheepishly, and Barry is on the verge of giggling with excitement, the berk. 3) I still want to be on an album cover somewhere, despite the fact that I was violently sick when I got to work this morning because I'd been up half the night smoking roll-ups made from dog-ends and drinking banana liqueur and missing Laura. (Is that good news? Maybe it's bad news, definite, final proof that I'm mad, but it's good news in that I still have an ambition of sorts, and that Melody Radio is not my only vision of the future.)

The bad news: 1) Marie brings someone out to sing with her for her encore. A bloke. Someone who shares her microphone with her with an intimacy I don't like, and sings harmonies on 'Love Hurts', and looks at her while he's doing so in a way that suggests that he's ahead of me in the queue for the album shoot. Marie still looks like Susan Dey, and this guy – she introduces him as 'T-Bone Taylor, the best-kept secret in Texas' – looks like a prettier version of Daryl Hall of Hall and Oates, if you can imagine such a creature. He's got long blond hair, and cheekbones, and he's well over nine feet tall, but he's got muscles too (he's wearing a denim waistcoat and no shirt) and a voice that makes that man who does the Guinness adverts sound soppy, a voice so deep that it seems to land with a thud on the stage and roll towards us like a cannonball.

I know my sexual confidence is not high at the moment, and I know that women are not necessarily interested in long blond hair, cheekbones and height; that sometimes they are looking for shortish dark hair, no cheekbones and width, but even so! Look at them! Susan Dey and Daryl Hall! Entwining the naked melody lines from 'Love Hurts'! Mingling their saliva, almost! Just as well I wore my favourite shirt when she came into the shop the other day, otherwise I wouldn't have stood a chance.

There is no other bad news. That's it.

When the gig finishes I pick my jacket up off the floor and start to go.

'It's only half-ten,' Barry says. 'Let's get another one in.'

'You can if you want. I'm going back.' I don't want to have a drink with someone called T-Bone, but I get the feeling that this is exactly what Barry would like to do. I get the feeling that having a drink with someone called T-Bone could be the high point of Barry's decade. 'I don't want to muck your evening up. I just don't feel like staying.'

'Not even for half an hour?'

'Not really.'

'Hold on a minute, then. I've got to go for a slash.'

'Me too,' Dick says.

When they're gone, I get out quick, and hail a black cab. It's brilliant, being depressed; you can behave as badly as you like.

Is it so wrong, wanting to be at home with your record collection? It's not like collecting records is like collecting stamps, or beermats, or antique thimbles. There's a whole world in here, a nicer, dirtier, more violent, more peaceful, more colourful, sleazier, more dangerous, more loving world than the world I live in; there is history, and geography, and poetry, and countless other things I should have studied at school, including music.

When I get home (twenty quid, Putney to Crouch End, and no tip) I make myself a cup of tea, plug in the headphones, and plough through every angry song about women by Bob Dylan and Elvis Costello I own, and when I've got through those I stick on a Neil Young live album until I have a head ringing with feedback, and when I've finished with Neil Young I go to bed and stare at the ceiling, which is no longer the dreamy, neutral activity it once was. It was a joke, wasn't it, all that Marie stuff? I was kidding myself that there was something I could go on to, an easy, seamless transition to be made. I can see that now. I can see everything once it's already happened – I'm very good at the past. It's the present I can't understand.

I get to work late, and Dick has already taken a message from Liz. I'm to ring her at work, urgently. I have no intention of ringing her at work. She wants to cancel our drink this evening, and I know why, and I'm not going to let her. She'll have to cancel to my face.

I get Dick to ring her back and tell her that he'd forgotten I wouldn't be in all day – I've gone to a record fair in Colchester and I'm coming back specially for a date this evening. No, Dick doesn't have a number.

No, Dick doesn't think I'll be ringing the shop. I don't answer the phone for the rest of the day, just in case she tries to catch me out.

We've arranged to meet in Camden, in a quiet Youngs pub on Parkway. I'm early, but I've got a *Time Out* with me, so I sit in a corner with my pint and some cashews and work out which films I'd see if I had anyone to go with.

The date with Liz doesn't take long. I see her stomping towards my table – she's nice, Liz, but she's huge, and when she's angry, like she is now, she's pretty scary – and I try a smile, but I can see it's not going to work, because she's too far gone to be brought back like that.

'You're a fucking arsehole, Rob,' she says, and then she turns round and walks out, and the people on the next table stare at me. I blush, stare at the *Time Out* and take a big pull on my pint in the hope that the glass will obscure my reddening face.

She's right, of course. I am a fucking arsehole.

SEVEN

For a couple of years, at the end of the eighties, I was a DJ at a club in Kentish Town and it was there I met Laura. It wasn't much of a club, just a room above a pub, really, but for a six-month period it was popular with a certain London crowd – the almost fashionable, right-on, black-501s-and-DMs crowd that used to move in herds from the market to the Town and Country to Dingwalls to the Electric Ballroom to the Camden Plaza. I was a good DJ, I think. At any rate, people seemed happy; they danced, stayed late, asked me where they could buy some of the records I played and came back week after week. We called it the Groucho Club, because of Groucho Marx's thing about not wanting to join any club that would have him as a member; later on we found out that there was another Groucho Club somewhere in the West End, but nobody seemed to get confused about which was which. (Top five floor-fillers at the Groucho, incidentally: 'It's A Good Feeling' by Smokey Robinson and the Miracles; 'No Blow No Show' by Bobby Bland; 'Mr Big Stuff' by Jean Knight; 'The Love You Save' by the Jackson Five; 'The Ghetto' by Donny Hathaway.)

And I loved, loved doing it. To look down on a room full of heads all bobbing away to the music you have chosen is an uplifting thing, and for that six-month period when the club was popular, I was as happy as I have ever been. It was the only time I have ever really had a sense of momentum, although later I could see that it was a false momentum, because it didn't belong to me at all, but to the music: anyone playing their favourite dance records very loud in a crowded place, to people who had paid to hear them, would have felt exactly the same thing. Dance music, after all, is supposed to have momentum – I just got confused.

Anyway, I met Laura right in the middle of that period, in the summer of '87. She reckons she had been to the club three or four times before I noticed her, and that could well be right – she's small, and skinny, and pretty, in a sort of Sheena Easton pre-Hollywood makeover way (although she looked tougher than Sheena Easton, with her radical lawyer spiky hair and her boots and her scary pale blue eyes), but there were prettier women there, and when you're looking on in that idle kind of way, it's the prettiest ones you look at. So, on this third or fourth time, she came up to my little rostrum thing and spoke to me, and I liked her straight away: she asked me to play a record that I really loved ('Got To Get You Off My Mind' by Solomon Burke, if anyone cares), but which had cleared the floor whenever I'd tried it.

'Were you here when I played it before?'

'Yeah.'

'Well, you saw what happened. They were all about to go home.'

It's a three-minute single, and I'd had to take it off after about a minute and a half. I played 'Holiday' by Madonna instead; I used modern stuff every now and again, at times of crisis, just like people who believe in homeopathy have to use conventional medicine sometimes, even though they disapprove of it.

'They won't this time.'

'How do you know that?'

'Because I brought half of this lot here, and I'll make sure they dance.'

So I played it, and sure enough Laura and her mates flooded the dance floor, but one by one they all drifted off again, shaking their heads and laughing. It is a hard song to dance to; it's a mid-tempo R&B thing, and the intro sort of stops and starts. Laura stuck with it, and though I wanted to see whether she'd struggle gamely through to the end, I got nervous when people weren't dancing, so I put 'The Love You Save' on quick.

She wouldn't dance to the Jackson Five, and she marched over to me, but she was grinning and said she wouldn't ask again. She just wanted to know where she could buy the record. I said if she came next week I'd have a tape for her, and she looked really pleased.

I spent hours putting that cassette together. To me, making a tape is like writing a letter – there's a lot of erasing and rethinking and starting again, and I wanted it to be a good one, because . . . to be honest, because I hadn't met anyone as promising as Laura since I'd started the DJing, and meeting promising women was partly what the DJing was supposed to be about. A good compilation tape, like breaking up, is hard to do. You've got to kick off with a corker, to hold the attention (I started with 'Got To Get You Off My Mind', but then realized that she might not get any further than track one, side one if I delivered what she wanted straight away, so I buried it in the middle of side two), and then you've got to up it a notch, or cool it a notch, and you can't have white music and black music together, unless the white music sounds like black music, and you can't have two tracks by the same artist side by side, unless you've done the whole thing in pairs, and . . . oh, there are loads of rules.

Anyway, I worked and worked at this one, and I've still got a couple of early demos knocking around the flat, prototype tapes I changed my mind about when I was checking them through. And on Friday night, club night, I produced it from my jacket pocket when she came over to me, and we went on from there. It was a good beginning.

Laura was, is, a lawyer, although when I met her she was a different kind of lawyer to the one she is now: then, she worked for a legal aid firm (hence, I guess, the clubbing and the black leather motorcycle jacket). Now, she works for a City law firm (hence, I guess, the restaurants and the expensive suits and the disappearance of the spiky haircut and a previously unrevealed taste for weary sarcasm) not because she underwent any kind of political conversion, but because she was made redundant and couldn't find any legal aid work. She had to take a job that paid about forty-five grand a year because she couldn't find one that paid under twenty; she said that this was all you need to know about Thatcherism, and I suppose she had a point. She changed when she got the new job. She was always intense, but, before, the intensity had somewhere to go: she could worry about tenants' rights, and slum landlords, and kids living in places without running water. Now she's just intense about *work* – how much she has, the pressure she's under, how she's doing, what the partners think of her, that kind of stuff. And when she's not being intense about work, she's being intense about why she shouldn't be intense about work, or this kind of work, anyway.

Sometimes – not so often recently – I could do something or say something that allowed her to escape from herself, and that's when we worked best; she complains frequently about my 'relentless triviality', but it has its uses.

I never had any wild crush on her, and that used to worry me about the long-term future: I used to think – and given the way we ended up, maybe I still do – that all relationships need the kind of violent shove that a crush brings, just to get you started and to push you over the humps. And then, when the energy from that shove has gone and you come to something approaching a halt, you have a look around and see what you've got. It could be something completely different, it could be something roughly the same, but gentler and calmer, or it could be nothing at all.

With Laura, I changed my mind about that whole process for a while. There weren't any sleepless nights or losses of appetite or agonizing waits for the phone to ring for either of us. But we just carried on regardless, anyway, and, because there was no steam to lose, we never had to have that look around to see what we'd got, because what we'd got was the same as what we'd always had. She didn't make me miserable, or anxious, or ill-at-ease, and when we went to bed I didn't panic and let myself down, if you know what I mean and I think you do.

We went out a lot, and she came to the club every week, and when she lost the lease on her flat in Archway she moved in, and everything was good, and stayed that way for years and years. If I was being obtuse, I'd say that money changed everything: when she switched jobs, she suddenly had loads, and when I lost the club work, and the recession seemed to make the shop suddenly invisible to passers-by, I had none. Of course things like that complicate life, and there are all kinds of readjustments to think about, battles to fight and lines to draw. But really, it wasn't the money. It was me. Like Liz said, I'm an arsehole.

The night before Liz and I were supposed to have a drink in Camden, Liz and Laura met up somewhere for something to eat, and Liz had a go at Laura about Ian, and Laura wasn't planning on saying anything in her own defence, because that would have meant assaulting me, and she has a powerful and sometimes ill-advised sense of loyalty. (I, for example, would not have been able to restrain myself.) But Liz pushed it too far, and Laura snapped, and all these things about me poured out in a torrent, and then they both cried, and Liz apologized between fifty and one hundred times for speaking out of turn. So the following day Liz snapped, tried to phone me and then marched into the pub and called me names. I don't know any of this for sure, of course. I have had no contact at all with Laura and only a brief and unhappy meeting with Liz. But, even so, one does not need a sophisticated understanding of the characters in question to guess this much.

I do not know what, precisely, Laura said, but she would have revealed at least two, maybe even all four, of the following pieces of information:

1) That I slept with somebody else while she was pregnant.
2) That my affair contributed directly to her terminating the pregnancy.
3) That, after her abortion, I borrowed a large sum of money from her and have not yet repaid any of it.
4) That, shortly before she left, I told her I was unhappy in the relationship, and I was kind of sort of maybe looking out for someone else.

Did I do and say these things? Yes, I did. Are there any mitigating circumstances? Not really, unless any circumstances (in other words, context) can be regarded as mitigating. And before you judge, although you have probably already done so, go away and write down the worst four things that you have done to your partner, even if – especially if – your partner doesn't know about them. Don't dress these things up, or try to explain them; just write them down, in a list, in the plainest language possible. Finished? OK, so who's the arsehole now?

EIGHT

'Where the fuck have you been?' I ask Barry when he turns up for work on Saturday morning. I haven't seen him since we went to Marie's gig at the White Lion – no phone calls, no apologies, nothing.

'Where the fuck have I been? Where the fuck have *I* been? God, you're an arsehole,' Barry says by way of an explanation. 'I'm sorry, Rob. I know things aren't going so well for you and you have problems and stuff, but, you know. We spent fucking hours looking for you the other night.'

'Hours? More than one hour? At least two? I left at half-ten, so you abandoned the search at half-twelve, right? You must have walked from Putney to Wapping.'

'Don't be a smartarse.'

One day, maybe not in the next few weeks, but certainly in the conceivable future, somebody will be able to refer to me without using the word 'arse' somewhere in the sentence.

'OK, sorry. But I'll bet you looked for ten minutes, and then had a drink with Marie and thingy. T-Bone.'

I hate calling him T-Bone. It sets my teeth on edge, like when you have to ask for a Big Heap Buffalo Billburger, when all you want is a quarter-pounder, or a Just Like Mom Used to Make, when all you want is a piece of apple pie.

'That's not the point.'

'Did you have a good time?'

'It was great. T-Bone's played on two Guy Clark albums and a Jimmie Dale Gilmore album.'

'Far out.'

'Oh, fuck off.'

I'm glad it's Saturday because we're reasonably busy, and Barry and I don't have to find much to say to each other. When Dick's making a cup of coffee and I'm looking for an old Shirley Brown single in the stockroom, he tells me that T-Bone's played on two Guy Clark albums and a Jimmie Dale Gilmore album.

'And do you know what? He's a really nice guy,' he adds, astonished that someone who has reached these dizzy heights is capable of exchanging a few civil words in a pub. But that's about it as far as staff interaction goes. There are too many other people to talk to.

Even though we get a lot of people into the shop, only a small percentage of them buy anything. The best customers are the ones who just *have* to buy a record on a Saturday, even if there's nothing they really want; unless they go home clutching a flat, square carrier bag they feel uncomfortable. You can spot the vinyl addicts because after a while they get fed up with the rack they are flicking through, march over to a completely different section of the shop, pull a sleeve out from the middle somewhere, and come over to the counter; this is because they have been making a list of possible purchases in their head ('If I don't find anything in the next five minutes, that blues compilation I saw half an hour ago will have to do'), and suddenly sicken themselves with the amount of time they have wasted looking for something they don't really want. I know that feeling well (these are my people, and I understand them better than I understand anybody in the world): it is a prickly, clammy, panicky sensation, and you go out of the shop reeling. You walk much more quickly afterwards, trying to recapture the part of the day that has escaped, and quite often you have the urge to read the international section of a newspaper, or go to see a Peter Greenaway film, to consume something solid and meaty which will lie on top of the candyfloss worthlessness clogging up your head.

The other people I like are the ones who are being driven to find a tune that has been troubling them, distracting them, a tune that they can hear in their breath when they run for a bus, or in the rhythm of their windscreen wipers when they're driving home from work. Sometimes something banal and obvious is responsible for the distraction: they have heard it on the radio, or at a club. But sometimes it has come to them as if by magic. Sometimes it has come to them because the sun was out, and they saw someone who looked nice, and they suddenly found themselves humming a snatch of a song they haven't heard for fifteen or twenty years; once, a guy came in because he had *dreamed* a record, the whole thing, melody, title and artist. And when I found it for him (it was an old reggae thing, 'Happy Go Lucky Girl' by the Paragons), and it was more or less exactly as it had appeared to him in his sleep, the look on his face made me feel as though I was not a man who ran a record shop, but a midwife, or a painter, someone whose life is routinely transcendental.

You can really see what Dick and Barry are for on Saturdays. Dick is as patient and as enthusiastic and as gentle as a primary school teacher:

he sells people records they didn't know they wanted because he knows intuitively what they should buy. He chats, then puts something on the record deck, and soon they're handing over fivers almost distractedly as if that's what they'd come in for in the first place. Barry, meanwhile, simply bulldozes customers into submission. He rubbishes them because they don't own the first Jesus and Mary Chain album, and they buy it, and he laughs at them because they don't own *Blonde On Blonde* so they buy that, and he explodes in disbelief when they tell him that they have never heard of Ann Peebles, and then they buy something of hers, too. At around four o'clock most Saturday afternoons, just when I make us all a cup of tea, I have a little glow on, maybe because this is after all my work, and it's going OK, maybe because I'm proud of us, of the way that, though our talents are small and peculiar, we use them to their best advantage.

So when I come to close the shop, and we're getting ready to go out for a drink as we do every Saturday, we are all happy together again; we have a fund of goodwill which we will spend over the next few empty days, and which will have completely run out by Friday lunchtime. We are so happy, in fact, that between throwing the customers out and leaving for the day, we list our top five Elvis Costello songs (I go for 'Alison', 'Little Triggers', 'Man Out Of Time', 'King Horse' and a Merseybeat-style version of 'Everyday I Write The Book' I've got on a bootleg tape somewhere, the obscurity of the last cleverly counteracting the obviousness of the first, I thought, and thus pre-empting scorn from Barry) and, after the sulks and rows of the last week, it feels good to think about things like this again.

But when we walk out of the shop, Laura's waiting there for me, leaning against the strip of wall that separates us from the shoe shop next door, and I remember that it's not supposed to be a feel-good period of my life.

NINE

The money is easy to explain: she had it, I didn't, and she wanted to give it to me. This was when she'd been in the new job a few months and her salary was starting to pile up in the bank a bit. She lent me five grand; if she hadn't, I would have gone under. I have never paid her back because I've never been able to, and the fact that she's moved out and is seeing somebody else doesn't make me five grand richer. The other day on the phone, when I gave her a hard time and told her she'd fucked my life up, she said something about the money, something about whether I'd start paying her back in instalments, and I said I'd pay her back at a pound a week for the next hundred years. That's when she hung up.

So that's the money. The stuff I told her about being unhappy in the relationship, about half-looking around for someone else: she pushed me into saying it. She *tricked* me into saying it. That sounds feeble, but she did. We were having a state-of-the-nation conversation and she said, quite matter-of-factly, that we were in a pretty unhappy phase at the moment, and I agreed; she asked whether I ever thought about meeting somebody else, and I denied it, and she laughed, and said that people in our position were always thinking about meeting somebody else. So I asked if she was always thinking about meeting somebody else, and she said of course, so I admitted that I did daydream about it sometimes. At the time I thought it was a let's-be-grown-up-about-life's-imperfectibility sort of conversation, an abstract, adult analysis; now I see that we were really talking about her and Ian, and that she suckered me into absolving her. It was a sneaky lawyer's trick, and I fell for it, because she's much smarter than me.

I didn't know she was pregnant, of course I didn't. She hadn't told me because she knew I was seeing somebody else. (She knew I was seeing somebody else because I'd told her. We thought we were being grown-up, but we were being preposterously naive, childish even, to think that one or other of us could get up to no good, and own up to the misdemeanour, while we were living together.) I didn't find out until ages afterwards: we were going through a good period and I made some joke about having kids and she burst into tears. So I made her tell me what it was all about, and she did, after which I had a brief and ill-advised bout of noisy self-righteousness (the usual stuff – my child too, what right did she have, blah blah) before her disbelief and contempt shut me up.

'You didn't look a very good long-term bet at the time,' she said. 'I didn't like you very much, either. I didn't want to have a baby by you. I didn't want to think about some awful visiting-rights relationship that stretched way on into the future. And I didn't want to be a single mother. It wasn't a very hard decision to make. There wasn't any point in consulting you about it.'

These were all fair points. In fact, if I'd got pregnant by me at the time, I would have had an abortion for exactly the same reasons. I couldn't think of anything to say.

Later on the same evening, after I'd rethought the whole pregnancy thing using the new information I had at my disposal, I asked her why she had stuck with it.

She thought for a long time.

'Because I'd never stuck at anything before, and I'd made a promise to myself when we started seeing each other that I'd make it through at least one bad patch, just to see what happened. So I did. And you were so pathetically sorry about that idiotic Rosie woman . . .' – Rosie, the four-bonk, simultaneous-orgasm, pain-in-the-arse girl, the girl I was seeing when Laura was pregnant – '. . . that you were very nice to me for quite a long time, and that was just what I needed. We go quite deep, Rob, if only because we've been together a reasonable length of time. And I didn't want to knock it all over and start again unless I really had to. So.'

And why had I stuck with it? Not for reasons as noble and as adult as that. (Is there anything more adult than sticking with a relationship that's falling apart in the hope that you can put it right? I've never done that in my life.) I stuck with it because, suddenly, right at the end of the Rosie thing, I found myself really attracted to Laura again; it was like I needed Rosie to spice Laura up a bit. And I thought I'd blown it (I didn't know then that she was experimenting with stoicism). I could see her losing interest in me, so I worked like mad to get that interest back, and when I got it back, I lost interest in her all over again. That sort of thing happens to me a lot, I find. I don't know how to sort it out. And that more or less brings us up to date. When the whole sorry tale comes out in a great big lump like that, even the most short-sighted jerk, even the most self-deluding and self-pitying of jilted, wounded lovers can see that there is some cause and effect going on here, that abortions and Rosie and Ian and money all belong to, *deserve* each other.

Dick and Barry ask us if we want to go with them to the pub for a quick one, but it's hard to imagine us all sitting round a table laughing about the customer who confused Albert King with Albert Collins ('He didn't even twig when he was looking at the record for scratches and he saw the Stax label,' Barry told us, shaking his head at the previously unsuspected depths of human ignorance), and I politely decline. I presume that we're going back to the flat, so I walk towards the bus stop, but Laura tugs me on the arm and wheels around to look for a cab.

'I'll pay. It wouldn't be much fun on the twenty-nine, would it?'

Fair point. The conversation we need to have is best conducted without a conductor – and without dogs, kids and fat people with huge John Lewis bags.

We're pretty quiet in the cab. It's only a ten-minute ride from the Seven Sisters Road to Crouch End, but the journey is so uncomfortable and intense and unhappy that I feel I'll remember it for the rest of my life. It's raining, and the fluorescent lights make patterns on our faces; the taxi driver asks us if we've had a good day, and we grunt, and he slams the partition shut behind him. Laura stares out of the window, and I sneak the odd look at her, trying to see if the last week has made any difference to her face. She's had her hair cut, same as usual, very short, sixties short, like Mia Farrow, except – and I'm not just being creepy – she's better suited to this sort of cut than her. It's because her hair is so dark, nearly black, that when it's short her eyes seem to take up most of her face. She's not wearing any make-up, and I reckon this is for my benefit. It's an easy way of showing me that she's careworn, distracted, too miserable for fripperies. There's a nice symmetry here: when I gave her that tape with the Solomon Burke song on it, all those years ago, she was wearing loads of make-up, much more than she was used to wearing, and much more than she had worn the previous week, and I knew, or hoped, that this was for my benefit too. So you get loads at the beginning, to show that things are good, positive, exciting, and none at the end, to show that things are desperate. Neat, eh?

(But later, just as we're turning the corner into my road, and I'm beginning to panic about the pain and difficulty of the impending conversation, I see a woman on her own, Saturday-night-smart, off to meet somebody somewhere, friends, or a lover. And when I was living with Laura, I missed . . . what? Maybe I missed somebody travelling on a bus or tube or cab, *going out of their way*, to meet me, maybe dressed up a little, maybe wearing more make-up than usual, maybe even slightly nervous; when I was younger, the knowledge that I was responsible for any of this, even the bus ride, made me feel pathetically grateful. When you're with someone permanently, you don't get that: if Laura wanted to see me, she only had to turn her head, or walk from the bathroom to the bedroom, and she never bothered to dress up for the trip. And when she came home, she came home because she lived in my flat, not because we were lovers, and when we went out, she sometimes dressed up and sometimes didn't, depending on where we were going, but again, it was nothing whatsoever to do with me. Anyway, all this is by way of saying that the woman I saw out of the cab window inspired me and consoled me, momentarily: maybe I am not too old to provoke a trip from one part of London to another, and if I ever do have another date, and I arrange to meet that date in, say, Islington, and she has to come all the way from Stoke Newington, a journey of some three to four miles, I will thank her from the bottom of my wretched thirty-five-year-old heart.)

Laura pays the cabbie and I unlock the front door, put the timer light on and usher her inside. She stops and goes through the post on the windowsill, just through force of habit, I guess, but of course she gets herself in difficulties immediately: as she's shuffling through the envelopes, she comes across Ian's TV licence reminder, and she hesitates, just for a second, but long enough to remove any last remaining trace of doubt from my mind, and I feel sick.

'You can take it with you if you want,' I say, but I can't look at her, and she doesn't look at me. 'Save me having to redirect it.' But she just puts it back in the pile, and then puts the pile back among the takeaway menus and minicab cards on the windowsill, and starts walking up the stairs.

When we get into the flat, it's weird seeing her there. But what's particularly odd is how she tries to avoid doing the things that she used to do – you can see her checking herself. She takes her coat off; she used to chuck it over one of the chairs, but she doesn't want to do that tonight. She stands there holding it for a little while, and I take it off her and chuck it over one of the chairs. She starts to go into the kitchen, either to put the kettle on or to pour herself a glass of wine, so I ask her, politely, whether she'd like a cup of tea, and she asks me, politely, whether there's anything stronger, and when I say that there's a half-empty bottle of wine in the fridge, she manages not to say that there was a whole one when she left, and she bought it. Anyway, it's not hers any more, or it's not the same bottle, or something. And when she sits down, she chooses the chair nearest the stereo – my chair – rather than the one nearest the TV – her chair.

'Have you done them yet?' She nods towards the shelves full of albums.

'What?' I know what, of course.

'The Great Reorganization.' I can hear the capital letters.

'Oh. Yes. The other night.' I don't want to tell her that I did it the evening after she'd gone, but she gives an irritating little, well-fancy-that smile anyway.

'What?' I say. 'What's that supposed to mean?'

'Nothing. Just, you know. Didn't take you long.'

'Don't you think there are more important things to talk about than my record collection?'

'Yes, I do, Rob. I've always thought that.'

I'm supposed to have the moral high ground here (she's the one who's been sleeping with the neighbours, after all), but I can't even get out of base camp.

'Where have you been staying for the last week?'

'I think you know that,' she says quietly.

'Had to work it out for myself, though, didn't I?'

I feel sick again, really sick. I don't know how it shows on my face, but suddenly Laura loses it a little: she looks tired, and sad, and she stares hard straight ahead to stop herself from crying.

'I'm sorry. I made some bad decisions. I haven't been very fair to you. That's why I came to the shop this evening, because I thought it was time to be brave.'

'Are you scared now?'

'Yes, of course I am. I feel terrible. This is really hard, you know.'

'Good.'

Silence. I don't know what to say. There are loads of things I want to ask, but they are all questions I don't really want answered: when did you start seeing Ian, and was it because of the-you know-the ceiling-noise thing, and is it better (What? she'd ask; Everything, I'd say), and is this really definitely it, or just some sort of phase, and – this is how feeble I'm becoming – have you missed me at all even one bit, do you love me, do you love him, do you want to end up with him, do you want to have babies with him, and is it better, *is it better*, IS IT BETTER?

'Is it because of my job?'

Where did that one come from? Of course it's not because of my fucking job. Why did I ask that?

'Oh, Rob, of course it isn't.'

That's why I asked that. Because I felt sorry for myself, and I wanted some sort of cheap consolation: I wanted to hear 'Of course it isn't' said with a tender dismissiveness, whereas if I'd asked her the Big Question I might have got an embarrassed denial, or an embarrassed silence, or an embarrassed confession, and I didn't want any of them.

'Is that what you think? That I've left you because you're not grand enough for me? Give me some credit, please.' But again, she says it nicely, in a tone of voice I recognize from a long time ago.

'I don't know. It's one of the things I thought of.'

'What were the others?'

'Just the obvious stuff.'

'What's the obvious stuff?'

'I don't know.'

'So it's not *that* obvious, then.'

'No.'

Silence again.

'Is it working out with Ian?'

'Oh, come on, Rob. Don't be childish.'

'Why is that childish? You're living with the bloke. I just wanted to know how it was going.'

'I'm not living with him. I've just been staying with him for a few days until I work out what I'm doing. Look, this is nothing to do with anyone else. You know that, don't you?'

They always say that. They always, always say that it's nothing to do with anyone else. I'll bet you any money that if Celia Johnson had run off with Trevor Howard at the end of *Brief Encounter*, she would have told her husband that it was nothing to do with anyone else. It's the first law of romantic trauma. I make a rather repulsive and inappropriately comic snorting noise to express my disbelief, and Laura nearly laughs, but thinks better of it.

'I left because we weren't really getting on, or even talking, very much, and I'm at an age where I want to sort myself out, and I couldn't see that ever happening with you, mostly because you seem incapable of sorting yourself out. And I was sort of interested in someone else, and then that went further than it should have done, so it seemed like a good time to go. But I've no idea what will happen with Ian in the long run. Probably nothing. Maybe you'll grow up a bit and we'll put things right. Maybe I'll never see either of you ever again. I don't know. All I do know is that it's not a good time to be living here.'

More silence. Why are people – let's face it, women – like this? It doesn't pay to think this way, with all this mess and doubt and grey, smudged lines where there should be a crisp, sharp picture. I agree that you need to meet somebody new in order to dispense with the old – you have to be incredibly brave and adult to pack something in just because it isn't working very well. But you can't go about it all half-heartedly, like Laura is doing now. When I started seeing Rosie the simultaneous-orgasm woman, I wasn't like this; as far as I was concerned, she was a serious prospect, the woman who was going to lead me painlessly out of one relationship and into another, and the fact that it didn't happen like that, that she was a disaster area, was just bad luck. At least there was a clear battle-plan in my head, and there was none of this irritating oh-Rob-I-need-time stuff.

'But you haven't definitely decided to pack me in? There's still a chance that we'll get back together?'

'I don't know.'

'Well, if you don't know, that must mean there's a chance.'

'I don't know if there's a chance.'

Jesus.

'That's what I'm saying. That if you don't know there's a chance, there must be a chance, mustn't there? It's like, if someone was in hospital, and he was seriously ill, and the doctor said, I don't know if he's got a chance of survival or not, then that doesn't mean the patient's definitely going to die, does it? It means he might live. Even if it's only a remote possibility.'

'I suppose so.'

'So we have a chance of getting back together again.'

'Oh, Rob, shut up.'

'I just want to know where I stand. What chance I have.'

'I don't bloody know what bloody fucking chance you have. I'm trying to tell you that I'm confused, that I haven't been happy for ages, that we got ourselves into a terrible mess, that I've been seeing someone else. These are the important things.'

'I guess. But if you could just tell me roughly, it would help.'

'OK, OK. We have a nine per cent chance of getting back together. Does that clarify the situation?' She's so sick of this, so near to bursting, that her eyes are clenched tight shut and she's speaking in a furious, poisonous whisper.

'You're just being stupid now.'

I know, somewhere in me, that it's not her that's being stupid. I understand, on one level, that she doesn't know, that everything's up in the air. But that's no use to me. You know the worst thing about being rejected? The lack of control. If I could only control the when and how of being dumped by somebody, then it wouldn't seem as bad. But then, of course, it wouldn't be rejection, would it? It would be by mutual consent. It would be musical differences. I would be leaving to pursue a solo career. I know how unbelievably and pathetically childish it is to push and push like this for some degree of probability, but it's the only thing I can do to grab any sort of control back from her.

When I saw Laura outside the shop I knew *absolutely*, without any question at all, that I wanted her again. But that's probably because she's the one doing the rejecting. If I can get her to concede that there is a chance we'll patch things up, that makes things easier for me: if I don't have to go around feeling hurt, and powerless, and miserable, I can cope without her. In other words, I'm unhappy because she doesn't want me; if I can convince myself that she does want me a bit, then I'll be OK again, because then I won't want her, and I can get on with looking for someone else.

Laura is wearing an expression I have come to know well in recent months, a look that denotes both infinite patience and hopeless frustration. It doesn't feel good to know that she has invented this look just for me. She never needed it before. She sighs, and puts her head on her hand, and stares at the wall.

'OK, it could be that we sort things out. There may be a chance of that happening. I would say not a good chance, but a chance.'

'Great.'

'No, Rob, it's not great. Nothing's great. Everything's shit.'

'But it won't be, you'll see.'

She shakes her head, apparently in disbelief. 'I'm too tired for this now. I know I'm asking a lot, but will you go back to the pub and have a drink with the others while I'm sorting some stuff out? I need to be able to think while I'm doing it, and I can't think with you here.'

'No problem. If I can ask one question.'

'OK. One.'

'It sounds stupid.'

'Never mind.'

'You won't like it.'

'Just . . . just ask it.'

'Is it better?'

'Is what better? Is what better than what?'

'Well. Sex, I guess. Is sex with him better?'

'Jesus Christ, Rob. Is that really what's bothering you?'

'Of course it is.'

'You really think it would make a difference either way?'

'I don't know.' And I don't.

'Well, the answer is that I don't know either. We haven't done it yet.'

Yes!

'Never?'

'No. I haven't felt like it.'

'But not even before, when he was living upstairs?'

'Oh, thanks a lot. No. I was living with you then, remember?'

I feel a bit embarrassed and I don't say anything.

'We've slept together but we haven't made love. Not yet. But I'll tell you one thing. The sleeping together is better.'

Yes! Yes! This is fantastic news! Mr Sixty Minute Man hasn't even clocked on yet! I kiss her on the cheek and go to the pub to meet Dick and Barry. I feel like a new man, although not very much like a New Man. I feel so much better, in fact, that I go straight out and sleep with Marie.

TEN

FACT: over three million men in this country have slept with ten or more women. And do they all look like Richard Gere? Are they all as rich as Croesus, as charming at Clark Gable, as preposterously endowed as Errol Flynn, as witty as Clive James? Nope. It's nothing to do with any of that. Maybe half a dozen or so of that three million have one or more of these attributes, but that still leaves . . . well, three million, give or take half a dozen. And they're just blokes. *We're* just blokes, because I, even I, am a member of the exclusive three million club. Ten is not so many if you're unmarried and in your mid-thirties. Ten partners in a couple of decades of sexual activity is actually pretty feeble, if you think about it: one partner every two years, and if any of those partners was a one-night stand, and that one-night stand came in the middle of a two-year drought, then you're not *in trouble* exactly, but you're hardly the Number One Lurve Man in your particular postal district. Ten isn't a lot, not for the thirtysomething bachelor. Twenty isn't a lot, if you look at it that way. Anything over thirty, I reckon, and you're entitled to appear on an *Oprah* about promiscuity.

Marie is my seventeenth lover. 'How does he do it?' you ask yourselves. 'He wears bad jumpers, he gives his ex-girlfriend a hard time, he's grumpy, he's skint, he hangs out with the Musical Moron Twins, and yet he gets to go to bed with an American recording artiste who looks like Susan Dey. What's going on?'

First off, let's not get carried away here. Yes, she's a recording artiste, but she records with the ironically titled Blackpool-based Hit Records, and it's the type of record contract where you sell your own tapes during the interval of your own show in London's prestigious Sir Harry Lauder nightspot. And if I know Susan Dey, and after a relationship that has endured for over twenty years I feel I do, I reckon she'd be the first to admit that looking like Susan Dey in *LA Law* is not the same as looking like, say, Vivien Leigh in *Gone With the Wind*.

But yes, even so, the night with Marie is my major sexual triumph, my *bonkus mirabilis*. And do you know how it comes about? Because I ask questions. That's it. That's my secret. If someone wanted to know how to get off with seventeen women, or more, no less, that's what I'd tell them: ask questions. It works precisely because that isn't how you're supposed to do it, if you listen to the collective male wisdom. There are still enough of the old-style, big-gobbed, self-opinionated egomaniacs around to make someone like me appear refreshingly different; Marie even says something like that to me halfway through the evening . . .

I had no idea that Marie and T-Bone were going to be in the pub with Dick and Barry, who had apparently promised them a real English Saturday night out – pub, curry, night bus and all the trimmings. But

I'm happy to see them, both of them; I'm really up after the triumph with Laura, and seeing as Marie has only ever seen me tongue-tied and grumpy, she must wonder what has happened. Let her wonder. It's not often that I get the chance to be enigmatic and perplexing.

They're sitting round a table, drinking pints of bitter. Marie shuffles along to let me sit down, and the moment she does that I'm lost, gone, away. It's the Saturday-night-date woman I saw through the window of the cab who has set me off, I think. I see Marie's shuffle along the seat as a miniature but meaningful romantic accommodation: hey, she's doing this for me! Pathetic, I know, but immediately I start to worry that Barry or Dick – let's face it, Barry – has told her about where I was and what I was doing. Because if she knows about Laura, and about the split, and about me getting uptight, then she'll lose interest and, as she had no interest in the first place, that would put me into a minus-interest situation. I'd be in the red, interest-wise.

Barry and Dick are asking T-Bone about Guy Clark; Marie's listening, but then she turns to me and asks me, conspiratorially, if everything went all right. Bastard Barry bigmouth.

I shrug.

'She just wanted to pick some stuff up. No big deal.'

'God, I hate that time. That picking-up-stuff time. I just went through that before I came here. You know that song called "Patsy Cline Times Two" I play? That's about me and my ex dividing up our record collections.'

'It's a great song.'

'Thank you.'

'And you wrote it just before you came here?'

'I wrote it on the way here. The words, anyway. I'd had the tune for a while, but I didn't know what to do with it until I thought of the title.'

It begins to dawn on me that T-Bone, if I may Moulinex my foodstuffs, is a red herring.

'Is that why you came to London in the first place? Because of, you know, dividing up your record collection and stuff?'

'Yup.' She shrugs, then thinks, and then laughs, because the affirmative has told the entire story, and there's nothing else to say, but she tries anyway.

'Yup. He broke my heart, and suddenly I didn't want to be in Austin any more, so I called T-Bone, and he fixed up a couple of gigs and an apartment for me, and here I am.'

'You share a place with T-Bone?'

She laughs again, a big snorty laugh, right into her beer. 'No *way*! T-Bone wouldn't want to share a place with me. I'd cramp his style. And I wouldn't want to listen to all that stuff happening on the other side of the bedroom wall. I'm way too unattached for that.'

She's single. I'm single. I'm a single man talking to an attractive single woman who may or may not have just confessed to feelings of sexual frustration. Oh my God.

A while back, when Dick and Barry and I agreed that what really matters is what you like, not what you *are* like, Barry proposed the idea of a questionnaire for prospective partners, a two- or three-page multiple-choice document that covered all the music/film/TV/book bases. It was intended a) to dispense with awkward conversation, and b) to prevent a chap from leaping into bed with someone who might, at a later date, turn out to have every Julio Iglesias record ever made. It amused us at the time, although Barry, being Barry, went one stage further: he compiled the questionnaire and presented it to some poor woman he was interested in, and she hit him with it. But there was an important and essential truth contained in the idea, and the truth was that these things matter, and it's no good pretending that any relationship has a future if your record collections disagree violently, or if your favourite films wouldn't even speak to each other if they met at a party.

If I'd given Marie a questionnaire, she wouldn't have hit me with it. She would have understood the validity of the exercise. We have one of those conversations where everything clicks, meshes, corresponds, locks, where even our pauses, even our punctuation marks, seem to be nodding in agreement. Nanci Griffith and Kurt Vonnegut, the Cowboy Junkies and hip-hop, *My Life as a Dog* and *A Fish Called Wanda*, Pee-Wee Herman and *Wayne's World*, sport and Mexican food (yes, yes, yes, no, yes, no, no, yes, no, yes) . . . You remember that kid's game, Mousetrap? That ludicrous Heath Robinson machine you had to build, where silver balls went down chutes, and little men went up ladders, and one thing knocked into another to set off something else, until in the end the cage fell on to the mouse and trapped it? The evening goes with that sort of breathtaking joke precision, where you can kind of see what's supposed to happen but you can't believe it's ever going to get there, even though afterwards it seems obvious.

When I begin to get the feeling that we're having a good time, I give her chances to get away: when there's a silence I start to listen to T-Bone telling Barry what Guy Clark is really like in real life as a human being, but Marie sets us back down a private road each time. And when we move from the pub to the curry house, I slow down to the back of the group, so that she can leave me behind if she wants, but she slows down with me. And in the curry house I sit down first, so she can choose where she wants to be, and she chooses the place next to me. It's only at the end of the evening that I make anything that could be interpreted as a move: I tell Marie that it makes sense for the two of us to share a cab. It's more or less true anyway, because T-Bone is staying in Camden and both Dick and Barry live in the East End, so it's not like I've redrawn the entire *A–Z* for my own purposes. And it's not like I've told her that it makes sense for me to stay the night at her place, either – if she doesn't want any further company, all she has to do is get out of the cab, try to shove a fiver at me, and wave me on my way. But when we get to her place, she asks me if I want to break into her duty free, and I find that I do. So.

So. Her place is very much like my place, a boxy first-floor flat in a north London three-storey house. In fact, it's so much like my place that it's depressing. Is it really as easy as this to approximate my life? One quick phone call to a friend and that's it? It's taken me a decade or more to put down roots even as shallow as these. The acoustics are all wrong, though; there are no books, there's no wall of records and there's very little furniture, just a sofa and an armchair. There's no hi-fi, just a little radiocassette and a few tapes, some of which she bought from us. And, thrillingly, there are two guitars leaning against the wall.

She goes into the kitchen, which is actually in the living room but distinguishable because the carpet stops and the lino begins, and gets some ice and a couple of glasses (she doesn't ask me if I want ice, but this is the first bum note she's played all evening, so I don't feel like complaining) and sits down next to me on the sofa. I ask her questions about Austin, about the clubs and the people there; I also ask her loads of questions about her ex, and she talks *well* about him. She describes the set-up and her knock-back with wisdom and honesty and a dry self-deprecating humour, and I can see why her songs are as good as they are. I don't talk well about Laura, or, at least, I don't talk with the same sort of depth. I cut corners and trim edges and widen the margins and speak in big letters to make it all look a bit more detailed than it really is, so she gets to hear a bit about Ian (although she doesn't get to hear the noises I heard), and a bit about Laura's work, but nothing about abortions or money or pain-in-the-arse simultaneous-orgasm women. It feels, even to me, like I'm being intimate: I speak quietly, slowly, thoughtfully, I express regret, I say nice things about Laura, I hint at a deep ocean of melancholy just below the surface. But it's all bollocks, really, a cartoon sketch of a decent, sensitive guy which does the trick because I am in a position to invent my own reality and because – I think – Marie has already decided she likes me.

I have completely forgotten how to do the next bit, even though I'm never sure whether there's going to be a next bit. I remember the juvenile stuff, where you put your arm along the sofa and let it drop on to her shoulder, or press your leg against hers; I remember the mock-tough adult stuff I used to try when I was in my mid-twenties, where I looked someone in the eye and asked if they wanted to stay the night. But none of that seems appropriate any more. What do you do when you're old enough to know better? In the end – and if you'd wanted to place a bet, you would have got pretty short odds on this one – it's a clumsy collision standing up in the middle of the living room. I get up to go to the loo, she says she'll show me, we bump into each other, I grab, we kiss, and I'm back in the land of sexual neurosis.

Why is failure the first thing I think of when I find myself in this sort of situation? Why can't I just enjoy myself? But if you have to ask the question, then you know you're lost: self-consciousness is a man's worst enemy. Already I'm wondering whether she's as aware of my erection as I am, and if she is what she feels about it; but I can't even maintain that worry, let alone anything else, because so many other worries are crowding it out, and the next stage looks intimidatingly difficult, unfathomably terrifying, absolutely impossible.

Look at all the things that can go wrong for men. There's the nothing-happening-at-all problem, the too-much-happening-too-soon problem, the dismal-droop-after-a-promising-beginning problem; there's the size-doesn't-matter-except-in-my-case problem, the failing-to-deliver-the-goods problem . . . and what do women have to worry about? A handful of cellulite? Join the club. A spot of I-wonder-how-I-rank? Ditto.

I'm happy to be a bloke, I think, but sometimes I'm not happy being a bloke in the late twentieth century. Sometimes I'd rather be my dad. He never had to worry about delivering the goods, because he never knew that there were any goods to deliver; he never had to worry about how he ranked in my mother's all-time hot one hundred, because he was first and last on the list. Wouldn't it be great if you could talk about this sort of thing to your father?

One day, maybe, I'll try. 'Dad, did you ever have to worry about the female orgasm in either its clitoral or its (possibly mythical) vaginal form? Do you, in fact, know what the female orgasm is? What about the G-spot? What did "good in bed" mean in 1955, if it meant anything at all? When was oral sex imported to Britain? Do you envy me my sex life, or does it all look like terribly hard work to you? Did you ever fret about how long you could keep going for, or didn't you think about that sort of thing then? Aren't you glad that you've never had to buy vegetarian cookery books as the first small step on the road to getting inside someone's knickers? Aren't you glad that you've never had the "You might be right-on but do you clean the toilet?" conversation? Aren't you relieved that you've been spared the perils of childbirth that all modern men have to face?' (And what would he say, I wonder, if he were not tongue-tied by his class and his sex and his diffidence? Probably something like, 'Son, stop whingeing. The good fuck wasn't even *invented* in my day, and however many toilets you clean and vegetarian recipes you have to read, you still have more fun than we were ever allowed.' And he'd be right, too.)

This is the sort of sex education I never had – the one that deals in G-spots and the like. No one ever told me about anything that mattered, about how to take your trousers off with dignity or what to say to someone when you can't get an erection or what 'good in bed' meant in 1975 or 1985, never mind 1955. Get this: no one ever told me about *semen* even, just sperm, and there's a crucial difference. As far as I could tell, these microscopic tadpole things just leapt invisibly out of the end of your whatsit, and so when, on the occasion of my first . . . well, never you mind. But this disastrously partial grasp of the male sex organs caused distress and embarrassment and shame until one afternoon in a Wimpy Bar, a school friend, apropos of nothing, remarked that the saliva he had left in his glass of Wimpy cola 'looked like spunk', an enigmatic observation that had me puzzling feverishly for an entire weekend, although at the time, of course, I tittered knowingly. It is difficult to stare at foreign matter floating on the top of a glass of cola and from this minimal information work out the miracle of life itself, but that is what I had to do, and I did it, too.

Anyway. We stand up and kiss, and then we sit down and kiss, and half of me is telling myself not to worry, and the other half is feeling pleased with myself, and these two halves make a whole and leave no room for the here and now, for any pleasure or lust, so then I start wondering whether I have *ever* enjoyed this stuff, the physical sensation rather than the fact of it, or whether it's just something I feel I ought to do, and when this reverie is over I find that we're no longer kissing but hugging, and I'm staring at the back of the sofa. Marie pushes me away so that she can have a look at me and, rather than let her see me gazing blankly into space, I squeeze my eyes tight shut, which gets me out of the immediate hole but which in the long run is probably a mistake, because it makes it look as though I have spent most of my life waiting for this moment, and that will either scare her rigid or make her assume some things that she shouldn't.

'You OK?' she says.

I nod. 'You?'

'For now. But I wouldn't be if I thought this was the end of the evening.'

When I was seventeen, I used to lie awake at night hoping that women would say things like that to me; now, it just brings back the panic.

'I'm sure it isn't.'

'Good. In that case, I'll fix us something else to drink. You sticking to the Irish, or you want a coffee?'

I stick to the Irish, so I'll have an excuse if nothing happens, or if things happen too quickly, or if blah blah blah.

'You know, I really thought you hated me,' she says. 'You'd never said more than two words to me before this evening, and they were real crotchety words.'

'Is that why you were interested?'

'Yeah, kind of, I guess.'

'That's not the right answer.'

'No, but . . . if a guy's kind of weird with me, I want to find out what's going on, you know?'

'And you know now?'
'Nope. Do you?'
Yep.
'Nope.'
We laugh merrily; maybe if I just keep laughing I'll be able to postpone the moment. She tells me that she thought I was cute, a word that no one has ever previously used in connection with me, and soulful, by which I think she means that I don't say much and I always look vaguely pissed off. I tell her that I think she's beautiful, which I sort of do, and talented, which I definitely do. And we talk like this for a while, congratulating ourselves on our good fortune and each other for our good taste, which is the way these post-kiss pre-sex conversations always go, in my experience; and I'm grateful for every stupid word of it, because it buys me time.

I've never had the sexual heebie-jeebies this bad before. I used to get nervous, sure, but I was never in any doubt that I wanted to go through with it; now, it seems more than enough to know that I can if I want to, and if there was a way of cheating, of circumnavigating the next bit – getting Marie to sign some sort of affidavit which said I'd spent the night, for example – I'd take it. It's hard to imagine, in fact, that the thrill of actually doing it will be any greater than the thrill of finding myself in a *position* to do it, but then maybe sex has always been like that for me. Maybe I never really enjoyed the naked part of sex, just the dinner, coffee and get-away-that's-*my*-favourite-Hitchcock-film-*too* part of sex, as long as it's a sexual preamble, and not just a purposeless chat, and . . .

Who am I kidding? I'm just trying to make myself feel better. I used to love sex, all of it, the naked parts and the clothed parts and, on a good day, with a fair wind, when I hadn't had too much to drink and I wasn't too tired and I was just at the right stage of the relationship (not too soon, when I had the first-night nerves, and not too late, when I had the not-this-routine-again blues), I was OK at it. (By which I mean what exactly? Dunno. No complaints, I guess, but then there never are in polite company, are there?) The trouble is that it's been *years* since I've done anything like this. What if she laughs? What if I get my jumper stuck round my head? It does happen with this jumper. For some reason the neck-hole has shrunk but nothing else – either that or my head has got fat at a faster rate than the rest of me – and if I'd known this morning that . . . anyway.

'I've got to go,' I say. I have no idea that I'm going to say this, but when I hear the words they make perfect sense. But of course! What a fantastic idea! Just go home! You don't have to have sex if you don't want to! What a *grown-up*!

Marie looks at me. 'When I said before that I hoped it wasn't the end of the evening, I was, you know . . . talking about breakfast and stuff. I wasn't talking about another whiskey and another ten minutes of shooting the shit. I'd like it if you could stay the night.'

'Oh,' I say lamely. 'Oh. Right.'

'Jesus, so much for delicacy. Next time I ask a guy to stay the night when I'm here, I'll do it the American way. I thought you English were supposed to be the masters of understatement, and beating around the bush, and all that jazz.'

'We use it, but we don't understand it when other people use it.'

'You understand me now? I'd rather stop there, before I have to say something really crude.'

'No, that's fine. I just thought I should, you know, clear things up.'

'So they're clear?'

'Yeah.'

'And you'll stay?'

'Yeah.'

'Good.'

It takes genius to do what I have just done. I had the chance of going and I blew it; in the process I showed myself incapable of conducting a courtship with any kind of sophistication whatsoever. She uses a nice sexy line to ask me to stay the night, and I lead her to believe that it sailed right over my head, thus turning myself into the kind of person she wouldn't have wanted to sleep with in the first place. Brilliant.

But miraculously there are no more hiccups. We have the Durex conversation, as in I tell her I haven't brought anything with me and she laughs and says that she'd be appalled if I had and anyway she has something in her bag. We both know what we're talking about and why, but we don't elaborate any further. (You don't need to, do you? If you ask someone for a loo-roll, you don't have to have a conversation about what you're going to do with it.) And then she picks up her drink, grabs me by the hand and takes me into the bedroom.

Bad news: there's a bathroom interlude. I hate bathroom interludes, all that 'You can use the green toothbrush and the pink towel' stuff.

Don't get me wrong: personal hygiene is of the utmost importance, and people who don't clean their teeth are shortsighted and very silly, and I wouldn't let a child of mine etc., and so on. But, you know, can't we take some time out every now and again? We're supposed to be in the grip of a passion that neither of us can control here, so how comes she can find time to think about Anne French and carrot moisturizer and cotton-wool balls and the rest of it? On the whole, I prefer women who are prepared to break the habit of half a lifetime in your honour, and in any case bathroom interludes do nothing for a chap's nerves, nor for his enthusiasm, if you catch my drift. I'm particularly disappointed to learn that Marie is an interluder, because I thought she'd be a little more Bohemian, what with the recording contract and all; I thought sex would be a little dirtier, literally and figuratively. Once we're in the bedroom she disappears straight away, and I'm left kicking my heels and worrying about whether I'm supposed to get undressed or not.

See, if I get undressed and she then offers me the green toothbrush, I'm sunk: that means either the long nude walk to the bathroom, and I'm just not ready for that yet, or going fully clothed and getting your jumper stuck over your head afterwards. (To *refuse* the green toothbrush is simply not on, for obvious reasons.) It's all right for her, of course; she can avoid all this. She can come in wearing an extra-large Sting T-shirt which she then slips off while I'm out of the room; she's given nothing away and I'm a humiliated wreck. But then I remember that I'm wearing a pair of reasonably snazzy boxers (a present from Laura) and a cleanish white running vest, so I can go for the underwear-in-bed option, a not unreasonable compromise. When Marie comes back I'm browsing through her John Irving paperback with as much cool as I can manage.

And then I go to the bathroom, and clean my teeth; and then I come back; and then we make love; and then we talk for a bit; and then we turn the light out, and that's it. I'm not going into all that other stuff, the who-did-what-to-who stuff. You know 'Behind Closed Doors' by Charlie Rich? That's one of my favourite songs.

You're entitled to know some things, I suppose. You're entitled to know that I didn't let myself down, that none of the major problems afflicted me, that I didn't deliver the goods but Marie said she had a nice time anyway, and I believed her; and you're entitled to know that I had a nice time too, and that at some point or other along the way I remembered what it is I like about sex: what I like about sex is that I can lose myself in it entirely. Sex, in fact, is the most absorbing activity I have discovered in adulthood. When I was a child I used to feel this way about all sorts of things – Meccano, *The Jungle Book*, *Biggles*, *The Man from U.N.C.L.E.*, the ABC Minors . . . I could forget where I was, the time of day, who I was with. Sex is the only thing I've found like that as a grown-up, give or take the odd film: books are no longer like that once you're out of your teens, and I've certainly never found it in my work. All the horrible pre-sex self-consciousness drains out of me, and I forget where I am, the time of day . . . and yes, I forget who I'm with, for the time being. Sex is about the only grown-up thing I know how to do; it's weird, then, that it's the only thing which can make me feel like a ten-year-old.

I wake up around dawn, and I have the same feeling I had the other night, the night I twigged about Laura and Ray: that I've got no ballast, nothing to weight me down, and if I don't hang on I'll just float away. I like Marie a lot, she's funny and smart and pretty and talented, but who the hell is she? I don't mean that philosophically. I just mean, I don't know her from Eve, so what am I doing in her bed? Surely there's a better, safer, more friendly place for me than this? But I know there isn't, not at the moment, and that scares me rigid.

I get up, find my snazzy boxers and my vest, go into the living room, fumble in my jacket pocket for my fags and sit in the dark smoking. After a little while Marie gets up too, and sits down next to me.

'You sitting here wondering what you're doing?'

'No. I'm just, you know . . .'

''Cos that's why I'm sitting here, if it helps.'

'I thought I'd woken you up.'

'I ain't even been to sleep yet.'

'So you've been wondering for a lot longer than me. Worked anything out?'

'Bits. I've worked out that I was real lonely, and I went and jumped into bed with the first person who'd have me. And I've also worked out that I was lucky it was you, and not somebody mean, or boring, or crazy.'

'I'm not mean, anyway. And you wouldn't have gone to bed with anyone who was any of those things.'

'I'm not so sure about that. I've had a bad week.'

'What's happened?'

'Nothing's happened. I've had a bad week in my head, is all.'

Before we slept together, there was at least some pretence that it was something we both wanted to do, that it was the healthy, strong beginning of an exciting new relationship. Now all the pretence seems to have gone, and we're left to face the fact that we're sitting here because we don't know anybody else we could be sitting with.

'I don't care if you've got the blues,' Marie says. 'It's OK. And I wasn't fooled by you acting all cool about . . . what's her name?'

'Laura.'

'Laura, right. But people are allowed to feel horny and fucked-up at the same time. You shouldn't feel embarrassed about it. I don't. Why should we be denied basic human rights just because we've messed up our relationships?'

I'm beginning to feel more embarrassed about the conversation than about anything we've just done. Horny? They really use that word? Jesus. All my life I've wanted to go to bed with an American, and now I have, and I'm beginning to see why people don't do it more often. Apart from Americans, that is, who probably go to bed with Americans all the time.

'You think sex is a basic human right?'

'You bet. And I'm not going to let that asshole stand between me and a fuck.'

I try not to think about the peculiar anatomical diagram she has just drawn. And I also decide not to point out that though sex may well be a basic human right, it's kind of hard to insist on that right if you keep on busting up with the people you want to have sex with.

'Which arsehole?'

She spits out the name of a fairly well-known American singer-songwriter, someone you might have heard of.

'He's the one you had to split the Patsy Cline records with?'

She nods, and I can't control my enthusiasm.

'That's amazing!'

'What, that you've slept with someone who's slept with . . .' (Here she repeats the name of the fairly well-known American singer-songwriter, whom I shall hereafter refer to as Steve.)

She's right! Exactly that! Exactly that! I've slept with someone who's slept with . . . Steve! (That sentence sounds stupid without his real name in it. Like, I've danced with a man who danced with a girl who danced with . . . Bob. But just imagine the name of someone, not *really* famous, but quite famous – Lyle Lovett, say, although I should point out, for legal reasons, that it's not him – and you'll get the idea.)

'Don't be daft, Marie. I'm not that crass. I just meant, you know, it's amazing that someone who wrote—' (and here I name Steve's greatest hit, a drippy and revoltingly sensitive ballad) 'should be such a bastard.' I'm very pleased with this explanation for my amazement. Not only does it get me out of a hole, but it's both sharp and relevant.

'That song's about his ex, you know, the one before me. It felt real good listening to him sing that night after night, I can tell you.'

This is great. This is how I imagined it would be, going out with someone who had a recording contract.

'And then I wrote "Patsy Cline Times Two", and he's probably writing something about me writing a song about all that, and she's probably writing a song about having a song written about her, and . . .'

'That's how it goes. We all do that.'

'You all write songs about each other?'

'No, but . . .'

It would take too long to explain about Marco and Charlie, and how they wrote Sarah, in a way, because without Marco and Charlie there would have been no Sarah, and how Sarah and her ex, the one who wanted to be someone at the BBC, how they wrote me, and how Rosie the pain-in-the-arse simultaneous-orgasm girl and I wrote Ian. It's just that none of us had the wit or the talent to make them into songs. We made them into life, which is much messier, and more time-consuming, and leaves nothing for anybody to whistle.

Marie stands up. 'I'm about to do something terrible, so please forgive me.' She walks over to her radiocassette, ejects one tape, rummages around and then puts in another, and the two of us sit in the dark and listen to the songs of Marie LaSalle. I think I can understand why, too; I think if I were homesick and lost and unsure of what I was playing at, I'd do the same. Fulfilling work is a great thing at times like these. What am I supposed to do? Go and unlock the shop and walk around it?

'Is this gross or what?' she says after a little while. 'It's kind of like masturbation or something, listening to myself for pleasure. How d'you feel about that, Rob? Three hours after we made love and I'm already jerking off.'

I wish she hadn't said that. It kind of spoiled the moment.

*

We get back to sleep, in the end, and we wake up late, and I look and perhaps even smell a bit grottier than she might have wanted, in an ideal world, and she's friendly but distant; I get the feeling that last night is unlikely to be repeated. We go out for breakfast, to a place which is full of young couples who have spent the night together, and though we don't look out of place, I know we are: everybody else seems happy and comfortable and established, not nervy and new and sad, and Marie and I read our newspapers with an intensity that is designed to cut out any further intimacy. It's only afterwards that we really set ourselves apart from the rest, though: a quick and rueful peck on the cheek, and I have the rest of Sunday to myself, whether I want it or not.

What went wrong? Nothing and everything. Nothing: we had a nice evening, we had sex that humiliated neither of us, we even had a pre-dawn conversation that I and maybe she will remember for ages and ages. Everything: all that stupid business when I couldn't decide whether I was going home or not, and in the process giving her the impression that I was a half-wit; the way that we got on brilliantly and then had nothing much to say to each other; the manner of our parting; the fact that I'm no nearer to appearing in the sleeve notes than I was before I met her. It's not a case of the glass being half-full or half-empty; more that we tipped a whole half-pint into an empty pint pot. I had to see how much was there, though, and now I know.

ELEVEN

All my life I've hated Sundays, for the obvious British reasons (*Songs of Praise*, closed shops, congealing gravy that you don't want to go near but no one's going to let you escape from) and the obvious international reasons as well, but this Sunday is a corker. There are loads of things I could do; I've got tapes to make and videos to watch and phone calls to return. But I don't want to do any of them. I get back to the flat at one; by two, things have got so bad that I decide to go home – *home* home, Mum and Dad home, congealing gravy and *Songs of Praise* home. It was waking up in the middle of the night and wondering where I belonged that did it: I don't belong at home, and I don't *want* to belong at home, but at least home is somewhere I know.

Home home is near Watford, a bus-ride away from the Metropolitan Line station. It was a terrible place to grow up, I suppose, but I didn't really mind. Until I was thirteen or so it was just a place where I could ride my bike; between thirteen and seventeen a place where I could meet girls. And I moved when I was eighteen, so I only spent a year seeing the place for what it was – a suburban shit-hole – and hating it. My mum and dad moved house about ten years ago, when my mum reluctantly accepted that I had gone and wasn't coming back but they only moved around the corner, to a two-bedroom semi, and they kept their phone number and their friends and their life.

In Bruce Springsteen songs, you can either stay and rot, or you can escape and burn. That's OK; he's a songwriter, after all, and he needs simple choices like that in his songs. But nobody ever writes about how it is possible to escape and rot – how escapes can go off at half-cock, how you can leave the suburbs for the city but end up living a limp suburban life anyway. That's what happened to me; that's what happens to most people.

They're OK, if you like that sort of thing, which I don't. My dad is a bit dim but something of a know-all, which is a pretty fatal combination; you can tell from his silly, fussy beard that he's going to be the sort who doesn't talk much sense and won't listen to any reason. My mum is just a mum, which is an unforgivable thing to say in any circumstance except this one. She worries, she gives me a hard time about the shop, she gives me a hard time about my childlessness. I wish I wanted to see them more, but I don't, and when I've got nothing else to feel bad about, I feel bad about that. They'll be pleased to see me this afternoon, although my heart sinks when I see that fucking *Genevieve* is on TV this afternoon. (My dad's top five films: *Genevieve*, *The Cruel Sea*, *Zulu*, *Oh! Mr Porter*, which he thinks is hilarious, and *The Guns of Navarone*. My mum's top five films: *Genevieve*, *Gone With the Wind*, *The Way We Were*, *Funny Girl* and *Seven Brides for Seven Brothers*. You get the idea, anyway, and you'll get an even better idea when I tell you that going to the cinema is a waste of money, according to them, because sooner or later the films end up on television.)

*

When I get there, the joke's on me: they're not in. I've come a million stops on the Metropolitan Line on a Sunday afternoon, I've waited eight years for a bus, fucking *Genevieve* is on the fucking television and they're not here. They didn't even call to let me know they wouldn't be here, not that I called to let them know I was coming. If I was at all prone to self-pity, which I am, I would feel bad about the terrible irony of finding your parents out when, finally, you need them.

But just as I'm about to head back to the bus stop, my mum opens the window of the house opposite and yells at me.

'Rob! Robert! Come in!'

I've never met the people over the road, but it soon becomes obvious that I'm in a minority of one: the house is packed.

'What's the occasion?'

'Wine tasting.'

'Not Dad's home-made?'

'No. Proper wine. This afternoon it's Australian. We all chip in and a man comes and explains it all.'

'I didn't know you were interested in wine.'

'Oh, yes. And your dad loves it.'

Of course he does. He must be terrible to work with the morning after a wine-tasting session: not because of the reek of stale booze, or the bloodshot eyes, or the crabby behaviour, but because of all the facts he has swallowed. He'd spend half the day telling people things they didn't want to know. He's over the other side of the room, talking to a man in a suit – the visiting expert, presumably – who has a desperate look in his eye. Dad sees me, and mimes shock, but he won't break off the conversation.

The room is full of people I don't recognize. I've missed the part where the guy talks and hands out samples; I've arrived during the part where wine tasting becomes wine drinking and, though every now and again I spot someone swilling the wine around in their mouth and talking bollocks, mostly they're just pouring the stuff down their necks as fast as they can. I wasn't expecting this. I came for an afternoon of silent misery, not wild partying; the one thing I wanted from the afternoon was incontrovertible proof that my life may be grim and empty, but not as grim and empty as life in Watford. Wrong again. Nothing works, as Catweazle used to say. Life in Watford is grim, yes; but grim and full. What right do parents have to go to parties on Sunday afternoons for no reason at all?

'*Genevieve* is on the telly this afternoon, Mum.'

'I know. We're taping it.'

'When did you get a video?'

'Months ago.'

'You never told me.'

'You never asked.'

'Is that what I'm supposed to do every week? Ask you whether you've bought any consumer durables?'

A huge lady wearing what appears to be a yellow kaftan glides towards us.

'You must be Robert.'

'Rob, yeah. Hi.'

'I'm Yvonne. Your host. Hostess.' She laughs insanely, for no discernible reason. I want to see Kenneth More. 'You're the one who works in the music industry, am I right?'

I look at my mum, and she looks away. 'Not really, no. I own a record shop.'

'Oh, well. Same thing, more or less.' She laughs again, and though it would be consoling to think that she is drunk, I fear that this is not the case.

'I guess so. And the woman who develops your photos at Boots works in the film industry.'

'Would you like my keys, Rob? You can go home and put the kettle on.'

'Sure. Heaven forbid that I should be allowed to stay here and have fun.'

Yvonne mutters something and glides off. My mum's too pleased to see me to give me a hard time, but even so I feel a bit ashamed of myself.

'Perhaps it's time I had a cup of tea anyway.' She goes over to thank Yvonne, who looks at me, cocks her head on one side and makes a sad face; Mum's obviously telling her about Laura as an explanation for my rudeness. I don't care. Maybe Yvonne will invite me to the next session.

We go home and watch the rest of *Genevieve.*

My dad comes back maybe an hour later. He's drunk.

'We're all going to the pictures,' he says.

This is too much.

'You don't approve of the pictures, Dad.'

'I don't approve of the rubbish you go to watch. I approve of nice well-made films. British films.'

'What's on?' my mum asks him.

'*Howards End*. It's the follow-up to *A Room with a View*.'

'Oh, lovely,' my mum says. 'Is anyone else going from across the road?'

'Only Yvonne and Brian. But get a move on. It starts in half an hour.'

'I'd better be going back,' I say. I have exchanged hardly a word with either of them all afternoon.

'You're going nowhere,' my dad says. 'You're coming with us. My treat.'

'It's not the money, Dad.' It's Merchant and fucking Ivory. 'It's the time. I'm working tomorrow.'

'Don't be so feeble, man. You'll still be in bed by eleven. It'll do you good. Buck you up. Take your mind off things.' This is the first reference to the fact that I have things off which my mind needs taking.

And, anyway, he's wrong. Going to the pictures aged thirty-five with your mum and dad and their insane friends does not take your mind off things, I discover. It very much puts your mind on things. While we're waiting for Yvonne and Brian to purchase the entire contents of the Pick'n'Mix counter, I have a terrible, chilling, bone-shaking experience: the most pathetic man in the world gives me a smile of recognition. The Most Pathetic Man In The World has huge Dennis Taylor-style spectacles and buck teeth; he's wearing a dirty fawn anorak and brown cord trousers which have been rubbed smooth at the knee; he, too, is being taken to see *Howards End* by his parents, despite the fact that he's in his late twenties. And he gives me this terrible little smile *because he has spotted a kindred spirit*. It disturbs me so much that I can't concentrate on Emma Thompson and Vanessa and the rest, and by the time I rally it's too late, and the story's too far on down the road for me to catch up. In the end, a bookcase falls on someone's head.

I would go so far as to say that TMPMITW's smile has become one of my all-time top five low points, the other four of which temporarily escape me. I know I'm not as pathetic as the most pathetic man in the world (Did he spend last night in an American recording artiste's bed? I very much doubt it.); the point is that the difference between us is not immediately obvious to him, and I can see why. This, really, is the bottom line, the chief attraction of the opposite sex for all of us, old and young, men and women: we need someone to save us from the sympathetic smiles in the Sunday night cinema queue, someone who can stop us from falling down into the pit where the permanently single live with their mums and dads. I'm not going back there again; I'd rather stay in for the rest of my life than attract that kind of attention.

TWELVE

During the week, I think about Marie, and I think about The Most Pathetic Man In The World, and I think, at Barry's command, about my all-time top five episodes of *Cheers*: 1) The one where Cliff found a potato that looked like Richard Nixon. 2) The one where John Cleese offered Sam and Diane counselling sessions. 3) The one where they thought that the Chief of Staff of the US Forces – played by the real-life Admiral guy – had stolen Rebecca's earrings. 4) The one where Sam got a job as a sports presenter on TV. 5) The one where Woody sang his stupid song about Kelly. (Barry said I was wrong about four of the five, that I had no sense of humour, and that he was going to ask Channel 4 to scramble my reception between nine-thirty and ten every Friday night because I was an undeserving and unappreciative viewer.) But I don't think about anything Laura said that Saturday night until Wednesday, when I come home to find a message from her. It's nothing much, a request for a copy of a bill in our household file, but the sound of her voice makes me realize that there are some things we talked about which should have upset me but somehow didn't.

First of all – actually, first of all and last of all – this business about not sleeping with Ian. How do I know she's telling the truth? She could have been sleeping with him for weeks, *months*, for all I know. And anyway, she only said that she hasn't slept with him *yet*, and she said that on Saturday, five days ago. Five days! She could have slept with him five times since then! (She could have slept with him twenty times since then, but you know what I mean.) And even if she hasn't, she was definitely threatening to. What does 'yet' mean, after all? 'I haven't seen *Reservoir Dogs* yet.' What does that mean? It means you're going to go, doesn't it?

'Barry, if I were to say to you that I haven't seen *Reservoir Dogs* yet, what would that mean?'

Barry looks at me.

'Just ... come on, what would it mean to you? That sentence? "I haven't seen *Reservoir Dogs* yet"?'

'To me, it would mean that you're a liar. Either that or you've gone potty. You saw it twice. Once with Laura, once with me and Dick. We had that conversation about who killed Mr Pink or whatever fucking colour he was.'

'Yeah, yeah, I know. But say I hadn't seen it and I said to you, "I haven't seen *Reservoir Dogs* yet", what would you think?'

'I'd think, you're a sick man. And I'd feel sorry for you.'

'No, but would you think, from that one sentence, that I was going to see it?'

'I'd hope you were, yeah, otherwise I would have to say that you're not a friend of mine.'

'No, but—'

'I'm sorry, Rob, but I'm struggling here. I don't understand any part of this conversation. You're asking me what I'd think if you told me that you hadn't seen a film that you've seen. What am I supposed to say?'

'Just listen to me. If I said to you—'

'"I haven't seen *Reservoir Dogs* yet," yeah, yeah, I hear you—'

'Would you ... *would you get the impression that I wanted to see it?*'

'Well ... you couldn't have been desperate, otherwise you'd have already gone.'

'Exactly. We went first night, didn't we?'

'But the word "yet" ... yeah, I'd get the impression that you wanted to see it. Otherwise you'd say you didn't fancy it much.'

'But in your opinion, would I definitely go?'

'How am I supposed to know that? You might get run over by a bus, or go blind, or anything. You might go off the idea. You might be skint. You might just get sick of people telling you you've really got to go.'

I don't like the sound of that. 'Why would they care?'

'Because it's a brilliant film. It's funny, and violent, and it's got Harvey Keitel and Tim Roth in it, and everything. And a cracking soundtrack.'

Maybe there's no comparison between Ian sleeping with Laura and *Reservoir Dogs* after all. Ian hasn't got Harvey Keitel and Tim Roth in him. And Ian's not funny. Or violent. And he's got a crap soundtrack, judging from what we used to hear through the ceiling. I've taken this as far as it will go.

But it doesn't stop me worrying about the 'yet'.

I call Laura at work.

'Oh, hi, Rob,' she says, like I'm a friend she's pleased to hear from. (1. I'm not a friend. 2. She's not pleased to hear from me. Apart from that . . .) 'How's it going?'

I'm not letting her get away with this we-used-to-go-out-but-everything's-OK-now stuff.

'Bad, thanks.' She sighs. 'Can we meet? There're some things you said the other night that I wanted to go over.'

'I don't want . . . I'm not ready to talk about it all again yet.'

'So what am I supposed to do in the meantime?' I know how I'm sounding – whiny, whingey, bitter – but I don't seem to be able to stop myself.

'Just . . . live your life. You can't hang around waiting for me to tell you why I don't want to see you any more.'

'So what happened to us maybe getting back together?'

'I don't know.'

'Because the other night you said that might happen.' I'm getting nowhere fast here, and I know she's not in the right frame of mind to grant any concessions, but I push it anyway.

'I said nothing of the kind.'

'You did! You did! You said there was a chance! That's the same as "might"!' Jesus. This is truly pitiful.

'Rob, I'm at work. We'll talk when . . .'

'If you don't want me to call you at work, maybe you should give me your home number. I'm sorry, Laura, but I'm not going to put the phone down until you've agreed to meet up for a drink. I don't see why things should be on your terms all the time.'

She gives a short, bitter laugh. 'OK, OK, OK, OK, OK, OK. Tomorrow night? Come down and get me at the office.' She sounds utterly defeated.

'Tomorrow night? Friday? You're not busy? Fine. Great. It'll be nice to see you.' But I'm not sure she hears the positive, conciliatory, sincere bit at the end. She's hung up by then.

THIRTEEN

We're messing around at work, the three of us, getting ready to go home and rubbishing each other's five best side one, track ones of all time (mine: 'Janie Jones', the Clash, from *The Clash*; 'Thunder Road', Bruce Springsteen, from *Born To Run*; 'Smells Like Teen Spirit', Nirvana, from *Nevermind*; 'Let's Get It On', Marvin Gaye, from *Let's Get It On*'; 'Return Of The Grievous Angel', Gram Parsons, from *Grievous Angel.* Barry: 'Couldn't you make it any more obvious than that? What about the *Beatles*? What about the *Rolling Stones*? What about the fucking ... fucking ... *Beethoven*? Track one, side one of the Fifth Symphony? You shouldn't be allowed to run a record shop.' And then we have the argument about whether he's a snob obscurantist – are the Fire Engines, who appear on Barry's list, really better than Marvin Gaye, who does not? – or whether I'm a boring old middle-of-the-road fart.) And then Dick says, for the first time ever in his Championship Vinyl career, apart from maybe when he's gone somewhere miles away to see some ludicrous band, 'I can't make the pub tonight, guys.'

There's a mock-stunned silence.

'Don't mess about, Dick,' says Barry eventually.

Dick sort of smiles, embarrassed. 'No, really. I'm not coming.'

'I'm warning you,' says Barry. 'Unless there's an adequate explanation I shall have to give you the Weedy Wet of the Week award.'

Dick doesn't say anything.

'Come on. Who are you going to see?'

He still doesn't say anything.

'Dick, have you pulled?'

Silence.

'I don't believe it,' says Barry. 'Where is the justice in this world? Where is it? Justice! Where are you? Dick's out on a hot date, Rob's shagging Marie LaSalle, and the best-looking and most intelligent of the lot of them isn't getting anything at all.'

He's not just trying it on. There's no little sideways glance to see if he's hit the mark, no hesitation to see if I want to interject; he knows, and I feel both crushed and smug at the same time.

'How did you know about that?'

'Oh, come on, Rob. What do you take us for? I'm more bothered about Dick's date. How did this happen, Dick? What rational explanation can there possibly be? OK, OK. Sunday night you were in, because you made me that Creation B-sides tape. I was with you Monday night and last night, which leaves . . . Tuesday!'

Dick doesn't say anything.

'Where were you Tuesday?'

'Just at a gig with some friends.'

Was it that obvious? I guess a bit, on Saturday night, but Barry had no way of knowing that anything had actually happened.

'Well, what sort of gig is it where you just walk in and meet someone?'

'I didn't just walk in and meet her. She came with the friends I met there.'

'And you're going to meet her again tonight?'

'Yes.'

'Name?'

'Anna.'

'Has she only got half a name? Eh? Anna who? Anna Neagle? Anna Green Gables? Anna Conda? Come on.'

'Anna Moss.'

'Anna Moss. Mossy. The Moss Woman.'

I've heard him do this to women before, and I'm not sure why I don't like it. I talked about it to Laura once, because he tried it with her; some stupid pun on her surname, I can't remember what it was now. Lie-down, lied-on, something. And I hated him doing it. I wanted her to be *Laura*, to have a nice, pretty, girl's name that I could dream about when I felt like being dreamy. I didn't want him turning her into a bloke. Laura, of course, thought I was being a bit dodgy, thought I was trying to keep girls fluffy and silly and girly; she said I didn't want to think of them in the same way that I thought about my mates. She was right, of course – I don't. But that's not the point. Barry doesn't do this to strike a blow for equality: he does it because he's being spiteful, because he wants to puncture any sense of romantic well-being that Laura or Anna or whoever might have created in us. He's sharp, Barry. Sharp and nasty. He understands the power that girls' names have, and he doesn't like it.

'Is she all green and furry?'

This started out joky – Barry as demon counsel for the prosecution, Dick as defendant – but now those roles have started to harden. Dick looks guilty as all hell, and all he's done is meet someone.

'Leave it, Barry,' I tell him.

'Oh, yeah, you would say that, wouldn't you? You two have got to stick together now. Shaggers United, eh?'

I try to be patient with him. 'Are you coming to the pub or what?'

'No. Bollocks.'

'Fair enough.'

Barry leaves; Dick is now feeling guilty, not because he's met someone, but because I have nobody to drink with.

'I suppose I've got time for a quick one.'

'Don't worry about it, Dick. It's not your fault that Barry's a plonker. You have a nice evening.'

He flashes me a look of real gratitude, and it breaks your heart.

I feel as though I have been having conversations like this all my life. None of us is young any more, but what has just taken place could have happened when I was sixteen, or twenty, or twenty-five. We got to adolescence and just stopped dead; we drew up the map then and left the boundaries exactly as they were. And why does it bother Barry so much that Dick is seeing someone? Because he doesn't want a smile from a man with buck teeth and an anorak in the cinema queue, that's why; he's worried about how his life is turning out, and he's lonely, and lonely people are the bitterest of them all.

FOURTEEN

Ever since I've had the shop, we've been trying to flog a record by a group called the Sid James Experience. Usually we get rid of stuff we can't shift – reduce it to 10p, or throw it away – but Barry loves this album (he's got two copies of his own, just in case somebody borrows one and fails to return it), and he says it's rare, and that someday we'll make somebody very happy. It's become a bit of a joke, really. Regular customers ask after its health, and give it a friendly pat when they're browsing, and sometimes they bring the sleeve up to the counter as if they're going to buy it, and then say, 'Just kidding!', and put it back where they found it.

Anyway, on Friday morning, this guy I've never seen before starts flicking through the 'British Pop S–Z section', lets out a gasp of amazement and rushes up to the counter, clutching the sleeve to his chest as if he's afraid someone will snatch it from him. And then he gets out his wallet and pays for it, seven quid, just like that, no attempt to haggle, no recognition of the significance of what he is doing. I let Barry serve him – it's his moment – and Dick and I watch every move, holding our breath; it's like someone has walked in, tipped petrol over himself and produced a box of matches from his pocket. We don't exhale until he's struck the match and set himself alight, and when he's gone we laugh and laugh and laugh. It gives us all strength: if someone can just walk in and buy the Sid James Experience album, then surely anything good can happen at any time.

Laura's changed even since I last saw her. Partly it's the make-up: she's wearing it for work, and it makes her look less stressed-out, less tired, in control. But it's more than that, too. Something else has happened, maybe something real, or maybe something in her head. Whatever it is, you can see that she thinks she's started out on some new stage in her life. She hasn't. I'm not going to let her.

We go to a bar near her work – not a pub, a bar, with pictures of baseball players on the wall, and a food menu chalked up on a noticeboard, and a conspicuous lack of hand-pumps, and people in suits drinking American beer from the bottle. It's not crowded, and we sit in a booth near the back on our own.

And then she's straight in with the 'So, how are you?' as if I'm nobody very much. I mumble something, and I know that I'm not going to be able to control it, I'm going to come too quickly: then it's, bang, 'Have you slept with him yet?' and it's all over.

'Is that why you wanted to see me?'

'I guess.'

'Oh, Rob.'

I just want to ask the question again, straight away; I want an answer, I don't want 'Oh, Rob,' and a pitying stare.

'What do you want me to say?'

'I want you to say that you haven't, and for your answer to be the truth.'

'I can't do that.' She can't look at me when she's saying it, either.

She starts to say something else, but I don't hear it; I'm out in the street, pushing through all those suits and raincoats, angry and sick and on my way home to some more loud, angry records that will make me feel better.

The next morning the guy who bought the Sid James Experience album comes in to exchange it. He says it's not what he thought it was.

'What did you think it was?' I ask him.

'I don't know,' he says. 'Something else.' He shrugs, and looks at the three of us in turn. We are all staring at him, crushed, aghast; he looks embarrassed.

'Have you listened to all of it?' Barry asks.

'I took it off halfway through the second side. Didn't like it.'

'Go home and try it again,' Barry says desperately. 'It'll grow on you. It's a grower.'

The guy shakes his head helplessly. He's made up his mind. He chooses a second-hand Madness CD, and I put the Sid James Experience back in the rack.

Laura calls in the afternoon.

'You must have known it would happen,' she says. 'You couldn't have been entirely unprepared. Like you said, I've been living with the guy. We were bound to get around to it some time.' She gives a nervous and, to my way of thinking, highly inappropriate laugh.

'And, anyway, I keep trying to tell you, it's not really the point, is it? The point is, we got ourselves into an awful mess.'

I want to hang up, but people only hang up to get called back again, and why should Laura call me back? No reason at all.

'Are you still there? What are you thinking?'

I'm thinking: I've had a bath with this person (just one, years ago, but, you know, a bath's a bath), and I'm already beginning to find it hard to remember what she looks like. I'm thinking: I wish this stage was over, and we could go on to the next stage, the stage where you look in the paper and see that *Scent of a Woman* is on TV, and you say to yourself, Oh, I saw that with Laura. I'm thinking: am I supposed to fight, and what do I fight with, and who am I fighting?

'Nothing.'

'We can meet for another drink if you like. So I can explain better. I owe you that much.'

That much.

'How much would be too much?'

'Sorry?'

'Nothing. Look, I've got to go. I work too, you know.'

'Will you call me?'

'I haven't got your number.'

'You know you can call me at work. And we'll arrange to meet and talk properly.'

'OK.'

'Promise?'

'Yeah.'

'Because I don't want this to be the last conversation we have. I know what you're like.'

But she doesn't know what I'm like at all: I call her all the time. I call her later that afternoon, when Barry has gone out to get something to eat and Dick is busy sorting out some mail order stuff out the back. I call her after six, when Barry and Dick have gone. When I get home, I call Directory Enquiries and get Ian's new number, and I call about seven times, and hang up every time he answers; eventually, Laura guesses what's going on and picks up the phone herself. I call her the following morning, and twice that afternoon, and I call her from the pub that evening. And after the pub I go round to Ian's place, just to see what it looks like from the outside. (It's just another north London three-storey house, although I've no idea which storey is his, and there are no lights on in any of them anyway.) I've got nothing else to do. In short, I've lost it again, just like I lost it with Charlie, all those years ago.

There are men who call, and men who don't call, and I'd much, much rather be one of the latter. They are *proper* men, the sort of men that women have in mind when they moan about us. It's a safe, solid, meaningless stereotype: the man who appears not to give a shit, who gets ditched and maybe sits in the pub on his own for a couple of evenings, and then gets on with things; and though next time around he trusts even less than he did, he hasn't made a fool of himself, or frightened anybody, and this week I've done both of those things. One day Laura's sorry and guilty, and the next she's scared and angry, and I am entirely responsible for the transformation, and it hasn't done me any good at all. I'd stop if I could, but I don't seem to have any choice in the matter:

it's all I think about, all the time. 'I know what you're like,' Laura said, and she does, kind of: she knows that I'm someone who doesn't really bother, who has friends he hasn't seen for years, who no longer speaks to anybody that he has ever slept with. But she doesn't know how you have to work at that.

I want to see them now: Alison Ashworth, who ditched me after three miserable evenings in the park. Penny, who wouldn't let me touch her and who then went straight out and had sex with that bastard Chris Thomson. Jackie, attractive only while she was going out with one of my best friends. Sarah, with whom I formed an alliance against all the dumpers in the world and who then went and dumped me anyway. And Charlie. Especially Charlie, because I have her to thank for everything: my great job, my sexual self-confidence, the works. I want to be a well-rounded human being with none of these knotty lumps of rage and guilt and self-disgust. What do I want to do when I see them? I don't know. Just talk. Ask them how they are and whether they have forgiven me for messing them around, when I have messed them around, and tell them that I have forgiven them for messing me around, when they have messed me around. Wouldn't that be great? If I saw all of them in turn and there were no hard feelings left, just soft, *squidgy* feelings, Brie rather than old hard Parmesan, I'd feel clean, and calm, and ready to start again.

Bruce Springsteen's always doing it in his songs. Maybe not always, but he's done it. You know that one 'Bobby Jean', off *Born In The USA*? Anyway, he phones this girl up but she's left town years before and he's pissed off that he didn't know about it, because he wanted to say goodbye, and tell her that he missed her, and to wish her good luck. And then one of those sax solos comes in, and you get goosepimples, if you like sax solos. And Bruce Springsteen. Well, I'd like my life to be like a Bruce Springsteen song. Just once. I know I'm not born to run, I know that the Seven Sisters Road is nothing like Thunder Road, but *feelings* can't be so different, can they? I'd like to phone all those people up and say good luck, and goodbye, and then they'd feel good and I'd feel good. We'd all feel good. That would be good. Great even.

FIFTEEN

I am introduced to Anna. Dick brings her to the pub on a night when Barry isn't around. She's small, quiet, polite, anxiously friendly, and Dick obviously adores her. He wants my approval and I can give it easily, loads of it. Why would I want Dick to be unhappy? I wouldn't. I want him to be as happy as anybody has ever been. I want him to show the rest of us that it is possible to maintain a relationship and a large record collection simultaneously.

'Has she got a friend for me?' I ask Dick.

Normally, of course, I wouldn't refer to Anna in the third person while she's sitting with us, but I have an excuse: my question is both endorsement and allusion, and Dick smiles happily in recognition.

'Richard Thompson,' he explains to Anna. 'It's a song off a Richard Thompson album. "I Want To See The Bright Lights Tonight", isn't it, Rob?'

'Richard Thompson,' Anna repeats, in a voice which suggests that over the last few days she has had to absorb a lot of information very quickly. 'Now, which one was he? Dick's been trying to educate me.'

'I don't think we've got up to him yet,' says Dick. 'Anyway, he's a folk/rock singer and England's finest electric guitarist. Would you say that's right, Rob?' He asks the question nervously; if Barry were here, he'd take great pleasure in shooting Dick down at this point.

'That's right, Dick,' I reassure him. Dick nods with relief and satisfaction.

'Anna's a Simple Minds fan,' Dick confides, emboldened by his Richard Thompson success.

'Oh, right.' I don't know what to say. This, in our universe, is a staggering piece of information. We hate Simple Minds. They were number one in our Top Five Bands Or Musicians Who Will Have To Be Shot Come The Musical Revolution. (Michael Bolton, U2, Bryan Adams, and, surprise surprise, Genesis were tucked in behind them. Barry wanted to shoot the Beatles, but I pointed out that someone had already done it.) It is as hard for me to understand how he has ended up with a Simple Minds fan as it would be to fathom how he had paired off with one of the royal family, or a member of the shadow cabinet: it's not the attraction that baffles, so much as how on earth they got together in the first place.

'But I think she's beginning to understand why she shouldn't be. Aren't you?'

'Maybe. A bit.' They smile at each other. It's kind of creepy, if you think about it.

It's Liz that stops me phoning Laura all the time. She takes me to the Ship and gives me a good talking-to.

'You're really upsetting her,' she says. 'And him.'

'Oh, like I really care about him.'

'Well you should.'

'Why?'

'Because . . . because all you're doing is forming a little unit, them against you. Before you started all this, there was no unit. There were just three people in a mess. And now they've got something in common, and you don't want to make it any worse.'

'And why are you so bothered? I thought I was an arsehole.'

'Yeah, well, so is he. He's an even bigger arsehole, and he hasn't done anything wrong yet.'

'Why is he an arsehole?'

'You know why he's an arsehole.'

'How do *you* know I know why he's an arsehole?'

'Because Laura told me.'

'You had a conversation about what I thought was wrong with her new boyfriend? How did you get on to that?'

'We went the long way round.'

'Take me there the quick way.'

'You won't like it.'

'Come on, Liz.'

'OK. She told me that when you used to take the piss out of Ian, when you were living in the flat . . . that was when she decided she was going off you.'

'You have to take the piss out of someone like that, don't you? That Leo Sayer haircut and those dungarees, and the stupid laugh and the wanky right-on politics and the . . .'

Liz laughs. 'Laura wasn't exaggerating, then. You're not keen, are you?'

'I can't fucking stand the guy.'

'No, neither can I. For exactly the same reasons.'

'So what's she on about, then?'

'She said that your little Ian outbursts showed her how . . . *sour* was the word she used . . . how *sour* you've become. She said that she loved you for your enthusiasm and your warmth, and it was all draining away. You stopped making her laugh and you started depressing the hell out of her. And now you're scaring her as well. She could call the police, you know, if she wanted.'

The police. Jesus. One moment you're dancing round the kitchen to Bob Wills and the Texas Playboys (Hey! I made her laugh then, and that was only a few months ago!), and the next she wants to get you locked up. I don't say anything for ages. I can't think of anything to say that doesn't sound sour. 'What have I got to feel warm about?' I want to ask her. 'Where's the enthusiasm going to come from? How can you make someone laugh when they want to set the police on you?'

'But why do you keep calling her all the time? Why do you want her back so badly?'

'Why do you think?'

'I don't know. Laura doesn't know either.'

'Well if she doesn't know, what's the point?'

'There's always a point. Even if the point is to avoid this sort of mess next time, that's still a point.'

'Next time. You think there'll be a next time?'

'Come on, Rob. Don't be so pathetic. And you've just asked three questions to avoid answering my one.'

'Which was the one?'

'Ha, ha. I've seen men like you in Doris Day films, but I never thought they existed in real life.' She puts on a dumb, deep, American voice. 'The men who can't commit, who can't say "I love you" even when they want to, who start to cough and splutter and change the subject. But here you are. A living, breathing specimen. Incredible.'

I know the films she's talking about, and they're stupid. Those men don't exist. Saying 'I love you' is easy, a piece of piss, and more or less every man I know does it all the time. I've *acted* as though I haven't been able to say it a couple of times, although I'm not sure why. Maybe because I wanted to lend the moment that sort of corny Doris Day romance, make it more memorable than it otherwise would have been. You know, you're with someone, and you start to say something, and then you stop, and she goes 'What?' and you go 'Nothing', and she goes, 'Please say it', and you go, 'No, it'll sound stupid', and then she makes you spit it out, even though you'd been intending to say it all along, and she thinks it's all the more valuable for being hard-won. Maybe she knew all the time that you were messing about, but she doesn't mind anyway. It's like a quote: it's the nearest any of us get to being in the movies, those few days when you decide that you like somebody enough to tell her that you love her, and you don't want to muck it up with a glob of dour, straightforward, no-nonsense sincerity.

But I'm not going to put Liz straight. I'm not going to tell her that all this is a way of regaining control, that I don't know if I love Laura or not but I'm never going to find out while she's living with someone else; I'd rather Liz thought I was one of those anal, tongue-tied and devoted clichés who eventually see the light. I guess it won't do me any harm, in the long run.

SIXTEEN

I start at the beginning, with Alison. I ask my mum to look up her parents in the local phone book, and I take it from there.

'Is that Mrs Ashworth?'

'It is.' Mrs Ashworth and I were never introduced. We never really got to the meet-the-parents stage during our six-hour relationship.

'I'm an old friend of Alison's, and I'd like to get in touch with her again.'

'You want her address in Australia?'

'If . . . if that's where she lives, yeah.' I won't be forgiving Alison in a hurry. In fact, it will take me weeks: weeks to get around to writing a letter, weeks for a reply.

She gives me her daughter's address, and I ask what Alison's doing out there; it turns out that she's married to someone with a building business, and she's a nurse, and they have two children, both girls, and blah blah. I manage to resist asking whether she ever mentions me at all. You can only take self-absorption so far. And then I ask about David, and he's in London working for a firm of accountants, and he's married, and he's got two girls as well, and can't anybody in the family produce boys? Even Alison's cousin has just had a little girl! I express disbelief in all the right places.

'How did you know Alison?'

'I was her first boyfriend.'

There's a silence, and for a moment I worry that for the last twenty years I have been held responsible in the Ashworth house for some sort of sexual crime I did not commit.

'She married her first boyfriend. Kevin. She's Alison Bannister.'

She married Kevin Bannister. I was ousted by forces beyond my control. This is tremendous. What chance did I stand against kismet? No chance at all. It was nothing to do with me, or any failings on my part, and I can feel the Alison Ashworth scar healing over as we speak.

'If that's what she's saying, she's a liar.' This is meant to be a joke, but it comes out all wrong.

'I beg your pardon?'

'No, seriously, joking apart, ha ha, I went out with her before Kevin did. Only for a week or so' – I have to up it a bit, because if I told the truth, she'd think I was mad – 'but they all count, don't they? A snog's a snog, after all, ha ha.' I'm not going to be written out of history like this. I played my part. I did my bit.

'What did you say your name was?'

'Rob. Bobby. Bob. Robert. Robert Zimmerman.' Fucking hell.

'Well, Robert, I'll tell her you called, when I speak to her. But I'm not sure she'll remember you.'

She's right, of course. She'll remember the evening she got off with Kevin, but she won't remember the evening before. It's probably only me who remembers the evening before. I guess I should have forgotten about it ages ago, but forgetting isn't something I'm very good at.

This man comes into the shop to buy the *Fireball XL5* theme tune for his wife's birthday (and I've got one, an original, and it's his for a tenner). And he's maybe two or three years younger than me, but he's well spoken, and he's wearing a suit, and he's dangling his car keys and for some reason these three things make me feel maybe two decades younger than him, twenty or so to his fortysomething. And I suddenly have this burning desire to find out what he thinks of me. I don't give in to it, of course ('There's your change, there's your record, now come on, be honest, you think I'm a waster, don't you?'), but I think about it for ages afterwards, what I must look like to him.

I mean, he's married, which is a scary thing, and he's got the sort of car keys that you jangle confidently, so he's obviously got, like, a BMW or a Batmobile or something flash, and he does work which requires a suit, and to my untutored eye it looks like an expensive suit. I'm a bit smarter than usual today – I've got my newish black denims on, as opposed to my ancient blue ones, and I'm wearing a long-sleeved polo shirt thing that I actually went to the trouble of ironing – but even so I'm patently not a grown-up man in a grown-up job. Do I want to be like him? Not really, I don't think. But I find myself worrying away at that stuff about pop music again, whether I like it because I'm unhappy, or whether I'm unhappy because I like it. It would help me to know whether this guy has ever taken it seriously, whether he has ever sat surrounded by thousands and thousands of songs about . . . about . . . (say it, man, say it) . . . well, about love. I would guess that he hasn't. I would also guess Douglas Hurd hasn't, and the guy at the Bank of England hasn't; nor has David Owen or Nicholas Witchell or Kate Adie or loads of other famous people that I should be able to name, probably, but can't, because they never played for Booker T and the MGs. These people look as though they wouldn't have had the time to listen to the first side of *Al Green's Greatest Hits*, let alone all his other stuff (ten albums on the Hi label alone, although only nine of them were produced by Willie Mitchell); they're too busy fixing base rates and trying to bring peace to what was formerly Yugoslavia to listen to 'Sha La La (Make Me Happy)'.

So they might have the jump on me when it comes to accepted notions of seriousness (although as everyone knows, *Al Green Explores Your Mind* is as serious as life gets), but I ought to have the edge on them when it comes to matters of the heart. 'Kate,' I should be able to say, 'it's all very well dashing off to war zones. But what are you going to do about the only thing that really matters? You *know* what I'm talking about, baby.' And then I could give her all the emotional advice I gleaned from the College of Musical Knowledge. It hasn't worked out like that, though. I don't know anything about Kate Adie's love life, but it can't be in a worse state than mine, can it? I've spent nearly thirty years listening to people singing about broken hearts, and has it helped me any? Has it fuck.

So maybe what I said before, about how listening to too many records messes your life up . . . maybe there's something in it after all. David Owen, he's married, right? He's taken care of all that, and now he's a big-shot diplomat. The guy who came into the shop with the suit and the car keys, he's married too, and now he's, I don't know, a *businessman*. Me, I'm unmarried – at the moment as unmarried as it's possible to be – and I'm the owner of a failing record shop. It seems to me that if you place music (and books, probably, and films, and plays, and anything that makes you *feel*) at the centre of your being, then you can't afford to sort out your love life, start to think of it as the finished product. You've got to pick at it, keep it alive and in turmoil, you've got to pick at it and unravel it until it all comes apart and you're compelled to start all over again. Maybe we all live life at too high a pitch, those of us who absorb emotional things all day, and as a consequence we can never feel merely *content*: we have to be unhappy, or ecstatically, head-over-heels happy, and those states are difficult to achieve within a stable, solid relationship. Maybe Al Green is directly responsible for more than I ever realized.

See, records have helped me to fall in love, no question. I hear something new, with a chord change that melts my guts, and before I know it I'm looking for someone, and before I know it I've found her. I fell in love with Rosie the simultaneous-orgasm woman after I'd fallen in love with a Cowboy Junkies song: I played it and played it and played it, and it made me dreamy, and I needed someone to dream about, and I found her, and . . . well, there was trouble.

SEVENTEEN

Penny's easy. I don't mean, you know, *easy* (if I meant that, I wouldn't have to meet up with her and talk about knobbing and Chris Thomson, because I would have knobbed her first and he wouldn't have been able to shoot his mouth off in the classroom that morning); I mean she's easy to track down. My mum sees her mum quite often, and a while back Mum gave me her phone number and told me to get in touch, and Penny's mum gave her mine, and neither of us did anything about it, but I kept the number anyway. And she's surprised to hear from me – there's a long computer-memory silence while she tries to make sense of the name, and then a little laugh of recognition – but not, I think, displeased, and we arrange to go to a film together, some Chinese thing that she has to see for work, and to eat afterwards.

The film's OK, better than I thought it would be – it's about this woman who's sent off to live with this guy, and he's already got loads of wives, so it's about how she gets on with her rivals, and it all goes horribly wrong. Of course. But Penny's got one of these special film-critic pens that have a light in the end of them (even though she's not a film critic, just a BBC radio journalist) and people keep looking round at her and nudging each other, and I feel a bit of a berk sitting there with her. (I have to say, although it is ungallant, that she looks funny anyway, even without the special film-critic pen: she always was a girl for sensible clothes, but what she's wearing tonight – a big floral dress, a beige raincoat – pushes sensible over the edge towards death. 'What's that cool guy in the leather jacket doing with Virginia Bottomley's elder sister?' the audience is thinking. Probably.)

We go to this Italian place she knows, and they know her, too, and they do vulgar things with the pepper grinder that seem to amuse her. It's often the way that people who take their work seriously laugh at stupid jokes; it's as if they are under-humoured and, as a consequence, suffer from premature laugh-ejaculation. But she's OK, really. She's a good sort, a good sport, and it's easy to talk about Chris Thomson and knobbing. I just launch into it, with no real explanation.

I try to tell the story in a light-hearted, self-deprecatory way (it's about me, not him and her), but she's appalled, really disgusted: she puts her knife and fork down and looks away, and I can see that she's close to tears.

'Bastard,' she says. 'I wish you hadn't told me that.'

'I'm sorry. I just thought, you know, long time ago and all that.'

'Well, it obviously doesn't seem that long ago to you.'

Fair point.

'No. But I just thought I was weird.'

'Why this sudden need to tell me about it, anyway?'

I shrug. 'Dunno. Just . . .'

And then I show her that, on the contrary, I do know: I tell her about Laura and Ian (although I don't tell her about Marie or money or abortions or pain-in-the-arse Rosie) and about Charlie, maybe more about Charlie than she wants to know; and I try to explain to her that I feel like the Rejection Man, and that Charlie wanted to sleep with Marco and not me, and Laura wanted to sleep with Ian and not me, and Alison Ashworth, even all those years ago, wanted to snog with Kevin

Bannister and not me (although I do share with her my recent discovery about the invincibility of kismet), and that as she, Penny, wanted to sleep with Chris Thomson and not me, perhaps she would be able to help me understand why it kept happening, why I was apparently doomed to be left.

And she tells me, with great force, with *venom*, frankly speaking, about what she remembers: that she was mad about me, that she wanted to sleep with me, one day, but not when she was sixteen, and that when I packed her in – '*When you packed me in*,' she repeats, furiously, 'because I was, to use your charming expression, "tight", I cried and cried, and I hated you. And then that little shitbag asked me out, and I was too tired to fight him off, and it wasn't rape, because I said OK, but it wasn't far off. And I didn't have sex with anyone else until after university because I hated it so much. And now you want to have a chat about rejection. Well fuck you, Rob.'

So that's another one I don't have to worry about. I should have done this years ago.

EIGHTEEN

Sellotaped to the inside of the shop door is a handwritten notice, yellowed and faded with age. It reads as follows:

> HIP YOUNG GUNSLINGERS WANTED (BASS, DRUMS, GUITAR) FOR NEW BAND. MUST BE INTO REM, PRIMAL SCREAM, FANCLUB ETC. CONTACT BARRY IN THE SHOP.

The advertisement used to end with the intimidating postscript 'NO SLACKERS PLEASE', but after a disappointing response during the first couple of years of the recruitment drive, Barry decided that slackers were welcome after all, to no noticeable effect; perhaps they couldn't get it together to walk from the door to the counter. A while back, a guy with a drum kit made enquiries, and though this minimalist vocal/drums two-piece did rehearse a few times (no tapes survive, sadly), Barry eventually and perhaps wisely decided that he needed a fuller sound.

Since then, though, nothing . . . until today. Dick sees him first – he nudges me, and we watch fascinated as this guy stares at the notice, although when he turns round to see which of us might be Barry, we quickly get on with what we were doing. He's neither hip, nor young – he looks more like a Status Quo roadie than a *Smash Hits* cover star hopeful. He has long, lank dark hair tied back in a ponytail, and a stomach that has wriggled over his belt to give itself a bit more room. Eventually he comes up to the counter, and gestures back towards the door.

'Is this Barry geezer around?'

'I'll get him for you.'

I go into the stockroom, where Barry is having a lie-down.

'Oi, Barry. There's someone come to see you about your ad.'

'What ad?'

'For the band.'

He opens his eyes and looks at me. 'Fuck off.'

'Seriously. He wants to talk to you.'

He gets to his feet and walks through to the shop.

'Yeah?'

'You put that ad up?'

'That's right.'

'What can you play?'

'Nothing.' Barry's all-consuming desire to play at Madison Square Garden has never driven him to do anything as mundane as learn an instrument.

'But you can sing, right?'

'Yeah.'

'We're looking for a singer.'

'What sort of stuff are you into?'

'Yeah, the kind of stuff you, you know, mentioned. But we want to be a bit more experimental than that. We want to retain our pop sensibilities, but kind of stretch them a bit.'

God help us.

'Sounds great.'

'We haven't got any gigs or anything. We've only just got together. For a laugh, like. But we'll see how we go, yeah?'

'Fine.'

The Quo roadie jots down an address, shakes Barry's hand, and leaves. Dick and I gape at his back view, just in case he self-combusts, or disappears, or sprouts angel's wings; Barry just tucks the address into his jeans pocket and looks for a record to put on, as if what has just happened – a mysterious stranger walking in and granting him one of his dearest wishes – were not the kind of little miracle that most of us wait for in vain.

'What?' he says. 'What's up with you two? It's just a poxy little garage band. Nothing special.'

Jackie lives in Pinner, not far from where we grew up, with my friend Phil, of course. When I call her, she knows who I am straight away, presumably because I'm the only Other Man in her whole life, and at first she sounds guarded, suspicious, as if I want to go through the whole thing again. I tell her that my mum and dad are OK, that I have my own shop, that I'm not married and have no children, at which point the suspicion turns to sympathy, and maybe a touch of guilt (Is this my fault? you can hear her thinking. Did his love life just stop dead in 1975, when I got back together with Phil?); she tells me that they have two children and a small house, that they both work, and that she never went to college, just as she feared she wouldn't. To end the brief silence that occurs after this résumé, she invites me to their house for supper, and in the brief silence that occurs after the invitation, I accept.

Jackie has grey streaks in her hair, but otherwise still looks pretty and friendly and sensible and all the other things she used to be; I kiss her and offer Phil my hand. Phil is now a man, with a moustache and shirtsleeves and a bald patch and a loosened tie, but he makes a big show of pausing before he returns the gesture – he wants me to realize that this is a symbolic moment, that he is forgiving me for my misdemeanours of all those years ago. Jesus, I think, it's supposed to be elephants that never forget, not British Telecom after-sales people. But then, what am I doing here, if not to meddle around with things that most people would have forgotten about years ago?

Jackie and Phil are the most boring people in the south-east of England, possibly because they've been married too long, and therefore have nothing to talk about, apart from how long they've been married. In the end, I am reduced to asking them, in a joky sort of way, for the secret of their success; I was only saving time, because I think they would have told me anyway.

'If you've found the right person, you've found the right person, it doesn't matter how old you are.' (Phil)

'You have to work at relationships. You can't just walk out on them every time something goes wrong.' (Jackie)

'That's right. It would have been easy to pack it in and start all over again with someone else who's swept you off your feet, but then you're still going to get to the stage when you're going to have to work at the new one.' (Phil)

'There aren't too many candlelit dinners and second honeymoons, I can tell you. We're beyond all that. We're good friends more than anything.' (Jackie)

'You can't just jump into bed with the first person you fancy and hope that you don't damage your marriage, no matter what people think.' (Phil)

'The trouble with young people today is . . .' No. Just kidding. But they're . . . *evangelical* about what they have, as if I've come up from north London to arrest them for being monogamous. I haven't, but they're right in thinking that it's a crime where I come from: it's against the law because we're all cynics and romantics, sometimes simultaneously, and marriage, with its clichés and its steady low-watt glow, is as unwelcome to us as garlic is to a vampire.

I'm at home, making a tape of some old singles, when the phone goes.

'Hi. Is that Rob?'

I recognize the voice as belonging to someone I don't like, but I don't get any further than that.

'This is Ian. Ray.'

I don't say anything.

'I thought maybe we should have a chat? Sort a couple of things out?'

This is . . . *something* . . . gone mad. *Blank* gone mad. You know when people use that expression to communicate the fact that something OK has got right out of control? 'This is democracy gone mad.' Well, I want to use that expression, but I'm not sure what the something is. North London? Life? The nineties? I don't know. All I do know is that in a decent, sane society, Ian wouldn't be ringing me up to sort a couple of things out. Nor would I be ringing him up to sort a couple of things out. I'd be sorting *him* out, and if he wants to be eating dungarees for a week, he's going the right way about it.

'What needs sorting out?' I'm so angry my voice is shaky, like it used to be when I was on the verge of a fight at school, and consequently I don't sound angry at all: I sound scared.

'Come on, Rob. My relationship with Laura has obviously disturbed you a great deal.'

'Funnily enough I haven't been too thrilled about it.' Sharp and clear.

'We're not talking joky understatement here, Rob. We're talking harassment. Ten phone calls a night, hanging round outside my house . . .'

Fucking hell. How did he see that?

'Yeah, well I've stopped all that now.' Sharp and clear has gone; now I'm sort of mumbling, like a mad guilty person.

'We've noticed, and we're glad. But, you know . . . how are we going to make the peace here? We want to make things easier for you. What can we do? Obviously I know how special Laura is, and I know things can't be good for you at the moment. I'd hate it if I lost her. But I'd like to think that if she decided she didn't want to see me any more, I'd respect that decision. D'you see what I'm saying?'

'Yeah.'

'Good. So how shall we leave it then?'

'Dunno.' And then I put the phone down – not on a smart, crushing one-liner, or after a raging torrent of abuse, but on a 'dunno'. That's taught him a lesson he won't forget.

HIM: Good. So how shall we leave it then?
ME: I've already left it, you pathetic little twerp. Liz is quite right about you. [*Slams receiver down.*]

HIM: Good. So how shall we leave it then?
ME: We won't leave it, Ian. Or at least, I won't. I'd change your phone number, if I were you. I'd change your address. One day soon you'll look back on one visit to the house and ten phone calls a night as a golden age. Watch your step, boy. [*Slams receiver down.*]

HIM: But I'd like to think that if she decided she didn't want to see me any more, I'd respect that decision.
ME: If she decided she didn't want to see you any more, I'd respect that decision. I'd respect her. Her friends would respect her. Everybody would cheer. The world would be a better place.

HIM: This is Ian. Ray.
ME: Fuck off. [*Slams receiver down.*]

Oh, well.

Oh well, nothing. I should have said any of those things. I should have used at least one obscenity. I should certainly have threatened him with violence. I shouldn't have hung up on a 'dunno'. These things are going to eat away at me and eat away at me and I'm going to drop dead of cancer or heart disease or something. And I shake and shake, and I rewrite the script in my head until it's 100 per cent proof poison, and none of it helps at all.

NINETEEN

Sarah still sends me Christmas cards with her address and phone number on them. (She doesn't write it out: she uses those crappy little stickers.) They never say anything else, apart from 'Happy Xmas! Love, Sarah,' in her big round schoolteacher's handwriting. I send her equally blank ones back. I noticed a couple of years ago that the address had changed; I also noticed that it had changed from a Whole Number, Something Street to a number with a letter after it, and not even a 'b', which can still denote a house, but a 'c' or a 'd', which can only denote a flat. I didn't think much about it at the time, but now it seems faintly ominous. To me it suggests that the Whole Number, Something Street belonged to Tom, and that Tom isn't around any more. Smug? Me?

She looks the same – a bit thinner, maybe (Penny was a lot fatter, but then she's doubled her age since I last saw her; Sarah had only gone from thirty to thirty-five, and that's not life's most fattening journey), but she's still peering out from under her fringe. We go out for a pizza, and it's depressing how big a deal this is for her: not the act of eating pizza itself, but the date-ness of the evening. Tom *has* gone, and gone in a fairly spectacular fashion. Get this: he told her, not that he was unhappy in the relationship, not that he had met someone else he wanted to see, not that he was seeing someone else, but that he was *getting married* to someone else. Classic, eh? You've got to laugh, really, but I manage not to. It's one of those hard-luck stories that seem to reflect badly on the victims, somehow, so I shake my head at the cruel mysteries of the universe instead.

She looks at her wine. 'I can't believe I left you for him,' she says. 'Mad.'

I don't want to hear this. I don't want her rejecting the rejection; I want her to explain it so that I can absolve her.

I shrug. 'Probably seemed like a good idea at the time.'

'Probably. I can't remember why, though.'

I could end up having sex here, and the prospect doesn't appal me. What better way to exorcize rejection demons than to shag the person who rejected you? But you wouldn't just be sleeping with a person: you'd be sleeping with a whole sad single-person culture. If we went to her place there'd be a cat, and the cat would jump on the bed at a crucial point, and we'd have to break off while she shooed it out and shut it in the kitchen. And we'd probably have to listen to her Eurythmics records, and there'd be nothing to drink. And there'd be none of those Marie LaSalle hey-women-can-get-horny-too shrugs; there'd be phone calls and embarrassment and regret. So I'm not going to sleep with Sarah unless at some point during the evening I see quite clearly that it's her or nothing for the rest of my life, and I can't see that sort of vision descending on me tonight: that's how we ended up going out in the first place. That's why she left me for Tom. She made a calculation, worked out the odds, made a solid each-way bet and went. That she wants another go says more about me, and about her, than cash ever can: she's thirty-five, and she's telling herself that life isn't going to offer her any more than what she has here this evening, a pizza and an old boyfriend she didn't like that much in the first place. That's a pretty grim conclusion, but it's not difficult to see how she got there.

Oh, we know, both of us, that it shouldn't matter, that there's more to life than pairing off, that the media is to blame, blah blah blah. But it's hard to see that, sometimes, on a Sunday morning, when you're maybe ten hours from going down to the pub for a drink and the first conversation of the day.

I haven't got the heart for the rejection conversation. There are no hard feelings here, and I'm glad that she ditched me, and not the other way around. I already feel guilty enough as it is. We talk about films, a bit – she loved *Dances With Wolves*, but she didn't like the sound of

Reservoir Dogs – and work, and a bit more about Tom, and a bit about Laura, although I just tell her that we're going through a rough patch. And she asks me back, but I don't go, and we agree that we've had a nice time, and that we'll do it again soon. There's only Charlie left now.

TWENTY

'How's the experimenting going? Are you still stretching your pop sensibilities?'

Barry glowers at me. He hates talking about the band.

'Yeah. Are they really into the same sort of stuff as you, Barry?' asks Dick innocently.

'We're not "into stuff", Dick. We play songs. Our songs.'

'Right,' says Dick. 'Sorry.'

'Oh, bollocks, Barry,' I say. 'What do your songs sound like? The Beatles? Nirvana? Papa Abraham and the Smurfs?'

'You probably wouldn't be familiar with our immediate influences,' Barry says.

'Try me.'

'They're mostly German.'

'What, Kraftwerk and that?'

He looks at me pityingly. 'Er, hardly.'

'Who, then?'

'You wouldn't have heard of them, Rob, so just shut up.'

'Just name one.'

'No.'

'Give us the initial letters, then.'

'No.'

'You haven't got a fucking clue, have you?'

He stomps out of the shop.

I know this is everybody's answer to everything and I'm sorry, but if ever a chap needed to get laid, it's Barry.

She's still living in London. I get her phone number and address from Directory Enquiries – she lives in Ladbroke Grove, of course. I call, but

I hold the receiver about an inch away from the phone, so that I can hang up quick if anyone answers. Someone answers. I hang up. I try again, about five minutes later, although this time I hold the receiver a little nearer to my ear, and I can hear that a machine, not a person, is answering. I still hang up, though. I'm not ready to hear her voice yet. The third time, I listen to her message; the fourth time, I leave one of my own. It's incredible, really, to think that at any time over the last decade I could have done this: she has come to assume such an importance I feel she should be living on Mars, so that attempts to communicate with her would cost millions of pounds and take light-years to reach her. She's an extra-terrestrial, a ghost, a myth, not a person with an answering machine and a rusting wok and a two-zone travel pass.

She sounds older, I guess, and a little bit posher – London has sucked the life out of her Bristol burr – but it's obviously her. She doesn't say whether she's living with anyone – not that I was expecting a message giving details of her current romantic situation, but she doesn't say, you know, 'Neither Charlie nor Marco can come to the phone right now,' or anything like that. Just, 'There's no one here, please leave a message after the bleep.' I leave my name, including surname, and my phone number, and stuff about long time no see etc.

I don't hear anything back from her. A couple of days later I try again, and I say the same stuff. Still nothing. Now this is more like it, if you're talking about rejection: someone who won't even return your phone messages a decade after she rejected you.

Marie comes into the shop.

'Hi, guys.'

Dick and Barry disappear, conspicuously and embarrassingly.

''Bye, guys,' she says after they're gone, and shrugs.

She peers at me. 'You avoiding me, boy?' she asks, mock-angry.

'No.'

She frowns and cocks her head on one side.

'Honest. How could I, when I don't know where you've been the last few days?'

'Well, are you embarrassed, then?'

'Oh, God yes.'

She laughs. 'No need.'

This, it seems, is what you get for sleeping with an American, all this upfront goodwill. You wouldn't catch a decent British woman marching in here after a one-night stand. We understand that these things are, on the whole, best forgotten. But I suppose Marie wants to talk about it, explore what went wrong; there's probably some group counselling workshop she wants us to go to, with lots of other couples who spent a misguided one-off Saturday night together. We'll probably have to take our clothes off and re-enact what happened, and I'll get my jumper stuck round my head.

'I was wondering if you wanted to come see T-Bone play tonight.'

Of course I don't. We can't speak any more, don't you understand, woman? We had sex, and that was the end of it. That's the law in this country. If you don't like it, go back to where you came from.

'Yeah. Great.'

'Do you know a place called Stoke Newington? He's playing there. The Weavers Arms?'

'I know it.' I could just not turn up, I suppose, but I know I'll be there.

And we have a nice time. She's right to be American about it: just because we've been to bed together doesn't mean we have to hate each other. We enjoy T-Bone's set, and Marie sings with him for his encore (and when she goes up on stage, people look at the place where she was standing, and then they look at the person next to the place where she was standing, and I quite like that). And then the three of us go back to hers for a drink, and we talk about London and Austin and records, but not about sex in general or the other night in particular, as if it was just something we did, like going to the curry house, which also requires no examination or elaboration. And then I go home, and Marie gives me a nice kiss, and on the way back I feel as though there's one relationship, just one, that is OK really, a little smooth spot I can feel proud of.

Charlie phones, in the end; she's apologetic about not having called sooner, but she's been away, in the States, on business. I try to make out like I know how it is, but I don't, of course – I've been to Brighton on business, and to Redditch, and to Norwich, even, but I've never been to the States.

'So, how are you?' she asks, and for a moment, just a moment but even so, I feel like doing a misery number on her: 'Not very good, thanks, Charlie, but don't let that worry you. You just fly out to the States on business, never mind me.' To my eternal credit, however, I restrain myself, and pretend that in the twelve years since we last spoke I have managed to live life as a fully functioning human being.

'Fine, thanks.'

'Good. I'm glad. You are fine, and you deserve to be fine.'

Something's wrong, somewhere, but I can't put my finger on it.

'How are you?'

'Good. Great. Work's good, nice friends, nice flat, you know. College all seems a long time ago, now. You remember when we used to sit in the bar, wondering how life would turn out for us?'

Nope.

'Well . . . I'm really happy with mine, and I'm glad you're happy with yours.'

I didn't say I was happy with my life. I said that I was fine, as in no colds, no recent traffic accidents, no suspended prison sentences, but never mind.

'Have you got, you know, kids and stuff, like everybody else?'

'No. I could have had them if I'd wanted them, of course, but I didn't want them. I'm too young, and they're too . . .'

'Young?'

'Well, yes, young, obviously,' – she laughs nervously, as if I'm an idiot, which maybe I am, but not in the way she thinks – 'but too . . . I don't know, *time-consuming*, I guess is the expression I'm looking for.'

I'm not making any of this up. This is how she talks, as if nobody has ever had a conversation about this in the entire history of the world.

'Oh, right. I see what you mean.'

I just took the piss out of Charlie. Charlie! Charlie Nicholson! This is weird. Most days, for the last dozen or so years, I have thought about Charlie, and attributed to her, or at least to our break-up, most things that have gone wrong for me. Like: I wouldn't have packed in college; I wouldn't have gone to work in Record and Tape; I wouldn't be saddled with this shop; I wouldn't have had an unsatisfactory personal life. This is the woman who broke my heart, ruined my life, this woman is single-handedly responsible for my poverty and directionlessness and failure, the woman I dreamed about regularly for a good five years, and *I'm sending her up*. I've got to admire myself, really. I've got to take my own hat off, and say to myself, 'Rob, you're one cool character.'

'Anyway, are you in or out, Rob?'

'I'm sorry?' It is comforting to hear that she still says things that only she can understand. I used to like it, and to envy it; I could never think of anything to say that sounded remotely strange.

'No, I'm sorry. It's just . . . I find these long-lost boyfriend calls rather unnerving. There's been a spate of them, recently. Do you remember that guy Marco I went out with after you?'

'Um . . . Yeah, I think so.' I know what's coming, and I don't believe it. All that painful fantasy, the marriage and the kids, years and years of it, and she probably ended up packing him in six months after I last saw her.

'Well, he called a few months back, and I didn't really know what to say to him. I think he was going through, you know, some kind of what-does-it-all-mean thing, and he wanted to see me, and talk about stuff, and what have you, and I wasn't really up for it. Do all men go through this?'

'I haven't heard of it before.'

'It's just the ones I pick, then. I didn't mean . . .'

'No, no, that's OK. It must seem a bit funny, me ringing up out of the blue. I just thought, you know . . .' I don't know, so I don't see why she should. 'But what does "Are you in or out" mean?'

'It means, I don't know, are we pals or aren't we? Because if we are, fine, and if we're not, I don't see the point of messing about on the phone. Do you want to come to dinner Saturday? I'm having some friends over and I need a spare man. Are you a spare man?'

'I . . .' What's the point? 'Yes, at the moment.'

'So are you in or out?'

'I'm in.'

'Good. My friend Clara is coming, and she hasn't got a chap, and she's right up your street. Eight o'clockish?'

And that's it. Now I can put my finger on what's wrong: Charlie is awful. She didn't use to be awful, but something bad has happened to her, and she says terrible, stupid things and has no apparent sense of humour whatsoever. What would Bruce Springsteen make of Charlie?

I tell Liz about Ian phoning me up, and she says it's outrageous, and that Laura will be appalled, which cheers me up no end. And I tell her about Alison and Penny and Sarah and Jackie, and about the stupid little torch-pen thing, and about Charlie and how she'd just come back from the States on business, and Liz says that *she's* just about to go to the States on business, and I'm amusingly satirical at her expense, but she doesn't laugh.

'How come you hate women who have better jobs than you, Rob?'

She's like this sometimes, Liz. She's OK, but, you know, she's one of those *paranoid* feminists who see evil in everything you say.

'What are you on about now?'

'You hate this woman who took a little torch-pen into the cinema, which seems a perfectly reasonable thing to do if you want to write in the dark. And you hate the fact that . . . Charlie? . . . Charlie went to the States – I mean, maybe she didn't want to go to the States. I know I don't. And you didn't like Laura wearing clothes that she had no choice about wearing when she changed jobs, and now I'm beneath contempt because I've got to fly to Chicago, talk to some men in a hotel conference room for eight hours and then fly home again . . .'

'Well, I'm sexist, aren't I? Is that the right answer?'

You just have to smile and take it, otherwise it would drive you mad.

TWENTY-ONE

When Charlie opens the door, my heart sinks: she looks beautiful. She still has the short, blond hair, but the cut is a lot more expensive now, and she's ageing in a really elegant way – around her eyes there are faint, friendly, sexy crow's feet which make her look like Sylvia Sims, and she's wearing a self-consciously grown-up black cocktail dress (although it probably only seems self-conscious to me because as far as I'm concerned she's only just stepped out of a pair of baggy jeans and a Tom Robinson Band T-shirt). Straight away I start to worry that I'm going to fall for her again, and I'll make a fool of myself, and it's all going to end in pain, humiliation and self-loathing, just as it did before. She kisses me, hugs me, tells me I don't look any different and that it's great to see me, and then she points me to a room where I can leave my jacket. It's her bedroom (arty, of course, with a huge abstract painting on one wall and what looks like a rug on another); I have a sudden panic when I'm in there. The other coats on the bed are expensive, and for a moment I entertain the idea of going through the pockets and then doing a runner.

But I want to see Clara, Charlie's friend, who's right up my street. I want to see her because I don't know where my street is; I don't even know which part of town it's in, which *city*, which *country*, so maybe she'll enable me to get my bearings. And it'll be interesting, too, to see what street Charlie thinks I live on, whether it's the Old Kent Road or Park Lane. (Five women who don't live on my street, as far as I know, but would be very welcome if they ever decided to move into the area: the Holly Hunter of *Broadcast News*; the Meg Ryan of *Sleepless in Seattle*; a woman doctor I saw on the telly once, who had lots of long frizzy hair and carved up a Tory MP in a debate about embryos, although I don't know her name and I've never been able to find a pin-up of her; Katharine Hepburn in *The Philadelphia Story*; Valerie Harper in the TV series *Rhoda*. These are women who talk back, women with a mind of their own, women with snap and crackle and pop . . . but they are also women who seem to need the love of a good man. I could rescue them. I could redeem them. They could make me laugh, and I could make them laugh, maybe, on a good day, and we could stay in and watch one of their films or TV programmes or embryo debates on video and adopt disadvantaged children together and the whole family could play soccer in Central Park.)

When I walk into the sitting room, I can see immediately that I'm doomed to die a long, slow, suffocating death. There's a man wearing a sort of brick-red jacket and another man in a carefully rumpled linen suit and Charlie in her cocktail dress and another woman wearing fluorescent leggings and a dazzling white silk blouse and another woman wearing those trousers that look like a dress but which aren't. Isn't. Whatever. And the moment I see them I want to cry, not only through terror, but through sheer *envy*: *Why isn't my life like this?*

Both of the women who are not Charlie are beautiful – not pretty, not attractive, not appealing, *beautiful* – and to my panicking, blinking, twitching eye virtually indistinguishable: miles of dark hair, thousands of huge earrings, yards of red lips, hundreds of white teeth. The one wearing the white silk blouse shuffles along Charlie's enormous sofa, which is made of glass, or lead, or gold – some intimidating, un-sofa-like material, anyway – and smiles at me; Charlie interrupts the others ('Guys,

guys . . .') and introduces me to the rest of the party. Clara's on the sofa with me, as it were, ha ha, Nick's in the brick-red jacket, Barney's in the linen suit, Emma's in the trousers that look like a dress. If these people were ever up my street I'd have to barricade myself inside the flat.

'We were just talking about what we'd call a dog if we had one,' says Charlie. 'Emma's got a Labrador called Dizzy, after Dizzy Gillespie.'

'Oh, right,' I say. 'I'm not very keen on dogs.'

None of them says anything for a while; there's not much they *can* say, really, about my lack of enthusiasm for dogs.

'Is that size of flat, or childhood fear, or the smell, or . . . ?' asks Clara, very sweetly.

'I dunno. I'm just . . .' I shrug hopelessly, 'you know, not very keen.'

They smile politely.

As it turns out, this is my major contribution to the evening's conversation, and later on I find myself recalling the line wistfully as belonging to a Golden Age of Wit. I'd even use it again if I could, but the rest of the topics for discussion don't give me the chance – I haven't seen the films or the plays they've seen, and I haven't been to the places they've visited. I find out that Clara works in publishing, and Nick's in PR; I find out too that Emma lives in Clapham. Emma finds out that I live in Crouch End, and Clara finds out that I own a record shop. Emma has read the autobiography of John McCarthy and Jill Morrell; Charlie hasn't, but would very much like to, and may even borrow Emma's copy. Barney has been skiing recently. I could probably remember a couple of other things if I had to. For most of the evening, however, I sit there like a pudding, feeling like a child who's been allowed to stay up late for a special treat. We eat stuff I don't know about, and either Nick or Barney comments on each bottle of wine we drink apart from the one I brought.

The difference between these people and me is that they finished college and I didn't (they didn't split up with Charlie and I did); as a consequence, they have smart jobs and I have a scruffy job, they are rich and I am poor, they are self-confident and I am incontinent, they do not smoke and I do, they have opinions and I have lists. Could I tell them anything about which journey is the worst for jet-lag? No. Could they tell me the original line-up of the Wailers? No. They probably couldn't even tell me the lead singer's name.

But they're not bad people. I'm not a class warrior, and anyway they're not particularly posh – they probably have mothers and fathers just outside Watford or its equivalent too. Do I want some of what they've got? You bet. I want their opinions, I want their money, I want their clothes, I want their ability to talk about dogs' names without any hint of embarrassment. I want to go back to 1979 and start all over again.

It doesn't help that Charlie talks bollocks all night; she doesn't listen to anyone, she tries too hard to go off at obtuse angles, she puts on all sorts of unrecognizable and inappropriate accents. I would like to say that these are all new mannerisms, but they're not; they were there before, years ago. The not listening I once mistook for strength of character, the obtuseness I misread as mystery, the accents I saw as glamour and drama. How had I managed to edit all this out in the intervening years? How had I managed to turn her into the answer to all the world's problems?

I stick the evening out, even though I'm not worth the sofa space for most of it, and I outstay Clara and Nick and Barney and Emma. When they've gone, I realize that I spent the whole time drinking instead of speaking, and as a consequence I can no longer focus properly.

'I'm right, aren't I?' Charlie asks. 'She's just your type.'

I shrug. 'She's everybody's type.' I help myself to some more coffee. I'm drunk, and it seems like a good idea just to launch in. 'Charlie, why did you pack me in for Marco?'

She looks at me hard. 'I knew it.'

'What?'

'You *are* going through one of those what-does-it-all-mean things.' She says 'what-does-it-all-mean' in an American accent, and furrows her brow.

I cannot tell a lie. 'I am, actually, yes. Yes, indeed. Very much so.'

She laughs – at me, I think, not with me – and then plays with one of her rings.

'You can say what you like,' I tell her, generously.

'It's all kind of a bit lost in the . . . in the dense mists of time now.' She says 'dense mists of time' in an Irish accent, for no apparent reason, and waves her hand around in front of her face, presumably to indicate the density of the mist. 'It wasn't that I fancied Marco more, because I used to find you every bit as attractive as him.' (Pause.) 'It's just that he knew he was nice-looking, and you didn't, and that made a difference, somehow. You used to act as though I was a bit peculiar for wanting to spend time with you, and that got kind of tiring, if you know what I mean. Your self-image started to rub off on me, and *I* ended up thinking

I was peculiar. And I knew you were kind, and thoughtful, and you made me laugh, and I loved the way you got consumed by the things you loved, but . . . Marco seemed a bit more, I don't know, glamorous? More sure of himself, more in with the in-crowd?' (Pause.) 'Less hard work, 'cos I felt I was dragging you round a bit.' (Pause.) 'A bit sunnier, and a bit sparkier.' (Pause.) 'I don't know. You know what people are like at that age. They make very superficial judgements.'

Where's the superficial? I was, and therefore am, dim, gloomy, a drag, unfashionable, unfanciable and awkward. This doesn't seem like superficial to me. These aren't flesh wounds. These are life-threatening thrusts into the internal organs.

'Do you find that hurtful? He was a wally, if that's any consolation.'

It's not, really, but I didn't want consolation. I wanted the works, and I got them too. None of Alison Ashworth's kismet here; none of Sarah's rewriting of history, and no reminder that I'd got all the rejection stuff the wrong way round, like I did about Penny. Just a perfectly clear explanation of why some people have it and some people don't. Later on, in the back of a minicab, I realize that all Charlie has done is rephrase my own feelings about my genius for being normal; maybe that particular talent – my only one, as it happens – was overrated anyway.

TWENTY-TWO

Barry's band are going to play a gig, and he wants to put a poster up in the shop.

'No. Fuck off.'

'Thanks for your support, Rob. I really appreciate it.'

'I thought we had a rule about posters for crap bands.'

'Yeah, for people who come in off the street begging us. All the losers.'

'Like . . . let's see. Suede, you turned down. The Auteurs. St Etienne. Losers like that, you mean?'

'What's all this "*I* turned them down"? It was your rule.'

'Yeah, but you loved it, didn't you? It gave you great pleasure to tell all those poor kids to take a running jump.'

'Well, I was wrong, wasn't I? Oh, come on, Rob. We need the regulars from here, otherwise there'll be nobody.'

'OK, what's the name of the band? If it's any good, you can put a poster up.'

He thrusts a poster at me – just the name of the band, with some squiggly design.

'"Barrytown". "Barrytown"? Fucking hell. Is there no end to your arrogance?'

'It's not because of me. It's the Steely Dan song. And it was in *The Commitments*.'

'Yeah, but come on, Barry. You can't be called Barry and sing in a group called Barrytown. It just sounds . . .'

'They were fucking called that before I came along, OK? It wasn't my idea.'

'That's why you got the gig, isn't it?'

Barry of Barrytown says nothing.

'Isn't it?'

'That was one of the reasons why they asked me originally, yes. But . . .'

'Brilliant! Fucking brilliant! They only asked you to sing because of your name! Of course you can have a poster up, Barry. I want as many people to know as possible. Not in the window, OK? You can stick it above the browser racks over there.'

'How many tickets can I put you down for?'

I hold my sides and laugh mirthlessly. 'Ha, ha ha. Ho, ho ho. Stop, Barry, you're killing me.'

'You're not even coming?'

'Of course I'm not coming. Do I look like a man who'd want to listen to some terrible experimental racket played in some horrible north London pub? Where is it?' I look at the poster. 'The fucking Harry Lauder! Ha!'

'So much for mates, then. You're a bitter bastard, Rob, you know that?'

Sour. Bitter. Everyone seems to agree that I don't taste very nice.

'Bitter? Because I'm not in Barrytown? I hoped it wasn't that obvious. And you've been great to Dick about Anna, haven't you? Really made her feel a part of the Championship Vinyl family.'

I'd forgotten that I have been wishing nothing but everlasting happiness to Dick and Anna. How does that fit in with my sourness, eh? What's bitter about that?

'That Anna stuff was just a bit of fun. She's all right. It's just . . . it's not my fault that you're fucking up left, right and centre.'

'Oh, and you'd be first in the queue to see me play, wouldn't you?'

'Not first, maybe. But I'd be there.'

'Is Dick going?'

''Course. And Anna. And Marie and T-Bone.'

Is the world really that generous-spirited? I had no idea.

I guess you could see it as bitterness, if you wanted to. I don't think of myself as bitter, but I have disappointed myself; I thought I was going to turn out to be worth a bit more than this, and maybe that disappointment comes out all wrong. It's not just the work; it's not just the thirty-five and single thing, although none of this helps. It's . . . oh, I don't know. Have you ever looked at a picture of yourself when you were a kid? Or pictures of famous people when they were kids? It seems to me that they can either make you happy or sad. There's a lovely picture of Paul McCartney as a little boy, and the first time I saw it, it made me feel good: all that talent, all that money, all those years of blissed-out domesticity, a rock-solid marriage and lovely kids, and he doesn't even know it yet. But then there are others – JFK and all the rock deaths and fuck-ups, people who went mad, people who came off the rails, people who murdered, who made themselves or other people miserable in ways too numerous to mention – and you think, stop right there! This is as good as it gets!

Over the last couple of years, the photos of me when I was a kid, the ones that I never wanted old girlfriends to see . . . well, they've started to give me a little pang of something – not unhappiness, exactly, but some kind of quiet, deep regret. There's one of me in a cowboy hat, pointing a gun at the camera, trying to look like a cowboy but failing, and I can hardly bring myself to look at it now. Laura thought it was sweet (she used that word! Sweet, the opposite of sour!) and pinned it up in the kitchen, but I've put it back in a drawer. I keep wanting to apologize to the little guy: 'I'm sorry, I've let you down. I was the person who was supposed to look after you, but I blew it: I made wrong decisions at bad times, and I turned you into me.'

See, he would have wanted to see Barry's band; he wouldn't have worried too much about Ian's dungarees or Penny's torch-pen (he would have *loved* Penny's torch-pen) or Charlie's trips to the States. He wouldn't have understood, in fact, why I was so down on all of them. If he could be here now, if he could jump out of that photo and into this shop, he'd run straight out of the door and back to 1967 as fast as his little legs would carry him.

TWENTY-THREE

Finally, finally, a month or so after she's left, Laura comes to move her stuff out. There's no real argument about what belongs to who; the good records are mine, the good furniture, most of the cooking stuff and the hardback books are hers. The only thing I've done is to sort out a whole pile of records and a few CDs I gave her as presents, stuff that I wanted but thought she'd like, and which have somehow ended up being filed away in my collection. I've been really scrupulous about it: she wouldn't have remembered half of these, and I could have got away with it, but I've pulled out every single one.

I was scared she was going to bring Ian round, but she doesn't. In fact, she's obviously uncomfortable about the fact that he rang.

'Forget it.'

'He had no right to do that, and I told him so.'

'Are you still together?'

She looks at me to see if I'm joking, and then gives a little hard-luck grimace that actually isn't too attractive, if you think about it.

'Going all right?'

'I don't really want to talk about it, to be honest.'

'That bad, eh?'

'You know what I mean.'

She's borrowed her dad's Volvo estate for the weekend, and we fill every inch of it; she comes back inside for a cup of tea when we're done.

'It's a dump, isn't it?' I say. I can see her looking round the flat, staring at the dusty, discoloured spaces her things have left on the wall, so I feel I have to pre-empt criticism.

'Please do it up, Rob. It wouldn't cost you much, and it would make you feel better.'

'I'll bet you can't remember what you were doing here now, can you?'

'Yes, I can. I was here because I wanted to be with you.'

'No, I meant, you know . . . how much are you on now? Forty-five? Fifty? And you lived in this poky little hole in Crouch End.'

'You know I didn't mind. And it's not as if Ray's place is any better.'

'I'm sorry, but can we get this straight? What is his name, Ian or Ray? What do you call him?'

'Ray. I hate Ian.'

'Right. Just so's I know. Anyway, what's Ian's place like?' Childish, but it makes me happy. Laura puts on her pained, stoical face. I've seen that one a few times, I can tell you.

'Small. Smaller than here. But neater, and less cluttered.'

'That's 'cos he's only got about ten records. CDs.'

'And that makes him an awful person, does it?'

'In my book, yes. Barry, Dick and I decided that you can't be a serious person if you have—'

'Less than five hundred. Yes, I know. You've told me many, many times before. I disagree. I think it's possible to be a serious person even if you have no records whatsoever.'

'Like Kate Adie.'

She looks at me, frowns and opens her mouth, her way of indicating that I'm potty. 'Do you know for a fact that Kate Adie's got no records whatsoever?'

'Well, not *none*. She's probably got a couple. Pavarotti and stuff. Maybe some Tracey Chapman, and a copy of *Bob Dylan's Greatest Hits*, and two or three Beatles albums.'

She starts to laugh. I wasn't joking, to be honest, but if she thinks I'm funny then I'm prepared to act like I was.

'And I'll bet she was one of the people at parties who used to go "Woooh!" to the fade-out of "Brown Sugar".'

'There is no greater crime than that, as far as you're concerned, is there?'

'The only thing that runs it close is singing along to the chorus of "Hi Ho Silver Lining", at the top of your voice.'

'I used to do that.'

'You didn't.'

The joking has stopped now, and I look at her appalled. She roars.

'You believed me! You believed me! You must think I'm capable of *anything*.' She laughs again, catches herself having a good time, and stops.

I give her the cue. 'This is where you're supposed to say that you haven't laughed this much in ages, and then you see the error of your ways.'

She makes a so-what face. 'You make me laugh much more than Ray does, if that's what you're getting at.'

I give a mock-smug smile, but I'm not feeling mock-smug. I'm feeling the real thing.

'But it doesn't make any difference to anything, Rob. Really. We could laugh until I had to be taken away in an ambulance, but it doesn't mean I'm going to unload the car and move all my stuff back in. I already knew you could make me laugh. It's everything else I don't know about.'

'Why don't you just admit that Ian's an arsehole and have done with it? It would make you feel better.'

'Have you been talking to Liz?'

'Why? Does she think he's an arsehole too? That's interesting.'

'Don't spoil it, Rob. We've got on well today. Let's leave it at that.'

I pull out the stack of records and CDs that I've sorted out for her. There's *The Nightfly* by Donald Fagen, because she'd never heard it, and some blues compilation samplers I decided she ought to have, and a couple of jazz-dance things I bought for her when she started going to a jazz-dance class, although it turned out to be a different and frankly much crappier form of jazz-dance, and a couple of country things, in my vain attempt to change her mind about country, and . . .

She doesn't want any of it.

'But they're *yours*.'

'They're not really, though, are they? I know you bought them for me, and that was really sweet of you, but that was when you were trying to turn me into you. I can't take them. I know they'd just sit around staring at me, and I'd feel embarrassed by them, and . . . they don't fit in with the rest of what's mine, do you understand? That Sting record you bought me . . . that was a present for *me*. I like Sting and you hate him. But the rest of this stuff . . .' She picks up the blues sampler. 'Who the hell's Little Walter? Or Junior Wells? I don't know these people. I . . .'

'OK, OK. I get the picture.'

'I'm sorry to go on about it. But, I don't know, there's a lesson in here somewhere, and I want to make sure you get it.'

'I get it. You like Sting but you don't like Junior Wells, because you've never heard of him.'

'You're being deliberately obtuse.'

'I am, actually, yes.'

She gets up to go.

'Well, think about it.'

And later on, I think, what for? What's the point of thinking about it? If I ever have another relationship, I'll buy her, whoever she is, stuff that she ought to like but doesn't know about; that's what new boyfriends are for. And hopefully I won't borrow money off her, or have an affair, and she won't need to have an abortion, or run away with the neighbours, and then there won't be anything to think about. Laura didn't run off with Ray because I bought her CDs she wasn't that keen on, and to pretend otherwise is just . . . just . . . *psychowank*. If she thinks that, then she's missing the Brazilian rainforest for the twigs. If I can't buy specially priced compilation albums for new girlfriends, then I might as well give up, because I'm not sure that I know how to do anything else.

TWENTY-FOUR

I usually enjoy my birthday, but today I don't feel so good about it. Birthdays should be suspended in years like this one: there should be a law, of man if not of nature, that you are only allowed to age when things are ticking along nicely. What do I want to be thirty-six for now? I don't. It's not convenient. Rob Fleming's life is frozen at the moment, and he refuses to get any older. Please retain all cards, cakes and presents for use on another occasion.

Actually, that seems to be what people have done. Sod's law decrees that my birthday should fall on a Sunday this year, so cards and presents are not forthcoming; I didn't get anything Saturday either. I wasn't expecting anything from Dick or Barry, although I told them in the pub after work, and they looked guilty, and bought me a drink, and promised me all sorts of things (well, compilation tapes, anyway); but I never remember their birthdays – you don't, do you, unless you are of the female persuasion? – so a tantrum would not be particularly appropriate in this case. But Laura? Relatives? Friends? (Nobody you know, but I do have some, and I do see them sometimes, and one or two of them do know when my birthday is.) Godparents? Anyone else at all? I did get a card from my mum and pp my dad, but parents don't count; if you don't even get a card from your folks, then you're really in trouble.

On the morning of the day itself I spend much too much time fantasizing about some enormous surprise party organized by Laura, maybe, with the help of my mum and dad, who could have provided her with the addresses and phone numbers of some of the people she wouldn't know about; I even find myself irritated by their not having told me about it. Suppose I just took myself off to the pictures for a solitary birthday treat without letting them know? Then where would they be, eh? They'd all be hiding in some cupboard somewhere while I was watching a *Godfather* triple-bill at the Scala. That'd serve them right. I decide not to tell them where I'm going; I'll leave them squashed up in the dark, cramped and ill-tempered. ('I thought *you* were going to ring him?' 'I told you I didn't have time', etc.) After a couple of cups of coffee, however, I realize that this sort of thinking is not profitable, that it is, in fact, likely to drive me potty, and I decide to arrange something positive instead.

Like what?

Go to the video shop for a start, and rent loads of things I've been saving up for just such a dismal occasion as this: *Naked Gun 2½*, *Terminator 2*, *Robocop 2*. And then ring up a couple of people to see if they want a drink tonight. Not Dick and Barry. Marie maybe, or people I haven't seen for a long time. And then watch one or two of the videos, drink some beer and eat some crisps, maybe even some Kettle Chips. Sounds good. Sounds like the sort of birthday a brand-new thirty-six-year-old *should* have. (Actually, it is the *only* sort of birthday a brand-new thirty-six-year-old could have – the sort of thirty-six-year-old with no wife, family, girlfriend or money, anyway. Kettle Chips! Fuck off!)

You thought there was going to be nothing left in the video shop, didn't you? You thought I cut such a tragic figure that I'd be reduced to watching some Whoopi Goldberg comedy-thriller which never got a cinematic release in this country. But no! They're all there, and I walk out with all the rubbish I want tucked under my arm. It's just turned twelve, so I can buy some beer; I go home, pop a can, draw the curtains to keep out the March sunshine, and watch *Naked Gun*, which turns out to be pretty funny.

My mum calls just as I'm putting *Robocop 2* into the machine, and again, I'm disappointed that it isn't someone else. If you can't get a phone call from your mum on your birthday, then you're really in trouble.

She's nice to me, though. She's sympathetic about me spending the day on my own, even though she must be hurt that I'd rather spend the day on my own than spend it with her and Dad. ('D'you want to come to the pictures this evening with your father and Yvonne and Brian?' she asks me. 'No,' I tell her. That's all. Just 'No'. Restrained or what?) She can't really think of anything to say after that. It must be hard for parents, I guess, when they see that things aren't working out for their children, but that their children can no longer be reached by the old parental routes, because those roads are now much too long. She starts to talk about other birthdays, birthdays where I was ill because I ate too many hundreds-and-thousands sandwiches or drank too many rainbow cocktails, but these were at least pukes conceived in happiness, and her talking about them doesn't cheer me up much, and I stop her. And then she starts on a whiny, how-come-you've-got-yourself-into-this-mess speech, which I know is a result of her powerlessness and panic, but it's my day today, such as it is, and I'm not prepared to listen to that either. She's OK about me shutting her up, though: because she still treats me like a child, birthdays are times when I am allowed to behave like one.

Laura rings in the middle of *Robocop 2, from a callbox*. This is very interesting, but maybe now is not the time to talk about why – not with Laura anyway. Maybe later, with Liz or someone, but not now. This is obvious to anyone but a complete idiot.

'Why are you ringing from a callbox?'

'Am I?' she says. Not the smoothest answer.

'Did you have to put money or a card into a slot to speak to me? Is there a horrible smell of urine? If the answer to either of these questions is yes, it's a callbox. Why are you ringing from a callbox?'

'To wish you a happy birthday. I'm sorry I forgot to send you a card.'

'I didn't mean . . .'

'I was just on my way home, and I . . .'

'Why didn't you wait till you got back?'

'What's the point of me saying anything? You think you know the answer anyway.'

'I'd just like it confirmed.'

'Are you having a good day?'

'Not bad. *Naked Gun 2½*: very funny. *Robocop 2*: not as good as the first one. So far, anyway.'

'You're watching videos?'

'I am.'

'On your own?'

'Yep. Want to come round? I've still got *Terminator 2* to see.'

'I can't. I've got to get back.'

'Right.'

'Anyway.'

'How's your dad?'

'He's not too bad, at the moment, thanks for asking.'

'Good.'

'Have a nice day, OK? Do something good with it. Don't waste all day in front of the TV.'

'Right.'

'Come on, Rob. It's not my fault you're in on your own. I'm not the only person you know. And I am thinking of you, it's not like I've just jumped ship.'

'Tell Ian I said hi, OK?'

'Very funny.'

'I mean it.'

'I know you do. Very funny.'

Got her. He doesn't want her to phone, and she's not going to tell him she has. Cool.

I'm at a bit of a loss after *Terminator 2*. It's not six o'clock yet, and even though I've ploughed my way through three great crap videos and the best part of a six-pack, I still cannot shake the feeling that I'm not having much of a birthday. There are papers to read, and compilation tapes to make, but, you know. I pick up the phone instead, and start to organize my own surprise party in the pub. I shall gather a few people together, try to forget I called them, take myself off to the Crown or the Queen's

Head around eight for a quiet pint, and get my back slapped raw by well-wishers I never expected to see there in a million years.

It's harder than I thought, though. London, eh? You might as well ask people if they'd like to take a year off and travel around the world with you as ask them if they'd like to nip out for a quick drink later on: later on means later on in the month, or the year, or the nineties, but never later on the same day. 'Tonight?' they all go, all these people I haven't spoken to for months, ex-colleagues or old college friends, or people I've met through ex-colleagues or old college friends. 'Later on *tonight*?' They're aghast, they're baffled, they're kind of amused, but most of all they just can't believe it. Someone's phoning up and suggesting a drink tonight, out of the blue, no Filofax to hand, no lists of alternative dates, no lengthy consultation with a partner? Preposterous.

But a couple of them show signs of weakness, and I exploit that weakness mercilessly. It's not an ooh-I-shouldn't-really-but-I-quite-fancy-a-pint sort of weakness; it's an inability-to-say-no sort of weakness. They don't want to go out tonight, but they can hear the desperation, and they cannot find it in themselves to respond with the necessary firmness.

Dan Maskell (real first name Adrian, but it had to be done) is the first to crack. He's married, with a kid and he lives in Hounslow, and it's a Sunday night, but I'm not going to let him off the hook.

'Hello, Dan? It's Rob.'

'Hello, mate.' (Genuine pleasure at this point, which is something, I suppose.)

'How are you?'

So I tell him how I am, and then I explain the sad situation – sorry it's too last-minute, bit of a cock-up on the arrangement front (I manage to resist telling him there's been a bit of a cock-up on the life front generally), be nice to see him anyway, and so on and so forth, and I can hear the hesitation in his voice. And then – Adrian's a big music fan, which is how I met him at college, and why we kept in touch afterwards – I steal a trump card and play it.

'Have you heard of Marie LaSalle? She's a very good folky country kind of singer.'

He hasn't, not surprisingly, but I can tell that he's interested.

'Well, anyway, she's a . . . well, a friend, and she'll be coming along, so . . . she's great, and she's worth meeting, and . . . I don't know if . . .'

It's just about enough. To speak frankly with you, Adrian's a bit of an idiot, which is why I thought Marie might be an enticement. Why do I want to spend my birthday drinking with an idiot? That's a long story, most of which you already know.

Steven Butler lives in north London, doesn't have a wife, and doesn't have that many friends either. So why can't he come out tonight? He's already rented his video, that's why.

'Fucking hell, Steve.'

'Well you should have called me earlier. I've only just come back from the shop.''

'Why don't you watch it now?'

'No. I'm a bit funny about watching videos before my tea. It's like you're just watching for the sake of it, do you know what I mean? And every one you watch in the daytime, that's one less you can watch at night.'

'How d'you work that out?'

''Cos you're wasting them, aren't you?'

'Watch it another time, then.'

'Oh, yeah. I've got so much money I can give two pounds to the bloke in the video shop every night.'

'I'm not asking you to do it every night. I'm . . . Look, I'll give you the two quid, all right?'

'I dunno. Are you sure?'

I'm sure, and there we have it. Dan Maskell and Steve Butler. They don't know each other, they won't like each other, and they have nothing in common apart from a slight overlap in their record collections (Dan's not very interested in black music, Steve's not very interested in white music, they both have a few jazz albums). And Dan's expecting to see Marie, but Marie's not expecting to see Dan, nor does she even know of his existence. Should be a cracking night out.

Marie's got a phone now, and Barry has her number, and she's happy that I called, and more than happy to come out for a drink, and if she knew it was my birthday she'd probably explode with joy, but for some reason I decide not to tell her. I don't have to sell the evening to her, which is just as well, because I don't think I'd be able to give it away. She's got to do something else first, however, so there's an agonizing hour or so alone with Steve and Dan. I talk to Dan about rock music, while Steve stares at somebody getting lucky on the fruit machine, and I talk to Steve about soul music, while Dan does that trick with a beer mat which only the truly irritating person knows. And then we all talk about jazz, and then there's some pretty desultory what-do-you-do kind of stuff, and then we run out of petrol altogether, and we all watch the guy who's getting lucky on the fruit machine.

Marie and T-Bone and a very blonde, very glamorous and very young woman, also American, finally turn up around quarter to ten, so there's only forty-five minutes of drinking time left. I ask them what they want to drink, but Marie doesn't know, and comes up to the bar with me to have a look at what they've got.

'I see what you mean about T-Bone's sex life,' I say as we're waiting.

She raises her eyes to the ceiling. 'Isn't she something else? And you know what? That's the ugliest woman he's ever dated.'

'I'm glad you could come.'

'The pleasure is ours. Who are those guys?'

'Dan and Steve. I've known them for years. They're a bit dull, I'm afraid, but I have to see them sometimes.'

'Duck noires, right?'

'Sorry?'

'I call 'em duck noires. Sort of a mixture of lame duck and *bête noire*. People you don't want to see but kinda feel you should.'

Duck noires. Bang on. And I had to fucking beg mine, *pay* mine, to come out for a drink on my birthday.

I never think these things through, ever. 'Happy birthday, Rob,' says Steve when I put his drink down in front of him. Marie attempts to give me a look – of surprise, I would guess, but also of deepest sympathy and bottomless understanding, but I won't return it.

It's a pretty bad evening. When I was a kid, my granny used to spend Boxing Day afternoon with a friend's granny; my mum and dad would drink with Adrian's mum and dad, and I'd play with Adrian, and the two old codgers would sit in front of the TV exchanging pleasantries. The catch was that they were both deaf, but it didn't really matter: they were happy enough with their version of a conversation, which had the same gaps and nods and smiles as everyone else's conversation, but none of the connections. I haven't thought about that for years, but I remember it tonight.

Steve annoys me throughout: he has this trick of waiting until the conversation is in full flow, and then muttering something in my ear when I'm attempting either to talk or to listen to somebody else. So I can either ignore him and appear rude, or answer him, involve everyone else in what I'm saying and change their direction entirely. And once he's got everyone talking about soul, or *Star Trek* (he goes to conventions and things), or great bitters of the north of England (he goes to conventions and things), subjects nobody else knows anything about, we go through the whole process all over again. Dan yawns a lot, Marie is patient, T-Bone is tetchy, and his date, Suzie, is positively appalled. What is she doing in a grotty pub with these guys? She has no idea. Neither have I. Maybe Suzie and I should disappear off somewhere more intimate, and leave these losers to get on with it. I could take you through the whole evening, but you wouldn't enjoy it much, so I'll let you off with a dull but entirely representative sample:

MARIE: . . . just unbelievable, I mean, real *animals*. I was singing 'Love Hurts' and this guy shouted out, 'Not the way I do it, baby', and then he was sick all the way down his T-shirt, and he *didn't move a muscle*. Just stood there shouting at the stage and laughing with his buddies. [*Laughs.*] You were there, weren't you, T-Bone?

T-BONE: I guess.

MARIE: T-Bone *dreams* of fans as suave as that, don't you? The places he plays, you have to . . . [*Inaudible due to interruption from* . . .]

STEVE: [*Whispering in my ear*] They've brought *The Baron* out on video now, you know. Six episodes. D'you remember the theme music?

ME: No. I don't. [*Laughter from Marie, T-Bone, Dan*] Sorry, Marie, I missed that. You have to do what?

MARIE: I was saying, this place that T-Bone and me . . .

STEVE: It was brilliant. Der-der-DER! Der-der-der DER!

DAN: I recognize that. *Man in a Suitcase*?

STEVE: No. *The Baron*. 'S'out on video.

MARIE: *The Baron*? Who was in that?

DAN: Steve Forrest.

MARIE: I think we used to get that. Was that the one where the guy . . . [*Inaudible due to interruption from* . . .]

STEVE: [*Whispering in my ear*] D'you ever read *Voices from the*

Shadows? Soul magazine? Brilliant. Steve Davis owns it, you know. The snooker player.

[*Suzie makes a face at T-Bone. T-Bone looks at his watch.*]

Etc.

Never again will this combination of people be seated around a table; it just couldn't possibly happen, and it shows. I thought the numbers would provide a feeling of security and comfort, but they haven't. I don't really know any of these people, not even the one I've slept with, and for the first time since I split up with Laura I really feel like slumping on to the floor and bawling my eyes out. I'm homesick.

It's supposed to be women who allow themselves to become isolated by relationships: they end up seeing more of the guy's friends, and doing more of the guy's things (poor Anna, trying to remember who Richard Thompson is, and being shown the error of her Simple Minded ways), and when they're ditched, or when they ditch, they find they've floated too far away from friends they last saw properly three or four years before. And before Laura, that was what life was like for me and my partners too, most of them.

But Laura . . . I don't know what happened. I liked her crowd, Liz and the others who used to come down the Groucho. And for some reason – comparative career success, I guess, and the corresponding postponements that brings – her crowd were more single and more flexible than mine. So for the first time ever I played the woman's role, and threw my lot in with the person I was seeing. It wasn't that she didn't like my friends (not friends like Dick and Barry and Steve and Dan, but *proper* friends, the sort of people I have allowed myself to lose). It was just that she liked hers more, and wanted me to like them, and I did. I liked them more than I liked my own and, before I knew it (I never knew it, really, until it was too late), my relationship was what gave me my sense of location. And if you lose your sense of location, you get homesick. Stands to reason.

So now what? It feels as though I've come to the end of the line. I don't mean that in the American rock'n'roll suicide sense; I mean it in the English Thomas the Tank Engine sense. I've run out of puff, and come to a gentle halt in the middle of nowhere.

'These people are your friends?' Marie asks me the next day when she takes me for a post-birthday crispy bacon and avocado sandwich.

'It's not that bad. There were only two of them.'

She looks at me to see if I'm joking. When she laughs, it's clear that I am.

'But it was your *birthday*.'

'Well. You know.'

'Your *birthday*. And that's the best you can do?'

'Say it was your birthday today, and you wanted to go out for a drink tonight. Who would you invite? Dick and Barry? T-Bone? Me? We're not your bestest friends in the whole world, are we?'

'Come on, Rob. I'm not even in my own *country*. I'm thousands of miles from home.'

My point exactly.

I watch the couples that come into the shop, and the couples I see in pubs, and on buses, and through windows. Some of them, the ones that talk and touch and laugh and enquire a lot, are obviously new, and they don't count: like most people, I'm OK at being half of a new couple. It's the more established, quieter couples, the ones who have started to go through life back-to-back or side-to-side, rather than face-to-face, that interest me.

There's not much you can decipher in their faces, really. There's not much that sets them apart from single people; try dividing people you walk past into one of life's four categories – happily coupled, unhappily coupled, single and desperate – and you'll find you won't be able to do it. Or rather, you could do it, but you would have no confidence in your choices. This seems incredible to me. The most important thing in life, and you can't tell whether people have it or not. Surely this is wrong? Surely people who are happy should *look* happy, at all times, no matter how much money they have or how uncomfortable their shoes are or how little their child is sleeping; and people who are doing OK but have still not found their soul-mate should look, I don't know, well but anxious, like Billy Crystal in *When Harry Met Sally*; and people who are desperate should wear something, a yellow ribbon maybe, which would allow them to be identified by similarly desperate people. When I am no longer desperate, when I have got all this sorted out, I promise you here and now that I will never ever complain again about how the shop is doing, or about the soullessness of modern pop music, or the stingy fillings you get in the sandwich bar up the road (£1.60 for egg mayonnaise and crispy bacon, and none of us has ever had more than four pieces of crispy bacon in a whole round yet) or anything at all. I will beam beatifically at all times, just from sheer *relief*.

Nothing much, by which I mean even less than usual, happens for a couple of weeks. I find a copy of 'All Kinds Of Everything' in a junk shop near the flat, and buy it for fifteen pence, and give it to Johnny next time I see him, on the proviso that he fucks off and leaves us alone for ever. He comes in the next day complaining that it's scratched and demanding his money back. Barrytown make a triumphant debut at the Harry Lauder, and rock the place off its foundations, and the buzz is incredible, and there are loads of people there who look like A&R men, and they go absolutely mental, and honestly Rob you should have been there (Marie just laughs, when I ask her about it, and says that everyone has to start somewhere). Dick tries to get me to make up a foursome with him, Anna and a friend of Anna's who's twenty-one, but I don't go; we see Marie play at a folk club in Farringdon, and I think about Laura a lot more than I think about Marie during the sad songs, even though Marie dedicates a song to 'the guys at Championship Vinyl'; I go for a drink with Liz and she bitches about Ray the whole evening, which is great; and then Laura's dad dies, and everything changes.

TWENTY-FIVE

I hear about it on the same morning she does. I ring her number from the shop, intending just to leave a message on her machine; it's easier that way, and I only wanted to tell her about some ex-colleague who left a message for her on our machine. My machine. Her machine, actually, if we're talking legal ownership. Anyway. I wasn't expecting Laura to pick up the phone, but she does, and she sounds as though she's speaking from the bottom of the sea. Her voice is muffled, and low, and flat, and coated from first syllable to last in snot.

'Cor dear oh dear, that's a cold and a half. I hope you're in bed with a hot book and a good water bottle. It's Rob, by the way.'

She doesn't say anything.

'Laura? It's Rob.'

Still nothing.

'Are you all right?'

And then a terrible moment.

'Pigsty,' she says, although the first syllable's just a noise, really, so 'pig' is an educated guess.

'Don't worry about that,' I say. 'Just get into bed and forget about it. Worry about it when you're better.'

'Pig's died,' she says.

'Who the fuck's Pig?'

This time I can hear her. 'My dad's died,' she sobs. 'My dad, my dad.'

And then she hangs up.

I think about people dying all the time, but they're always people connected with me. I've thought about how I would feel if Laura died, and how Laura would feel if I died, and how I'd feel if my mum or dad died, but I never thought about Laura's mum or dad dying. I wouldn't, would I? And even though he was ill for the entire duration of my relationship with Laura, it never really bothered me: it was more like, my dad's got a beard, Laura's dad's got angina. I never thought it would actually *lead* to anything. Now he's gone, of course, I wish . . . what? What do I wish? That I'd been nicer to him? I was perfectly nice to him, the few times we met. That we'd been closer? He was my common-law father-in-law, and we were very different, and he was sick, and . . . we were as close as we needed to be. You're supposed to wish things when people die, to fill yourself full of regrets, to give yourself a hard time for all your mistakes and omissions, and I'm doing all that as best I can. It's just that I can't find any mistakes and omissions. He was my ex-girlfriend's dad, you know? What am I supposed to feel?

'You all right?' says Barry, when he sees me staring into space. 'Who were you talking to?'

'Laura. Her dad's died.'

'Oh, right. Bad one.' And then he wanders off to the post office with a pile of mail orders under his arm. See? From Laura, to me, to Barry: from grief, to confusion, to a fleeting, mild interest. If you want to find a way to extract death's sting, then Barry's your man. For a moment it feels strange that these two people, one who is so maddened by pain that she can hardly speak, the other who can hardly find the curiosity to shrug, should know each other; strange that I'm the link between them, strange that they live in the same place at the same time, even. But Ken was Barry's boss's ex-girlfriend's dad. What is he supposed to feel?

Laura calls back an hour or so later. I wasn't expecting her to.

'I'm sorry,' she says. It's still hard to make out what she's saying, what with the snot and the tears and the tone and the volume.

'No, no.'

Then she cries for a while. I don't say anything until she's a bit quieter.

'When are you going home?'

'In a minute. When I get it together.'

'Can I do anything?'

'No.' And then, after a sob, 'No' again, as if she's realized properly that there's nothing anybody can do for her, and maybe this is the first time she's ever found herself in that situation. I know I never have. Everything that's ever gone wrong for me could have been rescued by the wave of a bank manager's wand, or by a girlfriend's sudden change of mind, or by some quality – determination, self-awareness, resilience – that I might have found within myself, if I'd looked hard enough. I don't want to have to cope with the sort of unhappiness Laura's feeling, not ever. If people have to die, I don't want them dying near me. My mum and dad won't die near me, I've made bloody sure of that. When they go, I'll hardly feel a thing.

The next day she calls again.

'Mum wants you to come to the funeral.'

'Me?'

'My dad liked you. Apparently. And Mum never told him we'd split, because he wasn't up to it and . . . oh, I don't know. I don't really understand it, and I can't be bothered to argue. I think she thinks he'll be able to see what's going on. It's like . . .' She makes a strange noise which I realize is a manic giggle. 'Her attitude is that he's been through so much, what with dying and everything, that she doesn't want to upset him any more than she has to.'

I knew that Ken liked me, but I could never really work out why, apart from once he was looking for the original London cast recording of *My Fair Lady*, and I saw a copy at a record fair, and sent it to him. See where random acts of kindness get you? To fucking funerals, that's where.

'Do *you* want me there?'

'I don't care. As long as you don't expect me to hold your hand.'

'Is Ray going?'

'No, Ray's not going.'

'Why not?'

'Because he hasn't been invited, OK?'

'I don't mind, you know, if that's what you want.'

'Oh, that's so sweet of you, Rob. It's your day, after all.'

Jesus.

'Look, are you coming or not?'

'Yes, of course.'

'Liz'll give you a lift. She knows where to go and everything.'

'Fine. How are you?'

'I haven't got time to chat, Rob. I've got too much to do.'

'Sure. I'll see you Friday.' I put the phone down before she can say anything, to let her know I'm hurt, and then I want to phone her back and apologize, but I know I mustn't. It's like you can never do the right thing by someone if you've stopped sleeping with them. You can't see a way back, or through, or round, however hard you try.

There aren't really any pop songs about death – not good ones, anyway. Maybe that's why I like pop music, and why I find classical music a bit creepy. There was that Elton John instrumental, 'Song For Guy', but, you know, it was just a plinky-plonky piano thing that would serve you just as well at the airport as at your funeral.

'OK guys, best five pop songs about death.'

'Magic,' says Barry. 'A Laura's Dad Tribute List. OK, OK. "Leader Of The Pack". The bloke dies on his motorbike, doesn't he? And then there's "Dead Man's Curve" by Jan and Dean, and "Terry", by Twinkle. Ummm . . . that Bobby Goldsboro one, you know, "And Honey, I Miss You . . ."' He sings it off-key, even more so than he would have done normally, and Dick laughs. 'And what about "Tell Laura I Love Her". That'd bring the house down.' I'm glad that Laura isn't here to see how much amusement her father's death has afforded us.

'I was trying to think of serious songs. You know, something that shows a bit of respect.'

'What, you're doing the DJing at the funeral, are you? Ouch. Bad job. Still, the Bobby Goldsboro could be one of the smoochers. You know, when people need a breather. Laura's mum could sing it.' He sings the same line, off-key again, but this time in a falsetto voice to show that the singer is a woman.

'Fuck off, Barry.'

'I've already worked out what I'm having at mine. "One Step Beyond", by Madness. "You Can't Always Get What You Want".'

'Just 'cos it's in *The Big Chill*.'

'I haven't seen *The Big Chill*, have I?'

'You lying bastard. You saw it in a Lawrence Kasdan double bill with *Bodyheat*.'

'Oh, yeah. But I'd forgotten about that, honestly. I wasn't just nicking the idea.'

'Not much.'

And so on.

I try again later.

'"Abraham, Martin and John",' says Dick. 'That's quite a nice one.'

'What was Laura's dad's name?'

'Ken.'

'"Abraham, Martin, John and Ken". Nah, I can't see it.'

'Fuck off.'

'Black Sabbath? Nirvana? They're all into death.'

Thus is Ken's passing mourned at Championship Vinyl.

I have thought about the stuff I want played at my funeral, although I could never list it to anyone, because they'd die laughing. 'One Love' by Bob Marley; 'Many Rivers To Cross' by Jimmy Cliff; 'Angel' by Aretha Franklin. And I've always had this fantasy that someone beautiful and tearful will insist on 'You're The Best Thing That Ever Happened To Me' by Gladys Knight, but I can't imagine who that beautiful, tearful person will be. But that's my funeral, as they say, and I can afford to be generous and sentimental about it. It doesn't alter the point that Barry made, even if he didn't know he was making it: we have about seven squillion hours' worth of recorded music in here, and there's hardly a minute of it that describes the way Laura's feeling now.

I've got one suit, dark grey, last worn at a wedding three years ago. It doesn't fit too well now, in all the obvious places, but it'll have to do. I iron my white shirt, and find a tie that isn't made of leather and doesn't have saxophones all over it, and wait for Liz to come and pick me up. I haven't got anything to take with me – the cards in the newsagent's were all vile. They looked like the sort of thing the Addams Family would send to each other on their birthdays. I wish I'd been to a funeral before. One of my grandfathers died before I was born, and the other when I was very little; both my grandmothers are still alive, if you can call it that, but I never see them. One lives in a home, the other lives with Auntie Eileen, my dad's sister. And when they do die it will hardly be the end of the world. Just, you know, wow, stop press, extremely ancient person dies. And though I've got friends who have friends who've died – a gay guy that Laura was at college with got Aids, a mate of my mate Paul was killed in a motor-bike crash, and loads of them have lost parents – it's something I've always managed to put off. Now I can see that it's something I'll be doing for the rest of my life. Two grans, Mum and Dad, aunts and uncles, and, unless I'm the first person in my immediate circle to go, loads of people my age, eventually – maybe even sooner than eventually, given that one or two of them are bound to cop it before they're supposed to. Once I start to think about it, it seems terribly oppressive, as though I'll be going to three or four a week for the next forty years, and I won't have the time or the inclination to do anything else. How do people cope? Do you have to go? What happens if you refuse on the grounds of it being just too fucking grim? ('I'm sorry for you and everything, Laura, but it's not really my scene, you know?') I don't think I can bear to get any older than I already am, and I begin to develop a grudging admiration for my parents, just because they've been to scores of funerals and have never really moaned about it, not to me, anyway. Perhaps they just don't have the imagination to see that funerals are actually even more depressing than they look.

If I'm honest, I'm only going because it might do me some good in the long run. Can you get off with your ex-girlfriend at her father's funeral? I wouldn't have thought so. But you never know.

'So the vicar says nice things, and then, what, we all troop outside and they bury him?'

Liz is talking me through it.

'It's at a crematorium.'

'You're having me on.'

'Of course I'm not having you on, you fool.'

'A crematorium? Jesus.'

'What difference does it make?'

'Well, none, but . . . Jesus.' I wasn't prepared for this.

'What's the matter?'

'I don't know, but . . . bloody hell.'

She sighs. 'Do you want me to drop you off at a tube station?'

'No, of course not.'

'Shut up, then.'

'I just don't want to pass out, that's all. If I pass out because of lack of preparation, it'll be your fault.'

'What a pathetic specimen you are. You know that nobody actively enjoys these things, don't you? You know that we're all going to find this morning terribly upsetting? It's not just you. I've been to one cremation in my life and I hated it. And even if I'd been to a hundred it wouldn't be any easier. Stop being such a baby.'

'Why isn't Ray going, do you think?'

'Wasn't invited. Nobody in the family knows him. Ken was fond of you, and Jo thinks you're great.' Jo is Laura's sister, and I think she's great. She's like Laura to look at, but she hasn't got the sharp suits, or the sharp tongue, or any of the 'A' levels and degrees.

'Nothing more than that?'

'Ken didn't die for your benefit, you know. It's like everyone's a supporting actor in the film of your life story.'

Of course. Isn't that how it works for everybody?

'Your dad died, didn't he?'

'Yes. A long time ago. When I was eighteen.'

'Did it affect you?' Terrible. Stupid. 'For ages?' Saved. Just.

'It still does.'

'How?'

'I don't know. I still miss him, and think about him. Talk to him, sometimes.'

'What do you say?'

'That's between me and him.' But she says it gently, with a little smile. 'He knows more about me now he's dead than he ever did when he was alive.'

'And whose fault's that?'

'His. He was Stereotype Dad, you know, too busy, too tired. I used to feel bad about it, after he'd gone, but in the end I realized that I was just a little girl, and quite a good little girl, too. It was up to him, not me.'

This is great. I'm going to cultivate friendships with people who have dead parents, or dead friends, or dead partners. They're the most interesting people in the world. And they're accessible, too! They're all around us! Even if astronauts or former Beatles or shipwreck survivors did have more to offer – which I doubt – you never get to meet them anyway. People who know dead people, as Barbra Streisand might have sung but didn't, are the luckiest people in the world.

'Was *he* cremated?'

'Why does it matter?'

'I dunno. Just interested. Because you said you'd been to one cremation, and I was wondering, you know . . .'

'I'd give Laura a couple of days before you start pumping her with questions like this. It's not the kind of life experience that lends itself to idle chatter.'

'That's your way of telling me to shut up, right?'

'Right.'

Fair enough.

The crematorium is in the middle of nowhere, and we leave the car in a huge, almost empty car park and walk over to the buildings, which are new and horrible, too bright, not serious enough. You can't imagine that they're going to burn people in here; you can imagine, however, some iffy happy-clappy new religious group meeting for a sing-song once a week. I wouldn't have my old man buried here. I reckon I'd need some help from the atmosphere to get a really good head of grief going, and I wouldn't get it from all this exposed brickwork and stripped pine.

It's a three-chapel multiplex. There is even a sign on the wall telling you what's on in each, and at what time:

CHAPEL 1.	11.30	MR E BARKER
CHAPEL 2.	12.00	MR K LYDON
CHAPEL 3.	12.00	–

Good news in Chapel 3, at least. Cremation cancelled. Reports of death exaggerated, ha ha. We sit down in the reception area and wait while the place starts to fill up. Liz nods to a couple of people, but I don't know them; I try to think of men's names beginning with 'E'. I'm hoping that an old person is getting the treatment in Chapel 1, because if and when we see the mourners come out I don't want them to be too distressed. Eric. Ernie. Ebenezer. Ethelred. Ezra. We're all right. We're laughing. Well, not laughing, exactly, but whoever it is is at least four hundred years old, and no one will be grieving too much in those circumstances, will they? Ewan. Edmund. Edward. Bollocks. Could be any age.

No one's crying in the reception area yet, but there are a few people on the edge, and you can see they're going to go over it before the morning is over. They are all middle-aged, and they know the ropes. They talk quietly, shake hands, give wan smiles, kiss, sometimes; and then, for no reason I can see, and I feel hopelessly out of my depth, lost, ignorant, they stand, and troop through the door marked CHAPEL 2.

It's dark in there, at least, so it's easier to get into the mood. The coffin is up the front, slightly raised off the floor, but I can't work out what it's resting on; Laura, Jo and Janet Lydon are in the first row, standing very close, with a couple of men I don't know beside them. We sing a hymn, pray, there's a brief and unsatisfactory address from the vicar, some stuff from his book, and another hymn, and then there's this sudden, heart-stopping clanking of machinery and the coffin disappears slowly through the floor. And as it does so, there's a howl from in front of us, a terrible, terrible noise that I don't want to hear: I can only just tell that it's Laura's voice, but I know that it is, and at that moment I want to go to her and offer to become a different person, to remove all trace of what is me, as long as she will let me look after her and try to make her feel better.

When we get out into the light, people crowd around Laura and Jo and Janet, and hug them; I want to do the same, but I don't see how I can. But Laura sees Liz and me hovering on the fringe of the group, and comes to us, and thanks us for coming, and holds us both for a long time, and when she lets go of me I feel that I don't need to offer to become a different person: it has happened already.

TWENTY-SIX

It's easier in the house. You can feel that the worst is over, and there's a tired calm in the room, like the tired calm you get in your stomach when you've been sick. You even hear people talking about other stuff, although it's all big stuff – work, children, life. Nobody's talking about their Volvo's fuel consumption, or the names they'd choose for dogs. Liz and I get ourselves a drink and stand with our backs against a bookcase, right in the far corner away from the door, and we talk occasionally, but mostly we watch people.

It feels good to be in this room, even though the reasons for being here aren't so good. The Lydons have a large Victorian house, and it's old and tatty and full of things – furniture, paintings, ornaments, plants – which don't go together but which have obviously been chosen with care and taste. The room we're in has a huge, weird family portrait on the wall above the fireplace, done when the girls were about ten and eight. They are wearing what look like bridesmaids' dresses, standing self-consciously beside Ken; there's a dog, Allegro, Allie, who died before I came along, in front of them and partially obscuring them. He has his paws up on Ken's midriff, and Ken is ruffling the dog's fur and smiling. Janet is standing a little behind and apart from the other three, watching her husband. The whole family are much thinner (and splodgier, but that's the painting for you) than they are in real life. It's modern art, and bright and fun, and obviously done by someone who knew what they were about (Laura told me that the woman who did it has had exhibitions and all sorts), but it has to take its chances with a stuffed otter, which is on the mantelpiece underneath, and the sort of dark old furniture that I hate. Oh, and there's a hammock in one corner, loaded down with cushions, and a huge bank of new black hi-fi stuff in another corner, Ken's most treasured possession, despite the paintings and the antiques. It's all a mess, but you'd have to love the family that lived here, because you'd just know that they were interesting and kind and gentle. I realize now that I enjoyed being a part of this family, and though I used to moan about coming here for weekends or Sunday afternoons, I was never bored once. Jo comes up to us after a few minutes, and kisses both of us, and thanks us for coming.

'How are you?' Liz asks, but it's the 'How are you' which has an emphasis on the 'are', which makes the question sound meaningful and sympathetic. Jo shrugs.

'I'm all right. I suppose. And Mum's not too bad, but Laura . . . I dunno.'

'She's had a pretty rough few weeks already, without this,' says Liz, and I feel a little surge of something like pride: that was *me*. I made her feel like that. Me and a couple of others, anyway, including Laura herself, but never mind. I'd forgotten that I could make her feel anything and, anyway, it's odd to be reminded of your emotional power in the middle of a funeral which, in my limited experience, is when you lose sense of it altogether.

'She'll be OK,' says Liz decisively. 'But it's hard, when you're putting all your effort into one bit of your life, to suddenly find that it's the wrong bit.' She glances at me, suddenly embarrassed, or guilty, or something.

'Don't mind me,' I tell them. 'Really. No problem. Just pretend you're talking about somebody else.' I meant it kindly, honest I did. I was simply trying to say that if they wanted to talk about Laura's love life, any aspect of it, then I wouldn't mind, not today, of all days.

Jo smiles, but Liz gives me a look. 'We are talking about somebody else. Laura. Laura and Ray, really.'

'That's not fair, Liz.'

'Oh?' She raises an eyebrow, as if I'm being insubordinate.

'And don't fucking say "Oh" like that.' A couple of people look round when I use the 'f'-word, and Jo puts her hand on my arm. I shake it off. Suddenly, I'm raging and I don't know how to calm down. It seems like I've spent the whole of the last few weeks with someone's hand on my arm: I can't speak to Laura because she lives with somebody else and she calls from phone boxes and she pretends she doesn't, and I can't speak to Liz because she knows about the money and the abortion and me seeing someone else, and I can't speak to Barry and Dick because they're Barry and Dick, and I can't speak to my friends because I don't speak to my friends, and I can't speak now because Laura's father has died, and I just have to take it because otherwise I'm a bad guy, with the emphasis on guy, self-centred, blind and stupid. Well, I'm fucking *not*, not all the time, anyway, and I know this isn't the right place to say so – I'm not that daft – but when am I allowed to?

'I'm sorry, Jo. I'm really sorry.' I'm back to the funereal murmur now, even though I feel like screaming. 'But you know, Liz . . . I can either stick up for myself sometimes or I can believe anything you say about me and end up hating myself every minute of the day. And maybe you think I should, but it's not much of a life, you know?'

Liz shrugs.

'That's not good enough, Liz. You're dead wrong, and if you don't know it then you're dimmer than I thought.'

She sighs theatrically, and then sees the look on my face.

'Maybe I've been a little unfair. But is this really the time?'

'Only because it's never the time. We can't go on apologizing all our lives, you know.'

'If by "we" you are referring to men, then I have to say that just the once would do.'

I'm not going to walk out of Laura's dad's funeral in a sulk. I'm not going to walk out of Laura's dad's funeral in a sulk. I'm just not.

I walk out of Laura's dad's funeral in a sulk.

The Lydons live a few miles out of the nearest town, which is Amersham, and I don't know which way the nearest town is anyway. I walk round the corner, and round another corner, and come to some kind of main road, and see a bus stop, but it's not the sort of bus stop which fills you with confidence: there's nobody waiting, and nothing much there – a row of large detached houses on one side of the road, a playing field on the other. I wait there for a while, freezing in my suit, but just as I've worked out that it's the sort of bus stop that requires the investment of a few days, rather than a few minutes, I see a familiar green Volkswagen up the road. It's Laura, and she's come looking for me.

Without thinking, I jump over the wall that separates one of the detached houses from the pavement, and lie flat in somebody's flower bed. It's wet. But I'd rather get soaked to the skin than have Laura go mental at me for disappearing, so I stay there for as long as is humanly possible. Every time I think I have got to the bottom, I find a new way to sink even lower, but I know that this is the worst, and that whatever happens to me from now on, however poor or stupid or single I get, these few minutes will remain with me as a shining cautionary beacon. 'Is it better than lying face down in a flower bed after Laura's dad's funeral?' I shall ask myself when the bailiffs come into the shop, or when the next Laura runs off with the next Ray, and the answer will always, always be 'Yes'.

When I can't take it any more, when my white shirt is translucent and my jacket streaked with mud and I'm getting stabbing pains – cramp, or rheumatism, or arthritis, who knows? – in my legs, I stand up and brush myself off; and then Laura, who has obviously been sitting in her car by the bus stop all this time, winds down her window and tells me to get in.

What happened to me during the funeral was something like this: I saw, for the first time, how scared I am of dying, and of other people dying, and how this fear has prevented me from doing all sorts of things, like giving up smoking (because if you take death too seriously or not seriously enough, as I have been doing up till now, then what's the point?), and thinking about my life, especially my job, in a way that contains a concept of the future (too scary, because the future ends in death). But most of all it has prevented me from sticking with a relationship, because if you stick with a relationship, and your life becomes dependent on that person's life, and then they die, as they are bound to do, unless there are exceptional circumstances, e.g. they are a character from a science-fiction novel . . . well, you're up the creek without a paddle, aren't you? It's OK if I die first, I guess, but having to die before someone else dies isn't a necessity that cheers me up much: how do I know when she's going to die? Could be run over by a bus tomorrow, as the saying goes, which means I have to throw myself under a bus today. When I saw Janet Lydon's face at the crematorium . . . how can you be that brave? Now what does she do? To me, it makes more sense to hop from woman to woman until you're too old to do it any more, and then you live alone and die alone and what's so terrible about that, when you look at the alternatives? There were some nights with Laura when I'd kind of nestle into her back in bed when she was asleep, and I'd be filled with this enormous, nameless terror, except now I have a name for it: Brian. Ha, ha. OK, not really a name, but I could see where it came from, and why I wanted to sleep with Rosie the pain-in-the-arse simultaneous-orgasm woman, and if that sounds feeble and self-serving at the same time – Oh, right! He sleeps with other women because he has a fear of death! – well, I'm sorry, but that's the way things are.

When I nestled into Laura's back in the night, I was afraid because I didn't want to lose her, and we always lose someone, or they lose us, in the end. I'd rather not take the risk. I'd rather not come home from work one day in ten or twenty years' time to be faced with a pale, frightened woman saying that she'd been shitting blood – *I'm sorry, I'm sorry, but this is what happens to people* – and then we go to the doctor and then the doctor says it's inoperable and then . . . I wouldn't have the guts, you know? I'd probably just take off, live in a different city under an assumed name, and Laura would check in to the hospital to die and they'd say, 'Isn't your partner coming to visit?' and she'd say, 'No, when he found out about the cancer he left me.' Great guy! 'Cancer? Sorry, that's not for me! I don't like it!' Best not put yourself in that position. Best leave it all alone.

So where does this get me? The logic of it all is that I play a percentage game. I'm thirty-six now, right? And let's say that most fatal diseases – cancer, heart disease, whatever – hit you after the age of fifty. You might be unlucky, and snuff it early, but the fifty-plus age group get more than their fair share of bad stuff happening to them. So to play safe, you stop then: a relationship every couple of years for the next fourteen years, and then get out, stop dead, give it up. It makes sense. Will I explain this to whoever I'm seeing? Maybe. It's fairer, probably. And less emotional, somehow, than the usual mess that ends relationships. 'You're going to die, so there's not much point in us carrying on, is there?' It's perfectly acceptable if someone's emigrating, or returning to their own country, to stop a relationship on the grounds that any further involvement would be too painful, so why not death? The separation that death entails has got to be more painful than the separation of emigration, surely? I mean, with emigration, you can always go with her. You can always say to yourself, 'Oh, fuck it, I'll pack it all in and go and be a cowboy in Texas/tea-picker in India,' etc. You can't do that with the big D, though, can you? Unless you take the Romeo route, and if you think about it . . .

'I thought you were going to lie in that flower bed all afternoon.'

'Eh? Oh. Ha ha. No. Ha.' Assumed nonchalance is tougher than it looks in this sort of situation, although lying in a stranger's flower bed to hide from your ex-girlfriend on the day that her dad is buried – burned – is probably not a sort, a *genre* of situation at all, more a one-off, non-generic thing.

'You're soaking.'

'Mmm.'

'You're also an idiot.'

There will be other battles. There's not much point in fighting this one, when all the evidence is conspiring against me.

'I can see why you say that. Look, I'm sorry. I really am. The last thing I wanted was . . . that's why I went, because . . . I lost it, and I didn't want to blow my top in there, and . . . look, Laura, the reason I slept with Rosie and mucked everything up was because I was scared that you'd die. Or I was scared of you dying. Or whatever. And I know what that sounds like, but . . .' It all dries up as easily as it popped out, and I just stare at her with my mouth open.

'Well I will die. Nothing much has changed on that score.'

'No, no, I understand completely, and I'm not expecting you to tell me anything different. I just wanted you to know, that's all.'

'Thank you. I appreciate it.'

She's making no move to start the car.

'I can't reciprocate.'

'How do you mean?'

'I didn't sleep with Ray because I was scared of you dying. I slept with Ray because I was sick of you, and I needed something to get me out of it.'

'Oh, sure, no, I understand. Look, I don't want to take up any more of your time. You get back, and I'll wait here for a bus.'

'I don't want to go back. I've thrown a wobbler too.'

'Oh. Right. Great. I mean, not great, but, you know.'

The rain starts again, and she puts the windscreen wipers on so that we can see not very much out of the window.

'Who upset you?'

'Nobody. I just don't feel old enough. I want someone to look after me because my dad's died, and there's no one there who can, so when Liz told me you'd disappeared I used it as an excuse to get out.'

'We're a right pair, aren't we?'

'Who upset you?'

'Oh. Nobody. Well, Liz. She was . . .' I can't think of the adult expression, so I use the one closest to hand. 'She was picking on me.'

Laura snorts. 'She was picking on you, and you're sneaking on her.'

'That's about the size of it.'

She gives a short, mirthless laugh. 'It's no wonder we're all in such a mess, is it? We're like Tom Hanks in *Big*. Little boys and girls trapped in adult bodies and forced to get on with it. And it's much worse in a real life, because it's not just snogging and bunk beds, is it? There's all this as well.' She gestures through the windscreen at the field and the bus stop and a man walking his dog, but I know what she means. 'I'll tell you something, Rob. Walking out of that funeral was the worst thing I've ever done, and also the most exhilarating. I can't tell you how good and bad I felt. Yes I can: I felt like a baked Alaska.'

'It's not like you walked out of the funeral, anyway. You walked out of the party thing. That's different.'

'But my mum, and Jo, and . . . they'll never forget it. I don't care, though. I've thought so much about him and talked so much about him, and now our house is full of people who want to give me time and opportunity to think and talk about him some more, and I just wanted to scream.'

'He'd understand.'

'D'you think? I'm not sure I would. I'd want people to stay to the bitter end. That'd be the least they could do.'

'Your dad was nicer than you, though.'

'He was, wasn't he?'

'About five or six times as nice.'

'Don't push your luck.'

'Sorry.'

We watch a man trying to light a cigarette while holding a dog lead, a newspaper, and an umbrella. It can't be done, but he won't give up.

'When are you going to go back, actually?'

'I don't know. Some time. Later. Listen, Rob, would you sleep with me?'

'What?'

'I just feel like I want sex. I want to feel something else apart from misery and guilt. It's either that or I go home and put my hand in the fire. Unless you want to stub cigarettes out on my arm.'

Laura isn't like this. Laura is a lawyer by profession and a lawyer by nature, and now she's behaving as though she's after a supporting role in a Harvey Keitel movie.

'I've only got a couple left. I'm saving them for later.'

'It'll have to be the sex, then.'

'But where? And what about Ray? And what about . . .' I want to say 'everything'. What about everything?

'We'll have to do it in the car. I'll drive us somewhere.'

She drives us somewhere.

I know what you're saying: *You're a pathetic fantasist, Fleming, you wish, in your dreams*, etc. But I would never in a million years use anything that has happened to me today as the basis for any kind of sexual fantasy. I'm wet, for a start, and though I appreciate that the state of wetness has any number of sexual connotations, it would be tough for even the most determined pervert to get himself worked up about my sort of wetness, which involves cold, irritation (my suit trousers are unlined, and my legs are being rubbed raw), bad smells (none of the major perfume makers has ever tried to capture the scent of wet trouser, for obvious reasons), and there are bits of foliage hanging off me. And I've never had any ambition to do it in a car (my fantasies have always, always involved beds) and the funeral may have had a funny effect on the daughter of the deceased, but for me it's been a bit of a downer, quite frankly, and I'm not too sure how I feel about sex with Laura when she's living with someone else (is he better is he better is he better?), and anyway . . .

She stops the car, and I realize we've been bumping along for the last minute or two of the journey.

'Dad used to bring us here when we were kids.'

We're by the side of a long, rutted dirt road that leads up to a large house. There's a jungle of long grass and bushes on one side of the road, and a row of trees on the other; we're on the tree side, pointing towards the house, tilting into the road.

'It used to be a little private prep school, but they went bust years ago, and it's sat empty ever since.'

'What did he bring you here for?'

'Just a walk. In the summer there were blackberries, and in the autumn there were conkers. This is a private road, so it made it more exciting.'

Jesus. I'm glad I know nothing about psychotherapy, about Jung and Freud and that lot. If I did, I'd probably be extremely frightened by now: the woman who wants to have sex in the place where she used to go for walks with her dead dad is probably very dangerous indeed.

It's stopped raining, but the drips from the trees are bouncing off the roof, and the wind is knocking hell out of the branches, so every now and again large chunks of foliage fall on us as well.

'Do you want to get in the back?' Laura asks, in a flat, distracted voice, as if we're about to pick someone else up.

'I guess so. I guess that would be easier.'

She's parked too close to the trees, so she has to clamber out my side.

'Just shift all that stuff on to the back shelf.'

There's an *A–Z*, a big road map, a couple of empty cassette cases, an opened bag of Opal Fruits and a handful of sweet papers. I take my time getting them out of the way.

'I knew there was a good reason for putting on a skirt this morning,' she says as she gets in. She leans over and kisses me on the mouth, tongues and everything, and I can feel some interest despite myself.

'Just stay there.' She makes some adjustments to her dress and sits on top of me. 'Hello. It doesn't seem so long ago that I looked at you from here.' She smiles at me, kisses me again, reaches underneath her for my fly. And then there's foreplay and stuff, and then – I don't know why – I remember something you're supposed to remember but only rarely do.

'You know with Ray . . .'

'Oh, Rob, we're not going to go through that again.'

'No, no. It's not . . . are you still on the pill?'

'Yes, of course. There's nothing to worry about.'

'I didn't mean that. I mean . . . was that all you used?'

She doesn't say anything, and then she starts to cry.

'Look, we can do other things,' I say. 'Or we can go into town and get something.'

'I'm not crying because we can't do it,' she says. 'It's not that. It's just that . . . I lived with you. You were my partner just a few weeks ago. And now you're worried I might kill you, and you're entitled to worry. Isn't that a terrible thing? Isn't that sad?' She shakes her head and sobs, and climbs off me, and we sit there side by side in the back seat saying nothing, just watching the drips crawl down the windows.

Later, I wonder whether I was really worried about where Ray has been. Is he bisexual, or an intravenous drug user? I doubt it. (He wouldn't have the guts for either.) Has he ever slept with an intravenous drug user, or has he ever slept with someone who's slept with a bisexual male? I have no idea, and that ignorance gives me every right to insist on protection. But in truth it was the symbolism that interested me more than the fear. I wanted to hurt her, on this day of all days, just because it's the first time since she left that I've been able to.

We drive to a pub, a twee little mock-country place that serves nice beer and expensive sandwiches, and sit in a corner and talk. I buy some more fags and she smokes half of them or, rather, she lights one, takes a drag or two, grimaces, stubs it out and then five minutes later takes another. She stubs them out with such violence that they cannot be salvaged, and when she does it I can't concentrate on what she's saying, because I'm too busy watching my fags disappear. Eventually she notices and says she'll buy me some more and I feel mean.

We talk about her dad, mostly, or rather, what life will be like without him. And then we talk about what life will be like generally without dads, and whether it's the thing that makes you feel grown-up, finally. (Laura thinks not, on the evidence available to date.) I don't want to talk about this stuff, of course: I want to talk about Ray and me and whether we'll ever come as close to having sex again and whether the warmth and intimacy of this conversation means anything, but I manage to hold myself back.

And then, just as I have begun to accept that none of this is going to be about me me me, she sighs, and slumps back against her chair, and says, half-smiling, half-despairing, 'I'm too tired not to go out with you.'

There's a kind of double negative here – 'too tired' is a negative because it's not very positive – and it takes me a while to work out what she means.

'So, hold on: if you had a bit more energy, we'd stay split. But as it is, what with you being knackered, you'd like us to get back together.'

She nods. 'Everything's too hard. Maybe another time I would have had the guts to be on my own, but not now I haven't.'

'What about Ray?'

'Ray's a disaster. I don't know what that was all about, really, except sometimes you need someone to lob into the middle of a bad relationship like a hand grenade, and blow it all apart.'

I'd like to talk, in some detail, about all the ways in which Ray is a disaster; in fact, I'd like to make a list on the back of a beer mat and keep it for ever. Maybe another time.

'And now you're out of the bad relationship, and you have blown it all apart, you want to be back in it, and put it back together again.'

'Yes. I know none of this is very romantic, and there will be romantic bits at some stage, I'm sure. But I need to be with someone, and I need to be with someone I know and get on with OK, and you've made it clear that you want me back, so . . .'

And wouldn't you know it? Suddenly I feel panicky, and sick, and I want to get record label logos painted on my walls and sleep with American recording artistes. I take Laura's hand and kiss her on the cheek.

There's a terrible scene back at the house, of course. Mrs Lydon is in tears, and Jo is angry, and the few guests that are left stare into their drinks and don't say anything. Laura takes her mum through to the kitchen and shuts the door, and I stand in the sitting room with Jo, shrugging my shoulders and shaking my head and raising my eyebrows and shifting from foot to foot and doing anything else I can think of to suggest embarrassment, sympathy, disapproval and misfortune. When my eyebrows are sore, and I have nearly shaken my head off its hinges, and I have walked the best part of a mile on the spot, Laura emerges from the kitchen in a state and tugs me by the arm.

'We're going home,' she says, and that is how our relationship resumes its course.

TWENTY-SEVEN

Five conversations:

1. (Third day, out for a curry, Laura paying.)

'I'll bet you did. I'll bet you sat there, five minutes after I'd gone, smoking a *fag*' – she always emphasizes the word, to show that she disapproves – 'and thinking to yourself, cor, this is all right, I can cope with this. And then you sat and thought up some stupid idea for the flat . . . I know, I know, you were going to get some guy to paint record label logos on the wall before I moved in, weren't you? I'll bet you sat there, smoking a *fag*, and thinking, I wonder if I've still got that guy's phone number?'

I look away so she can't see me smile, but it's no use. 'God, I'm so right, aren't I? I'm so right I can't believe it. And then – hold on, hold on' – she puts her fingers to her temples, as if she's receiving the images into her brain – 'and then you thought, plenty more fish in the sea, been feeling like a bit of new for ages, and then you stuck something on the hi-fi, and everything was right in your pathetic little world.'

'And then what?'

'And then you went to work, and you didn't say anything to Dick or Barry, and you were fine until Liz let the cat out of the bag, and then you became suicidal.'

'And then I slept with someone else.'

She doesn't hear me.

'When you were fucking around with that prat Ray, I was screwing an American singer-songwriter who looks like Susan Dey out of *LA Law*.'

She still doesn't hear me. She just breaks off a bit of poppadum and dips it in the mango chutney.

'And I was all right. Not too bad. Quite good, in fact.'

No reaction. Maybe I should try again, this time out loud, with my voice instead of the inside of my head.

'You know it all, don't you?'

She shrugs, and smiles, and makes her smug face.

2. (Seventh day, bed, afterwards.)

'You don't really expect me to tell you.'

'Why not?'

'Because what purpose would it serve? I could describe every second of every time, and there weren't that many of them, and you'd be hurt, but you still wouldn't understand the first thing about anything that mattered.'

'I don't care. I just want to know.'

'Want to know what?'

'What it was like.'

She huffs. 'It was like sex. What else could it be like?'

Even this answer I find hurtful. I had hoped it wouldn't be like sex at all; I had hoped that it would be like something much more boring or unpleasant instead.

'Was it like good sex or was it like bad sex?'

'What's the difference?'

'You know the difference.'

'I never asked you how your extra-curricular activities went.'

'Yes you did. I remember. "Have a nice time, dear?"'

'It was a rhetorical question. Look, we're OK now. We've just had a nice time. Let's leave it at that.'

'OK, OK. But the nice time we've just had . . . was it nicer, as nice, or less nice than the nice times you were having a couple of weeks ago?'

She doesn't say anything.

'Oh, come on, Laura. Just say anything. Fib, if you want. It'd make me feel better, and it'd stop me asking you questions.'

'I was going to fib, and now I can't, because you'd know I was fibbing.'

'Why would you want to fib anyway?'

'To make you feel better.'

And so it goes. I want to know (except, of course, I don't want to know) about multiple orgasms and ten times a night and blow jobs and positions that I've never even heard of, but I haven't the courage to ask, and she would never tell me. I know they've done it, and that's bad enough; all I can hope for now is damage limitation. I want her to say that it was dull, that it was bog-standard, lie-back-and-think-of-Rob sort of sex, that Meg Ryan had more fun in the delicatessen than Laura had at Ray's place. Is that too much to ask?

She props herself up on an elbow and kisses me on the chest. 'Look, Rob. It happened. It was good that it happened in lots of ways, because we were going nowhere, and now we might be going somewhere. And if great sex was as important as you think it is, and if I'd had great sex, then we wouldn't be lying here now. And that's my last word on the subject, OK?'

'OK.' There could have been worse last words, although I know she's not saying anything much.

'I wish your penis was as big as his, though.'

This, it would appear, judging from the length and volume of the ensuing snorts, giggles, guffaws and roars, is the funniest joke Laura has ever made in her life – the funniest joke that anyone has ever made, in fact, in the entire history of the world. It is an example, I presume, of the famous feminist sense of humour. Hilarious or what?

3. (Driving down to her mum's, second weekend, listening to a compilation tape she has made that features Simply Red *and* Genesis *and* Art Garfunkel singing 'Bright Eyes'.)

'I don't care. You can make all the faces you want. That's one thing that's changing around here. *My* car. *My* car stereo. *My* compilation tape. On the way to see *my* parents.'

We let the 's' hang in the air, watch it try to crawl back where it came from, and then forget it. I give it a moment before I return to fight possibly the bitterest of all the bitter battles between men and women.

'How can you like Art Garfunkel *and* Solomon Burke? It's like saying you support the Israelis *and* the Palestinians.'

'It's not like saying that at all, actually, Rob. Art Garfunkel and Solomon Burke make pop records, the Israelis and the Palestinians don't. Art Garfunkel and Solomon Burke are not engaged in a bitter territorial dispute, the Israelis and the Palestinians are. Art Garfunkel and Solomon Burke . . .'

'OK, OK. But . . .'

'And who says I like Solomon Burke anyway?'

This is too much.

'Solomon Burke! "Got To Get You Off My Mind"! That's our song! Solomon Burke is responsible for our entire relationship!'

'Is that right? Do you have his phone number? I'd like a word with him.'

'But don't you remember?'

'I remember the song. I just couldn't remember who sung it.'

I shake my head in disbelief.

'See, this is the sort of moment where men just want to give up. Can you really not see the difference between "Bright Eyes" and "Got To Get You Off My Mind"?'

'Yes, of course. One's about rabbits and the other has a brass band playing on it.'

'A brass band! A brass band! It's a *horn section*! Fucking hell.'

'Whatever. I can see why you prefer Solomon to Art. I understand, really I do. And if I was asked to say which of the two was better, I'd go for Solomon every time. He's authentic, and black, and legendary, and all that sort of thing. But I like "Bright Eyes". I think it's got a pretty tune, and beyond that, I don't really care. There are so many other things to worry about. I know I sound like your mum, but they're only pop records, and if one's better than the other, well, who cares, really, apart from you and Barry and Dick? To me, it's like arguing the difference between McDonald's and Burger King. I'm sure there must be one, but who can be bothered to find out what it is?'

The terrible thing is, of course, that I already know the difference, that I have complicated and informed views on the subject. But if I start going on about BK Flamers versus Quarter Pounders with Cheese, we will both feel that I have somehow proved her point, so I don't bother.

But the argument carries on, goes round corners, crosses the road, turns back on itself and eventually ends up somewhere neither of us has ever been before – at least, not sober, and not during daylight hours.

'You used to care more about things like Solomon Burke than you do now,' I tell her. 'When I first met you, and I made you that tape, you were really enthused. You said – and I quote – "it was so good that it made you ashamed of your record collection".'

'Shameless, wasn't I?'

'What does that mean?'

'Well, I fancied you. You were a DJ, and I thought you were groovy, and I didn't have a boyfriend, and I wanted one.'

'So you weren't interested in the music at all?'

'Well, yes. A bit. And more so then than I am now. That's life, though, isn't it?'

'But you see . . . *That's all there is of me.* There isn't anything else. If you've lost interest in that, you've lost interest in everything. What's the point of us?'

'You really believe that?'

'Yes. Look at me. Look at the flat. What else has it got, apart from records and CDs and tapes?'

'And do you like it that way?'

I shrug. 'Not really.'

'*That's* the point of us. You have potential. I'm here to bring it out.'

'Potential as what?'

'As a human being. You have all the basic ingredients. You're really very likeable, when you put your mind to it. You make people laugh, when you can be bothered, and you're kind, and when you decide you like someone then that person feels as though she's the centre of the whole world, and that's a very sexy feeling. It's just that most of the time you can't be bothered.'

'No,' is all I can think of to say.

'You just . . . you just don't *do* anything. You get lost in your head, and you sit around thinking instead of getting on with something, and most of the time you think rubbish. You always seem to miss what's really happening.'

'This is the second Simply Red song on this tape. One's unforgivable. Two's a war crime. Can I fast forward?' I fast forward without waiting for a reply. I stop on some terrible post-Motown Diana Ross thing, and I groan. Laura ploughs on regardless.

'Do you know that expression, "Time on his hand and himself on his mind"? That's you.'

'So what should I be doing?'

'I don't know. Something. Working. Seeing people. Running a scout troop, or running a club even. Something more than waiting for life to change and keeping your options open. You'd keep your options open for the rest of your life, if you could. You'll be lying on your deathbed, dying of some smoking-related disease, and you'll be thinking, well, at least I've kept my options open. At least I never ended up doing something I couldn't back out of. And all the time you're keeping your options open, you're closing them off. You're thirty-six and you don't have children. So when are you going to have them? When you're forty? Fifty? Say you're forty, and say your kid doesn't want kids until *he's* thirty-six. That means you'd have to live much longer than your allotted three-score years and ten just to catch so much as a *glimpse* of your grandchild. See how you're denying yourself things?'

'So it all boils down to that.'

'What?'

'Have kids or we split up. The oldest threat in the book.'

'Fuck *off*, Rob. That's not what I'm saying to you. I don't care whether you want kids or not. I do, I know that, but I don't know whether I want them with you, and I don't know whether you want them at all. I've got to sort that out for myself. I'm just trying to wake you up. I'm just trying to show you that you've lived half your life, but for all you've got to show for it you might as well be nineteen, and I'm not talking about money or property or furniture.'

I know she's not. She's talking about detail, clutter, the stuff that stops you floating away.

'It's easy for you to say that, isn't it, Mzzzz Hot Shot City Lawyer. It's not my fault that the shop isn't doing very well.'

'Jesus Christ.' She changes gears with an impressive violence, and doesn't speak to me for a while. I know we nearly got somewhere; I know that if I had any guts I would tell her that she was right, and wise, and that I needed and loved her, and I would have asked her to marry me or something. It's just that, you know, I want to keep my options open, and anyway, there's no time, because she hasn't finished with me yet.

'Do you know what really annoys me?'

'Yeah. All the stuff you just told me. About the way I keep my options open and all that.'

'Apart from that.'

'Fucking hell.'

'I can tell you exactly – exactly – what's wrong with you and what you should be doing about it, and you couldn't even begin to do the same for me. Could you?'

'Yeah.'

'Go on, then.'

'You're fed up with your job.'

'And that's what's wrong with me, is it?'

'More or less.'

'See? You haven't got a clue.'

'Give me a chance. We've only just started living together again. I'll probably spot something else in a couple of weeks.'

'But I'm not even fed up with my job. I quite enjoy it, in fact.'

'You're just saying that to make me look stupid.'

'No, I'm not. I enjoy my work. It's stimulating, I like the people I work with, I've got used to the money . . . but I don't like liking it. It confuses me. I'm not who I wanted to be when I grew up.'

'Who did you want to be?'

'Not some woman in a suit, with a secretary and half an eye on a partnership. I wanted to be a legal aid lawyer with a DJ boyfriend, and it's all going wrong.'

'So find yourself a DJ. What do you want me to do about it?'

'I don't want you to do anything about it. I just want you to see that I'm not entirely defined by my relationship with you. I want you to see that just because we're getting sorted out, it doesn't mean that I'm getting sorted out. I've got other doubts and worries and ambitions. I don't know what kind of life I want, and I don't know what sort of house I want to live in, and the amount of money I'll be making in two or three years frightens me, and . . .'

'Why couldn't you have just come out with it in the first place? How am I supposed to guess? What's the big secret?'

'There's no secret. I'm simply pointing out that what happens to us isn't the whole story. That I continue to exist even when we're not together.'

I would have worked that out for myself, in the end. I would have seen that just because I go all fuzzy around the edges when I don't have a partner, it doesn't mean that everybody else does.

4. (In front of the TV, the following evening.)

'... somewhere nice. Italy. The States. The West Indies, even.'

'Excellent idea. What I'll do is, tomorrow I'll get hold of a box full of mint Elvis Presley 78s on Sun, and I'll pay for it that way.' I remember the Wood Green lady with the errant husband and the amazing singles collection, and feel a quick pang of regret.

'I presume that's some kind of sarcastic male record collector joke.'

'You know how skint I am.'

'You know I'll pay for you. Even though you still owe me money. What's the point of me doing this job if I have to spend my holiday in a tent on the Isle of Wight?'

'Oh yeah, and where am I going to find the money for half a tent?'

We watch Jack Duckworth trying to hide a fifty-pound note he won on the horses from Vera.

'It doesn't matter, you know, about the money. I don't care how little you earn. I'd like you to be happier in your work, but beyond that you can do what you like.'

'But it wasn't supposed to be like this. When I met you we were the same people, and now we're not, and ...'

'How were we the same people?'

'You were the sort of person that came to the Groucho, and I was the sort of person that played the records. You wore leather jackets and T-shirts, and so did I. And I still do, and you don't.'

'Because I'm not *allowed* to. I do during the evenings.'

I'm trying to find a different way of saying that we're not the same people we used to be, that we've grown apart, blah blah blah, but the effort is beyond me.

'"We're not the same people we used to be. We've grown apart."'

'Why are you putting on that silly voice?'

'It's supposed to indicate inverted commas. I was trying to find a new way of saying it. Like you tried to find a new way of saying that either we have babies or split up.'

'I did *not* ...'

'Just joking.'

'So we should pack it in? Is that what you're arguing? Because if you are, I'm going to run out of patience.'

'No, but . . .'

'But what?'

'But why doesn't it matter that we're not the same people we used to be?'

'First, I feel I should point out that you are entirely blameless.'

'Thank you.'

'You are exactly the same person you used to be. You haven't changed so much as a pair of socks in the years I've known you. If we've grown apart, then I'm the one that's done the growing. And all I've done is changed jobs.'

'And hairstyles and clothes and attitude and friends and . . .'

'That's not fair, Rob. You know I couldn't go to work with my hair all spiked. And I can afford to go out shopping more now. And I've met a couple of people I like over the last year or so. Which leaves attitude.'

'You're tougher.'

'More confident, maybe.'

'Harder.'

'Less neurotic. Are you intending to stay the same for the rest of your life? Same friends, or lack of them? Same job? Same attitude?'

'I'm all right.'

'Yeah, you're all right. But you're not perfect, and you're certainly not happy. So what happens if you *get* happy, and yes I know that's the title of an Elvis Costello album, I used the reference deliberately to catch your attention, do you take me for a complete idiot? Should we split up then, because I'm used to you being miserable? What happens if you, I don't know, if you start your own record label and it's a success? Time for a new girlfriend?'

'You're being stupid.'

'How? Show me the difference between you running a record label and me moving from legal aid to the City.'

I can't think of one.

'All I'm saying is that if you believe in a long-term monogamous relationship at all, then you have to allow for things happening to people, and you have to allow for things not happening to people. Otherwise what's the use?'

'No use.' I say it mock-meekly, but I am cowed – by her intelligence, and her ferocity, and the way she's always right. Or at least, she's always right enough to shut me up.

5. (In bed, sort of beforehand and sort of during, if you see what I mean, two nights later.)

'I don't know. I'm sorry. I think it's because I feel insecure.'

'I'm sorry, Rob, but I don't believe that for a moment. I think it's because you're half-cut. When we've had this sort of trouble before, it's usually been because of that.'

'Not this time. This time is because of insecurity.' I have trouble with the word 'insecurity', which in my rendition loses its second 'i'. The mispronunciation doesn't strengthen my case.

'What would you say you're insecure about?'

I let out a short, mirthless 'Ha!', a textbook demonstration of the art of the hollow laugh.

'I'm still none the wiser.'

'"I'm too tired to split up with you." All that. And Ray, and you seem ... *cross* with me all the time. Angry that I'm so hopeless.'

'Are we giving up on this?' She's referring to the lovemaking, rather than the conversation or the relationship.

'I s'pose.' I roll off her, and lie on the bed with an arm around her, looking at the ceiling.

'I know. I'm sorry, Rob. I haven't been very ... I haven't really given the impression that this is something I want to do.'

'And why's that, do you think?'

'Hold on. I want to try to explain this properly. OK. I thought that we were bound by one simple little cord, our relationship, and if I cut it then that would be that. So I cut it, but that wasn't that. There wasn't just one cord, there were hundreds, thousands, everywhere I turned – Jo going quiet when I said we'd split up, and me feeling funny on your birthday, and me feeling funny ... not *during* sex with Ray, but afterwards, and I felt sick when I played a tape you'd made me that was in the car, and I kept wondering how you were and ... oh, millions of things. And then you were more upset than I thought you'd be, and that made it harder ... and then on the day of the funeral ... it was me that wanted you to be there, not my mum. I mean, she was quite pleased, I think, but it never occurred to me to ask Ray, and that's when I felt tired. I wasn't prepared to do all that work. It wasn't worth it, just to be shot of you.' She laughs a little.

'This is the nice way of saying it?'

'You know I'm not very good at slushy stuff.' She kisses me on the shoulder.

You hear that? She's not very good at slushy stuff? That, to me, is a problem, as it would be to any male who heard Dusty Springfield singing 'The Look Of Love' at an impressionable age. That was what I thought it was all going to be like when I was married (I called it 'married' then – I call it 'settled' or 'sorted' now). I thought there was going to be this sexy woman with a sexy voice and lots of sexy eye make-up whose devotion to me shone from every pore. And there is such a thing as the look of love – Dusty didn't lead us up the garden path entirely – it's just that the look of love isn't what I expected it to be. It's not huge eyes almost bursting with longing situated somewhere in the middle of a double bed with the covers turned down invitingly; it's just as likely to be the look of benevolent indulgence that a mother gives a toddler, or a look of amused exasperation, even a look of pained concern. But the Dusty Springfield look of love? Forget it. As mythical as the exotic underwear.

Women get it wrong when they complain about media images of women. Men understand that not everyone has Bardot's breasts, or Jamie Lee Curtis's neck, or Felicity Kendall's bottom, and we don't mind at all. Obviously we'd take Kim Basinger over Hattie Jacques, just as women would take Keanu Reeves over Bernard Manning, but it's not the body that's important, it's the level of abasement. We worked out very quickly that Bond girls were out of our league, but the realization that women don't ever look at us the way Ursula Andress looked at Sean Connery, or even in the way that Doris Day looked at Rock Hudson, was much slower to arrive, for most of us. In my case I'm not at all sure that it ever did.

I'm beginning to get used to the idea that Laura might be the person I spend my life with, I think (or at least, I'm beginning to get used to the idea that I'm so miserable without her that it's not worth thinking about alternatives). But it's much harder to get used to the idea that my little-boy notion of romance, of négligés and candlelit dinners at home and long, smouldering glances, had no basis in reality at all. That's what women ought to get all steamed up about; that's why we can't function properly in a relationship. It's not the cellulite or the crow's feet. It's the . . . the . . . the *disrespect.*

TWENTY-EIGHT

About two weeks in, after a lot of talking and a lot of sex and a tolerable amount of arguing, we go for dinner with Laura's friends Paul and Miranda. This might not sound very exciting to you, but it's a really big deal to me: it's a vote of confidence, an endorsement, a sign to the world that I'm going to be around for a few months at least. Laura and I have never seen eye-to-eye about Paul and Miranda, not that I've ever met either of them. Laura and Paul joined the law firm around the same time, and they got on well, so when she (and I) were asked round, I refused to go. I didn't like the sound of him, nor Laura's enthusiasm for him, although when I heard that there was a Miranda I could see I was being stupid, so I made up a load of other stuff. I said that he sounded typical of the sort of people she was going to be meeting all the time now she had this flash new job, and I was being left behind, and she got cross, so I upped the ante and prefaced his name with the words 'this' and 'wanker' whenever I mentioned him, and I attributed to him a hoity-toity voice and a whole set of interests and attitudes he probably hasn't got, and then Laura got *really* cross and went on her own. And having called him a wanker so many times I felt that Paul and I had got off on the wrong foot, and when Laura invited them round to ours I went out until two in the morning just to make sure I didn't bump into them, even though they've got a kid and I knew they'd be gone by half past eleven. So when Laura said we'd been invited again I knew it was a big deal, not only because she was prepared to give it another go, but because it meant she'd been saying stuff about us living together again, and the stuff she'd been saying couldn't have been all bad.

As we stand on the doorstep of their house (nothing swanky, a three-bedroomed terraced in Kensal Green), I fiddle with the fly button on my 501s, a nervous habit that Laura strongly disapproves of, for perhaps understandable reasons. But tonight she looks at me and smiles, and gives my hand (my other hand, the one that isn't scrabbling frantically at my groin) a quick squeeze, and before I know it we're in the house amid a flurry of smiles and kisses and introductions.

Paul is tall and good-looking, with long (untrendy, can't-be-bothered-to-have-it-cut, computer-nerdy long, as opposed to hairdressery long) dark hair and a shadow that's nearer six-thirty than five o'clock. He's wearing a pair of old brown cords and a Body Shop T-shirt depicting something green, a lizard or a tree or a vegetable or something. I wish a few of the buttons on my fly were undone, just so I wouldn't feel overdressed. Miranda, like Laura, is wearing a baggy jumper and leggings, and a pair of pretty cool rimless specs, and she's blonde and round and pretty, not quite Dawn French round, but round enough for you to notice straight away. So I'm not intimidated by the clothes, or by the house, or the people, and anyway the people are so nice to me that for a moment I almost feel a bit weepy: it's obvious to even the most insecure that Paul and Miranda are delighted that I am here, either because they have decided that I am a Good Thing, or because Laura has told them that she is happy with the way things are (and if I've got it all wrong, and they're just acting, then who cares anyway, when the actors are this good?).

There isn't any what-would-you-call-your-dog stuff, partly because everyone knows what everyone does (Miranda is an English lecturer at an FE college), and partly because the evening isn't like that for a moment. They ask about Laura's dad, and Laura tells them about the funeral, or at least some of it, and also some stuff I didn't know – like, she says she felt a little thrill, momentarily, before all the pain and the grief and everything hit her – 'Like, God, this is the most grown-up thing that's ever happened to me.'

And Miranda talks a bit about her mum dying, and Paul and I ask questions about that, and Paul and Miranda ask questions about my mum and dad, and then it all somehow moves on from there to aspirations, and what we want, and what we're not happy about, and . . . I don't know. It sounds stupid to say it, but despite what we're talking about, I really enjoy myself – I don't feel afraid of anybody, and whatever I say people take seriously, and I catch Laura looking fondly at me from time to time, which helps morale. It's not like anyone says any one thing that's memorable, or wise, or acute; it's more a mood thing. For the first time in my life I felt as though I'm in an episode of *thirtysomething* rather than an episode of . . . of . . . of some sitcom that hasn't been made yet about three guys who work in a record shop and talk about sandwich fillings and sax solos all day, and I love it. And I know *thirtysomething* is soppy and clichéd and American and naff, I can see that. But when you're sitting in a one-bedroom flat in Crouch End and your business is going down the toilet and your girlfriend's gone off with the guy from the flat upstairs, a starring role in a real-life episode of *thirtysomething*, with all the kids and marriages and jobs and barbecues and k.d. lang CDs that this implies, seems more than one could possibly ask of life.

The first time I had a crush on anyone was four or five years before Alison Ashworth came along. We were on holiday in Cornwall, and a couple of honeymooners had the next breakfast table to us, and we got talking to them, and I fell in love with both of them. It wasn't one or the other, it was the unit. (And now I come to think about it, it was maybe these two as much as Dusty Springfield that gave me unrealistic expectations about relationships.) I think that each was trying, as newlyweds sometimes do, to show that they were brilliant with kids, that he'd make a brilliant dad and she'd make a fantastic mum, and I got the benefit of it: they took me swimming and rockpooling, and they bought me Sky Rays, and when they left I was heartbroken.

It's kind of like that tonight, with Paul and Miranda. I fall in love with both of them – with what they have, and the way they treat each other, and the way they make me feel as if I am the new centre of their world. I think they're great, and I want to see them twice a week every week for the rest of my life.

Only right at the end of the evening do I realize that I've been set up. Miranda's upstairs with their little boy; Paul's gone to see whether there's any ropy holiday liqueurs mouldering in the back of a cupboard anywhere, so that we can stoke up the log-fire glow we all have in our stomachs.

'Go and look at their records,' says Laura.

'I don't have to. I am capable of surviving without turning my nose up at other people's record collections, you know.'

'Please. I want you to.'

So I wander over to the shelf, and turn my head on one side and squint, and sure enough, it's a disaster area, the sort of CD collection that is so poisonously awful that it should be put in a steel case and shipped off to some Third World waste dump. They're all there: Tina

Turner, Billy Joel, Kate Bush, Pink Floyd, Simply Red, the Beatles, of course, Mike Oldfield (*Tubular Bells I* and *II*), Meat Loaf . . . I don't have much time to examine the vinyl, but I see a couple of Eagles records, and I catch a glimpse of what looks suspiciously like a Barbara Dickson album.

Paul comes back into the room.

'I shouldn't think you approve of many of those, do you?'

'Oh, I don't know. They were a good band, the Beatles.'

He laughs. 'We're not very up on things, I'm afraid. We'll have to come into the shop, and you can put us right.'

'Each to his own, I say.'

Laura looks at me. 'I've never heard you say it before. I thought "each to his own" was the kind of sentiment that'd be enough to get you hung in the brave new Fleming world.'

I manage a crooked smile, and hold out my brandy glass for some ancient Drambuie out of a sticky bottle.

'You did that deliberately,' I say to her on the way home. 'You knew all along I'd like them. It was a trick.'

'Yeah. I tricked you into meeting some people you'd think were great. I conned you into having a nice evening.'

'You know what I mean.'

'Everybody's faith needs testing from time to time. I thought it would be amusing to introduce you to someone with a Tina Turner album, and then see whether you still felt the same.'

I'm sure I do. Or at least, I'm sure I will. But tonight, I have to confess (but only to myself, obviously) that maybe, given the right set of peculiar, freakish, probably unrepeatable circumstances, it's not what you like but what you're like that's important. I'm not going to be the one that explains to Barry how this might happen, though.

TWENTY-NINE

I take Laura to see Marie; she loves her.

'But she's brilliant!' she says. 'Why don't more people know about her? Why isn't the pub packed?'

I find this pretty ironic, as I've spent our entire relationship trying to make her listen to people who should be famous but aren't, though I don't bother pointing this out.

'You need pretty good taste to see how great she is, I suppose, and most people haven't got that.'

'And she's been to the shop?'

Yeah. I slept with her. Pretty cool, eh?

'Yeah. I served her in the shop. Pretty cool, eh?'

'Starfucker.' She claps the back of the hand that's holding the half of Guinness when Marie finishes a song. 'Why don't you get her to play in the shop? A personal appearance? You've never done one of those before.'

'I haven't been in a position to before.'

'Why not? It would be fun. She probably wouldn't even need a mike.'

'If she needed a mike in Championship Vinyl she'd have some kind of major vocal cord disorder.'

'And you'd probably sell a few of her tapes, and probably a couple of extra things besides. And you could get it put into the *Time Out* gigs list.'

'Ooer, Lady Macbeth. Calm down and listen to the music.' Marie's singing a ballad about some uncle who died, and one or two people look round when Laura's excitement gets the better of her.

But I like the sound of it. A personal appearance! Like at HMV! (Do people sign cassettes? I suppose they must do.) And maybe if the Marie one goes well, then other people would want to do it – bands maybe, and if it's true about Bob Dylan buying a house in north London . . . well, why not? I know that pop superstars don't often do in-store appearances to help flog second-hand copies of their back-catalogue, but if I could get shot of that mono copy of *Blonde On Blonde* at an inflated price, I'd go halves with him. Maybe even sixty–forty, if he threw in a signature.

And from a small, one-off acoustic event like Bob Dylan at Championship Vinyl (with a limited-edition live album, maybe? Could be some tricky contractual stuff to deal with, but nothing impossible, I wouldn't have thought), it's easy to see bigger, better, brighter days ahead. Maybe I could reopen the Rainbow? It's only down the road, and nobody else wants it. And I could launch it with a charity one-off, maybe a re-enactment of Eric Clapton's Rainbow Concert . . .

We go to see Marie in the interval, when she's selling her tapes.

'Oh, hiii! I saw Rob out there with someone, and I hoped it might be you,' she says to Laura, with a big smile.

I was so busy with all the promotion stuff going on in my head that I forgot to be nervous about Laura and Marie face-to-face (Two Women. One Man. Any fool could see there was going to be trouble. Etc.), and already I have some explaining to do. I served Marie in the shop a couple of times, according to me. On what basis, then, was Marie hoping that Laura is Laura? ('That'll be five pounds ninety-nine, please. Oh, my girlfriend's got a wallet like that. My ex-girlfriend, actually. I'd really like you to meet her, but we've split up.')

Laura looks suitably mystified, but ploughs on.

'I love your songs. And the way you sing them.' She colours slightly, and shakes her head impatiently.

'I'm glad you did. Rob was right. You *are* special.' ('There's four pounds and a penny change. My ex-girlfriend's special.')

'I didn't realize you two were such pals,' says Laura, with more acidity than is good for my stomach.

'Oh, Rob's been a good friend to me since I've been here. And Dick and Barry. They've made me feel real welcome.'

'We'd better let Marie sell her tapes, Laura.'

'Marie, will you do a PA in Rob's shop?'

Marie laughs. She laughs, and doesn't reply. We stand there gormlessly.

'You're kidding me, right?'

'Not really. On a Saturday afternoon, when the shop's busy. You could stand on the counter.' This last embellishment is Laura's own, and I stare at her.

Marie shrugs. 'OK. But I get to keep any money I make from the tapes.'

'Sure.' Laura again. I'm still staring at her from before, so I have to content myself with staring at her even harder.

'Thanks, it was nice to meet you.'

We go back to where we were standing.

'See?' she says. 'Easy.'

Occasionally, during the first few weeks of Laura's return, I try to work out what life is like now: whether it's better or worse, how my feelings for Laura have changed, if they have, whether I'm happier than I was, how near I am to getting itchy feet again, whether Laura's any different, what it's like living with her. The answers are easy – better, kind of, yes, not very near, not really, quite nice – but also unsatisfying, because I know they're not answers that come from down deep. But somehow, there's less time to think since she came back. We're too busy talking, or working, or having sex (there's a lot of sex at the moment, much of it initiated by me as a way of banishing insecurity), or eating, or going to the pictures. Maybe I should stop doing these things, so as I can work it all out properly, because I know these are important times. But there again, maybe I shouldn't; maybe this is how it's done. Maybe this is how people manage to have relationships.

'Oh, great. You never asked us to play here, did you?'

Barry. Pillock. I might have known he'd find something in Marie's imminent in-store performance to moan about.

'Didn't I? I thought I did, and you said no.'

'How are we ever going to get going if even our friends won't give us a break.'

'Rob let you put the poster up, Barry. Be fair.' This is quite assertive for Dick, but there is something in him that doesn't like the idea of Barry's band anyway. For him, I think, a band is too much like action, and not enough like fandom.

'Oh, fucking great. Big fucking deal. A poster.'

'How would a band fit in here? I'd have to buy the shop next door, and I'm not prepared to do that just so's you can make a terrible racket one Saturday afternoon.'

'We could have done an acoustic set.'

'Oh, right. Kraftwerk unplugged. That'd be nice.'

This gets a laugh from Dick, and Barry looks round at him angrily.

'Shut up, jerk. I told you, we're not doing the German stuff any more.'

'What would be the point? What do you have to sell? Have you ever made a record? No? Well, there you are then.'

So forceful is my logic that Barry has to content himself with stomping around for five minutes, and then sitting on the counter with his head buried in an old copy of *Hot Press*. Every now and again he says something feeble – 'Just because you've shagged her', for example, and, 'How can you run a record shop when you have no interest in music at all?' But mostly he's quiet, lost in contemplation of what might have been had I given Barrytown the opportunity to play live in Championship Vinyl.

It's a stupid little thing, this gig. All it will be, after all, is half a dozen songs played on an acoustic guitar in front of half a dozen people. What depresses me is how much I'm looking forward to it, and how much I've enjoyed the pitiful amount of preparation (a few posters, a couple of phone calls to try and get hold of some tapes) it has involved. What if I'm about to become dissatisfied with my lot? What do I do then? The notion that the amount of . . . of *life* I have on my plate won't be enough to fill me up alarms me. I thought we were supposed to ditch anything superfluous and get by on the rest, and that doesn't appear to be the case at all.

The big day itself goes by in a blur, like it must have done for Bob Geldof at Live Aid. Marie turns up, and loads of people turn up to watch her (the shop's packed, and though she doesn't stand on the counter to play, she does have to stand behind it, on a couple of crates we found for her), and they clap, and at the end some of them buy tapes and a few of them buy other stuff they see in the shop; my expenses came to about ten pounds, and I sell thirty or forty quid's worth of stock, so I'm laughing. Chuckling. Smiling broadly, anyway.

Marie flogs the stuff for me. She plays about a dozen songs, only half of which are her own; before she starts, she spends some time rummaging through the browser racks checking that I've got all the cover versions she was intending to play, and writing down the names and the prices of the albums they come from. If I haven't got it, she crosses the song off her set list and chooses one I do have.

'This is a song by Emmylou Harris called "Boulder to Birmingham",' she announces. 'It's on the album *Pieces Of The Sky*, which Rob is selling this afternoon for the unbelievable price of five pounds and ninety-nine pence, and you can find it right over there in the "Country Artists – (Female)" section.' 'This is a song by Butch Hancock called . . .' And at the end, when people want to buy the songs but have forgotten the names, Marie is there to help them out. She's great, and when she sings, I wish that I wasn't living with Laura, and that my night with Marie had gone better than it did. Maybe next time, if there is a next time, I won't feel so miserable about Laura going, and then things might be different with Marie, and . . . but I'm always going to feel miserable about Laura going. That's what I've learned. So I should be happy that she's staying, right? That's how it should work, right? And that's how it does work. Kind of. When I don't think about it too hard.

It could be argued that my little event is, on its own terms, more successful than Live Aid, at least from the technical point of view. There are no glitches, no technical fuck-ups (although admittedly it would be hard to see what could go wrong, apart from a broken guitar string, or Marie falling over), and only one untoward incident: two songs in, a familiar voice emerges from the back of the shop, right next to the door.

'Will you play "All Kinds Of Everything"?'

'I don't know that,' says Marie sweetly. 'But if I did, I'd sing it for you.'

'You don't know it?'

'Nope.'

'*You don't know it?*'

'Nope again.'

'Jesus, woman, it won the Eurovision Song Contest.'

'Then I guess I'm pretty ignorant, huh? I promise that the next time I play live here, I'll have learned it.'

'I should fockin' hope so.'

And then I push through to the door, and Johnny and I do our little dance, and I shove him out. But it's not like Paul McCartney's microphone conking out during 'Let It Be', is it?

'I had a terrific time,' says Marie afterwards. 'I didn't think it would work, but it did. And we all made money! That always makes me feel good.'

I don't feel good, not now it's all over. For an afternoon I was working in a place that other people wanted to come to, and that made a difference to me – I felt, I felt, I felt, go on say it, *more of a man*, a feeling both shocking and comforting.

Men don't work in quiet, deserted side streets in Holloway: they work in the City or the West End, or in factories, or down mines, or in stations or airports or offices. They work in places where other people work, and they have to fight to get there, and perhaps as a consequence they do not get the feeling that real life is going on elsewhere. I don't even feel as if I'm the centre of my own world, so how am I supposed to feel as though I'm the centre of anyone else's? When the last person has been ushered out of this place, and I lock the door behind him, I suddenly feel panicky. I know I'm going to have to do something about the shop – let it go, burn it down, whatever – and find myself a career.

THIRTY

But look:

My five dream jobs

1. NME journalist, 1976–1979
Get to meet the Clash, Sex Pistols, Chrissie Hynde, Danny Baker, etc. Get loads of free records – good ones too. Go on to host my own quiz show or something.

2. Producer, Atlantic Records, 1964–1971 (approx)
Get to meet Aretha, Wilson Pickett, Solomon Burke, etc. Get loads of free records (probably) – good ones too. Make piles of money.

3. Any kind of musician (apart from classical or rap)
Speaks for itself. But I'd have settled just for being one of the Memphis Horns – I'm not asking to be Hendrix or Jagger or Otis Redding.

4. Film director
Again, any kind, although preferably not German or silent.

5. Architect
A surprise entry at number 5, I know, but I used to be quite good at technical drawing at school.

And that's it. It's not even as though this list is my *top* five, either: there isn't a number six or seven that I had to omit because of the limitations of the exercise. To be honest, I'm not even that bothered about being an architect – I just thought that if I failed to come up with five, it would look a bit feeble.

It was Laura's idea for me to make a list, and I couldn't think of a sensible one, so I made a stupid one. I wasn't going to show it to her, but something got to me – self-pity, envy, something – and I do anyway.

She doesn't react.

'It's got to be architecture, then, hasn't it?'

'I guess.'

'Seven years' training.'

I shrug.

'Are you prepared for that?'

'Not really.'

'No, I didn't think so.'

'I'm not sure I really want to be an architect.'

'So you've got a list here of five things you'd do if qualifications and time and history and salary were no object, and one of them you're not bothered about.'

'Well, I did put it at number five.'

'You'd really rather have been a journalist for the *NME*, than, say, a sixteenth-century explorer, or King of France?'

'God, yes.'

She shakes her head.

'What would you put down, then?'

'Hundreds of things. A playwright. A ballet dancer. A musician, yes, but also a painter or a university don or a novelist or a great chef.'

'A chef?'

'Yes. I'd love to have that sort of talent. Wouldn't you?'

'Wouldn't mind. I wouldn't want to work evenings, though.' I wouldn't, either.

'Then you might just as well stay at the shop.'

'How d'you work that out?'

'Wouldn't you rather do that than be an architect?'

'I suppose.'

'Well, there you are then. It comes in at number five in your list of dream jobs, and as the other four are entirely impractical, you're better off where you are.'

I don't tell Dick and Barry that I'm thinking of packing it in. But I do ask them for their five dream jobs.

'Are you allowed to subdivide?' Barry asks.

'How d'you mean?'

'Like, does saxophonist and pianist count as two jobs?'

'I should think so.'

There's silence in the shop; for a few moments it has become a primary school classroom during a quiet drawing period. Biros are sucked, crossings out are made, brows are furrowed, and I look over shoulders.

'And what about bass guitarist and lead guitarist?'

'I don't know. Just the one, I should think.'

'What, so Keith Richards had the same job as Bill Wyman, according to you?'

'I didn't say they've got . . .'

'Someone should have told them that. One of them could have saved himself a lot of trouble.'

'What about, say, film reviewer and album reviewer?' says Dick.

'One job.'

'Brilliant. That frees me up for other things.'

'Oh yeah? Like?'

'Pianist and saxophonist, for a start. And I've still got two places left.'

And so on, and on. But the point is, my own list wasn't freakish. It could have been made by anybody. Just about anybody. Anybody who works here, anyway. Nobody asks how to spell 'solicitor'. Nobody wants to know whether 'vet' and 'doctor' count as two choices. Both of them are lost, away, off in recording studios and dressing rooms and Holiday Inn bars.

THIRTY-ONE

Laura and I go to see my mum and dad, and it feels sort of official, like we're announcing something. I think that feeling comes from them rather than from us. My mum's wearing a dress, and my dad doesn't buzz around doing things to his stupid and vile home-made wine, and nor does he reach for the TV remote control; he sits down in a chair and listens and asks questions, and in a dim light he would resemble an ordinary human being having a conversation with guests.

It's easier to have parents if you've got a girlfriend. I don't know why this is true, but it is. My mum and dad like me more when I have someone, and they seem more comfortable; it's as if Laura becomes a sort of human microphone, somebody we speak into to make ourselves heard.

'Have you been watching *Inspector Morse*?' Laura asks, apropos of nothing.

'No,' says my dad. 'They're repeats, aren't they? We've got them on video from the first time around.' See, this is typical of my dad. It's not enough for him to say that he never watches repeats, that he's the first on the block; he has to add an unnecessary and mendacious embellishment.

'You didn't have a video the first time around,' I point out, not unreasonably. My dad pretends he hasn't heard.

'What did you say that for?' I ask him. He winks at Laura, as if she's in on a particularly impenetrable family joke. She smiles back. Whose family is it anyway?

'You can buy them in the shops,' he says. 'Ready-made ones.'

'I know that. But you haven't got any, have you?'

My dad pretends he hasn't heard and, at this point, if it had been just the three of us, we would have had a row. I would have told him that he was mental and/or a liar; my mother would have told me not to make mountains out of molehills etc., and I would have asked her whether she had to listen to this stuff all day, and we would have taken it on from there.

When Laura's here, though . . . I wouldn't go so far as to say she actively likes my parents, but she certainly thinks that parents generally are a good thing, and that therefore their little quirks and idiocies are there to be loved, not exposed. She treats my father's fibs and boasts and non sequiturs as waves, giant breakers, and she surfs over them with skill and pleasure.

'They're really expensive, though, aren't they, those ready-made ones?' she says. 'I bought Rob a couple of things on video for his birthday a few years ago, and they came to nearly twenty-five pounds!'

This is shameless stuff. She doesn't think twenty-five pounds is a lot of money, but she knows they will, and my mum duly gives a loud, terrified, twenty-five-quid shriek. And then we're off on to the prices of things – chocolates, houses, anything we can think of, really – and my dad's outrageous lies are forgotten.

And while we're washing up, more or less the same thing happens with my mum.

'I'm glad you're back to sort him out,' she says. 'God knows what the flat would look like if he had to look after himself.'

This really fucks me off, a) because I'd told her not to mention Laura's recent absence, b) because you don't tell any woman, but especially not Laura, that one of her major talents is looking after me, and c) I'm the tidier one of the two of us, and the flat was actually cleaner during her absence.

'I didn't know you'd been letting yourself in to examine the state of our kitchen, Mum.'

'I don't need to, thanks all the same. I know what you're like.'

'You knew what I was like when I was eighteen. You don't know what I'm like now, bad luck.' Where did that 'bad luck' – childish, taunting, petulant – come from? Oh, I know where, really. It came from straight out of 1973.

'He's much tidier than me,' says Laura, simply and gravely. I've heard this sentence about ten times, with exactly the same intonation, ever since I was forced to bring Laura here for the first time.

'Oh, he's a good lad, really. I just wish he'd sort himself out.'

'He will.' And they both look at me fondly. So, yes, I've been rubbished and patronized and worried over, but there's a glow in the kitchen now, genuine three-way affection, where previously there might have been simply mutual antagonism, ending with my mum's tears and me slamming the door. I do prefer it this way, really; I'm happy Laura's here.

THIRTY-TWO

Fly posters. I'm for them. The only creative idea I have ever had in my life was for an exhibition of fly poster photographs. It would take two or three decades to get enough stuff, but it would look really good when it was finished. There are important historical documents on the window of the boarded-up shop opposite mine: posters advertising a Frank Bruno fight, and an Anti-Nazi rally, and the new Prince single, and a West Indian comedian, and loads of gigs, and in a couple of weeks they will be gone, covered over by the shifting sands of time – or at least, an advert for the new U2 album. You get a sense of the spirit of the age, right? (I'll let you into a secret: I actually started on the project. In 1988 I took about three pictures on my Instamatic of an empty shop on the Holloway Road, but then they let the shop, and I kind of lost enthusiasm.

The photos came out OK – OKish, anyway – but no one's going to let you exhibit three photos, are they?)

Anyway, every now and then I test myself. I stare at the shopfront to make sure that I've heard of the bands with gigs coming up, but the sad truth is that I'm losing touch. I used to know everyone, every single name, however stupid, whatever the size of the venue the band was playing. And then, three or four years ago, when I stopped devouring every single word in the music papers, I began to notice that I no longer recognized the names playing some of the pubs and smaller clubs; last year, there were a couple of bands playing at the Forum who meant absolutely nothing to me. The Forum! A fifteen hundred-capacity venue! One thousand five hundred people going to see a band I'd never heard of! The first time it happened I was depressed for the entire evening, probably because I made the mistake of confessing my ignorance to Dick and Barry. (Barry almost exploded with derision; Dick stared into his drink, too embarrassed for me even to meet my eye.)

Anyway again. I'm doing my spot check (Prince is there, at least, so I don't score *nul points* – one day I'm going to score *nul points*, and then I'll hang myself) and I notice a familiar-looking poster. 'BY POPULAR DEMAND!' it says. 'THE RETURN OF THE GROUCHO CLUB!' And then, underneath, 'EVERY FRIDAY FROM 20TH JULY, THE DOG AND PHEASANT.' I stand there looking at it for ages, with my mouth open. It's the same size and colour as ours used to be, and they've even had the cheek to copy our design and our logo – the Groucho Marx glasses and moustache in the second 'o' of 'Groucho', and the cigar coming out of the bumcrack (that's probably not the correct technical term, but that's what we used to call it) in the 'b' at the end of 'club'.

On our old posters, there used to be a line at the bottom listing the type of music I played; I used to stick the name of the brilliant, gifted DJ at the end, in the doomed hope of creating a cult following for him. You can't see the bottom of this one because some band has plastered a load of little flyers over it; so I peel them off, and there it is: 'STAX ATLANTIC MOTOWN R&B SKA MERSEYBEAT AND THE OCCASIONAL MADONNA SINGLE – DANCE MUSIC FOR OLD PEOPLE – DJ ROB FLEMING'. It's nice to see I'm still doing it after all these years.

What's going on? There are only three possibilities, really: a) this poster has been there since 1986, and fly poster archaeologists have just discovered it; b) I decided to restart the club, got the posters done, put them up, and then suffered a pretty comprehensive attack of amnesia; c) someone else has decided to restart the club for me. I reckon that explanation 'c' is the best bet, and go home to wait for Laura.

'It's a late birthday present. I had the idea when I was living with Ray, and it was such a good one that I was really annoyed that we weren't together any more. Maybe that's why I came back. Are you pleased?' she says. She's been out with a couple of people for a drink after work, and she's a bit squiffy.

I hadn't thought about it before, but I am pleased. Nervous and daunted – all those records to dig out, all that equipment to get hold of – but pleased. Thrilled, really.

'You had no right,' I tell her. 'Supposing . . .' What? 'Supposing I was doing something that couldn't be cancelled?'

'What do you ever do that can't be cancelled?'

'That's not the point.' I don't know why I have to be like this, all stern and sulky and what-business-is-it-of-yours. I should be bursting into tears of love and gratitude, not sulking.

She sighs, slumps back on the sofa and kicks her shoes off.

'Well, tough. You're doing it.'

'Maybe.'

One day, when something like this happens, I'm just going to go, thanks, that's great, how thoughtful, I'm really looking forward to it. Not yet, though.

'You know we're doing a set in the middle?' says Barry.

'Like fuck you are.'

'Laura said we could. If I helped out with the posters and all that.'

'Jesus. You're not going to take her up on it?'

'Course we are.'

'I'll give you ten per cent of the door if you don't play.'

'We're getting that anyway.'

'What's she fucking playing at? OK, twenty per cent.'

'No. We need the gig.'

'One hundred and ten per cent. That's my final offer.'

He laughs.

'I'm not kidding. If we get one hundred people paying a fiver a throw,

I'll give you five hundred and fifty pounds. That's how much it means to me not to hear you play.'

'We're not as bad as you think, Rob.'

'You couldn't be. Look, Barry. There's going to be people from Laura's work there, people who own dogs and babies and Tina Turner albums. How are you going to cope with them?'

'How are they going to cope with us, more like. We're not called Barrytown any more, by the way. They got sick of the Barry/Barrytown thing. We're called SDM. Sonic Death Monkey.'

'"Sonic Death Monkey".'

'What do you think? Dick likes it.'

'Barry, you're over thirty years old. You owe it to yourself and to your friends and to your mum and dad not to sing in a group called Sonic Death Monkey.'

'I owe it to myself to go out on the edge, Rob, and this group really does go out on the edge. Over it, in fact.'

'You'll be going fucking right over it if you come anywhere near me next Friday night.'

'That's what we want. Reaction. And if Laura's bourgeois lawyer friends can't take it, then fuck 'em. Let 'em riot, we can handle it. We'll be ready.' He gives what he fondly imagines to be a demonic, drug-crazed chuckle.

Some people would relish all this. They'd make an anecdote out of it, they'd be getting the phrasing right in their heads even as the pub was being torn apart, even as weeping lawyers with bleeding eardrums were heading for the exits. I am not one of those people. I just gather it all up into a hard ball of nervous anxiety, and put it in my gut, somewhere between the belly button and the arsehole, for safe keeping. Even Laura doesn't seem to be that worried.

'It's only the first one. And I've told them they can't go on for longer than half an hour. And OK, you might lose a couple of my friends, but they won't be able to get babysitters every week anyway.'

'I've got to pay a deposit, you know. As well as the rental on the room.'

'That's all taken care of.'

And just that one little sentence sets something off in me. I suddenly feel choked up. It's not the money, it's the way she's thought of everything: one morning I woke up to find her going through my singles, pulling out things that she remembered me playing and putting them into the little carrying cases that I used to use and put away in a cupboard somewhere years ago. She knew I needed a kick up the backside. She also knew how happy I was when I used to do this; and from whichever angle I examine it, it still looks as though she's done it because she loves me.

I cave in to something that has been eating away at me for a while, and put my arms around her.

'I'm sorry I've been a bit of a jerk. I do appreciate what you've done for me, and I know you've done it for the best possible reasons, and I do love you, even though I act as though I don't.'

'That's OK. You seem so cross all the time, though.'

'I know. I don't get myself.'

But if I had to take a wild guess, I'd say that I'm cross because I know I'm stuck, and I don't like it. It would be nicer, in some ways, if I wasn't so bound to her; it would be nicer if those sweet possibilities, that dreamy anticipation you have when you're fifteen or twenty or twenty-five, even, and you know that the most perfect person in the world might walk into your shop or office or friend's party at any moment . . . it would be nicer if all that was still around somewhere, in a back pocket or a bottom drawer. But it's all gone, I think, and that's enough to make anyone cross. Laura is who I am now, and it's no good pretending otherwise.

THIRTY-THREE

I meet Caroline when she comes to interview me for her newspaper, and I fall for her straight away, no messing, while she's at the bar in the pub waiting to buy me a drink. It's a hot day, the first of the year – we go and sit at a trestle table outside and watch the traffic – and she's pink-cheeked and wearing a sleeveless, shapeless summer dress with clumpy boots, and for some reason the outfit looks really good on her. But I think I would have gone for anyone today. The weather makes me feel as though I've lost all the dead nerve-ends that were stopping me from feeling and, anyway, how can you fail to fall in love with someone who wants to interview you for a newspaper?

She writes for the *Tufnell Parker*, one of those free magazines full of advertisements that people shove through your door and you shove into the rubbish bin. Actually, she's a student – she's doing a journalism course, and she's on work experience. And, actually, she says her editor isn't sure whether he'll want the piece, because he's never heard of the shop or the club, and Holloway is right on the borderline of his parish, or constituency, or catchment area, or whatever it is. But Caroline used to come to the club in the old days, and loved it, and wanted to give us a plug.

'I shouldn't have let you in,' I say. 'You must only have been about sixteen.'

'Dear me,' she says, and I can't see why until I think about what I've just said. I didn't mean it as a pathetic chat-up line, or indeed any sort of a chat-up line; I just meant that if she's a student now, she must have been at school then, even though she looks as though she's in her late twenties or early thirties. When I find out that she's a mature student and she worked as a secretary for some left-wing publishing company, I try to correct the impression I must have given without Tippexing it out altogether, if you see what I mean, and I make a bit of a hash of it.

'When I said that thing about not letting you in, I didn't mean you look young. You don't.' Jesus. 'You don't look old, either. You just look as old as you are.' Fucking hell. What if she's forty-five? 'Well, you do. A bit younger, maybe, but not a lot. Not too much. Just right. I'd forgotten about mature students, you see.' I'd rather be a smoothy slime-ball than a blundering, semi-coherent, gushing twit any day of the week.

Within minutes, however, I'm looking back fondly on those gushing twit days; they seem infinitely preferable to my next incarnation, Sleaze Man.

'You must have an enormous record collection,' Caroline says.

'Yeah,' I say. 'Do you want to come round and see it?'

I meant it! I meant it! I thought maybe they'd want a picture of me standing by it or something! But when Caroline looks at me over the top of her sunglasses, I rewind and listen to what I said, and let out an audible groan of despair. At least that makes her laugh.

'I'm not usually like this, honest.'

'Don't worry. I don't think he'll let me do one of those *Guardian*-type profiles anyway.'

'That wasn't why I was worried.'

'It's OK, really.'

It's all forgotten, though, with her next question. All my life I have been waiting for this moment, and when it comes I can hardly believe it: I feel unprepared, caught short.

'What are your five favourite records of all time?' she says.

'Pardon?'

'What are your all-time top five records? Your desert island discs, minus – how many? Three?'

'Minus three what?'

'It's eight on *Desert Island Discs*, isn't it? So eight minus five is three, right?'

'Yeah. Plus three, though. Not minus three.'

'No, I just said . . . anyway. Your all-time top five records.'

'What, in the club, or at home?'

'Is there a difference?'

'OF COURSE . . .' Too shrill. I pretend I've got something in my throat, clear it, and start again. 'Well, yeah, a bit. There's my top five dance records of all time, and then there's my top five records of all time. See, one of my favourite-ever records is "Sin City" by the Flying Burrito Brothers, but I wouldn't play that at the club. It's a country-rock ballad. Everyone would go home.'

'Never mind. Any five. So four more.'

'What d'you mean, four more?'

'Well if one of them is this "Sin City" thing, that leaves four more.'

'NO!' This time I make no attempt to disguise the panic. 'I didn't say it was in my top five! I just said it was one of my favourites! It might turn out to be number six or seven!'

I'm making a bit of a berk of myself, but I can't help it: this is too important, and I've waited for it too long. But where have they gone, all these records I've had in my head for years, just in case Roy Plomley or Michael Parkinson or Sue Lawley or whoever used to do *My Top Twelve* on Radio One contacted me and asked me in as a late and admittedly unknown replacement for someone famous? For some reason I can think of hardly any record at all apart from 'Respect', and that's definitely not my favourite Aretha song.

'Can I go home and work it out and let you know? In a week or so?'

'Look, if you can't think of anything, it doesn't matter. I'll do one. My five favourites from the old Groucho Club or something.'

She'll do one! She'll rob me of my one and only chance to make a list for publication in a newspaper! I don't think so!

'Oh, I'm sure I can manage something.'

'A Horse With No Name'. 'Beep Beep'. 'Ma Baker'. 'My Boomerang Won't Come Back'. My head is suddenly flooded with the titles of terrible records, and I'm almost hyperventilating.

'OK, put "Sin City" down.' There must be one other good record in the entire history of pop.

'"Baby Let's Play House"!'

'Who's that by?'

'Elvis Presley.'

'Oh. Of course.'

'And . . .' Aretha. Think Aretha.

'"Think" by Aretha. Franklin.'

Boring, but it'll do. Three down. Two left. Come *on*, Rob.

'"Louie, Louie" by the Kingsmen. "Little Red Corvette" by Prince.'

'Fine. That's great.'

'Is that it?'

'Well, I wouldn't mind a quick chat, if you've got time.'

'Sure. But is that it for the list?'

'That's five. Do you want to change anything?'

'Did I say "Stir It Up"? Bob Marley?'

'No.'

'I'd better have that in.'

'What do you want to leave out?'

'Prince.'

'No problem.'

'And I'll have "Angel" instead of "Think".'

'Right.' She looks at her watch. 'I'd better ask you a couple of questions before I get back. Why did you want to start it up again?'

'It was a friend's idea really.' A friend. Pathetic. 'She organized it without telling me, as a sort of birthday present. I'd better have a James Brown in there, too, I think. "Papa's Got A Brand New Bag". Instead of the Elvis.'

I watch her carefully while she does the necessary crossing out and writing in.

'Nice friend.'

'Yeah.'

'What's her name?'

'Umm . . . Laura.'

'Surname?

'Just . . . Lydon.'

'And that motto, "Dance Music For Old People". Is that yours?'

'Laura's.'

'What does it mean?'

'Look, I'm sorry about this, but I'd like "Family Affair" by Sly and the Family Stone in there. Instead of "Sin City".'

She crosses out and scribbles again.

'"Dance Music for Old People"?'

'Oh, you know . . . a lot of people aren't too old for clubs, but they're too old for acid jazz and garage and ambient and all that. They want to hear a bit of Motown and vintage funk and Stax and a bit of new stuff and so on all jumbled together, and there's nowhere for them.'

'Fair enough. That'll do me, I think.' She drains her orange juice. 'Cheers. I'm looking forward to next Friday. I used to love the music you played.'

'I'll make you a tape, if you want.'

'Would you? Really? I could have my own Groucho Club at home.'

'No problem. I love making tapes.'

I know that I'll do it, tonight, probably, and I also know that when I'm peeling the wrapper off the cassette box and press the pause button, it will feel like a betrayal.

'I don't believe it,' says Laura when I tell her about Caroline. 'How could you?'

'What?'

'Ever since I've known you you've told me that "Let's Get It On" by Marvin Gaye was the greatest record of all time, and now it doesn't even make your top five.'

'Shit. Fuck. Bollocks. I knew I'd . . .'

'And what happened to Al Green? And the Clash? And Chuck Berry? And that man we had the argument about? Solomon somebody?'

Jesus.

*

I call Caroline the next morning. She's not there. I leave a message. She doesn't call back. I ring again. I leave another message. It's getting kind of embarrassing, but there's no way 'Let's Get It On' isn't going in that top five. The third time I try I get through to her, and she sounds embarrassed but apologetic, and when she realizes that I'm only calling to change the list she relaxes.

'OK. Definitive top five. Number one, "Let's Get It On" by Marvin Gaye. Number two, "This Is The House That Jack Built", Aretha Franklin. Number three, "Back In The USA", by Chuck Berry. Number four, "White Man In The Hammersmith Palais" by the Clash. And the last one, last but not least, ha ha, "So Tired Of Being Alone", by Al Green.'

'I can't change it again, you know. That's it.'

'Fine.'

'But I was thinking that maybe it would make sense to do your five favourite club records. The editor likes the story, by the way, the Laura stuff.'

'Oh.'

'Is it possible to get a quick list of floor-fillers off you, or is that too much to ask?'

'No. I know what they are.' I spell it all out for her (although when the article appears it says '*In* The Ghetto', like the Elvis song, a mistake that Barry pretends is due to my ignorance).

'I've nearly finished your tape.'

'Have you? That's really sweet of you.'

'Shall I send it to you? Or do you fancy a drink?'

'Umm . . . A drink would be great. I'd like to buy you one to thank you.'

'Great.'

Tapes, eh? They work every time.

'Who's it for?' Laura asks when she sees me fiddling around with fades and running orders and levels.

'Oh, just that woman who interviewed me for the free paper. Carol? Caroline? Something like that. She said it would be easier, you know, if she had a feel for the kind of music we play.' But I can't say it without blushing and staring intently at the cassette deck, and I know she doesn't really believe me. She of all people knows what compilation tapes represent.

*

The day before I'm supposed to be meeting Caroline for a drink, I develop all the textbook symptoms of a crush: nervous stomach, long periods spent daydreaming, an inability to remember what she looks like. I can bring back the dress and the boots, and I can see a fringe, but her face is a blank, and I fill it in with some anonymous rent-a-cracker details – pouty red lips, even though it was her well-scrubbed English clever-girl look that attracted me to her in the first place; almond-shaped eyes, even though she was wearing sunglasses most of the time; pale, perfect skin, even though I know she's quite freckly. When I meet her I know there'll be an initial twinge of disappointment – *this* is what all that internal fuss was about? – and then I'll find something to get excited about again: the fact that she's turned up at all, a sexy voice, intelligence, wit, something. And between the second and the third meeting a whole new set of myths will be born.

This time, something different happens, though. It's the daydreaming that does it. I'm doing the usual thing – imagining in tiny detail the entire course of the relationship, from first kiss, to bed, to moving in together, to getting married (in the past I have even organized the track listing of the party tapes), to how pretty she'll look when she's pregnant, to names of children – until suddenly I realize that there's nothing left to actually, like, *happen*. I've done it all, lived through the whole relationship in my head. I've watched the film on fast forward; I know the whole plot, the ending, all the good bits. Now I've got to rewind and watch it all over again in real time, and where's the fun in that?

And fucking . . . when's it all going to fucking stop? I'm going to jump from rock to rock for the rest of my life until there aren't any rocks left? I'm going to run each time I get itchy feet? Because I get them about once a quarter, along with the utilities bills. More than that, even, during British Summer Time. I've been thinking with my guts since I was fourteen years old, and frankly speaking, between you and me, I have come to the conclusion that my guts have shit for brains.

I know what's wrong with Laura. What's wrong with Laura is that I'll never see her for the first or second or third time again. I'll never spend two or three days in a sweat trying to remember what she looks like, never again will I get to a pub half an hour early to meet her, staring at the same article in a magazine and looking at my watch every thirty seconds, never again will thinking about her set something off in me like 'Let's Get It On' sets something off in me. And sure, I love her and like her and have good conversations, nice sex and intense rows with her, and she looks after me and worries about me and arranges the Groucho for me, but what does all that count for, when someone with bare arms, a nice smile and a pair of Doc Martens comes into the shop and says she wants to interview me? Nothing, that's what, but maybe it should count for a bit more.

Fuck it. I'll post the fucking tape. Probably.

THIRTY-FOUR

She's quarter of an hour late, which means I've been in the pub staring at the same article in a magazine for forty-five minutes. She's apologetic, although not *enthusiastically* apologetic, considering; but I don't say anything to her about it. Today's not the right day.

'Cheers,' she says, and clinks her spritzer against my bottle of Sol. Some of her make-up has sweated off in the heat of the day, and her cheeks are pink; she looks lovely. 'This is a nice surprise.'

I don't say anything. I'm too nervous.

'Are you worried about tomorrow night?'

'Not really.' I concentrate on shoving the bit of lime down the neck of the bottle.

'Are you going to talk to me, or shall I get my paper out?'

'I'm going to talk to you.'

'Right.'

I swish the beer around so it'll get really limey.

'What are you going to talk to me about?'

'I'm going to talk to you about whether you want to get married or not. To me.'

She laughs a lot. 'Ha ha ha. Hoo hoo hoo.'

'I mean it.'

'I know.'

'Oh, well thanks a fucking bunch.''

'Oh, I'm sorry. But two days ago you were in love with that woman who interviewed you for the local paper, weren't you?'

'Not in *love* exactly, but . . .'

'Well, forgive me if I don't feel that you're the world's safest bet.'

'Would you marry me if I was?'

'No, I shouldn't think so.'

'Right. OK, then. Shall we go home?'

'Don't sulk. What's brought all this on?'

'I don't know.'

'Very persuasive.'

'Are you persuadable?'

'No. I don't think so. I'm just curious about how one goes from making tapes for one person to marriage proposals to another in two days. Fair enough?'

'Fair enough.'

'So?'

'I'm just sick of thinking about it all the time.'

'All what?'

'This stuff. Love and marriage. I want to think about something else.'

'I've changed my mind. That's the most romantic thing I've ever heard. I do. I will.'

'Shut up. I'm only trying to explain.'

'Sorry. Carry on.'

'See, I've always been afraid of marriage because of, you know, ball and chain, I want my freedom, all that. But when I was thinking about that stupid girl I suddenly saw it was the opposite: that if you got married to someone you know you love, and you sort yourself out, it frees you up for other things. I know you don't know how you feel about me, but I do know how I feel about you. I know I want to stay with you and I keep pretending otherwise, to myself and you, and we just limp on and on. It's like we sign a new contract every few weeks or so, and I don't want that any more. And I know that if we got married I'd take it seriously, and I wouldn't want to mess about.'

'And you can make a decision about it just like that, can you? In cold blood, bang bang, if I do that, then this will happen? I'm not sure that it works like that.'

'But it *does*, you see. Just because it's a relationship, and it's based on soppy stuff, it doesn't mean you can't make intellectual decisions about it. Sometimes you just have to, otherwise you'll never get anywhere. That's where I've been going wrong. I've been letting the weather and my stomach muscles and a great chord change in a Pretenders single make up my mind for me, and I want to do it for myself.'

'Maybe.'

'What d'you mean, maybe?'

'I mean, maybe you're right. But that doesn't help me, does it? You're always like this. You work something out and everyone else has to fall into line. Were you really expecting me to say yes?'

'Dunno. Didn't think about it, really. It was the asking that was the important thing.'

'Well, you've asked.' But she says it sweetly, as if she knows that what I've asked is a nice thing, that it has some sort of meaning, even though she's not interested. 'Thank you.'

THIRTY-FIVE

Before the band come on, everything's brilliant. It used to take a bit of time to warm people up, but tonight they're up for it straight away. This is partly because most of the crowd here tonight are a few years older than they were a few years ago, if you see what I mean – in other words, this is exactly the same lot, not their 1994 equivalents – and they don't want to wait until half-twelve or one before they get going: they're too tired for that now, and anyway some of them have to go home to relieve babysitters. But mostly it's because there's a real party atmosphere, a genuine make-hay-while-the-sun-shines air of celebration, as though this is a wedding reception or a birthday party, rather than a club that will be here next week and maybe even the week after that.

But I have to say that I'm fucking good, that I haven't lost any of the old magic. One sequence – the O'Jays ('Back Stabbers'), Harold Melvin and the Bluenotes ('Satisfaction Guaranteed'), Madonna ('Holiday'), 'The Ghetto' (which gets a cheer, as if it's my song rather than Donny Hathaway's) and 'Nelson Mandela' by the Specials – has them begging for mercy. And then it's time for the band.

I've been told to introduce them; Barry has even written down what I'm supposed to say: 'Ladies and gentlemen, be afraid. Be very afraid. Here comes . . . SONIC DEATH MONKEY!' But bollocks to that, and in the end I just sort of mumble the name of the group into the microphone.

They're wearing suits and skinny ties, and when they plug in there's a terrible feedback whine which for a moment I fear is their opening number. But Sonic Death Monkey are no longer what they once were. They are no longer, in fact, Sonic Death Monkey.

'We're not called Sonic Death Monkey any more,' Barry says when he gets to the mike. 'We might be on the verge of becoming the Futuristics, but we haven't decided yet. Tonight, though, we're Backbeat. One two three . . . WELL SHAKE IT UP BABY . . .' And they launch into 'Twist and Shout', note perfect, and everyone in the place goes mad.

And Barry can sing.

They play 'Route 66' and 'Long Tall Sally' and 'Money' and 'Do You Love Me?', and they encore with 'In The Midnight Hour' and 'La Bamba'. Every song, in short, is naff and recognizable, and guaranteed to please a crowd of thirtysomethings who think that hip-hop is something their children do in music and movement classes. The crowd are so pleased, in fact, that they sit out the songs I have lined up to get them going again after Sonic Death Monkey have frightened and confused them.

'What was all that about?' I ask Barry when he comes up to the deck, sweaty and half-cut and pleased with himself.

'Was that all right?'

'It was better than what I was expecting.'

'Laura said we could only play if we learned some proper songs for the evening. But we loved it. The boys are talking about packing up the pop star thing and playing at silver wedding anniversaries.'

'How d'you feel about that?'

'All right, yeah. I was beginning to wonder about our musical direction anyway. I'd rather see people dancing to "Long Tall Sally" than running for the exit with their hands over their ears.'

'You enjoying the club?'

'It's OK. Bit, you know, populist for my taste,' he says. He's not joking.

The rest of the evening is like the end of a film. The entire cast is dancing: Dick with Anna (he's sort of standing still and shuffling, Anna is holding his hands and attempting to get him to let go a bit), Marie with T-Bone (Marie is drunk, T-Bone's looking over her shoulder at someone – Caroline! – that he's obviously interested in), Laura with Liz (who's talking animatedly and apparently angrily about something).

I play 'Got To Get You Off My Mind' by Solomon Burke, and everyone has a go, just out of duty, even though only the best dancers would be able to make something of it, and nobody in the room could claim to be among the best dancers, or even among the most average. When Laura hears the opening bars she spins round and grins and makes several thumbs-up signs, and I start to compile in my head a compilation tape for her, something that's full of stuff she's heard of, and full of stuff she'd play. Tonight, for the first time ever, I can sort of see how it's done.

About a Boy

*Love and thanks to David Evans,
Adrienne Maguire, Caroline Dawnay,
Virginia Bovell, Abigail Morris,
Wendy Carlton, Harry Ritchie and
Amanda Posey. Music provided by
Wood in Upper Street, London N1.*

In memory of Liz Knights

ONE

'Have you split up now?'

'Are you being funny?'

People quite often thought Marcus was being funny when he wasn't. He couldn't understand it. Asking his mum whether she'd split up with Roger was a perfectly sensible question, he thought: they'd had a big row, then they'd gone off into the kitchen to talk quietly, and after a little while they'd come out looking serious, and Roger had come over to him, shaken his hand and wished him luck at his new school, and then he'd gone.

'Why would I want to be funny?'

'Well, what does it look like to you?'

'It looks to me like you've split up. But I just wanted to make sure.'

'We've split up.'

'So he's gone?'

'Yes, Marcus, he's gone.'

He didn't think he'd ever get used to this business. He had quite liked Roger, and the three of them had been out a few times; now, apparently, he'd never see him again. He didn't mind, but it was weird if you thought about it. He'd once shared a toilet with Roger, when they were both busting for a pee after a car journey. You'd think that if you'd peed with someone you ought to keep in touch with them somehow.

'What about his pizza?' They'd just ordered three pizzas when the argument started, and they hadn't arrived yet.

'We'll share it. If we're hungry.'

'They're big, though. And didn't he order one with pepperoni on it?' Marcus and his mother were vegetarians. Roger wasn't.

'We'll throw it away, then,' she said.

'Or we could pick the pepperoni off. I don't think they give you much of it anyway. It's mostly cheese and tomato.'

'Marcus, I'm not really thinking about the pizzas right now.'

'OK. Sorry. Why did you split up?'

'Oh . . . this and that. I don't really know how to explain it.'

Marcus wasn't surprised that she couldn't explain what had happened. He'd heard more or less the whole argument, and he hadn't understood a word of it; there seemed to be a piece missing somewhere. When Marcus and his mum argued, you could hear the important bits: too much, too expensive, too late, too young, bad for your teeth, the other channel, homework, fruit. But when his mum and her boyfriends argued, you could listen for hours and still miss the point, the thing, the fruit and homework part of it. It was like they'd been told to argue and just came out with anything they could think of.

'Did he have another girlfriend?'

'I don't think so.'

'Have you got another boyfriend?'

She laughed. 'Who would that be? The guy who took the pizza orders? No, Marcus, I haven't got another boyfriend. That's not how it works. Not when you're a thirty-eight-year-old working mother. There's a time problem. Ha! There's an everything problem. Why? Does it bother you?'

'I dunno.'

And he didn't know. His mum was sad, he knew that – she cried a lot now, more than she did before they moved to London – but he had no idea whether that was anything to do with boyfriends. He kind of hoped it was, because then it would all get sorted out. She would meet someone, and he would make her happy. Why not? His mum was pretty, he thought, and nice, and funny sometimes, and he reckoned there must be loads of blokes like Roger around. If it wasn't boyfriends, though, he didn't know what it could be, apart from something bad.

'Do you mind me having boyfriends?'

'No. Only Andrew.'

'Well, yes, I know you didn't like Andrew. But generally? You don't mind the idea of it?'

'No. Course not.'

'You've been really good about everything. Considering you've had two different sorts of life.'

He understood what she meant. The first sort of life had ended four years ago, when he was eight and his mum and dad had split up; that was the normal, boring kind, with school and holidays and homework and weekend visits to grandparents. The second sort was messier, and there were more people and places in it: his mother's boyfriends and his dad's girlfriends; flats and houses; Cambridge and London. You wouldn't believe that so much could change just because a relationship ended, but he wasn't bothered. Sometimes he even thought he preferred the second sort of life to the first sort. More happened, and that had to be a good thing.

Apart from Roger, not much had happened in London yet. They'd only been here for a few weeks – they'd moved on the first day of the summer holidays – and so far it had been pretty boring. He had been to see two films with his mum, *Home Alone 2*, which wasn't as good as *Home Alone 1*, and *Honey, I Blew Up the Kid*, which wasn't as good as *Honey, I Shrunk the Kids*, and his mum had said that modern films were too commercial, and that when she was his age . . . something, he couldn't remember what. And they'd been to have a look at his school, which was big and horrible, and wandered around their new neighbourhood, which was called Holloway, and had nice bits and ugly bits, and they'd had lots of talks about London, and the changes that were happening to them, and how they were all for the best, probably. But really they were sitting around waiting for their London lives to begin.

The pizzas arrived and they ate them straight out of the boxes.

'They're better than the ones we had in Cambridge, aren't they?' Marcus said cheerfully. It wasn't true: it was the same pizza company, but in Cambridge the pizzas hadn't had to travel so far, so they weren't quite as soggy. It was just that he thought he ought to say something optimistic. 'Shall we watch TV?'

'If you want.'

He found the remote control down the back of the sofa and zapped through the channels. He didn't want to watch any of the soaps, because soaps were full of trouble, and he was worried that the trouble in the soaps would remind his mum of the trouble she had in her own life. So they watched a nature programme about this sort of fish thing that lived right down the bottom of caves and couldn't see anything, a fish that nobody could see the point of; he didn't think that would remind his mum of anything much.

TWO

How cool was Will Freeman? This cool: he had slept with a woman he didn't know very well in the last three months (five points). He had spent more than three hundred pounds on a jacket (five points). He had spent more than twenty pounds on a haircut (five points) (How was it possible to spend less than twenty pounds on a haircut in 1993?). He owned more than five hip-hop albums (five points). He had taken Ecstasy (five points), but in a club and not merely at home as a sociological exercise (five bonus points). He intended to vote Labour at the next general election (five points). He earned more than forty thousand pounds a year (five points), and he didn't have to work very hard for it (five points, and he awarded himself an extra five points for not having to work *at all* for it). He had eaten in a restaurant that served polenta and shaved parmesan (five points). He had never used a flavoured condom (five points), he had sold his Bruce Springsteen albums (five points), and he had both grown a goatee (five points) *and* shaved it off again (five points). The bad news was that he hadn't ever had sex with someone whose photo had appeared on the style page of a newspaper or magazine (minus two), and he did still think, if he was honest (and if Will had anything approaching an ethical belief, it was that lying about yourself in questionnaires was utterly wrong), that owning a fast car was likely to impress women (minus two). Even so, that gave him . . . sixty-six! He was, according to the questionnaire, sub-zero! He was dry ice! He was Frosty the Snowman! He would die of hypothermia!

Will didn't know how seriously you were supposed to take these questionnaire things, but he couldn't afford to think about it; being men's-magazine cool was as close as he had ever come to an achievement, and moments like this were to be treasured. Sub-zero! You couldn't get much cooler than sub-zero! He closed the magazine and put it on to a pile of similar magazines that he kept in the bathroom. He didn't save them all, because he bought too many for that, but he wouldn't be throwing this one out in a hurry.

Will wondered sometimes – not very often, because historical speculation wasn't something he indulged in very often – how people like him would have survived sixty years ago. ('People like him' was, he knew, something of a specialized grouping; in fact, there couldn't have been anyone like him sixty years ago, because sixty years ago no adult could have had a father who had made his money in quite the same way. So when he thought about people like him, he didn't mean people *exactly* like him, he just meant people who didn't really do anything all day, and didn't want to do anything much, either.) Sixty years ago, all the things Will relied on to get him through the day simply didn't exist: there was no daytime TV, there were no videos, there were no glossy magazines and therefore no questionnaires and, though there were probably record shops, the kind of music he listened to hadn't even been invented yet. (Right now he was listening to Nirvana and Snoop Doggy Dogg, and you couldn't have found too much that sounded like them in 1933.) Which would have left books. Books! He would have had to get a job, almost definitely, because he would have gone round the twist otherwise.

Now, though, it was easy. There was almost too much to do. You didn't have to have a life of your own any more; you could just peek over the fence at other people's lives, as lived in newspapers and *EastEnders* and films and exquisitely sad jazz or tough rap songs. The twenty-year-old Will would have been surprised and perhaps disappointed to learn that he would reach the age of thirty-six without finding a life for himself, but the thirty-six-year-old Will wasn't particularly unhappy about it; there was less clutter this way.

Clutter! Will's friend John's house was full of it. John and Christine had two children – the second had been born the previous week, and Will had been summoned to look at it – and their place was, Will couldn't help thinking, a disgrace. Pieces of brightly coloured plastic were strewn all over the floor, videotapes lay out of their cases near the TV set, the white throw over the sofa looked as if it had been used as a piece of gigantic toilet paper, although Will preferred to think that the stains were chocolate . . . How could people live like this?

Christine came in holding the new baby while John was in the kitchen making him a cup of tea. 'This is Imogen,' she said.

'Oh,' said Will. 'Right.' What was he supposed to say next? He knew there was something, but he couldn't for the life of him remember what it was. 'She's . . .' No. It had gone. He concentrated his conversational efforts on Christine. 'How are you, anyway, Chris?'

'Oh, you know. A bit washed out.'

'Been burning the candle at both ends?'

'No. Just had a baby.'

'Oh. Right.' Everything came back to the sodding baby. 'That would make you pretty tired, I guess.' He'd deliberately waited a week so that he wouldn't have to talk about this sort of thing, but it hadn't done him any good. They were talking about it anyway.

John came in with a tray and three mugs of tea.

'Barney's gone to his grandma's today,' he said, for no reason at all that Will could see.

'How is Barney?' Barney was two, that was how Barney was, and therefore of no interest to anyone apart from his parents, but, again, for reasons he would never fathom, some comment seemed to be required of him.

'He's fine, thanks,' said John. 'He's a right little devil at the moment, mind you, and he's not too sure what to make of Imogen, but . . . he's lovely.'

Will had met Barney before, and knew for a fact he wasn't lovely, so he chose to ignore the non sequitur.

'What about you, anyway, Will?'

'I'm fine, thanks.'

'Any desire for a family of your own yet?'

I would rather eat one of Barney's dirty nappies, he thought. 'Not yet,' he said.

'You are a worry to us,' said Christine.

'I'm OK as I am, thanks.'

'Maybe,' said Christine smugly. These two were beginning to make him feel physically ill. It was bad enough that they had children in the first place; why did they wish to compound the original error by encouraging their friends to do the same? For some years now Will had been convinced that it was possible to get through life without having to make yourself unhappy in the way that John and Christine were making themselves unhappy (and he was sure they were unhappy, even if they had achieved some peculiar, brain-washed state that prevented them from recognizing their own unhappiness). You needed money, sure – the only reason for having children, as far as Will could see, was so they could look after you when you were old and useless and skint – but he had money, which meant that he could avoid the clutter and the toilet-paper throws and the pathetic need to convince friends that they should be as miserable as you are.

John and Christine used to be OK, really. When Will had been going out with Jessica, the four of them used to go clubbing a couple of times a week. Jessica and Will split up when Jessica wanted to exchange the froth and frivolity for something more solid; Will had missed her, temporarily, but he would have missed the clubbing more. (He still saw her, sometimes, for a lunchtime pizza, and she would show him pictures of her children, and tell him he was wasting his life, and he didn't know what it was like, and he would tell her how lucky he was he didn't know what it was like, and she would tell him he couldn't handle it anyway, and he would tell her he had no intention of finding out one way or the other; then they would sit in silence and glare at each other.) Now John and Christine had taken the Jessica route to oblivion, he had no use for them whatsoever. He didn't want to meet Imogen, or know how Barney was, and he didn't want to hear about Christine's tiredness, and there wasn't anything else to them any more. He wouldn't be bothering with them again.

'We were wondering,' said John, 'whether you'd like to be Imogen's godfather?' The two of them sat there with an expectant smile on their faces, as if he were about to leap to his feet, burst into tears and wrestle them to the carpet in a euphoric embrace. Will laughed nervously.

'Godfather? Church and things? Birthday presents? Adoption if you're killed in an air crash?'

'Yeah.'

'You're kidding.'

'We've always thought you have hidden depths,' said John.

'Ah, but you see I haven't. I really am this shallow.'

They were still smiling. They weren't getting it.

'Listen. I'm touched that you asked. But I can't think of anything worse. Seriously. It's just not my sort of thing.'

He didn't stay much longer.

A couple of weeks later Will met Angie and became a temporary stepfather for the first time. Maybe if he had swallowed his pride and his hatred of children and the family and domesticity and monogamy and early nights, he could have saved himself an awful lot of trouble.

THREE

During the night after his first day Marcus woke up every half-hour or so. He could tell from the luminous hands of his dinosaur clock: 10.41, 11.19, 11.55, 12.35, 12.55, 1.31 . . . He couldn't believe he was going to have to go back there the next morning, and the morning after that, and the morning after that, and . . . well, then it would be the weekend, but more or less every morning for the rest of his life, just about. Every time he woke up his first thought was that there must be some kind of way past, or round, or even through, this horrible feeling; whenever he had been upset about anything before, there had usually turned out to be some kind of answer – one that mostly involved telling his mum what was bothering him. But there wasn't anything she could do this time. She wasn't going to move him to another school, and even if she did it wouldn't make a whole lot of difference. He'd still be who he was, and that, it seemed to him, was the basic problem.

He just wasn't right for schools. Not secondary schools, anyway. That was it. And how could you explain that to anyone? It was OK not to be right for some things (he already knew he wasn't right for parties, because he was too shy, or for baggy trousers, because his legs were too short), but not being right for school was a big problem. Everyone went to school. There was no way round it. Some kids, he knew, got taught by their parents at home, but his mum couldn't do that because she went out to work. Unless he paid her to teach him – but she'd told him not long ago that she got three hundred and fifty pounds a week from her job. Three hundred and fifty pounds a week! Where was he going to get that kind of money from? Not from a paper round, he knew that much. The only other kind of person he could think of who didn't go to school was the Macaulay Culkin kind. They'd had something about him on Saturday-morning TV once, and they said he got taught in a caravan sort of thing by a private tutor. That would be OK, he supposed. Better than OK, because Macaulay Culkin probably got three hundred and fifty pounds a week, maybe even more, which meant that if he were Macaulay Culkin he could pay his mum to teach him. But if being Macaulay

Culkin meant being good at drama, then forget it: he was crap at drama, because he hated standing up in front of people. Which was why he hated school. Which was why he wanted to be Macaulay Culkin. Which was why he was never going to be Macaulay Culkin in a thousand years, let alone in the next few days. He was going to have to go to school tomorrow.

All that night he thought like boomerangs fly: an idea would shoot way off into the distance, all the way to a caravan in Hollywood and, for a moment, when he had got as far away from school and reality as it was possible to go, he was reasonably happy; then it would begin the return journey, thump him on the head, and leave him in exactly the place he had started from. And all the time it got nearer and nearer to the morning.

He was quiet at breakfast. 'You'll get used to it,' his mum said as he was eating his cereal, probably because he was looking miserable. He just nodded, and smiled at her; it was an OK thing to say. There had been times when he knew, somewhere in him, that he would get used to it, whatever it was, because he had learnt that some hard things became softer after a very little while. The day after his dad left, his mum had taken him to Glastonbury with her friend Corinne and they'd had a brilliant time in a tent. But this was only going to get worse. That first terrible, horrible, frightening day was going to be as good as it got.

He got to school early, went to the form room, sat down at his desk. He was safe enough there. The kids who had given him a hard time yesterday were probably not the sort to arrive at school first thing; they'd be off somewhere smoking and taking drugs and raping people, he thought darkly. There were a couple of girls in the room, but they ignored him, unless the snort of laughter he heard while he was getting his reading book out had anything to do with him.

What was there to laugh at? Not much, really, unless you were the kind of person who was on permanent lookout for something to laugh at. Unfortunately, that was exactly the kind of person most kids were, in his experience. They patrolled up and down school corridors like sharks, except that what they were on the lookout for wasn't flesh but the wrong trousers, or the wrong haircut, or the wrong shoes, any or all of which sent them wild with excitement. As he was usually wearing the wrong shoes or the wrong trousers, and his haircut was wrong all the time, every day of the week, he didn't have to do very much to send them all demented.

Marcus knew he was weird, and he knew that part of the reason he was weird was because his mum was weird. She just didn't get this, any of it. She was always telling him that only shallow people made judgements on the basis of clothes or hair; she didn't want him to watch rubbish television, or listen to rubbish music, or play rubbish computer games (she thought they were all rubbish), which meant that if he wanted to do anything that any of the other kids spent their time doing he had to argue with her for hours. He usually lost, and she was so good at arguing that he felt good about losing. She could explain why listening to Joni Mitchell and Bob Marley (who happened to be her two favourite singers) was much better for him than listening to Snoop Doggy Dogg, and why it was more important to read books than to play on the Gameboy his dad had given him. But he couldn't pass any of this on to the kids at school. If he tried to tell Lee Hartley – the biggest and loudest and nastiest of the kids he'd met yesterday – that he didn't approve of Snoop Doggy Dogg because Snoop Doggy Dogg had a bad attitude to women, Lee Hartley would thump him, or call him something that he didn't want to be called. It wasn't so bad in Cambridge, because there were loads of kids who weren't right for school, and loads of mums who had made them that way, but in London it was different. The kids were harder and meaner and less understanding, and it seemed to him that if his mum had made him change schools just because she had found a better job, then she should at least have the decency to stop all that let's-talk-about-this stuff.

He was quite happy at home, listening to Joni Mitchell and reading books, but it didn't do him any good at school. It was funny, because most people would probably think the opposite – that reading books at home was bound to help, but it didn't: it made him different, and because he was different he felt uncomfortable, and because he felt uncomfortable he could feel himself floating away from everyone and everything, kids and teachers and lessons.

It wasn't all his mum's fault. Sometimes he was weird just because of who he was, rather than what she did. Like the singing . . . When was he going to learn about the singing? He always had a tune in his head, but every now and again, when he was nervous, the tune just sort of slipped out. For some reason he couldn't spot the difference between inside and outside, because there didn't seem to be a difference. It was like when you went swimming in a heated pool on a warm day, and you could get out of the water without noticing that you were getting out, because the temperatures were the same; that seemed to be what happened with the singing. Anyway, a song had slipped out yesterday during English, while the teacher was reading; if you wanted to make people laugh at you, really, really laugh, then the best way, he had discovered, better even than to have a bad haircut, was to sing out loud when everybody else in the room was quiet and bored.

This morning he was OK until the first period after break. He was quiet during registration, he avoided people in the corridors, and then it was double maths, which he enjoyed, and which he was good at, although they were doing stuff that he'd already done before. At break-time he went to tell Mr Brooks, one of the other maths teachers, that he wanted to join his computer club. He was pleased he did that, because his instinct was to stay in the form room and read, but he toughed it out; he even had to cross the playground.

But then in English things went bad again. They were using one of those books that had a bit of everything in them; the bit they were looking at was taken from *One Flew Over the Cuckoo's Nest.* He knew the story, because he'd seen the film with his mum, and so he could see really clearly, so clearly that he wanted to run from the room, what was going to happen.

When it happened it was even worse than he thought it was going to be. Ms Maguire got one of the girls who she knew was a good reader to read out the passage, and then she tried to get a discussion going.

'Now, one of the things this book is about is . . . How do we know who's mad and who isn't? Because, you know, in a way we're all a bit mad, and if someone decides that we're a bit mad, how do we . . . how do we show them we're sane?'

Silence. A couple of the kids sighed and rolled their eyes at each other. One thing Marcus had noticed was that when you came into a school late you could tell straight away how well the teachers got on with a class. Ms Maguire was young and nervous and she was struggling, he reckoned. This class could go either way.

'OK, let's put it another way. How can we tell if people are mad?'

Here it comes, he thought. Here it comes. This is it.

'If they sing for no reason in class, miss.'

Laughter. But then it all got worse than he'd expected. Everyone turned round and looked at him; he looked at Ms Maguire, but she had this big forced grin on and she wouldn't catch his eye.

'OK, that's one way of telling, yes. You'd think that someone who does that would be a little potty. But leaving Marcus out of it for a moment . . .'

More laughter. He knew what she was doing and why, and he hated her.

FOUR

Will first saw Angie – or, as it turned out, he didn't see her – in Championship Vinyl, a little record shop off the Holloway Road. He was browsing, filling up the time, vaguely trying to hunt down an old R & B anthology he used to own when he was younger, one of those he had loved and lost; he heard her tell the surly and depressive assistant that she was looking for a Pinky and Perky record for her niece. He was trawling through the racks while she was being served, so he never caught a glimpse of her face, but he saw a lot of honey-blond hair, and he heard the kind of vaguely husky voice that he and everyone else thought of as sexy, so he listened while she explained that her niece didn't even know who Pinky and Perky were. 'Don't you think that's terrible? Fancy being five and not knowing who Pinky and Perky are! What are they teaching these kids!'

She was trying to be jolly, but Will had learnt to his cost that jollity was frowned upon in Championship Vinyl. She was, as he knew she would be, met with a withering look of contempt and a mumble which indicated that she was wasting the assistant's valuable time.

Two days later, he found himself sitting next to the same woman in a café on Upper Street. He recognized her voice (they both ordered a cappuccino and croissant), the blond hair and her denim jacket. They both got up to get one of the café's newspapers – she took the *Guardian*, so he was left with the *Mail* – and he smiled, but she clearly didn't remember him, and he would have left it at that if she hadn't been so pretty.

'I like Pinky and Perky,' he said in what he hoped was a gentle, friendly and humorously patronizing tone, but he could see immediately that he had made a terrible mistake, that this was not the same woman, that she didn't have the faintest idea what he was talking about. He wanted to tear out his tongue and grind it into the wooden floor with his foot.

She looked at him, smiled nervously and glanced across at the waiter, probably calculating how long it would take for the waiter to hurl himself across the room and wrestle Will to the floor. Will both understood and sympathized. If a complete stranger were to sit down next to you in a coffee shop and tell you quietly that he liked Pinky and Perky as an opening conversational gambit, you could only presume that you were about to be decapitated and hidden under the floorboards.

'I'm sorry,' he said. 'I thought you were someone else.' He blushed, and the blush seemed to relax her: his embarrassment was some kind of indication of sanity, at least. They returned to their newspapers, but the woman kept breaking into a smile and looking across at him.

'I know this sounds nosy,' she said eventually, 'but I've got to ask you. Who did you think I was? I've been trying to come up with some kind of story, and I can't.'

So he explained, and she laughed again, and then finally he was given a chance to start over and converse normally. They talked about not working in the morning (he didn't own up to not working in the afternoon either), and the record shop, and Pinky and Perky, of course, and several other children's television characters. He had never before attempted to start a relationship cold in this way, but by the time they had finished their second cappuccino he had a phone number and a date for dinner.

When they met again she told him about her kids straight away; he wanted to throw his napkin on the floor, push the table over and run.

'So?' he said. It was, of course, the right thing to say.

'I just thought you ought to know. It makes a difference to some people.'

'In what way?'

'Guys, I mean.'

'Well, yes, I worked that out.'

'I'm sorry, I'm not making this very easy, am I?'

'You're doing fine.'

'It's just that . . . if this is a date date, and it feels like one to me, then I thought I ought to tell you.'

'Thank you. But really, it's no problem. I would have been disappointed if you didn't have children.'

She laughed. 'Disappointed? Why?'

This was a good question. Why? Obviously he had said it because he thought it sounded smooth and winning, but he couldn't tell her that.

'Because I've never been out with someone who was a mum before, and I've always wanted to. I think I'd be good at it.'

'Good at what?'

Right. Good at what? What was he good at? This was the million-dollar question, the one he had never been able to answer about anything. Maybe he would be good at children, even though he hated them and everyone responsible for bringing them into the world. Maybe he had written John and Christine and baby Imogen off too hastily. Maybe this was it! Uncle Will!

'I don't know. Good at kids' things. Messing about things.'

He must be, surely. Everyone was, weren't they? Maybe he should have been working with kids all this time. Maybe this was a turning point in his life!

It had to be said that Angie's beauty was not irrelevant to his decision to reassess his affinity with children. The long blond hair, he now knew, was accompanied by a calm, open face, big blue eyes and extraordinarily sexy crow's feet – she was beautiful in a very winning, wholesome, Julie Christie-type way. And that was the point. When had he ever been out with a woman who looked like Julie Christie? People who looked like Julie Christie didn't go out with people like him. They went out with other film stars, or peers of the realm, or Formula One drivers. What was happening here? He decided that children were what was happening here; that children served as a symbolic blemish, like a birthmark or obesity, which gave him a chance where previously there would have been none. Maybe children *democratized* beautiful single women.

'I'll tell you,' Angie was saying, although he had missed much of the cogitation that had brought her to this point, 'when you're a single mother, you're far more likely to end up thinking in feminist clichés. You know, all men are bastards, a woman without a man is like a . . . a . . . something without a something that doesn't have any relation to the first something; all that stuff.'

'I'm sure,' said Will, sympathetically. He was getting excited now. If single mothers really thought that all men were bastards, then he could clean up. He could go out with women who looked like Julie Christie for ever. He nodded and frowned and pursed his lips while Angie ranted, and while he plotted his new, life-changing strategy.

For the next few weeks he was Will the Good Guy, Will the Redeemer, and he loved it. It was effortless, too. He never managed to strike up much of a rapport with Maisy, Angie's mysteriously sombre five-year-old, who seemed to regard him as frivolous to his core. But Joe, the three-year-old, took to him almost at once, mostly because during their first meeting Will held him upside-down by his ankles. That was it. That was all it took. He wished that relationships with proper human beings were that easy.

They went to McDonald's. They went to the Science Museum and the Natural History Museum. They went on a boat down the river. On the very few occasions when he had thought about the possibility of children (always when he was drunk, always in the first throes of a new relationship), he had convinced himself that fatherhood would be a sort of sentimental photo-opportunity, and fatherhood Angie-style was exactly like that: he could walk hand-in-hand with a beautiful woman, children gambolling happily in front of him, and everyone could see him doing it, and when he had done it for an afternoon he could go home again if he wanted to.

And then there was the sex. Sex with a single mother, Will decided after his first night with Angie, beat the sort of sex he was used to hands down. If you picked the right woman, someone who'd been messed around and eventually abandoned by the father of her children, and who hadn't met anyone since (because the kids stopped you going out and anyway a lot of men didn't like kids that didn't belong to them, and they didn't like the kind of mess that frequently coiled around these kids like a whirlwind) . . . if you picked one of these, then she loved you for it. All of a sudden you became better-looking, a better lover, a better person.

As far as he could see, it was an entirely happy arrangement. All those so-so couplings going on out in the world of the childless singles, to whom a night in a foreign bed was just another fuck . . . they didn't know what they were missing. Sure, there were right-on people, men and women, who would be repelled and appalled by his logic, but that was fine by him. It reduced the competition.

In the end, the thing that swung it for him in his affair with Angie was that he was not Someone Else. That meant in this case he wasn't Simon, her ex, who had problems with drink and work, and who, with a cavalier disregard for cliché, turned out to be screwing his secretary. Will found it easy not to be Simon; he had a positive flair for not being Simon, he was brilliant at it. It seemed unfair, in fact, that something he found so effortless should bring him any kind of reward at all, but it did: he was loved for not being Simon more than he had ever been loved simply for being himself.

Even the end, when it came, had an enormous amount to recommend it. Will found endings difficult: he had never quite managed to grasp the bull by the horns, and as a consequence there had hitherto always been some kind of messy overlap. But with Angie it was easy – indeed, it was so easy that he felt there had to be some kind of catch.

They had been going out for six weeks, and there were certain things that he was beginning to find unsatisfactory. Angie wasn't very flexible, for a start, and the whole kid thing really got in the way sometimes – the week before he had bought tickets for the new Mike Leigh film on the opening night, but she didn't make it to the cinema until thirty minutes after it had started because the babysitter hadn't turned up. That really pissed him off, although he felt he managed to disguise his annoyance pretty well, and they had a reasonable evening out anyway. And she could never stay over at his place, so he always had to go round there, and she didn't have many CDs, and there was no VCR or satellite or cable, so on a Saturday night they always ended up watching *Casualty* and a crap made-for-TV movie about some kid with a disease. He was just beginning to wonder whether Angie was exactly what he was looking for when she decided to finish it.

They were in an Indian restaurant on Holloway Road when she told him.

'Will, I'm so sorry, but I'm not sure this is working out.'

He didn't say anything. In the past, any conversation that began in this way usually meant that she had found something out, or that he had done something mean, or stupid, or grotesquely insensitive, but he really thought that he had kept a clean sheet in this relationship. His silence bought him time while he scanned through the memory bank for any indiscretions he might have forgotten about, but there was nothing. He would have been extremely disappointed if he had found something, an overlooked infidelity, say, or a casual, unmemorable cruelty. As the whole point of this relationship was his niceness, any blemish would have meant that his untrustworthiness was so deeply ingrained as to be ungovernable.

'It's not you. You've been great. It's me. Well, my situation, anyway.'

'There's nothing wrong with your situation. Not as far as I'm concerned.' He was so relieved that he felt like being generous.

'There are things you don't know. Things about Simon.'

'Is he giving you a hard time? Because if he is . . .' You'll what? he wanted to ask himself contemptuously. You'll roll yourself a joint when you get home and forget them? You'll go out with someone a lot easier?

'No, not really. Well, I suppose it would look like that from the outside. He's not very happy about me seeing somebody else. And I know how that sounds, but I know him, and he just hasn't come to terms with us splitting up. And I'm not sure I have either, more to the point. I'm not ready to launch into a relationship with anybody new yet.'

'You've been doing pretty well.'

'The tragedy is that I've met someone just right for me at precisely the wrong time. I should have started with a meaningless fling, not a . . . not with someone who . . .'

This, he couldn't help feeling, was kind of ironic. If she but knew it, he was exactly right; if there was a man better equipped for the meaningless fling, he wouldn't like to meet him. I've been putting this on! he wanted to tell her. I'm horrible! I'm much shallower than this, honest! But it was too late.

'I did wonder whether I was rushing you. I've really cocked this up, haven't I?'

'No, Will, not at all. You've been brilliant. I'm so sorry that . . .'

She was starting to get a little tearful, and he loved her for it. He had never before watched a woman cry without feeling responsible, and he was rather enjoying the experience.

'You don't have to be sorry for anything. Really.' Really, really, really.

'Oh, I do.'

'You don't.'

When was the last time he had been in a position to bestow forgiveness? Certainly not since school, and possibly not even then. Of all the evenings he had spent with Angie, he loved the last one the best.

This, for Will, was the clincher. He knew then that there would be other women like Angie – women who would start off by thinking that they wanted a regular fuck, and end up deciding that a quiet life was worth any number of noisy orgasms. As he felt something not dissimilar, although for very different reasons, he knew he had a lot to offer. Great sex, a lot of ego massage, temporary parenthood without tears and a guilt-free parting – what more could a man want? Single mothers – bright, attractive, available women, thousands of them, all over London – were the best invention Will had ever heard of. His career as a serial nice guy had begun.

FIVE

One Monday morning his mother started crying before breakfast, and it frightened him. Morning crying was something new, and it was a bad, bad sign. It meant that it could now happen at any hour of the day without warning; there was no safe time. Up until today the mornings had been OK; she seemed to wake up with the hope that whatever was making her unhappy would somehow have vanished overnight, in her sleep, the way colds and upset stomachs sometimes did. And she had sounded OK this morning – not angry, not unhappy, not mad, just kind of normal and mum-like – when she shouted for him to get a move on. But here she was, already at it, slumped over the kitchen table in her dressing-gown, a half-eaten piece of toast on her plate, her face all puffed-up, snot pouring out of her nose.

Marcus never said anything when she cried. He didn't know what to say. He didn't understand why she did it, and because he didn't understand he couldn't help, and because he couldn't help, he just ended up standing there and staring at her with his mouth open, and she'd just carry on as if nothing was happening.

'Do you want some tea?'

He had to guess at what she was saying, because she was so snuffled up.

'Yeah. Please.' He took a clean bowl from the draining board and went to the larder to choose his cereal. That cheered him up. He'd forgotten that she'd let him put a variety pack in the supermarket trolley on Saturday morning. He went through all the usual agonies of indecision: he knew he should get through the boring stuff, the cornflakes and the one with fruit in it, first of all, because if he didn't eat them now he'd never eat them, and they'd just sit on the shelf until they got stale, and Mum would get cross with him, and for the next few months he'd have to stick to an economy-sized packet of something horrible. He understood all that, yet still he went for the Coco Pops, as he always did. His mother didn't notice – the first advantage of her terrible depression that he'd found so far. It wasn't a big advantage, though; on the whole he'd rather she was cheerful enough to send him back to the larder. He'd quite happily give up Coco Pops if she'd give up crying all the time.

He ate his cereal, drank his tea, picked up his bag and gave his mother a kiss, just a normal one, not a soppy, understanding one, and went out. Neither of them said a word. What else was he supposed to do?

On the way to school he tried to work out what was wrong with her. What could be wrong with her that he wouldn't know about? She was in work, so they weren't poor, although they weren't rich either – she was a music therapist, which meant that she was a sort of teacher of handicapped children, and she was always saying that the money was pitiful, pathetic, lousy, a crime. But they had enough for the flat, and for food, and for holidays once a year, and even for computer games, once in a while. What else made you cry, apart from money? Death? But he'd know if anybody important had died; she would only cry that much about Grandma, Grandpa, his uncle Tom and Tom's family, and they'd seen them all the previous weekend, at his cousin Ella's fourth birthday party. Something to do with men? He knew she wanted a boyfriend; but he knew because she joked about it sometimes, and he couldn't see that it was possible to go from joking about something now and again to crying about it all the time. Anyway, she was the one who had got rid of Roger, and if she was desperate she would have kept it going. So what else was there? He tried to remember what people cried about in *EastEnders*, apart from money, death and boyfriends, but it wasn't very helpful: prison sentences, unwanted pregnancies, Aids, stuff that didn't seem to apply to his mum.

He'd forgotten about it all by the time he was inside the school gates. It wasn't like he'd *decided* to forget about it. It was simply that an instinct for self-preservation took over. When you were having trouble with Lee Hartley and his mates, it hardly mattered whether your mum was going round the bend or not. But it was OK, this morning. He could see them all leaning against the wall of the gym, huddled around some item of treasure, safe in the distance, so he reached the form room without any difficulty.

His friends Nicky and Mark were already there, playing Tetris on Mark's Gameboy. He went over to them.

'All right?'

Nicky said hello, but Mark was too absorbed to notice him. He tried to position himself so he could see how Mark was getting on, but Nicky was standing in the only place that offered a glimpse of the Gameboy's tiny screen, so he sat on a desk waiting for them to finish. They didn't finish. Or rather, they did, but then they just started again; they didn't offer him a game or put it away because he had arrived. Marcus felt he was being left out deliberately, and he didn't know what he was supposed to have done wrong.

'Are you going to the computer room at lunchtime?' That was how he knew Nicky and Mark – through the computer club. It was a stupid question, because they always went. If they didn't go, then like him they would be tiptoeing timidly around the edges of lunchtime, trying not to get noticed by anybody with a big mouth and a sharp haircut.

'Dunno. Maybe. What do you reckon, Mark?'

'Dunno. Probably.'

'Right. See you there, then, maybe.'

He'd see them before then. He was seeing them now, for example – it wasn't like he was going anywhere. But it was something to say.

Breaktime was the same: Nicky and Mark on the Gameboy, Marcus hovering around on the outside. OK, they weren't real friends – not like the friends he'd had in Cambridge – but they got on OK, usually, if only because they weren't like the other kids in their class. Marcus had even been to Nicky's house once, after school one day. They knew they were nerdy and geeky and all the other things some of the girls called them (all three of them wore specs, none of them was bothered about clothes, Mark had ginger hair and freckles, and Nicky looked a good three years younger than everyone else in year seven), but it didn't worry them much. The important thing was that they had each other, that they weren't hugging the corridors trying desperately not to get noticed.

'Oi! Fuzzy! Give us a song.' A couple of year eights were standing in the doorway. Marcus didn't know them, so his fame was obviously spreading. He tried to look more purposeful: he craned his neck to make it look as though he was concentrating on the Gameboy, but he still couldn't see anything, and anyway Mark and Nicky started to back away, leaving him on his own.

'Hey, Ginger! Chris Evans! Speccy!' Mark started to redden.

'They're all speccy.'

'Yeah, I forgot. Oi, Ginger Speccy! Is that a love bite on your neck?'

They thought this was hilarious. They always made jokes about girls and sex; he didn't know why. Probably because they were sex-mad.

Mark gave up the struggle and turned the Gameboy off. This had been happening a lot recently, and there wasn't much you could do about it. You just had to stand there and take it until they got bored. It was finding something to do in the meantime, some way to be and to look, that made it difficult. Marcus had recently taken to making lists in his head; his mum had a game where you had cards with categories on them, like, say, 'Puddings', and the other team had to guess what twelve examples were on the card, and then you swapped round and had to guess what twelve examples were on the other team's card, like 'Football teams'. He couldn't play it here because he didn't have the cards and there wasn't another team, but he played a variation of this: he thought of something that had lots of examples, like, say, 'Fruit', and tried to think of as many different fruits as he could before whoever it was who was giving them a hard time went away again.

Chocolate bars. Mars, of course. Snickers. Bounty. Were there any more ice-cream ones? He couldn't remember. Topic. Picnic.

'Hey, Marcus, who's your favourite rapper? Tupac? Warren G?' Marcus knew these names, but he didn't know what they meant, or any of their songs, and anyway he knew he wasn't meant to give an answer. If he gave an answer he'd be sunk.

His mind had gone blank, but then this was part of the point of the game. It would be easy to think of the names of chocolate bars at home, but here, with these kids giving him a hard time, it was almost impossible.

Milky Way.

'Oi, Midget, do you know what a blow job is?' Nicky was pretending to stare out of the window, but Marcus could tell he wasn't seeing anything at all.

Picnic. No, he'd already had that one.

'Come on, this is boring.'

And they were gone. Only six. Pathetic.

The three of them didn't say anything for a while. Then Nicky looked at Mark, and Mark looked at Nicky, and finally Mark spoke.

'Marcus, we don't want you hanging around with us any more.'

He didn't know how to react, so he said, 'Oh,' and then, 'Why not?'

'Because of them.'

'They're nothing to do with me.'

'Yes they are. We never got in any trouble with anyone before we knew you, and now we get this every day.'

Marcus could see that. He could imagine that if they had never met him, Nicky and Mark would have had as much contact with Lee Hartley and the rest of them as koala bears have with piranha fish. But now, because of him, the koala bears had fallen into the sea and the piranhas were taking an interest in them. Nobody had hurt them, not yet, and Marcus knew all the stuff about sticks and stones and names. But insults were hurled in just the same way as missiles, if you thought about it, and if other people happened to be standing in the line of fire they got hit too. That's what had happened with Nicky and Mark: he had made them visible, he had turned them into targets, and if he was any kind of a friend at all he'd take himself well away from them. It's just that he had nowhere else to go.

SIX

I'm a single father. I have a two-year-old boy. I'm a single father. I have a two-year-old boy. I'm a single father. I have a two-year-old boy. However many times Will told himself this, he could always find some reason that prevented him from believing it; in his own head – not the place that counted the most, but important nevertheless – he didn't feel like a parent. He was too young, too old, too stupid, too smart, too groovy, too impatient, too selfish, too careless, too careful (whatever the contraceptive circumstances of the woman he was seeing, he always, always used a Durex, even in the days before you had to), he didn't know enough about kids, he went out too often, he drank too much, he took too many drugs. When he looked in the mirror, he didn't, couldn't, see a dad, especially a single dad.

He was trying to see a single dad in the mirror because he had run out of single mums to sleep with; in fact, Angie had so far proved to be both the beginning and the end of his supply. It was all very well deciding that single mums were the future, that there were millions of sad, Julie Christie-like waifs just dying for his call, but the frustrating truth was that he didn't have any of their phone numbers. Where did they hang out?

It took him longer than it should have done to realize that, by definition, single mothers had children, and children, famously, prevented one from hanging out anywhere. He had made a few gentle, half-hearted enquiries of friends and acquaintances, but had so far failed to make any real headway; the people he knew either didn't know any single mothers, or were unwilling to effect the necessary introductions due to Will's legendarily poor romantic track record. But now he had found the ideal solution to this unexpected dearth of prey. He had invented a two-year-old son called Ned and had joined a single parent group.

Most people would not have bothered to go to these lengths to indulge a whim, but Will quite often bothered to do things that most people wouldn't bother to do, simply because he had the time to bother. Doing nothing all day gave him endless opportunities to dream and scheme and pretend to be something he wasn't. He had, after a fit of remorse following a weekend of extreme self-indulgence, volunteered to work in a soup kitchen, and even though he never actually reported for duty, the phone call had allowed him to pretend, for a couple of days, that he was the kind of guy who might. And he had thought about VSO and filled in the forms, and he had cut out an advert in the local paper about teaching slow learners to read, and he had contacted estate agents about opening a restaurant and then a bookshop . . .

The point was that if you had a history of pretending, then joining a single parent group when you were not a single parent was neither problematic nor particularly scary. If it didn't work out, then he'd just have to try something else. It was no big deal.

SPAT (Single Parents – Alone Together) met on the first Thursday of the month in a local adult education centre, and tonight was Will's first time. He was almost sure that tonight would be his last time, too: he'd get something wrong, like the name of Postman Pat's cat, or the colour of Noddy's car (or, more crucially, the name of his own child – for some reason he couldn't stop thinking of him as Ted, and he had only christened him Ned this morning), and he'd be exposed as a fraud and frogmarched off the premises. If there was a chance of meeting someone like Angie, however, it had to be worth a try.

The car park at the centre contained just one other vehicle, a beaten-up B-reg 2CV which had, according to the stickers in its window, been to Chessington World of Adventures and Alton Towers; Will's car, a new GTi, hadn't been anywhere like that at all. Why not? He couldn't think of any reason why not, apart from the glaringly obvious one, that he was a childless single man aged thirty-six and therefore had never had the desire to drive miles and miles to plunge down a plastic fairy mountain on a tea-tray.

The centre depressed him. He hadn't set foot inside a place with classrooms and corridors and home-made posters for nearly twenty years, and he had forgotten that British education smelt of disinfectant. It hadn't occurred to him that he wouldn't be able to find the SPAT party. He thought he'd be led straight to it by the happy buzz of people forgetting their troubles and getting roaring drunk, but there was no happy buzz, just the distant, mournful clank of a bucket. Finally he spotted a piece of file paper pinned to a classroom door with the word SPAT! scrawled on it in felt-tip pen. The exclamation mark put him off. It was trying too hard.

There was only one woman in the room. She was taking bottles – of white wine, beer, mineral water and supermarket-brand cola – out of a cardboard box and putting them on to a table in the centre of the room. The rest of the tables had been pushed to the back; the chairs were stacked in rows behind them. It was the most desolate party venue Will had ever seen.

'Have I come to the right place?' he asked the woman. She had pointy features and red cheeks; she looked like Worzel Gummidge's friend Aunt Sally.

'SPAT? Come in. Are you Will? I'm Frances.'

He smiled and shook her hand. He had spoken to Frances on the phone earlier in the day.

'I'm sorry there's nobody else here yet. We quite often get off to a slow start. Babysitters.'

'Of course.' So he was wrong to be prompt. He had more or less given himself away already. And, of course, he should never have said 'of course', which implied that she had clarified something he was finding puzzling. He should have rolled his eyes and said, 'Tell me about it', or, 'Don't talk to me about babysitters', something weary and conspiratorial.

Maybe it wasn't too late. He rolled his eyes. 'Don't talk to me about babysitters,' he said. He laughed bitterly and shook his head, just for good measure. Frances ignored the eccentric conversational timing and took the cue.

'Did you have trouble tonight, then?'

'No. My mother's looking after him.' He was proud of the use of the pronoun. It implied familiarity. On the debit side, though, there had been an awful lot of head-shaking, eye-rolling and bitter laughter for a man with no apparent babysitting difficulties.

'I've had trouble before, though,' he added hastily. The conversation was less than two minutes old and already he was a nervous wreck.

'Haven't we all?' said Frances.

Will laughed heartily. 'Yes,' he said. 'I know I have.'

It was now perfectly clear, he felt, that he was either a liar or a lunatic, but before he could dig himself any deeper into a hole which was already shipping water other SPAT members – all of them women, all but one of them in their thirties – started to arrive. Frances introduced him to each of them: Sally and Moira, who looked tough, ignored him completely, helped themselves to a paper cupful of white wine and disappeared off to the further corner of the room (Moira, Will noted with interest, was wearing a Lorena Bobbitt T-shirt); Lizzie, who was small, sweet and scatty; Helen and Susannah, who obviously regarded SPAT as beneath their dignity, and made rude comments about the wine and the location; Saskia, who was ten years younger than anybody else in the room, and looked more like somebody's daughter than somebody's mother; and Suzie, who was tall, blonde, pale, nervy-looking and beautiful. She would do, he thought, and stopped looking at anyone else who came in. Blonde and beautiful were two of the qualities he was looking for; pale and nervy-looking were two of the qualities that gave him the right to do so.

'Hello,' he said. 'I'm Will, I'm new, and I don't know anybody.'

'Hello, Will. I'm Suzie, I'm old, and I know everybody.' He laughed. She laughed. He spent as much of the evening as courtesy allowed in her company.

His conversation with Frances had sharpened him up, so he did better on the Ned front. In any case Suzie wanted to talk, and in these circumstances he was extremely happy to listen. There was a lot to listen to. Suzie had been married to a man called Dan, who had started an affair when she was six months pregnant and had left her the day before she went into labour. Dan had only seen his daughter Megan once, accidentally, in the Body Shop in Islington. He hadn't seemed to want to see her again. Suzie was now poor (she was trying to retrain as a nutritionist) and bitter, and Will could understand why.

Suzie looked around the room.

'One of the reasons I like coming here is that you can be angry and no one thinks any the less of you,' she said. 'Just about everyone's got something they're angry about.'

'Really?' They didn't look that angry to Will.

'Let's see who's here . . . The woman in the denim shirt over there? Her husband went because he thought their little boy wasn't his. Ummm . . . Helen . . . boring . . . he went off with someone from work . . . Moira . . . he came out . . . Susannah Curtis . . . I think he was running two families . . .'

There were endless ingenious variations on the same theme. Men who took one look at their new child and went, men who took one look at their new colleague and went, men who went for the hell of it. Immediately Will understood Moira's sanctification of Lorena Bobbitt completely; by the time Suzie had finished her litany of treachery and deceit, he wanted to cut off his own penis with a kitchen knife.

'Aren't there any other men who come to SPAT?' he asked Suzie.

'Just one. Jeremy. He's on holiday.'

'So women do leave sometimes?'

'Jeremy's wife was killed in a car crash.'

'Oh. Oh well.'

Will was becoming so depressed about his sex that he decided to redress the balance.

'So. I'm on my own,' he said, in what he hoped was a mysteriously wistful tone.

'I'm sorry,' said Suzie. 'I haven't asked you anything about yourself.'

'Oh . . . It doesn't matter.'

'Did you get dumped then?'

'Well, I suppose I did, yes.' He gave her a sad, stoical smile.

'And does your ex see Ned?'

'Sometimes. She's not really that bothered.' He was beginning to feel better; it was good to be the bearer of bad news about women. True, this bad news was entirely fictitious, but there was, he thought, an emotional truth here somewhere, and he could see now that his role-playing had a previously unsuspected artistic element to it. He was acting, yes, but in the noblest, most profound sense of the word. He wasn't a fraud. He was Robert De Niro.

'How does he cope with that?'

'Oh . . . he's a good little boy. Very brave.'

'They have amazing resources, kids, don't they?'

To his astonishment he found himself blinking back a tear, and Suzie put a reassuring hand on his arm. He was in here, no doubt about it.

SEVEN

Some things carried on as normal. He went to his dad's in Cambridge for the weekend and watched a load of telly. On the Sunday he and his dad and Lindsey, his dad's girlfriend, went to Lindsey's mum's house in Norfolk, and they went for a walk on the beach and Lindsey's mum gave him a fiver for no reason. He liked Lindsey's mum. He liked Lindsey, too. Even his mum liked Lindsey, although she said nasty things about her every now and again. (He never stuck up for her. In fact, he stored up stupid things that Lindsey said or did and told his mum about them when he got home; it was easier that way.) Everyone was OK, really. It was just that there were so many of them now. But he got on with them all OK, and they didn't think he was weird, or at least they didn't seem to. He went back to school wondering whether he'd been making a fuss about nothing.

On the way home, though, it all started again, in the newsagent's round the corner. They were nice in there, and they didn't mind him looking at the computer magazines. He could stand browsing for ten minutes or so before they said anything, and even then they were gentle and jokey about it, not mean and anti-kid, like in so many of the shops. 'Only three children allowed in at the same time.' He hated all that. You were a thief just because of how old you were . . . He wouldn't go in shops that had that sign in the window. He wouldn't give them his money.

'How's your lovely mum, Marcus?' the man behind the counter asked when he walked in. They liked his mother here, because she talked to them about the place where they came from; she had been there once, a long time ago, when she was a real hippy.

'She's OK.' He wasn't going to tell them anything.

He found the magazine he'd got halfway through last week, and forgot about everything else. The next thing he knew they were all in there, crowded in really close, and they were laughing at him again. He was sick of that sound. If no one laughed again in the whole world for the rest of his life, he wouldn't care.

'What you singing, Fuzzy?'

He'd done it again. He'd been thinking of one of his mum's songs, a Joni Mitchell one about a taxi, but it had obviously slipped out again. They all started humming tunelessly, throwing in nonsense words every now and again, prodding him to get him to turn round. He ignored them, and tried to concentrate on what he was reading. He didn't need to think of stuff like chocolate bars when he had a computer article to lose himself in. He started off just pretending, but within seconds he was properly lost, and he forgot all about them, and the next thing he knew they were on their way out of the shop.

'Oi, Mohammed,' one of them shouted. That wasn't Mr Patel's name. 'You ought to check his pockets. He's been thieving.' And then they were gone. He checked his own pockets. They were full of chocolate bars and packets of chewing gum. He hadn't even noticed. He felt sick. He started trying to explain, but Mr Patel interrupted him.

'I was watching them, Marcus. It's OK.'

He walked over to the counter and piled the stuff on top of the newspapers.

'Are they at your school?'

Marcus nodded.

'You'd better keep out of their way.'

Yeah, right. Bloody hell. Keep out of their way.

When he got home his mother was lying on the floor with a coat draped over her, watching children's cartoons. She didn't look up.

'Didn't you go to work today?'

'This morning. I took the afternoon off sick.'

'What kind of sick?'

No answer.

This wasn't right. He was only a kid. He'd been thinking that more and more recently, as he got older and older. He didn't know why. Maybe it was because, when he really was only a kid, he wasn't capable of recognizing it – you had to be a certain age before you realized that you were actually quite young. Or maybe when he was little there was nothing to worry about – five or six years ago his mum never spent half the day shivering under a coat watching stupid cartoons, and even if she had he might not have thought it was anything out of the ordinary.

But something was going to have to give. He was having a shit time at school and a shit time at home, and as home and school was all there was to it, just about, that meant he was having a shit time all the time, apart from when he was asleep. Someone was going to have to do something about it, because he couldn't do anything about it himself, and he couldn't see who else there was, apart from the woman under the coat.

She was funny, his mum. She was all for talking. She was always on at him to talk and tell her things, but he was sure she didn't really mean it. She was fine on the little things, but he knew that if he went for the big stuff then there'd be trouble, especially now, when she cried and cried about nothing. But at the moment he couldn't see any way of avoiding it. He was only a kid, and she was his mum, and if he felt bad it was her job to stop him feeling bad, simple as that. Even if she didn't want to, even if it meant that she'd end up feeling worse. Tough. Too bad. He was angry enough to talk to her now.

'What are you watching this for? It's rubbish. You're always telling me.'

'I thought you liked cartoons.'

'I do. I just don't like this one. It's terrible.'

They both stared at the screen without speaking. This weird dog-type thing was trying to get at a boy who could turn himself into a kind of flying saucer.

'What sort of sick?' He asked the question roughly, the way a teacher would ask someone like Paul Cox whether he'd done his homework.

No answer again.

'Mum, what sort of sick?'

'Oh, Marcus, it's not the sort of sick that—'

'Don't treat me like an idiot, Mum.'

She started crying again, long, low sobs that terrified him.

'You've got to stop this.'

'I can't.'

'You've got to. If you can't look after me properly then you'll have to find someone who can.'

She rolled over on to her stomach and looked at him.

'How can you say I don't look after you?'

'Because you don't. All you do is make my meals and I could do that. The rest of the time you just cry. That's . . . that's no good. That's no good to me.'

She cried even harder then, and he let her. He went upstairs to his room and played NBA Basketball with the earphones on, even though he wasn't supposed to on school nights. But when he came downstairs she was up and the duvet had been put away. She was spooning pasta and sauce on to plates, and she seemed OK. He knew she wasn't OK – he may have been just a kid, but he was old enough to know that people didn't stop being nuts (and that, he was beginning to realize, was what sort of sick it was) just because you told them to stop – but he didn't care, as long as she was OK in front of him.

'You're going to a picnic on Saturday,' she said out of the blue.

'A picnic?'

'Yes. In Regent's Park.'

'Who with?'

'Suzie.'

'Not that SPAT lot.'

'Yes, that SPAT lot.'

'I hate them.' Fiona had taken Marcus to a SPAT summer party in someone's garden when they first moved to London, but she hadn't been back since; Marcus had been to more meetings than she had, because Suzie had taken him on one of their outings.

'*Tant pis.*'

What did she have to say things like that for? He knew it was French for 'tough shit', but why couldn't she just say 'tough shit'? No wonder he was a weirdo. If you had a mum who spoke French for no reason, you were more or less bound to end up singing out loud in newsagents' without meaning to. He put loads and loads of cheese on his pasta and stirred it around.

'Are you going?'

'No.'

'So why do I have to?'

'Because I'm having a rest.'

'I can keep out of your way.'

'I'm doing what you said. I'm getting someone else to look after you. Suzie's much more capable than I am.'

Suzie was her best friend; they'd known each other since school-days. She was nice; Marcus liked her a lot. But he still didn't want to go on a picnic with her and all those horrible little kids from SPAT. He was ten years older than most of them, and every time he'd done anything with them before, he'd hated it. The last time, when they all went to the zoo, he'd come home and told his mum he wanted a vasectomy. That made her laugh a lot, but he'd meant it. He knew for a fact that he was never going to have children, so why not get it over and done with now?

'I could do anything. I could sit in my room all day playing games. You wouldn't even know I was in the house.'

'I want you to get out. Do something normal. It's too intense here.'

'What do you mean?'

'I mean . . . Oh, I don't know what I mean. I just know that we're not doing each other any good.'

Hold on a moment. They didn't do *each other* any good? For the first time since his mother had started crying, he wanted to cry too. He knew she wasn't doing him any good, but he had no idea that it worked both ways. What had he done to her? He couldn't think of a single thing. One day he'd ask her what she was on about, but not today, not now. He wasn't sure he'd like the answer.

EIGHT

'What a *bitch.*'

Will looked at his feet and made noises intended to convey to Suzie that his ex-wife wasn't that bad, not really.

'Will, it's just not on. You can't ring up five minutes in advance and change plans like that. You should've told her to . . .' – she looked around to see whether Marcus, the strange kid they were apparently stuck with for the day, was still listening – '. . . eff off.'

His ex (who, according to Suzie, was called Paula, a name he must have mentioned the other night) was always going to get the blame for Ned's non-appearance at the picnic, but he felt obscurely loyal to her in the face of Suzie's empathetic anger. Had he pushed it too far?

'Oh, well,' he kept saying, while Suzie raged on, 'you know.'

'You can't afford to be soft. You'll just get messed around all the time.'

'She's never done it before.'

'No, but she'll do it again. You watch. You're too nice. This is a nasty business. You'll have to toughen up.'

'I suppose so.' Being told that he was too nice, that he needed to be meaner, was an unusual experience for Will, but he was feeling so weedy that it was easy to see how Paula had walked all over him.

'And the car! I can't believe she took the car.'

He had forgotten about the car. Paula had also taken that, first thing this morning, for reasons too complicated to explain, thus obliging Will to phone up Suzie and ask for a lift to Regent's Park.

'I know, I know. She's . . .' Words failed him. If you looked at the whole picture, the Ned thing and the car thing, Paula had behaved outrageously, he could see that, but it was still hard for him to summon up the requisite anger. He was going to have to, though, if only to show Suzie that he wasn't a hopeless, spineless wimp. 'She's a cow.'

'That's more like it.'

It was much more confusing than he had imagined, making people up, and he was beginning to realize that he hadn't thought it through properly at all. He already had a cast of three – Paula, Ned and his mother (who wasn't imaginary in quite the same way, having at least been alive once, although not, admittedly, recently) – and he could see that if he was going to carry this through, then there would soon be a cast of thousands. But how could he carry it through? How many times could Ned reasonably be whisked away by his mother, or maternal grandmother, or international terrorists? What reasons could he give for not inviting Suzie round to his flat, where there were no toys or cots or nappies or bowls, where there was no second bedroom even? Could he kill Ned off with some awful disease, or a car crash – tragic, tragic, life goes on? Maybe not. Parents got pretty cut up about kids dying, and he'd find the requisite years of grief a real drain on his thespian resources. What about Paula? Couldn't he just pack Ned off to her, even though she didn't want to see him much? Except . . . except then he wouldn't be a single father any more. He'd lose the point of himself, somehow.

No, disaster was approaching, and there was nothing he could do about it. Best pull out now, walk away, leave them all with the impression that he was an inadequate eccentric, nothing more – certainly not a pervert, or a fantasist, or any of the bad things he was about to turn into. But walking away wasn't Will's style. He always felt something would turn up, even though nothing ever did, or even could, most of the time. Once, years ago, when he was a kid, he told a schoolfriend (having first ascertained that this friend was not a C. S. Lewis fan) that it was possible to walk through the back of his wardrobe into a different world, and invited him round to explore. He could have cancelled, he could have told him anything, but he was not prepared to suffer a moment's mild embarrassment if there was no immediate need to do so, and the two of them scrabbled around among the coathangers for several minutes until Will mumbled something about the world being closed on Saturday afternoons. The thing was, he could still remember feeling genuinely hopeful, right up until the last minute: maybe there will be something there, he had thought, maybe I won't lose face. There wasn't and he did, loads of it, a whole headful of face, but he hadn't learnt a thing from the experience: if anything, it seemed to have left him with the feeling that he was bound to be lucky next time. So here he was, in his mid-thirties, knowing in all the places there were to know that he didn't have a two-year-old son, but still working on the presumption that, when it came to the crunch, one would pop up from somewhere.

'I'll bet you could do with a coffee,' said Suzie.

'I could murder one. What a morning!' He shook his head in amazement, and Suzie blew her cheeks out sympathetically. It occurred to him that he was really enjoying himself.

'I don't even know what you do,' Suzie said, when they were settled into the car. Megan was in the baby seat beside her; Will was in the back with Marcus, the weird kid, who was humming tunelessly.

'Nothing.'

'Oh.'

He usually made something up, but he had made too much up already over the last few days . . . if he added a fictitious job to the list, not only would he begin to lose track, he'd be offering Suzie nothing real at all.

'Well, what did you do before?'

'Nothing.'

'You've never worked?'

'I've done the odd day here and there, but—'

'Oh. Well, that's . . .'

She trailed off, and Will knew why. Not having a job ever, that's . . . nothing. There was nothing to say about it at all, not immediately, anyway.

'My dad wrote a song. In nineteen thirty-eight. It's a famous song, and I live off the royalties.'

'You know Michael Jackson, right? He makes a million pounds a minute,' said the weird kid.

'I'm not sure it's a million pounds a minute,' said Suzie doubtfully. 'That's an awful lot.'

'A million pounds a minute!' Marcus repeated. 'Sixty million pounds an hour!'

'Well I don't make sixty million pounds an hour,' said Will. 'Nothing like.'

'How much, then?'

'Marcus,' said Suzie. 'So what's this song, Will? If you can live off it, we must have heard of it.'

'Umm . . . "Santa's Super Sleigh",' said Will. He said it neutrally, but it was useless, because there was no way of saying it that didn't make it sound silly. He wished his father had written any other song in the world, with the possible exception of 'Itsy Bitsy Teeny Weeny Yellow Polka Dot Bikini', or 'How Much Is That Doggie In The Window?'

'Really? "Santa's Super Sleigh"?' Suzie and Marcus both started singing the same part of the song:

So just leave out the mince pies, and a glass of sherry,
And Santa will visit you, and leave you feeling merry,
Oh, Santa's super sleigh,
Santa's super sleigh . . .

People always did this. They always sang, and they always sang the same part. Will had friends who began every single phone call with a quick burst of 'Santa's Super Sleigh', and when he didn't laugh they accused him of a sense of humour failure. But where was the joke? And even if there was one, how was he supposed to make himself laugh at it every time, year after year after year?

'I expect people always do that, don't they?'

'You two are the first, actually.'

Suzie glanced at him in the rear-view mirror. 'Sorry.'

'No, it's OK. I ask for it, really.'

'But I don't understand. How does that make money? Do carol singers have to pay you ten per cent?'

'They should do. But you can't always catch them. No, it's on every Christmas album ever made. Elvis did it, you know. And the Muppets.' And Des O'Connor. And the Crankies. And Bing Crosby. And David Bowie, in a duet with Zsa Zsa Gabor. And Val Doonican, and Cilla Black, and Rod Hull and Emu. And an American punk band called the Cunts, and, at the last count, at least a hundred other recording artists. He knew the names from the royalty statements, and he didn't like any of them. Will prided himself on his cool; he hated making his living from Val Doonican.

'But haven't you ever wanted to work?'

'Oh, yes. Sometimes. It's just . . . I don't know. I never seem to get round to it.' And that was the long and the short of it. He never seemed to get round to it. Every day for the last eighteen years he had got up in the morning with the intention of sorting out his career problem once and for all; as the day wore on, however, his burning desire to seek a place for himself in the outside world somehow got extinguished.

*

Suzie parked the car in the Outer Circle and unfolded Megan's buggy, while Will stood awkwardly on the pavement with Marcus. Marcus had shown no interest in him whatsoever, although he could hardly claim to have made a vigorous effort to get to know the boy. It did occur to Will, however, that there were few adult males better equipped than him to deal with a teenager (if that is what Marcus was – it was hard to tell. He had a strange frizzy bush of hair, and he dressed like a twenty-five-year-old chartered accountant on his day off: he was wearing brand-new jeans and a Microsoft T-shirt). After all, Will was a sports fan and a pop music fan, and he of all people knew how heavy time could hang on one's hands; to all intents and purposes he *was* a teenager. And it wouldn't do him any harm with Suzie if he were to strike up a sparky, mutually curious relationship with her friend's son. He'd work on Megan later. A quick tickle would probably do the trick.

'So, Marcus. Who's your favourite footballer?'

'I hate football.'

'Right. What a shame.'

'Why?'

Will ignored him.

'Who are your favourite singers then?'

Marcus snorted. 'Are you getting these questions out of a book?'

Suzie laughed. Will blushed.

'No, I was just interested.'

'OK. My favourite singer is Joni Mitchell.'

'Joni Mitchell? Don't you like MC Hammer? Or Snoop Doggy Dogg? Or Paul Weller?'

'No, don't like any of them.' Marcus looked Will up and down, taking in the trainers, the haircut and the sunglasses, and added cruelly, 'Nobody does. Only old people.'

'What, everyone in your school listens to Joni Mitchell?'

'Most people.'

Will knew about hip-hop and acid house and grunge and Madchester and indie; he read *Time Out* and *iD* and the *Face* and *Arena* and the *NME*, still. But nobody had ever mentioned anything about a Joni Mitchell revival. He felt dispirited.

Marcus went on ahead, and Will made no move to keep up with him. At least his failure gave him a chance to talk to Suzie.

'Do you have to look after him often?'

'Not as often as I'd like, eh, Marcus?'

'What?' Marcus stopped and waited for them to catch up.

'I said, I don't look after you as often as I'd like.'

'Oh.'

He walked on ahead again, but not as far as before, so Will was unsure about how much he could hear.

'What's up with his mum?' Will asked Suzie quietly.

'She's just a bit . . . I don't know. Under the weather.'

'She's going nuts,' said Marcus matter-of-factly. 'Cries all the time. Doesn't go to work.'

'Oh, come on, Marcus. She's just had a couple of afternoons off. We all do that when we're, you know, off colour.'

'Off colour? Is that what you call it?' said Marcus. 'I call it nuts.' Will had only previously heard that note of amused belligerence in the voices of old people who were trying to tell you things were much worse than you wanted to pretend: his father had been like that in the last few years of his life.

'Well, she doesn't seem nuts to me.'

'That's because you don't see her very often.'

'I see her as often as I can.'

Will noted the tetchy defensiveness in her voice. What was it with this kid? Once he had seen where you were vulnerable, he was merciless.

'Maybe.'

'Maybe? What does "maybe" mean?'

Marcus shrugged. 'Anyway, she's not nuts with you. She's only nuts at home, when it's the two of us.'

'She'll be fine,' said Suzie. 'She just needs a weekend taking it easy. We'll have a nice picnic, and when you get back tonight she'll be rested up and ready to go.'

Marcus snorted and ran on. They were in the park now, and they could see the SPAT crowd over by the lake in front of them, filling juice containers and unwrapping silver-foil packages.

'I see her at least once a week,' said Suzie. 'And I phone as well. Does he really expect more than that? It's not as if I'm messing around all day. I study. I've got Megan. Jesus.'

'I don't believe all these kids are listening to Joni Mitchell,' said Will. 'I would have read about it. I'm not that out of touch.'

'I suppose I'm going to have to ring every day,' said Suzie.

'I'm giving up those magazines. They're useless,' said Will.

They trudged towards the picnic, feeling old and beaten and found out.

Will felt that his apologies and explanations for Ned's absence were taken at face value by the SPAT picnickers, although there was, he knew, absolutely no reason why they should not have been. Nobody was so desperate for an egg-and-cress sandwich and a game of rounders that they would go to all the trouble of inventing a child. But he still felt a little uncomfortable, and as a consequence threw himself into the afternoon with an enthusiasm that he was only usually able to muster with chemical or alcoholic assistance. He played ball, he blew bubbles, he burst crisp packets (a mistake – many tears, lots of irritated glances), he hid, he sought, he tickled, he dangled . . . He did more or less anything that would keep him away from the knot of adults sitting on blankets under a tree, and away from Marcus, who was wandering around the boating lake throwing pieces of leftover sandwich at the ducks.

He didn't mind. He was better at hiding and seeking than he was at talking, and there were worse ways to spend an afternoon than making small children happy. After a while Suzie and Megan, asleep in her buggy, came over to join him.

'You miss him, don't you?'

'Who?'

He meant it; he had no idea what she was talking about. But Suzie smiled knowingly, and so Will, on the case again, smiled back.

'I'll see him later. It's no big deal. He would have enjoyed it here, though.'

'What's he like?'

'Oh . . . Nice. He's a really nice boy.'

'I can imagine. Who does he look like?'

'Ummm . . . Me, I guess. He drew the short straw.'

'Oh, he could have done worse. Anyway, Megan looks just like Dan, and I hate it.'

Will looked at the sleeping child. 'She's beautiful.'

'Yeah. That's why I hate it. When I see her like this, I think, what a gorgeous baby, and then I think, you bastard, and then I think . . . I don't know what I think. I get into a mess. You know, she's a bastard, he's gorgeous . . . You end up hating your own child and loving the man who dumped her.'

'Oh, well,' said Will. He was beginning to feel cheap and churned up. If the conversation was taking a mournful turn, it was time to make a move. 'You'll meet someone else.'

'D'you reckon?'

'Well. There'll be lots of men . . . I mean, you know, you're a very . . . You know. I mean, you've met me, and I know I don't count, but . . . You know, there are plenty . . .' He trailed off hopefully. If she didn't bite, forget it.

'Why don't you count?'

Bingo.

'Because . . . I don't know . . .'

Suddenly Marcus was in front of them, hopping from foot to foot as if he were about to wet himself.

'I think I've killed a duck,' he said.

NINE

Marcus couldn't believe it. Dead. A dead duck. OK, he'd been *trying* to hit it on the head with a piece of sandwich, but he *tried* to do all sorts of things, and none of them had ever happened before. He'd *tried* to get the highest score on the Stargazer machine in the kebab shop on Hornsey Road – nothing. He'd *tried* to read Nicky's thoughts by staring at the back of his head every maths lesson for a week – nothing. It really annoyed him that the only thing he'd ever achieved through trying was something he hadn't really wanted to do that much in the first place. And anyway, since when did hitting a bird with a sandwich ever kill it? Kids must spend half their lives throwing things at the ducks in Regent's Park. How come he managed to pick a duck that pathetic? There must have been something wrong with it. It was probably just about to die from a heart attack or something; it was just a coincidence. But if it was, nobody would believe him. If there were any witnesses, they'd only have seen the bread hit the duck right on the back of the head, and then seen it keel over. They'd put two and two together and make five, and he'd be imprisoned for a crime he never committed.

Will, Suzie, Megan and Marcus stood on the path at the edge of the lake, staring at the dead body floating in the water.

'There's nothing we can do about it now,' said Will, the trendy bloke who was trying to get off with Suzie. 'Just leave it. What's the problem?'

'Well . . . Supposing someone saw me?'

'D'you think anyone did?'

'I don't know. Maybe. Maybe they said they were going to tell the park-keeper.'

'Maybe someone saw you, or definitely? Maybe they said they were going to get the park-keeper, or definitely?' Marcus didn't like this bloke, so he didn't answer him.

'What's that floating next to it?' Will asked. 'Is that the bread you threw at it?'

Marcus nodded unhappily.

'That's not a sandwich, that's a bloody French loaf. No wonder it keeled over. That would have killed me.'

'Oh, Marcus,' Suzie sighed. 'What were you playing at?'

'Nothing.'

'No, it looks like it,' said Will. Marcus hated him even more. Who did this Will think he was?

'I'm not sure it was me.' He was going to test out his theory. If Suzie didn't believe him, there was no chance the police and judges would.

'How do you mean?'

'I think it must have been ill. I think it was going to die anyway.' Nobody said anything; Will shook his head angrily. Marcus decided this line of defence was a waste of time, even though it was true.

They were staring so hard at the scene of the crime that they didn't notice the park-keeper until he was standing right next to them. Marcus felt his insides turn to mush. This was it.

'One of your ducks has died,' said Will. He made it sound as if it were the saddest thing he'd ever seen. Marcus looked up at him; maybe he didn't hate him after all.

'I was told that you had something to do with it,' said the park-keeper. 'You know that's a criminal offence, don't you?'

'You were told that I had something to do with it?' said Will. 'Me?'

'Maybe not you, but your lad here.'

'You're suggesting that Marcus killed this duck? Marcus *loves* ducks, don't you, Marcus?'

'Yeah. They're my favourite animal. Well, second favourite. After dolphins. They're definitely my favourite bird, though.' This was rubbish, because he hated all animals, but he thought it helped.

'I was told he was throwing bloody great French loaves at it.'

'He was, but I've stopped him now. Boys will be boys,' said Will. Marcus hated him again. He might have known he'd grass him up.

'So he killed it?'

'Oh, God no. Sorry, I see what you mean. No, he was throwing bread at the body. I think he was trying to sink it, because Megan here was getting upset.'

The park-keeper looked at the sleeping form in the buggy.

'She doesn't look very upset now.'

'No. She cried herself to sleep, poor love.'

There was a silence. Marcus could see that this was the crucial time;

the attendant could either accuse them all of lying, and call the police or something, or forget all about it.

'I'll have to wade in and get it,' he said. They were in the clear. Marcus wasn't going to jail for a crime he probably – OK, possibly – didn't commit.

'I hope there's not some sort of epidemic,' said Will sympathetically, as they started to walk back towards the others.

It was then that Marcus saw – or thought he saw – his mum. She was standing in front of them, blocking the path, and she was smiling. He waved and turned around to tell Suzie that she'd turned up, but when he looked back his mum wasn't there. He felt stupid and didn't say anything about it to anyone, ever.

Marcus was never able to work out why Suzie had insisted on coming back to the flat with him. He'd been out with her before, and she'd just dropped him off outside, waited until he'd let himself in and then driven off. But that day she parked the car, lifted Megan out in her car seat, and came in with him. She was never able to explain why she had done it.

Will wasn't invited, but he followed them in, and Marcus didn't tell him not to. Everything about that two minutes was mysteriously memorable, even at the time, somehow: climbing the stairs, the cooking smells that got trapped in the hall, the way he noticed the pattern on the carpet for the first time ever. Afterwards he thought he could recall being nervous, too, but he must have made that up, because there wasn't anything to be nervous about. Then he put the key in the door and opened it, and a new part of his life began, bang, without any warning at all.

His mum was half on and half off the sofa: her head was lolling towards the floor. She was white, and there was a pool of sick on the carpet, but there wasn't much on her – either she'd had the sense to puke away from herself, or she'd just been lucky. In the hospital they told him it was a miracle she hadn't choked on her own vomit and killed herself. The sick was grey and lumpy, and the room stank.

He couldn't speak. He didn't know what to say. He didn't cry either. It was much too serious for that. So he just stood there. But Suzie dropped the car seat and ran over to her and started screaming at her and slapping her. Suzie must have seen the empty pill bottle as soon as she walked in, but Marcus didn't spot it until later, when the ambulancemen came, so at first he was just confused; he couldn't understand why Suzie was so mad at someone who was not very well.

Suzie yelled at Will to call for an ambulance and told Marcus to make some black coffee; his mum was moving now and making a terrible moaning noise that he had never heard before and never wanted to hear again. Suzie was crying, and then Megan started up too, so in seconds the room had gone from a terrifying silence and stillness to noisy, terrifying panic.

'Fiona! How could you do this?' Suzie screamed. 'You've got a kid. How could you do this?'

It was only then it occurred to Marcus that all this reflected badly on him.

Marcus had seen some things, mostly on video at other people's houses. He had seen a bloke put another bloke's eye out with a kebab skewer in *Hellhound 3*. He had seen a man's brains come out of his nostrils in *Boilerhead – The Return*. He had seen arms taken off with a single swing of a machete, he had seen babies with swords where their willies should be, he had seen eels coming out of a woman's belly-button. None of it had ever stopped him sleeping or given him nightmares. OK, he hadn't seen many things in real life, but up until now he hadn't thought it mattered: shocks are shocks, wherever you find them. What got him about this was that there wasn't even anything very shocking, just some puke and some shouting, and he could see his mum wasn't dead or anything. But this was the scariest thing he'd ever seen, by a million miles, and he knew the moment he walked in that it was something he'd have to think about for ever.

TEN

When the ambulance came there was a long, complicated discussion about who would go to the hospital and how. Will was hoping he'd be packed off home, but it didn't work out like that. The ambulancemen didn't want to take Suzie and Marcus and the baby, so in the end he had to drive Megan and Marcus there in Suzie's car, while she went with Marcus's mother in the ambulance. He tried to stay tucked in behind them, but he lost them the moment they got out on to the main road. He would have liked nothing better than to pretend he had a flashing blue light on the top of the car, drive on the wrong side of the road and crash through as many red lights as he wanted, but he doubted whether either of the mothers ahead of him would thank him for it.

In the back seat Megan was still crying hard; Marcus was staring grimly through the windscreen.

'See if you can do anything with her,' said Will.

'Like what?'

'I don't know. Think of something.'

'You think of something.'

Fair enough, Will thought. Asking a kid to do anything at all in these circumstances was probably unreasonable.

'How do you feel?'

'I don't know.'

'She'll be OK.'

'Yeah. I suppose so. But . . . that's not the point, is it?'

Will knew it wasn't the point, but he was surprised that Marcus had worked it out quite so quickly. For the first time it occurred to him that the boy was probably pretty bright.

'What do you mean?'

'Work it out for yourself.'

'Are you worried she'll try it again?'

'Just shut up, all right?'

So he did, and they travelled to the hospital in as much silence as a screaming baby would allow.

When they arrived Fiona had already been carted off somewhere, and Suzie was sitting in the waiting room clutching a styrofoam cup. Marcus dumped the car seat and its apoplectic load down next to her.

'So what's happening?' Will only just managed to restrain himself from rubbing his hands together. He was completely absorbed in all of this – absorbed almost to the point of enjoyment.

'I don't know. They're pumping her stomach or something. She was talking a little in the ambulance. She was asking after you, Marcus.'

'That's nice of her.'

'This isn't anything to do with you, Marcus. You know that, don't you? I mean, you're not the reason she . . . You're not the reason she's here.'

'How do you know?'

'I just do.' She said it with warmth and humour, shaking her head and ruffling Marcus's hair, but everything about the intonation and her gestures was wrong: they belonged to other, quieter, more domestic circumstances, and though they might have been appropriate for a twelve-year-old, they were not appropriate for the oldest twelve-year-old in the world, which Marcus had suddenly become. Marcus pushed her hand away.

'Has anyone got any change? I want to get something from the machine.'

Will gave him a handful of silver, and he wandered off.

'Fucking hell,' said Will. 'What are you supposed to tell a kid whose mum has just tried to top herself?' He was merely curious, but luckily the question came out as if it were rhetorical, and therefore sympathetic. He didn't want to sound like someone watching a really good disease-of-the-week film.

'I don't know,' said Suzie. She had Megan on her lap, and she was trying to get her to chew on a breadstick. 'But we'll have to try and think of something.'

Will didn't know if he was a part of the 'we' or not, but it didn't matter one way or the other. However absorbing he was finding the evening's entertainment, he certainly didn't intend repeating it: this lot were just too weird.

The evening dragged on. Megan cried, then whined, then fell asleep; Marcus made repeated visits to the vending machine and came back with cans of Coke and Kit-Kats and bags of crisps. None of them talked much, although occasionally Marcus grumbled about the people waiting for treatment.

'I hate this lot. They're drunk, most of them. Look at them. They've all been fighting.'

It was true. More or less everyone in the waiting room was some kind of deadbeat – a vagrant, or a drunk, or a junkie, or just mad. The few people who were there through sheer bad luck (there was a woman who had been bitten by a dog and was waiting for a shot, and a mother with a little girl who looked as though she might have broken her ankle in a fall) looked anxious, pale, drained; tonight was really something out of the ordinary for them. But the rest had simply transferred the chaos of their daily life from one place to another. It made no difference to them if they were roaring at passers-by in the street or abusing nurses in a hospital casualty department – it was all just business.

'My mum's not like these people.'

'No one said she was,' said Suzie.

'Supposing they think she is, though?'

'They won't.'

'They might. She took drugs, didn't she? She came in with sick all over her, didn't she? How would they know the difference?'

'Of course they'll know the difference. And if they don't, we'll tell them.'

Marcus nodded, and Will could see that Suzie had said the right thing: who could believe that Fiona was any kind of derelict with friends like these? For once, Will thought, Marcus was asking the wrong question. The right question was: what the hell difference did it make? Because if the only things that separated Fiona from the rest of them were Suzie's reassuring car keys and Will's expensive casual clothes, then she was in trouble anyway. You had to live in your own bubble. You couldn't force your way into someone else's, because then it wouldn't be a bubble any more. Will bought his clothes and his CDs and his cars and his Heal's furniture and his drugs for himself, and himself alone; if Fiona couldn't afford these things, and didn't have an equivalent bubble of her own, then that was her lookout.

Right on cue, a woman came over to see them – not a doctor or a nurse, but somebody official.

'Hello. Did you come in with Fiona Brewer?'

'Yes. I'm her friend Suzie, and this is Will, and this is Fiona's son Marcus.'

'Right. We're going to be keeping Fiona in overnight, and obviously we don't want you to have to stay. Is there somewhere Marcus could go? Is there anyone else at home, Marcus?'

Marcus shook his head.

'He'll be staying with me tonight,' said Suzie.

'OK, but I'll have to get his mother's permission for that,' said the woman.

'Sure.'

'That's where I want to go,' Marcus said to the woman's retreating back. She turned round and smiled. 'Not that anyone cares.'

'Of course they do,' said Suzie.

'You reckon?'

The woman came back a couple of minutes later, smiling and nodding as if Fiona had given birth to a baby, rather than given permission for an overnight stay.

'That's fine. She says thank you.'

'Great. Come on, then, Marcus. You can help me open the sofa bed.'

Suzie put Megan back into the car seat and they made their way out to the car park.

'I'll see you,' said Will. 'I'll call you.'

'I hope you get things sorted out with Ned and Paula.'

Again the momentary blankness: Ned and Paula, Ned and Paula . . . Ah, yes, his ex-wife and his son.

'Oh, it'll be fine. Thanks.' He kissed Suzie on the cheek, punched Marcus on the arm, waved to Megan and went off to hail a cab. It had all been very interesting, but he wouldn't want to do it every night.

ELEVEN

It was there, on the kitchen table. He was just putting the flowers in the vase, like Suzie had told him to do, when he spotted it. Everyone had been in such a hurry and a mess last night that they hadn't noticed. He picked it up and sat down.

Dear Marcus,

I think that whatever I say in this letter, you'll end up hating me. Or maybe end up is a bit too final: perhaps when you're older, you'll feel something else other than hate. But there's certainly going to be a long period of time when you'll think I did a wrong, stupid, selfish, unkind thing. So I wanted to give myself a chance to explain, even if it doesn't do any good.

Listen. A big part of me knows that I'm doing a wrong, stupid, selfish, unkind thing. Most of me, in fact. The trouble is that it's not the part that controls me any more. That's what's so horrible about the sort of illness I've had for the last few months – it just doesn't listen to anything or anybody else. It just wants to do its own thing. I hope you never get to find out what that's like.

None of this is anything to do with you. I've loved being your mum, always, even though it's been hard for me and I've found it difficult sometimes. And I don't know why being your mum isn't enough for me, but it isn't. And it isn't that I'm so unhappy I don't want to live any more. That's not what it feels like. It feels more like I'm tired and bored and the party's gone on too long and I want to go home. I feel flat and there doesn't seem to be anything to look forward to, so I'd rather call it a day. How can I feel like that when I've got you? I don't know. I do know that if I kept it all going just for your sake, you wouldn't thank me, and I reckon that once you've got over this things will be better for you than they were before. Really. You can go to your dad's, or Suzie has always said she'll look after you if anything happened to me.

I'll watch out for you if I am able to. I think I will be. I think that when something happens to a mother, she's allowed to do that, even if it's her fault. I don't want to stop writing this, but I can't think of any reason to keep it going.

Love you,

Mum.

He was still sitting at the kitchen table when she came back from the hospital with Suzie and Megan. She could see straight away what he had found.

'Shit, Marcus. I'd forgotten about it.'

'You forgot? You forgot a suicide letter?'

'Well, I didn't think I'd ever have to remember it, did I?' She laughed at that. She actually laughed. That was his mother. When she wasn't crying over the breakfast cereal, she was laughing about killing herself.

'Jesus,' said Suzie. 'Is that what it was? I shouldn't have left him here before I went to get you. I thought it would be nice if he tidied the place up.'

'Suzie, I don't honestly think you're to blame for anything.'

'I should have thought.'

'Maybe Marcus and I ought to have a little talk on our own.'

'Of course.'

Suzie and his mum hugged, and Suzie came over to give him a kiss.

'She's fine,' Suzie whispered, loud enough for his mum to hear. 'Don't worry about her.'

When Suzie had gone, Fiona put the kettle on and sat down at the table with him.

'Are you angry with me?'

'What do you think?'

'Because of the letter?'

'Because of the letter, because of what you did, everything.'

'I can understand that. I don't feel the same as I did on Saturday, if that's any help.'

'What, it's all just gone away, all that?'

'No, but . . . at the moment I feel better.'

'At the moment's no good to me. I can see that you're better at the moment. You've just put the kettle on. But what happens when you've finished your tea? What happens when I go back to school? I can't be here to watch you all the time.'

'No, I know. But we've got to look after each other. It shouldn't all be one way.'

Marcus nodded, but he was in a place where words didn't matter. He had read her letter, and he was no longer very interested in what she said; it was what she did, and what she was going to do, that counted. She wasn't going to do anything today. She'd drink her tea, and tonight they'd get a takeaway and watch TV, and they would feel as though it were the beginning of a different, better time. But that time would run out, and then there would be something else. He had always trusted his mother – or rather, he had never *not* trusted her. But for him, things would never be the same again.

Two wasn't enough, that was the trouble. He'd always thought that two was a good number, and that he'd hate to live in a family of three or four or five. But he could see the point of that now: if someone dropped off the edge, you weren't left on your own. How could you make a family grow if there was no one around to, you know, help it along? He was going to have to find a way.

'I'll make the tea,' he said brightly. At least now he had something to work on.

They decided to have a quiet, normal evening. They ordered a delivery curry, and Marcus went to the newsagent's to get a video, but it took him ages: everything he looked at seemed to have something about death in it, and he didn't want to watch anything about death. He didn't want his mum to watch anything about death, come to that, although he wasn't sure why. What did he think would happen if his mum saw Steven Seagal blast some guys in the head with a gun? That wasn't the kind of death they were trying not to think about tonight. The kind of death they were trying not to think about was the quiet, sad, real kind, not the noisy, who-cares kind. (People thought that kids couldn't tell the difference, but they could, of course.) In the end he got *Groundhog Day*, which he was pleased with, because it was new on video and it said it was funny on the back of the box.

They didn't start watching it until the food arrived. Fiona served it up, and Marcus wound the tape on past the trailers and adverts so that they would be ready to go the moment they took their first bite of poppadum. The back of the box was right: it was a funny film. This guy was stuck in the same day, over and over again, although they didn't really explain how that happened, which Marcus thought was weak – he liked to know how things worked. Maybe it was based on a true story, and there had been this guy who was stuck in the same day over and over again, and he didn't know himself how it had happened. This alarmed Marcus. Supposing he woke up tomorrow and it was yesterday again, with the duck and the hospital and everything? Best not to think about it.

But then the film changed, and became all about suicide. This guy was so fed up with being stuck in the same day over and over for hundreds of years that he tried to kill himself. It was no good, though. Whatever he did, he still woke up the next morning (except it wasn't the next morning. It was this morning, the morning he always woke up on).

Marcus was really angry. They hadn't said anything about suicide on the video box, and yet this film had a bloke trying to kill himself about three thousand times. OK, he didn't succeed, but that didn't make it funny. His mum hadn't succeeded either, and nobody felt like making a comedy film about it. Why wasn't there any warning? There must be loads of people who wanted to watch a good comedy just after they'd tried to kill themselves. Supposing they all chose this one?

At first Marcus was quiet, so quiet that he almost stopped breathing. He didn't want his mum to hear his breaths, in case she thought they were noisier than usual because he was upset. But then he couldn't stand it any more, and he turned the film off with the remote.

'What's up?'

'I just wanted to watch this.' He gestured at the TV screen, where a man with a French accent and a chef's hat was trying to teach one of the Gladiators how to cut open a fish and take its guts out. It didn't look like the sort of programme Marcus usually watched, especially as he hated cooking. And fish. And he wasn't very keen on *Gladiators*, either.

'This? What do you want to watch this for?'

'We're doing cooking at school, and they said we had to watch this for homework.'

'*Au revoir,*' said the man in the chef's hat. 'See you,' said the Gladiator. They waved and the programme ended.

'So you'll be in trouble tomorrow,' said his mum. 'Why didn't you tell me you had to watch this tonight?'

'I forgot.'

'Anyway, we can watch the rest of the film now.'

'Do you really want to?'

'Yes. It's funny. Don't you think it's funny?'

'It's not very realistic, is it?'

She laughed. 'Oh, Marcus! You make me watch things where people jump from exploding helicopters on to the tops of trains, and you complain about realism.'

'Yeah, but you can see them doing it. You can actually see them doing those things. You don't know for sure he's waking up on the same day over and over again, because they can just pretend that, can't they?'

'You do talk some rot.'

This was great. He was trying to save his mum from watching a man committing suicide for hours on end, and she was calling him an idiot.

'Mum, you must know why I turned it off really?'

'No.'

He couldn't believe it. Surely she must be thinking about it all the time, like he was?

'Because of what he was trying to do.'

She looked at him.

'I'm sorry, Marcus, I'm still not with you.'

'The . . . thing.'

'Marcus, you're an articulate boy. You can do better than this.'

She was driving him mad. 'He's spent the last five minutes trying to kill himself. Like you did. I didn't want to watch it, and I didn't want you to watch it.'

'Ah.' She reached for the remote control and turned the TV off. 'I'm sorry. I was being pretty thick, wasn't I?'

'Yes.'

'I just never made the connection at all. Incredible. God.' She shook her head. 'I'm going to have to get my act together.'

Marcus was starting to lose track of his mother. Right up until recently he had always thought she was . . . not *perfect*, because they had arguments, and she didn't let him do things that he wanted to do, and so on, but he had never spent any time thinking she was stupid, or mad, or wrong. Even when they had arguments, he could see what she was on about: she was just saying the things that mothers were supposed to say. But at the moment, he wasn't getting her at all. He hadn't understood the crying, and now, when he had been expecting her to be twice as miserable as she had been before, she was completely normal. He was beginning to doubt himself. Wasn't trying to kill yourself a really big deal? Didn't you have long talks about it afterwards, and tears, and hugs? Apparently not. You just sat on the sofa and watched videos and acted as though nothing had happened.

'Shall I put the film back on?' he asked her. This was like a test. The old mum would know he didn't mean that.

'Do you mind?' she said. 'I'd like to see how it turns out.'

TWELVE

Filling days had never really been a problem for Will. He might not have been proud of his lifelong lack of achievement, but he was proud of his ability to stay afloat in the enormous ocean of time he had at his disposal; a less resourceful man, he felt, might have gone under and drowned.

The evenings were fine; he knew people. He didn't know how he knew them, because he'd never had colleagues, and he never spoke to girlfriends when they became ex-girlfriends. But he had managed to pick people up along the way – guys who once worked in record shops that he frequented, guys he played football or squash with, guys from a pub quiz team he once belonged to, that kind of thing – and they sort of did the job. They wouldn't be much use in the unlikely event of some kind of suicidal depression, or the even more unlikely event of a broken heart, but they were pretty good for a game of pool, or a drink and a curry.

No, the evenings were OK; it was the days that tested his patience and ingenuity, because all of these people were at work – unless they were on paternity leave, like John, father of Barney and Imogen, and Will didn't want to see them anyway. His way of coping with the days was to think of activities as units of time, each unit consisting of about thirty minutes. Whole hours, he found, were more intimidating, and most things one could do in a day took half an hour. Reading the paper, having a bath, tidying the flat, watching *Home and Away* and *Countdown*, doing a quick crossword on the toilet, eating breakfast and lunch, going to the local shops . . . That was nine units of a twenty-unit day (the evenings didn't count) filled by just the basic necessities. In fact, he had reached a stage where he wondered how his friends could juggle life and a job. Life took up so much time, so how could one work *and*, say, take a bath on the same day? He suspected that one or two people he knew were making some pretty unsavoury short cuts.

Occasionally, when the mood took him, he applied for jobs advertised in the media pages of the *Guardian*. He liked the media pages, because he felt he was qualified to fill most of the vacancies on offer. How hard could it be to edit the building industry's in-house journal, or run a small arts workshop, or write copy for holiday brochures? Not very hard at all, he imagined, so he doggedly wrote letters explaining to potential employers why he was the man they were looking for. He even enclosed a CV, although it only just ran on to a second page. Rather brilliantly, he thought, he had numbered these two pages 'one' and 'three', thus implying that page two, the page containing the details of his brilliant career, had got lost somewhere. The idea was that people would be so impressed by the letter, so dazzled by his extensive range of interests, that they would invite him in for an interview, where sheer force of personality would carry him through. Actually, he had never heard from anybody, although occasionally he received a standard rejection letter.

The truth was he didn't mind. He applied for these jobs in the same spirit that he had volunteered to work in the soup kitchen, and in the same spirit that he had become the father of Ned: it was all a dreamy alternative reality that didn't touch his real life, whatever that was, at all. He didn't need a job. He was OK as he was. He read quite a lot; he saw films in the afternoon; he went jogging; he cooked nice meals for himself and his friends; he went to Rome and New York and Barcelona every now and again, when boredom became particularly acute . . . He couldn't say that the need for change burned within him terribly fiercely.

In any case, this morning he was somewhat distracted by the curious events of the weekend. For some reason – possibly because he encountered real drama very rarely in the course of an average twenty-time-unit quick-crossword-on-the-toilet day – he kept being drawn back to thinking about Marcus and Fiona, and wondering how they were. He had also, in the absence of a *Media Guardian* advertisement that had really grabbed him, begun to entertain strange and probably unhealthy notions of entering their lives in some way. Maybe Fiona and Marcus needed him more than Suzie did. Maybe he could really . . . *do* something with those two. He could take an avuncular interest in them, give their lives a bit of shape and gaiety. He would bond with Marcus, take him somewhere every now and again – to Arsenal, possibly. And perhaps Fiona would like a nice dinner somewhere, or a night out at the theatre.

Mid-morning he phoned Suzie. Megan was having a nap, and she was just sitting down to a cup of coffee.

'I was wondering how things are up the road,' he said.

'Not too bad, I think. She hasn't gone back to work, but Marcus went to school today. How about you?'

'Fine, thanks.'

'You sound pretty cheerful. Did things get sorted out?'

If he sounded cheerful, then obviously they must have done. 'Oh, yes. It's all blown over now.'

'And Ned's OK?'

'Yes, he's fine. Aren't you, Ned?' Why had he done that? It was a completely unnecessary embellishment. Why couldn't he just leave well alone?

'Good.'

'Listen, do you think there's any way I could help with Marcus and Fiona? Take Marcus out or something?'

'Would you like to?'

'Of course. He seemed . . .' What? What did Marcus seem, other than slightly batty and vaguely malevolent? 'He seemed nice. We got on OK. Maybe I could, you know, build on the other day.'

'Why don't I ask Fiona?'

'Thanks. And it'd be nice to see you and Megan again soon.'

'I'm still dying to meet Ned.'

'We'll fix something up.'

So, there it was then: an enormous, happy, extended family. True, this happy family included an invisible two-year-old, a barmy twelve-year-old and his suicidal mother; but sod's law dictated that this was just the sort of family you were bound to end up with when you didn't like families in the first place.

Will bought a *Time Out* and read it from cover to cover in an attempt to find something that a twelve-year-old boy might want to do on a Saturday afternoon – or rather, something that might make it clear to Marcus that he was not dealing with your average, desperately unhip thirty-six-year-old here. He started with the children's section, but soon realized that Marcus was not a brass-rubbing sort of a child, or a puppet theatre sort of a child, or even a child at all; at twelve, his childhood was over. Will tried to remember what he liked doing at that age, but could come up with nothing, although he could remember what he hated doing. What he hated doing were things that adults made him do, however well intentioned those adults were. Maybe the coolest thing he could do for Marcus was let him run wild on Saturday – give him some money, take him to Soho and leave him there. He had to admit, though, that while this might score points on the coolometer, it didn't do quite so well on the responsible *in loco parentis* scale: if Marcus were to embark on a career as a rent-boy and his mother never saw him again, Will would end up feeling responsible and possibly even regretful.

Films? Video arcades? Ice-skating? Museums? Art galleries? Brent Cross? McDonald's? Jesus, how did anyone get through childhood without falling into a slumber lasting several years? If he were forced to relive his childhood, he would go to bed when *Blue Peter* had ceased to exert its allure and ask to be woken up when it was time to sign on. It was no wonder young people were turning to crime and drugs and prostitution. They were turning to crime and drugs and prostitution simply because they were on the menu now, an exciting, colourful and tasty new range of options that he had been denied. The real question was why his generation had been quite so apathetically, unenterprisingly law-abiding – especially given the lack of even the token sops to teens, the Australian soaps and the chicken dippers, that passed for youthful entertainment in contemporary society.

He was in the process of wondering whether the British Gas Wildlife Photographer of the Year Exhibition could possibly be any duller than it sounded, when the telephone rang.

'Hi, Will, it's Marcus.'

'Hi. Funnily enough, I was just wondering—'

'Suzie said you want to take me out for the day somewhere.'

'Yeah, well, that's just—'

'I'll come if my mum can come.'

'I'm sorry?'

'I'll come if you can take my mum too. And she hasn't got any money, so either we'll have to go somewhere cheap or you'll have to treat us.'

'Right. Hey, say what you mean, Marcus. Don't beat around the bush.'

'I don't know how else to say it. We're broke. You're not. You pay.'

'It's OK. I was joking.'

'Oh. I didn't get it.'

'No. Listen, I'm quite safe, you know. I thought it might be better just you and me.'

'Why?'

'Give your mum a break?'

'Yeah, well.'

Suddenly, belatedly, he got it. Giving Marcus's mum a break was what they had been doing last weekend; she had spent the leisure time tipping a bottle of pills down her throat and having her stomach pumped.

'I'm sorry, Marcus. I was being dim.'

'Yeah.'

'Of course your mum can come. That would be great.'

'We haven't got a car either. You'll have to bring yours.'

'Fine.'

'You can bring your little boy if you like.'

He laughed. 'Thanks.'

'That's OK,' Marcus said generously. 'It's only fair.' Sarcasm, Will was beginning to see, was a language that Marcus found peculiarly baffling, which as far as Will was concerned meant it was absolutely irresistible.

'He'll be with his mum again on Saturday.'

'Fine. Come round about half-past twelve or something. You remember where we live? Flat 2, 31 Craysfield Road, Islington, London N1 2SF.'

'England, the world, the universe.'

'Yeah,' Marcus said blankly – simple confirmation for a simpleton.

'Right. See you then.'

In the afternoon Will went out to buy a car seat in Mothercare. He had no intention of filling his whole flat with cots and potties and high chairs, but if he was going to start ferrying people around at weekends, he felt he should at least make some concession to Ned's reality.

'That's sexist, you know,' he said to the assistant smugly.

'Sorry?'

'Mothercare. What about the fathers?'

She smiled politely.

'Fathercare,' he added, just in case she was missing his point.

'You're the first person ever to say that.'

'Really?'

'No.' She laughed. He felt like Marcus.

'Anyway. How can I help you?'

'I'm looking for a car seat.'

'Yes.' They were in the car-seat section. 'What make are you looking for?'

'Dunno. Anything. The cheapest.' He laughed matily. 'What do most people get?'

'Well. Not the cheapest. They're usually worried about safety.'

'Ah. Yes.' He stopped laughing. Safety was a serious business. 'Not much point in saving a few quid if he ends up through the windscreen, is there?'

In the end – possibly to over-compensate for his previous callousness – he bought the most expensive car seat in the store, an enormous padded bright blue contraption that looked as though it might last Ned until he was a father himself.

'He'll love it,' he said to the assistant as he handed over his credit card.

'It looks nice now, but he'll mess it up soon enough with his biscuits and crisps and what have you.'

Will hadn't thought about his biscuits and crisps and what have you, so on the way home he stopped off for some chocolate-chip cookies and a couple of bags of cheese and onion, squashed everything up, and sprinkled the crumbs generously over his new purchase.

THIRTEEN

Contrary to what he told Will, Marcus wasn't really bothered about leaving his mum on her own. He knew that if she did try anything again it wouldn't be for a while, because right now she was still in this weird, calm mood. But telling Will that he wanted his mum to come with them was a way of getting her and Will together, and after that, he reckoned, it should be easy. His mum was pretty, and Will seemed quite well off, they could go and live with Will and his kid, and then there'd be four of them, and four was twice as good as two. And maybe, if they wanted to, they could have a baby. His mum wasn't too old. She was thirty-eight. You could have a baby when you were thirty-eight. So then there would be five of them, and it wouldn't matter quite so much if one of them died. Well, it would matter, of course it would matter, but at least it wouldn't leave somebody, him or his mum or Will or his little boy, completely on their own. Marcus didn't even know whether he liked Will or not, but that didn't come into it any more; he could see he wasn't bad, or a drunk, or violent, so he would have to do.

It wasn't as if he didn't know anything about Will, because he did: Marcus had checked him out. On his way back from school one afternoon he had seen Will out shopping, and he had followed him home like a private detective. He hadn't really found out much about him, apart from where he lived and what shops he went in. But he seemed to be on his own – no girlfriend, no wife, no little boy, even. Unless the little boy was with his girlfriend at home. But if he had a girlfriend, why was he trying to chat up Suzie?

'What time is this guy coming?' his mum asked. They were tidying the house and listening to *Exodus* by Bob Marley.

'In about ten minutes. You're going to get changed, aren't you?'

'Why?'

'Because you look a wreck, and he's going to take us to Planet Hollywood for lunch.' Will didn't know that last bit yet, because Marcus hadn't told him, but he wouldn't mind.

She looked at him. 'Why does it bother you what I wear?'

'Planet Hollywood.'

'What about it?'

'You don't want to look like an old bag there. In case one of them sees you.'

'In case one of who sees me?'

'Bruce Willis or one of them.'

'Marcus, they won't be there, you know.'

'They're there all the time. Unless they're working. And even then they try to make films in London so they can go for lunch.'

Fiona laughed and laughed. 'Who told you that?'

A kid at his old school called Sam Lovell had told him that. Now Marcus thought about it, Sam had told him some other things that turned out not to be true: that Michael Jackson and Janet Jackson were the same person, and that Mr Harrison the French teacher had been in the Beatles.

'It's just well known.'

'Do you still want to go there if you're not going to see any stars?'

He didn't really, but he wasn't going to let her know that.

'Yeah. Course.'

His mum shrugged and went off to get changed.

Will came into the flat before they went out. He introduced himself, which Marcus thought was pretty stupid as everyone knew who everyone else was anyway.

'Hi. I'm Will,' he said. 'We've . . . Well, I . . .' But he obviously couldn't think of a polite way of saying that he'd seen her conked out on the sofa by a pool of her own sick the week before, so he stopped and just smiled.

'I'm Fiona.' His mum looked good, Marcus thought. She was wearing her best leggings and a baggy, hairy jumper, and she was wearing make-up for the first time since the hospital, and a pair of nice dangly earrings someone had sent her from Zimbabwe. 'Thanks for all you did last weekend. I really appreciate it.'

'Pleasure. I hope you're feeling . . . I hope you've—'

'My stomach's fine. I suppose I must still be a bit barmy, though. That sort of thing doesn't clear up so quickly, does it?'

Will looked shocked, but she just laughed. Marcus hated it when she made jokes to people who didn't know her very well.

'Have you decided where you want to go, then, young Marcus?'

'Planet Hollywood.'

'Oh, God. Really?'

'Yeah. Supposed to be brilliant.'

'Is it? We obviously don't read the same restaurant reviews.'

'It wasn't a restaurant reviewer. It was Sam Lovell from my old school.'

'Oh, well, in that case . . . Shall we go?'

Will opened the door and waved at Fiona to go through. Marcus wasn't sure what to look for, but he had a feeling that this was going to work.

They didn't take the car, because Will said Planet Hollywood was in Leicester Square and they wouldn't be able to park, so they caught the bus. On the way to the bus stop Will showed them his car.

'This is mine. The one with the car seat in the back. Look at it. What a mess.'

'Gosh,' said Fiona.

'Right,' said Marcus.

They couldn't think of much else to say about it, so they walked on.

There were loads of people outside Planet Hollywood waiting to get in, and it was raining. They were the only people that spoke English in the whole queue.

'Are you sure this is where you want to go, Marcus?' his mum asked him.

'Yeah. Where else is there, anyway?' If someone came up with an even half-decent suggestion, he'd take it. He didn't want to stand around with a load of French and Italian people. It wasn't right.

'There's a Pizza Express round the corner,' said Will.

'No thanks.'

'You're always on about wanting to go out for a pizza,' said his mum.

'No, I'm not.' He was, but pizza was too cheap, he reckoned.

They went back to queuing in silence. Nobody was going to get married to anybody at this rate. It was too wet and too horrible.

'Tell me why you want to go to Planet Hollywood and I'll see if I can think of anywhere like it,' said Will.

'I don't know. Because it's famous. And it's got the sort of food I like. Fries and things.'

'So if I can think of somewhere famous that serves fries, we can go there?'

'Yeah. But it's got to be my sort of famous, not your sort of famous.'

'What does that mean?'

'It's got to be the sort of famous that kids know about. You can't just tell me it's famous, because if I've never heard of it then it's not.'

'So if I said to you, how about Twenty-Eight, you wouldn't want to go.'

'No. Not famous. Never heard of it.'

'But famous people go there.'

'Like who?'

'Actors and so on.'

'Which actors?'

'I should think they've all been there at some time or another. But they don't tell you in advance. I'll be straight with you, Marcus. We could go there now and we might bump into Tom Cruise and Nicole Kidman. Or we might see nobody at all. But they do good fries. The thing is, we'll be standing here for an hour, and then when we get in there'll be nobody there worth seeing anyway.'

'OK then.'

'Seriously?'

'Yeah.'

'Good man.'

No famous people ever went to this Twenty-Eight place. You could tell. It was nice, and the fries were good, but it was just normal; it didn't have anything on the walls, like Clint Eastwood's jacket, or the mask Michael Keaton wore in *Batman*. It didn't even have any signed photos. The Indian restaurant near their flat that delivered their takeaways wasn't famous at all, but even that had a signed picture of someone who used to play for Arsenal ages ago. He didn't mind though. The main thing was that they were sat down and dry, and Will and his mother could begin to talk.

They needed some help at first; nobody said anything until the waiter came to take their order.

'Mushroom omelette and fries, please. And a Coke,' said Marcus.

'I'll have the swordfish steak,' said Will. 'No vegetables, just a side salad.'

Fiona was having difficulty deciding.

'Why don't you have the swordfish steak?' said Marcus.

'Ummm . . .'

He tried to get his mother's attention across the table without Will noticing. He nodded hard, once, and then he coughed.

'Are you all right, sweetie?'

He just felt it would help if his mum ordered the same food as Will. He didn't know why. It wasn't like you could talk for ages about swordfish steak or anything, but maybe it would show them that they had something in common, that sometimes they thought the same way about things. Even if they didn't.

'We're vegetarian,' said Marcus. 'But we eat fish.'

'So we're not really vegetarian.'

'We don't eat fish very often though. Fish and chips sometimes. We never cook fish at home, do we?'

'Not often, no.'

'Never.'

'Oh, don't show me up.'

He didn't know how saying she never cooked fish was showing her up – did men like women who cooked fish? Why? – but that was the last thing he wanted to do.

'All right,' he said. 'Not never. Sometimes.'

'Shall I come back in a couple of minutes?' said the waiter. Marcus had forgotten he was still there.

'Ummm . . .'

'Have the swordfish,' said Marcus.

'I'll have the penne pesto,' said his mother. 'With a mixed salad.'

Will ordered a beer, and his mum ordered a glass of white wine. Nobody said anything again.

Marcus didn't have a girlfriend, nor had he ever come close to having one, unless you counted Holly Garrett, which he didn't. But he knew this: if a girl and a boy met, and they didn't have a boyfriend or a girlfriend, and they both looked all right, and they didn't mind each other, then they might as well go out together. What was the point in not? Will didn't have a girlfriend, unless you counted Suzie, which he didn't, and his mum didn't have a boyfriend, so . . . It would be good for all of them. The more he thought about it, the more obvious it seemed.

It wasn't that he needed someone to replace his dad. He'd talked about that with his mum ages ago. They'd been watching a programme on TV about the family, and some silly fat Tory woman said that everyone should have a mother and a father, and his mum got angry and later depressed. Then, before the hospital thing, he'd thought the Tory woman was stupid, and he'd told his mum as much, but at the time he hadn't worked out that two was a dangerous number. Now he had worked that out, he wasn't sure it made much difference to what he thought about the fat Tory woman's idea; he didn't care whether the family he wanted were all men, or all women, or all children. He simply wanted people.

'Don't just sit there,' he said suddenly.

Will and his mother looked at him.

'You heard me. Don't just sit there. Talk to each other.'

'I'm sure we will in a moment,' said his mother.

'Lunch will be over before you two've thought of anything to say,' Marcus grumbled.

'What do you want us to talk about?' Will asked.

'Anything. Politics. Films. Murders. I don't care.'

'I'm not sure that's how conversation happens,' said his mother.

'Maybe you should have worked it out by now. You're old enough.'

'Marcus!'

Will was laughing, though.

'He's right. We have, I don't know how old you are, Fiona, but we have at least sixty years of conversational experience between us here, and maybe we ought to be able to get something going.'

'OK then.'

'So.'

'After you.'

They both laughed, but neither of them said anything.

'Will,' said Marcus.

'Yes, Marcus,' said Will.

'What do you think of John Major?'

'Not much.'

'What about you, Mum?'

'You know what I think of him.'

'Tell Will.'

'Not much.'

This was useless.

'Why?'

'Oh, Marcus, leave us alone. You're making it more difficult, not easier. You're making us self-conscious. We'll start talking soon.'

'When?'

'Stop it.'

'Have you ever been married, Will?'

'Marcus, I'm going to get cross with you in a minute.'

'It's OK, Fiona. No, I haven't. Have you?'

'No, course not. I'm not old enough.'

'Oh.'

'Now ask Mum.'

'Fiona, have you ever been married?'

'No.'

For a moment, Marcus was confused; when he was a real kid, a little kid, he used to think that you had to be married to be a father or mother, in the same way that you had to have a driving licence to drive. He knew now that this wasn't true, and he knew too that his parents had never been married, but somehow the ideas you grew up with were hard to shake off.

'Did you want to get married, Mum?'

'Not really. It didn't seem important.'

'So why do other people bother?'

'Oh, all sorts of reasons. Security. Pressure from family. Misguided notions of romance.'

Will laughed at this. 'Cynic,' he said.

Marcus didn't understand this, but that was good: his mum and Will now had something that he hadn't started.

'Do you still see Marcus's dad?'

'Sometimes. Not very often. Marcus sees him quite a lot. How about you? Do you still see your ex?'

'Ummm . . . Well, yes. All the time. She picked Ned up this morning.' He said this in a funny way, Marcus thought. Almost like he'd forgotten and then remembered.

'And is that all right?'

'Oh, it's OK. We have our moments.'

'How come you ended up looking after Ned? I mean, I'm sure you're a brilliant dad and everything, but that's not usually how it works, is it?'

'No. She was going through a *Kramer vs Kramer* kind of thing at the time. You know, a sort of I-want-to-find-out-who-I-am malarkey.'

'And did she find out who she was?'

'Not really. I don't know if anyone really does, do they?'

The food arrived, but the two adults hardly noticed; Marcus dug happily into his omelette and fries. Would they move into Will's place, he wondered, or buy somewhere new?

FOURTEEN

Will knew that Fiona was not his type. For a start, she didn't look the way he wanted women to look – in fact, he doubted whether looks were important to her at all. He couldn't be doing with that. People, women and men, had a duty to care, he felt, even if they didn't have the requisite raw material – unless they weren't interested in the sexual side of life at all, in which case, fair enough. You could do what you wanted then. Einstein, for example . . . Will didn't know the first thing about Einstein's private life, but in his photos he looked like a guy with other things on his mind. But Fiona wasn't Einstein. She might have been as brainy as Einstein, for all he knew, but she was clearly interested in relationships, judging from the conversation they had had over lunch, so why didn't she make more of an effort? Why didn't she have a decent haircut, instead of all that frizz, and why didn't she wear clothes which looked like they mattered to her? He didn't get that at all.

And she was just too hippy. He could see now why Marcus was so weird. She believed in alternative things, like aromatherapy and vegetarianism and the environment, stuff he didn't give much of a shit about, really. If they went out they'd fight terribly, he knew, and that would upset her, and the last thing he wanted to do at the moment was upset her.

He had to say that the thing he found most attractive about her was that she had tried to kill herself. Now that was interesting – sexy, almost, in a morbid kind of way. But how can you contemplate dating a woman who might top herself at any moment? Before, he thought that going out with a mother was a heavy number; how much heavier would it be going out with a suicidal mother? But he didn't want to let it drop. He still had this sense that Fiona and Marcus could replace soup kitchens and *Media Guardian* jobs, possibly for ever. He wouldn't have to do that much, after all – the occasional swordfish steak, the odd visit to a crappy film that he might have gone to anyway. How hard could that be? It was a damn sight easier than trying to force-feed vagrants. Good works! Helping people! That was the way forward for him now. The way he saw it, he'd helped Angie by sleeping with her (although admittedly there had been a little speck of self-interest there) and now he was going to find out whether it was possible to help someone without sleeping with them. It had to be, surely? Other people had managed, Mother Teresa and Florence Nightingale and so on, although he suspected that when he entered the good-works fray his style would be somewhat different.

They had made no further arrangement after the lunch. They left the restaurant, wandered around Covent Garden, caught the tube back to north London, and he was back home in time for *Sports Report.* But he knew they'd all started something that wasn't finished.

Within a few days he'd changed his mind completely. He had no interest in good works. He had no interest in Marcus and Fiona. He would, he felt sure, break out into a cold sweat of embarrassment every time he thought of them. He would never see them again; he doubted, in fact, whether he would ever be able to go to Holloway again, just in case he bumped into them. He knew he was overreacting, but not by much. Singing! How could you have anything to do with someone who makes you sing! He knew they were both a little flaky, but . . .

It began ordinarily enough, with an invitation to supper, and though he didn't like what they had to eat – something vegetarian with chickpeas and rice and tinned tomatoes – he quite enjoyed the conversation. Fiona told him about her job as a music therapist, and Marcus told Fiona that Will earned millions of pounds a minute because his dad had written a song. Will helped with the washing up, and Fiona made them a cup of tea, and then she sat down at the piano and started to play.

She wasn't bad. The piano playing was better than her voice, but her voice wasn't awful, simply adequate, if a little thin, and she could certainly carry a tune. No, it wasn't the quality that embarrassed him, it was the sincerity. He'd been with people who had picked up guitars and sat down at pianos before (although not for a very long time), but they had always sent themselves up in some way: they had chosen stupid songs to play, or sung them in a stupid way, or camped them up or done anything to show they didn't mean it.

Fiona meant it. She meant 'Knocking On Heaven's Door', and then she meant 'Fire And Rain', and then she meant 'Both Sides Now'. There was nothing between her and the songs; she was inside them. She even closed her eyes when she was singing.

'Do you want to come over here so you can see the words?' she asked him after 'Both Sides Now'. He'd been sitting at the dining table staring hard at Marcus, until Marcus started singing too, at which point he turned his attention to the wall.

'Ummm . . . What's next?'

'Any requests?'

He wanted her to play something that she couldn't close her eyes to, 'Roll Out The Barrel,' say, or 'Knees Up, Mother Brown', but the mood had already been set.

'Anything.'

She chose 'Killing Me Softly With His Song'. There was nothing he could do but stand next to her and let the odd half-syllable of lyric crawl choking out of his mouth. 'Smile . . . While . . . Boy . . . Ling . . .' He knew, of course he knew, that the song couldn't last for ever, that the evening couldn't last for ever, that he would soon be home tucked up in bed, that singing round the piano with a depressive hippy and her weirdo son wouldn't kill him. He knew all that, but he didn't *feel* it. He couldn't do anything with these people after all, he could see that now. He'd been stupid to think there was anything here for him.

When he got home he put a Pet Shop Boys CD on, and watched *Prisoner: Cell Block H* with the sound down. He wanted to hear people who didn't mean it, and he wanted to watch people he could laugh at. He got drunk, too; he filled a glass with ice and poured himself Scotch after Scotch. And as the drink began to take hold, he realized that people who meant it were much more likely to kill themselves than people who didn't: he couldn't recall having even the faintest urge to take his own life, and he found it hard to imagine that he ever would. When it came down to it, he just wasn't that engaged. You had to be engaged to be a vegetarian; you had to be engaged to sing 'Both Sides Now' with your eyes closed; when it came down to it, you had to be engaged to be a mother. He wasn't much bothered either way about anything, and that, he knew, would guarantee him a long and depression-free life. He'd made a big mistake thinking that good works were a way forward for him. They weren't. They drove you mad. Fiona did good works and they had driven her mad: she was vulnerable, messed-up, inadequate. Will had a system going here that was going to whizz him effortlessly to the grave. He didn't want to fuck it up now.

*

Fiona called him once more, soon after the excruciating supper; she left a message on the machine, and he didn't answer it. Suzie called him too, and though he wanted to see her, he suspected she was ringing on Fiona's behalf, so he was vague and non-committal. It looked to him like he'd taken the single-mum thing as far as it would go, and he was preparing for a return to the life he had been living before he met Angie. Maybe it was for the best.

He went record shopping, he went clothes shopping, he played a bit of tennis, he went to the pub, he watched telly, he went to see films and bands with friends. Time units were filled effortlessly. He had even gone back to reading books in the afternoon; he was halfway through a James Ellroy thriller one Thursday, in that horrible dead dark time between *Countdown* and the news, when the doorbell went.

He was expecting to see someone selling J-cloths and brushes, so he found himself looking at nothing when he opened the door, because his visitor was a good foot shorter than the average hawker.

'I've come to see you,' said Marcus.

'Oh. Right. Come in.' He said it warmly enough, as far as he could tell, but for some reason he felt a rising tide of panic.

Marcus marched into the sitting room, sat down on the sofa and stared intently at everything.

'You haven't got a kid, have you?'

That was certainly one explanation for the panic.

'Well,' said Will, as if he were about to launch into a very long and involved story, the details of which were currently eluding him.

Marcus got up and walked around the flat.

'Where's your loo? I'm dying for a pee.'

'Just down the hall there.'

While Marcus was gone, Will tried to think of a story that would account for the complete absence of anything Ned-related, but there was nothing. He could either tell Marcus that *of course* he had a child, and that the lack of both child and child-related paraphernalia was simply . . . simply something he would think of later; or he could dissolve into tears and own up to being a pathetic fantasist. He decided against the latter version.

'You've only got one bedroom,' said Marcus when he got back.

'Have you been nosing around?'

'Yeah. You've got one bedroom, you've got no children's toys in the bathroom, there are no toys in here . . . You haven't even got any photos of him.'

'What business is it of yours?'

'None. Apart from you've been lying to me and my mum and my mum's friend.'

'Who told you where I lived?'

'I followed you home once.'

'Where from?'

'I saw you out wandering around and I followed you.'

This was plausible. He was often out wandering around and, in any case, he hadn't told Suzie or Fiona or the SPAT woman where he lived, so there was no other explanation.

'Why?'

'Dunno. Something to do.'

'Why don't you just go home, Marcus?'

'All right. But I'm going to tell my mum.'

'Ooooh. I'm scared.'

Will could feel himself tumbling down a hill towards the kind of panicky guilt he hadn't felt since schooldays, and it seemed natural to resort to the kind of phrases he used then. There was no explanation he could give Marcus, other than the truth – that he had invented a child so he could meet women – and the truth sounded much seedier than it was ever intended to be.

'Go on then, off you go.'

'I'll do you a deal. I won't say anything to my mum if you go out with her.'

'Why do you want your mum to go out with someone like me?'

'I don't think you're too bad. I mean, you told lies, but apart from that you seem OK. And she's sad, and I think she'd like a boyfriend.'

'Marcus, I can't go out with someone just because you want me to. I'd have to like the person as well.'

'What's wrong with her?'

'Nothing's wrong with her, but—'

'You want to go out with Suzie, don't you?'

'I don't want to talk about this with you.'

'I thought so.'

'I didn't say anything. All I said was . . . Listen, I really don't want to talk about this with you. Go home.'

'OK. But I'll be back.' And off he went.

When Will had conceived this fantasy and joined SPAT, he had imagined sweet little children, not children who would be able to track him down and come to his house. He had imagined entering their world, but he hadn't foreseen that they might be able to penetrate his. He was one of life's visitors; he didn't want to be visited.

FIFTEEN

Marcus wasn't daft. Well, OK, he was daft sometimes, like with the singing, but he wasn't stupid-daft, just brush-daft. He could see instantly that the things he knew about Will, the stuff about him not having a kid and not having an ex, were too good to give up all at once; they were worth something. If he'd gone straight home after his first visit to Will's flat and told his mum and Suzie everything immediately, then that would have been the end of it. They would have stopped him from talking to Will, and he didn't want that.

He wasn't sure why he didn't want that. He just knew that he didn't want to spend this information straight away, in the same way that he didn't want to spend birthday money straight away: he wanted to leave it in his pocket while he looked around, to work out what it was worth. He knew he couldn't make Will go out with his mum if he wasn't bothered, but he could make him do something else, maybe, something he hadn't even thought of yet, so he started going round to Will's house more or less every day after school to get some ideas.

The first time he went back, Will wasn't too pleased to see him. He just stood in the doorway with his hand on the latch.

'What?' said Will.

'Nothing. Thought I'd pop round.' That made Will smile, although Marcus couldn't see why. 'What are you doing?'

'What am I doing?'

'Yeah.'

'Watching TV.'

'What are you watching?'

'*Countdown.*'

'What's that?' Marcus knew what it was. Every kid who had ever come home from school knew what it was: it was the most boring programme in the history of television.

'A quiz show. Words and numbers.'

'Oh. Would I like it?' Of course he wouldn't like it. Nobody liked it, apart from his dad's girlfriend's mum.

'I'm not sure I care.'

'I could watch it with you, if you want.'

'That's very nice of you, Marcus, but I usually manage on my own.'

'I'm good at anagrams. And maths. I'd be really helpful, if you were serious about doing well.'

'So you do know what *Countdown* is.'

'Yes. I remember now. I really like it. I'll go when it's finished.'

Will looked at him and shook his head. 'Oh, hell. Come in.'

Marcus was almost in anyway. He sat down on Will's long cream sofa, kicked his shoes off and stretched himself out. It was as useless as he remembered, *Countdown*, but he didn't complain or ask to watch another channel. (Will had cable, Marcus noted for future reference.) He just sat there patiently. Will didn't do anything while the programme was on: he didn't shout the answers at the screen, or tut when somebody got something wrong. He just smoked.

'You need a pen and paper to do it properly,' Marcus observed at the end.

'Yeah, well.'

'Do you ever do that?'

'Sometimes.'

'Why didn't you today?'

'I don't know. Jesus.'

'You could have done. I wouldn't have minded.'

'That's very big of you.'

He turned the TV off with the remote and they sat in silence.

'What do you want, Marcus? Haven't you got any homework to do?'

'Yeah. Do you want to help me?'

'That wasn't what I meant. I meant, why don't you go home and do it?'

'I'll do it after supper. You shouldn't smoke, you know.'

'No, I know. Thank you for telling me. What time does your mum get home?'

'About now.'

'So?'

Marcus ignored him and started poking around the flat. Last time he'd only noticed that there was no Ned, and he'd missed a lot of things: the flash hi-fi, the hundreds of CDs and thousands of records and tapes, the black and white photos of people playing saxophones and the film posters on the wall, the wooden floors, the rug. It was small, which surprised Marcus. If Will earned what Marcus thought he earned, then he could afford something a lot bigger than this. It was cool, though. If Marcus had a flat of his own, he'd make it look just like this, although he'd probably choose different film posters. Will had posters of old films he'd never heard of – *Double Indemnity, The Big Sleep*. Marcus would have *Honey, I Shrunk the Kids*, definitely, and *Free Willy* and . . . he wouldn't have *Hellhound 3* or *Boilerhead*, though. Not now. The Dead Duck Day had really put him off things like that.

'Nice flat.'

'Thank you.'

'Quite small, though.'

'It's big enough for me.'

'But you could get something bigger if you wanted to.'

'I'm happy with this one.'

'You've got a lot of CDs. More than anyone I've met.' Marcus went over to look at them, but he didn't really know what he was looking for. 'Iggy Pop,' he said, and laughed at the funny name, but Will just looked at him.

'Who are those people on the wall? The ones with the saxophones and the trumpets?'

'Saxophonists and trumpeters.'

'But who are they? And why are they on your wall?'

'That's Charlie Parker, and that's Chet Baker. And they're on my wall because I like their music and they're cool.'

'Why are they cool?'

Will sighed. 'I don't know. Because they took drugs and died, probably.'

Marcus looked at him to see if he was joking, but he didn't seem to be. Marcus wouldn't want pictures on his walls of people who took drugs and died. He'd want to forget all about that kind of thing, not look at it every day of his life.

'Do you want anything? A cup of tea or a Coke or something?'

'Yeah, OK.'

Marcus followed him into the kitchen. It wasn't like their kitchen at home. It was much smaller and whiter, and it had loads more gadgets, all of which looked as though they had never been used. At home, they had a liquidizer and a microwave, both of which were covered in stains that had gradually become black.

'What's this?'
'Espresso machine.'
'And this?'
'Ice-cream maker. What do you want?'
'I'll have some ice-cream, if you're making it.'
'I'm not. It takes hours.'
'Might as well buy it from the shop, then.'
'Coke?'
'Yeah.'
Will handed him a can and he snapped it open.
'Do you watch telly all day then?'
'No, of course not.'
'So what else do you do?'
'Read. Shop. See friends.'
'Nice life. Did you go to school when you were a kid?'
'Yeah, course.'
'Why? I mean, you didn't really need to, did you?'
'How d'you work that out? What do you think school's for?'
'Getting a job.'
'What about reading and writing?'
'I could do that years ago, and I'm still going to school. Because I've got to get a job. You could have left school when you were about six or seven. Saved yourself all the hassle. You don't really need to do history to go shopping or read, do you?'
'Depends if you want to read about history.'
'Is that what you read about?'
'Not often, no.'
'OK, so why did you go to school?'
'Shut up, Marcus.'
'If I knew I wasn't going to get a job, I wouldn't bother.'
'Don't you like it?' Will was making himself a cup of tea. When he'd put the milk in they went back into the living room and sat down on the sofa.
'No. I hate it.'
'Why?'
'It doesn't suit me. I'm not a school sort of person. I'm the wrong personality type.' His mum had told him about personality types a while ago, just after they had moved. They were both introverts, she said, which

made a lot of things – making new friends, starting at new schools and new places of work – more difficult for them. She'd said it as if it would make him feel better, but of course it hadn't helped at all, and he couldn't understand how on earth she thought it might: as far as he could see, being an introvert just meant that it wasn't even worth trying.

'Do people give you a hard time?'

Marcus looked at him. How did he know that? Things must be worse than he thought, if people knew even before he had said anything.

'Not really. Just a couple of kids.'

'What do they give you a hard time about?'

'Nothing really. Just, you know, my hair and glasses. And singing and stuff.'

'What about singing?'

'Oh, just . . . sometimes I sing without noticing.'

Will laughed.

'It's not funny.'

'I'm sorry.'

'I can't help it.'

'You could do something about the hair.'

'Like what?'

'Get it cut.'

'Like who?'

'Like who! Like how you want it.'

'This is how I want it.'

'You'll have to put up with the other kids, then. Why do you want your hair like that?'

''Cos that's how it grows, and I hate going to the hairdresser.'

'I can see that. How often do you go?'

'Never. My mum cuts it.'

'Your mum? Jesus. How old are you? Twelve? I would have thought you're old enough to get your own hair cut.'

Marcus was interested in that 'old enough'. It wasn't something he was told very often. 'D'you think?'

'Course. Twelve? You could get married in four years' time. Are you going to get your mum to cut your hair then?'

Marcus didn't think he'd be getting married in four years' time, but he could see what Will was telling him.

'She wouldn't like it, would she?' he said.

'Who?'

'My wife. If I had a wife, but I don't think I will. Not in four years.'

'I wasn't really thinking of that. I was thinking that you might feel a bit of a wally if your mum had to come round and do everything like that. Cut your hair and cut your toenails and scrub your back—'

'Oh, right. Yeah, I see what you mean.'

And yes, he saw what Will meant, and yes, Will was right. In those circumstances he would feel like a wally. But there was another way of looking at it: if his mum was coming round in four years' time to cut his hair, then that would mean nothing terrible had happened in the meantime. The way he was feeling at the moment, he'd settle for looking like a bit of a wally once every couple of months.

Marcus visited Will a lot that autumn, and by about the third or fourth time he felt that Will was getting used to him. They had a bit of an argument the second time – Will didn't want to let him in again, and Marcus had to insist, but eventually they reached a stage where Marcus would ring the bell and Will would open the door without even bothering to check who it was; he'd just wander back into the living room and expect Marcus to follow him. A couple of times he was out, but Marcus didn't know whether he went out deliberately, and he didn't want to know, either, so he didn't ask him.

They didn't talk about much at first, but eventually, when the visits became routine, Will seemed to think they should have proper conversations. He wasn't very good at them, though. The first time it happened they were talking about this fat bloke who kept winning on *Countdown*, when Will said, 'How's it going at home?', for no reason at all that Marcus could see.

'You mean my mum?'

'I suppose.'

It was so obvious that Will would rather talk about the fat bloke on *Countdown* than about what had happened before that for a moment Marcus felt a little stab of temper because he didn't have the same kind of choice. If it was up to him he'd spend all his time thinking about the fat bloke on *Countdown*, but he couldn't because there were too many other things to think about. He wasn't annoyed for long, though. It wasn't Will's fault and at least he was trying, even though it was difficult for him.

'She's all right, thanks,' Marcus said, in a way that suggested she was always all right.

'No, you know—'

'Yeah, I know. No, nothing like that.'

'Does it still bother you?'

He'd never talked about it since the night it happened, and even then he'd never said what he felt. What he felt, all the time, every single day, was a horrible fear. In fact, the main reason he came round to Will's after school was that he was able to put off going back to the flat; he could no longer climb the stairs at home without looking at his feet and remembering the Dead Duck Day. By the time he got to the bit where he had to put his key in the lock, his heart was thumping in his chest and his arms and his legs, and when he saw his mum watching the news or cooking or preparing work on the dining table, it was all he could do not to cry, or be sick, or something.

'A bit. When I think about it.'

'How often do you think about it?'

'I dunno.' All the time, all the time, all the time. Could he say that to Will? He didn't know. He couldn't say it to his mum, he couldn't say it to his dad, he couldn't say it to Suzie; they'd all make too much of a fuss. His mum would get upset, Suzie would want to talk about it, his dad would want him to move back to Cambridge . . . he didn't need that. So why tell anyone anything? What was the point? All he wanted was a promise from someone, anyone, that it wouldn't happen again, ever, and no one could do that.

'Fucking hell,' said Will. 'Sorry, I shouldn't say that in front of you, should I?'

'It's OK. People say it at school all the time.'

And that was it. That was all Will said. 'Fucking hell.' Marcus didn't know why Will had sworn like that, but Marcus liked it; it made him feel better. It was serious, it wasn't too much and it made him see that he wasn't being pathetic to get so scared.

'You might as well stay for *Neighbours* now,' Will said. 'Otherwise you'll miss the beginning.' Marcus never watched *Neighbours*, and didn't know how Will had got the idea that he did, but he stayed anyway. He felt he should. They watched in silence, and when the theme music started up, Marcus said thank you politely and went home.

SIXTEEN

Will found himself working Marcus's visits into the fabric of his day. This wasn't difficult to do, since the fabric of his day was tatty, and filled with any number of large and accommodating holes, but even so, he could have filled them with other, easier things, like more shopping, or more afternoon cinema visits; nobody could argue that Marcus was the equivalent of a crap Steve Martin film and a sackful of liquorice allsorts. It wasn't that he behaved badly when he came round, because he didn't, and it wasn't that he was hard to talk to, because he wasn't. Marcus was difficult simply because he frequently gave the impression that he was merely stopping off on this planet on his way to somewhere else, somewhere he might fit in better. Periods of blankness, when he seemed to disappear into his own head completely, were followed by periods when he seemed to be trying to compensate for these absences, and would ask question after question.

Once or twice Will decided he couldn't face it and went shopping or to the cinema; but most of the time he was in at four-fifteen, waiting for the buzzer – sometimes because he couldn't be bothered to go out, sometimes because he felt he owed Marcus something. What and why he owed him he didn't know, but he could see he was serving some purpose in the kid's life at the moment, and as he served no purpose in anybody else's he was hardly going to die of compassion fatigue. It was still a bit of a drag, though, having some kid inflict himself on you every afternoon. Will would be relieved when Marcus found a purpose to life somewhere else.

On the third or fourth visit he asked Marcus about Fiona, and ended up wishing he hadn't, because it was quite clear that the boy was messed up about it. Will couldn't blame him, but couldn't think of anything to say that would be of even the smallest consolation or value, so he ended up simply swearing sympathetically and, given Marcus's age, inappropriately. Will wouldn't make that mistake again. If Marcus wanted to talk about his suicidal mother, he could do it with Suzie, or a counsellor, or someone like that, someone capable of something more than an obscenity.

The thing was, Will had spent his whole life avoiding real stuff. He was, after all, the son and heir of the man who wrote 'Santa's Super Sleigh'. Santa Claus, whose existence most adults had real cause to doubt, bought him everything he wore and ate and drank and sat on and lived in; it could reasonably be argued that reality was not in his genes. He liked watching real stuff on *EastEnders* and *The Bill*, and he liked listening to Joe Strummer and Curtis Mayfield and Kurt Cobain singing about real stuff, but he'd never had real stuff sitting on his sofa before. No wonder, then, that once he'd made it a cup of tea and offered it a biscuit he didn't really know what to do with it.

Sometimes they managed conversations about Marcus's life that skirted round the twin disasters of school and home.

'My dad's stopped drinking coffee,' Marcus suddenly said one evening after Will had complained of caffeine poisoning (an occupational hazard, he supposed, of those with no occupation).

Will had never really thought about Marcus's father. Marcus seemed so much a product of his mother that the idea of a father seemed almost incongruous.

'What does he do, your dad?'

'He works for Cambridge Social Services.'

That figured, Will thought. All of these people came from another country, a country full of things that Will knew nothing about and had no use for, like music therapists and housing officers and health-food shops with noticeboards and aromatherapy oils and brightly coloured sweaters and difficult European novels and feelings. Marcus was the fruit of their loins.

'What does he do for them?'

'I dunno. He doesn't get much money, though.'

'Do you see him often?'

'Quite often. Some weekends. Half-terms. He's got a girlfriend called Lindsey. She's nice.'

'Oh.'

'Do you want me to say more about him?' Marcus asked helpfully. 'I will if you want.'

'Do you want to say more about him?'

'Yeah. We don't talk about him at home much.'

'What do you want to say?'

'I dunno. I could tell you what car he's got, and whether he smokes.'

'OK, does he smoke?' Will was no longer thrown by Marcus's somewhat eccentric conversational patterns.

'No. Given up,' Marcus said triumphantly, as if he had lured Will into a trap.

'Ah.'

'It was hard, though.'

'I'll bet. Do you miss your dad?'

'How do you mean?'

'Well, you know. Do you . . . I don't know . . . do you miss him? You understand what that means.'

'I see him. How can I miss him?'

'Do you wish you saw him more than you do?'

'No.'

'Oh. That's all right, then.'

'Can I have another Coke?'

Will didn't understand at first why Marcus had introduced the subject of his father, but clearly there was a value in talking about something that didn't remind Marcus of the awful messes that surrounded him. The triumph over nicotine addiction wasn't Marcus's triumph, exactly, but in a life that was at the moment decidedly triumph-free it was the closest he had come for a while.

Will could see how sad this was, but he could also see that it wasn't his problem. No problem was his problem. Very few people were in a position to say they had no problems, but then, that wasn't his problem either. Will didn't see this as a source of shame, but as a cause for wild and raucous celebration; to reach the age he had without encountering any serious difficulties seemed to him a record worth preserving, and though he didn't mind giving Marcus the odd can of Coke, he wasn't about to embroil himself in the sorry dog's dinner that was Marcus's life. Why would he want to do that?

The following week Will's date with *Countdown* was interrupted by a hail of what sounded like gravel against his sitting-room window, followed quickly by a continuous, urgent-sounding and annoying ring on the doorbell. Will knew it was trouble – you didn't get gravel smashing into your windows and frantic doorbell-ringing without trouble, he imagined – and his first instinct was to turn the volume on the TV up and ignore it all. But in the end some sense of self-respect drove the cowardice away, and he propelled himself off the sofa towards the front door.

Marcus was standing on the step being bombarded with some kind of confectionery, rock-shaped and rock-hard lumps that could easily do as much damage as rocks. Will knew this because he took several direct hits himself. He ushered Marcus in and managed to locate the bombardiers, two mean-looking French-cropped teenage boys.

'What do you think you're doing?'

'Who are you?'

'Never mind who I am. Who the fuck are you?' Will couldn't remember the last time he felt like thumping someone, but he felt like thumping these two. 'Fuck off.'

'Ooo-er,' said one of them obscurely. Will presumed it was intended to indicate their lack of fear, but their bravado was somewhat undercut by their immediate and rapid disappearance. This was a surprise and a relief. Will would never have run away from Will in a million years (or rather, in the admittedly unlikely event that Will should meet himself down a dark alley, both Wills would have run away at equal and very fast speeds in opposite directions). But he was an adult now, and though it was of course true that teenagers had lost all respect, bring back National Service and so on and so forth, only the very bad or very armed were likely to risk a confrontation with someone bigger and older than them. Will went back into the flat feeling bigger and older, and not altogether displeased with himself.

Marcus had helped himself to a biscuit, and was sat on the sofa watching TV. He looked just as he normally looked, absorbed in the programme, the biscuit poised halfway to the mouth; there was no visible sign of distress at all. If this boy, the one on the sofa watching *Countdown*, had ever been bullied, it was ages ago, and he had long since forgotten all about it.

'Who were they, then?'

'Who?'

'Who? Those kids who were just trying to embed sweets into your skull.'

'Oh, them,' said Marcus, his eyes still on the screen. 'I don't know their names. They're in year nine.'

'And you don't know their names?'

'No. They just started following me home after school. So I thought I'd better not go home, so they wouldn't find out where I lived. I thought I'd come round here.'

'Thanks a lot.'
'They won't chuck sweets at you. They were after me.'
'And does this happen often?'
'They've never chucked sweets before. They thought of that today. Just now.'
'I'm not talking about the sweets. I'm talking about . . . older kids trying to kill you.'
Marcus looked at him.
'Yeah. I told you before.'
'You didn't make it sound so dramatic before.'
'What do you mean?'
'You said a couple of kids gave you a hard time. You didn't say that people you don't even know follow you around and chuck things at you.'
'They hadn't done it then,' said Marcus patiently. 'They've only just invented it.'
Will was beginning to lose his temper; if he'd had any sweets to hand he would have started flinging them at Marcus himself. 'Marcus, for Christ's sake, I'm not talking about the bloody sweets. Are you always this bloody literal-minded? I understand that they've never done that before. But they've been giving you a hard time for ages.'
'Oh yeah. Not those two . . .'
'No, OK, OK, not those two. But others like them.'
'Yeah. Loads.'
'Right. That's all I've been trying to find out.'
'You could have just asked.'
Will walked into the kitchen and put the kettle on, if only to give himself something to do which wouldn't result in a prison sentence, but he couldn't let it drop.
'So what are you going to do about it?'
'How do you mean?'
'Are you going to let it go on like this for the next however many years?'
'You're like the teachers at school.'
'What do they say?'
'Oh, you know. "Keep out of their way." I mean, I don't try to get in their way.'
'But it must make you unhappy.'
'I s'pose so. I just don't think about it. Like when I broke my wrist falling off that climbing-frame thing.'

'You've lost me.'

'I tried not to think about that. It happened and I wished it hadn't, but it's just life, isn't it?'

Sometimes Marcus sounded as though he were a hundred years old, and it broke Will's heart.

'It doesn't have to be life, though, does it?'

'I dunno. You tell me. I haven't done anything. I just started at a new school and then I got all this. I don't know why.'

'What about your old school?'

'It was different there. Not every kid was the same. There were clever ones and thick ones and trendy ones and weird ones. I didn't feel different there. Here I feel different.'

'They can't be different sorts of kids here. Kids are kids.'

'So where are all the weird ones, then?'

'Maybe they start off weird, and then they get their act together. They're still weird but you just can't see them. The trouble is, these kids can see you. You make yourself obvious.'

'So I've got to make myself invisible?' Marcus snorted at the magnitude of the task. 'How do I do that? Is one of the machines in your kitchen an invisible machine?'

'You don't have to make yourself invisible. You just have to go in disguise.'

'What, with a moustache and stuff?'

'Yeah, right, with a moustache. Nobody would notice a twelve-year-old boy with a moustache, would they?'

Marcus looked at him. 'You're joking. Everyone would notice. I'd be the only one in the whole school.'

Will had forgotten about the sarcasm thing. 'OK, no moustache, then. Bad idea. But how about if you wore the same clothes and haircut and glasses as everyone else? You can be as weird as you want on the inside. Just do something about the outside.'

They started with his feet. Marcus wore the kind of shoes that Will didn't think they made any more, plain black slip-ons whose only discernible ambition was to get their owner up and down school corridors without attracting the attention of the deputy head.

'Do you like those shoes?' Will asked him. They were walking up Holloway Road to look at trainers. Marcus peered down at his feet through the early-evening gloom and promptly collided with a large woman carrying several overstuffed Lo-Cost bags.

'How do you mean?'

'I mean, do you like them?'

'They're my school shoes. I'm not supposed to like them.'

'You can like everything you wear, if you can be bothered.'

'Do you like everything you wear?'

'I don't wear anything I hate.'

'What do you do with the stuff you hate, then?'

'I don't buy it, do I?'

'Yeah, because you haven't got a mum. Sorry to say it like that, but you haven't.'

'It's OK. I've got used to the idea.'

The trainer shop was huge and crowded, and the lighting made all the customers look ill; everyone had a green tinge, regardless of their original colour. Will caught sight of the pair of them in a mirror, and was shocked to see that they could easily pass for father and son; he had somehow imagined himself as Marcus's elder brother, but the reflection threw age and youth into sharp relief – Will's stubble and crow's feet versus Marcus's smooth cheeks and gleaming white teeth. And the hair . . . Will prided himself on having avoided even the tiniest of bald patches, but he still had less on top than Marcus, almost as if life had worn some of it away.

'What do you fancy?'

'I don't know.'

'It's got to be Adidas, I think.'

'Why?'

'Because that's what everyone wears.'

The shoes were displayed according to manufacturer, and the Adidas section of the shop was attracting more than its fair share of shoppers.

'Sheep,' said Marcus as they were approaching. 'Baaaa.'

'Where did you get that from?'

'That's what my mum says when she thinks people haven't got a mind of their own.'

Will suddenly remembered that a boy at his old school had had a mum like Fiona – not exactly like her, because it seemed to Will that Fiona was a peculiarly contemporary creation, with her seventies albums, her eighties politics and her nineties foot lotion, but certainly a sixties equivalent of Fiona. Stephen Fullick's mother had a thing about TV, that it turned people into androids, so they didn't have a set in the house. 'Did you see *Thund . . .*' Will would say every Monday morning and then remember and blush, as if the TV were a parent who had just died. And what good had that done Stephen Fullick? He was not, as far as Will was aware, a visionary poet, or a primitive painter; he was probably stuck in some provincial solicitor's office, like everyone else from school. He had endured years of pity for no discernible purpose.

'The whole idea of this expedition, Marcus, is that you learn to become a sheep.'

'Is it?'

'Of course. You don't want anyone to notice you. You don't want to look different. Baaaa.'

Will picked out a pair of Adidas basketball boots that looked cool but relatively unshowy.

'What do you think of them?'

'They're sixty pounds.'

'Never mind how much they cost. What do you think of them?'

'Yeah, good.'

Will grabbed an assistant and asked him to bring the right size, and Marcus stomped up and down for a while. He looked at himself in the mirror and tried to repress a smile.

'You think you look cool, don't you?' said Will.

'Yeah. Except . . . except now the rest of me looks all wrong.'

'So next time we'll make the rest of you look OK.'

Marcus went straight home afterwards, his boots stuffed into his school bag; Will walked back beaming at his own munificence. So this was what people meant by a natural high! He couldn't recall having felt like this before, so at peace with himself, so convinced of his own self-worth. And, unbelievably, it had only cost him sixty quid! How much would he have had to pay for an equivalent unnatural high? (Probably about twenty-five quid, thinking about it, but unnatural highs were indisputably inferior.) He had made an unhappy boy temporarily happy, and there hadn't been anything in it for him at all. He didn't even want to sleep with the boy's mother.

The following day Marcus turned up at Will's door, tearful, a pair of soggy black socks where his Adidas basketball boots should have been; they'd stolen them, of course.

SEVENTEEN

Marcus would have told his mum where the trainers had come from, if she'd asked, but she didn't because she didn't even notice he was wearing them. OK, his mum wasn't the most observant person in the world, but the trainers seemed so big and white and peculiar and attention-seeking that Marcus felt as though he wasn't wearing shoes at all, but something alive – a pair of rabbits, maybe.

But she noticed they had gone. Typical. She didn't notice the rabbits, which you never see on feet, but she spotted the socks, which were only where they should be.

'Where are your shoes?' she shrieked when he came home. (Will had given him a lift, but it was November, and wet, and during the short walk across the pavement and up the stairs to the front door of the flats he had soaked his socks through again.) He looked at his feet, and for a moment he didn't say anything: he toyed with the idea of acting all surprised and telling her he didn't know, but he quickly realized she wouldn't believe him.

'Stolen,' he said eventually.

'Stolen? Why would anyone steal your shoes?'

'Because . . .' He was going to have to tell the truth, but the problem was that the truth would lead to a whole lot more questions. 'Because they were nice ones.'

'They were just ordinary black slip-on shoes.'

'No, they weren't. They were new Adidas trainers.'

'Where did you get new Adidas trainers from?'

'Will bought them for me.'

'Will who? Will the guy who took us out to lunch?'

'Yeah, Will. The bloke from SPAT. He's sort of become my friend.'

'He's sort of become your friend?'

Marcus was right. She had loads more questions, except the way she asked them was a bit boring: she just repeated the last thing he said, stuck a question mark on the end of it and shouted.

'I go round his flat after school.'

'YOU GO ROUND HIS FLAT AFTER SCHOOL?'

Or:

'Well, you see, he doesn't really have a kid.'

'HE DOESN'T REALLY HAVE A KID?'

And so on. Anyway, at the end of the question session he was in a lot of trouble, although probably not as much trouble as Will.

Marcus put his old shoes back on, and then he and his mother went straight back to Will's flat. Fiona started raging at Will the moment they had been invited in and, at the beginning, when she was having a go at him about SPAT and his imaginary son he looked embarrassed and apologetic – he had no answers to any of her questions, so he stood there staring at the floor. But as it went on he started to get angry too.

'OK,' Fiona was saying. 'Now what the hell are these little after-school tea parties about?'

'I'm sorry?'

'Why would a grown man want to hang out with a twelve-year-old boy day after day?'

Will looked at her. 'Are you suggesting what I think you're suggesting?'

'I'm not suggesting anything.'

'I don't think that's true, is it? You're suggesting that I've been . . . fiddling with your son.'

Marcus looked at Fiona. Was that really what she was on about? Fiddling?

'I'm simply asking why you entertain twelve-year-olds in your flat.'

Will lost his temper. He went red in the face and started shouting very loud. 'I don't have any fucking choice, do I? Your son comes round fucking uninvited every night. Sometimes he's pursued by gangs of savages. I could leave him outside to take his chances, but I've been letting him in for his own safety. I won't fucking bother next time. Sod the pair of you. Now, if you've finished, you can piss off.'

'I haven't finished yet, actually. Why did you buy him a pair of expensive trainers?'

'Because . . . because look at him.' They looked at him. Marcus even looked at himself.

'What's wrong with him?'

Will looked at her. 'You haven't got a clue, have you? You really haven't got a clue.'

'About what?'

'Marcus is being eaten alive at school, you know. They take him to pieces every single fucking day of the week, and you're worried about where his trainers come from and whether I'm molesting him.'

Marcus suddenly felt exhausted. He hadn't properly realized how bad things were until Will started shouting, but it was true, he really was being taken to pieces every single fucking day of the week. Up until now he hadn't linked the days of the week in that way: each day was a bad day, but he survived by kidding himself that each day was somehow unconnected to the day before. Now he could see how stupid that was, and how shit everything was, and he wanted to go to bed and not get up until the weekend.

'Marcus is doing fine,' his mother said. At first he didn't believe she'd said it, and then, when he'd had a chance to listen to the words ringing in his ears, he tried to find a different meaning for them. Maybe there was another Marcus? Maybe there was something else he was doing fine at, something he'd forgotten about? But of course there was no other Marcus, and he wasn't doing fine at anything; his mum was just being blind and stupid and nuts.

'You're kidding,' said Will.

'I know he's taking some time to settle at his new school, but—'

Will laughed. 'Yeah. Give him a couple of weeks and he'll be OK, eh? Once they've stopped stealing his shoes and following him home from school everything'll be great.'

That was wrong. They were all mad. 'I don't think so,' said Marcus. 'It's going to take longer than a couple of weeks.'

'It's OK, I know,' said Will. 'I was joking.'

Marcus didn't think it was the sort of conversation that jokes fitted into, but at least it meant that someone understood what was going on. How come it was Will, though, whom he'd known for two minutes, and not his mum, whom he'd known for, well, all his life?

'I think you're being a bit melodramatic,' said Fiona. 'Maybe you haven't had very much contact with kids before.'

Marcus didn't know what the 'melo' bit of 'melodramatic' meant, but it made Will even angrier.

'I used to be a fucking kid,' said Will. He was swearing a lot now. 'And I used to go to a fucking school. I know the difference between kids who can't settle down and kids who are just plain miserable, so don't give me any shit about being melodramatic. I'm supposed to take this from someone who—'

'Ow!' Marcus shouted. 'Cowabunga!'

They both stared at him and he stared back. He had no way of explaining his outburst; he had made the first two noises he could think of, because he could see that Will was going to bring up the subject of the hospital, and he didn't want that. It wasn't fair. Just because his mum was being dim, it didn't mean that Will had the right to have a go at her about that. The way he saw it the hospital stuff was more serious than the sweets and trainers stuff, and no one should mix them in together.

'What's wrong with you?' asked Will.

Marcus shrugged. 'Nothing. Just . . . I don't know. Wanted to have a shout.'

Will shook his head. 'Jesus,' he said. 'What a family.'

Marcus hadn't enjoyed the afternoon's rows, but when they had finished he could see the point of them. His mum knew about Will not having a kid, which was probably a good thing, and she knew that he visited Will after school most days, which was also a good thing, probably, because he'd had to tell her a lot of fibs recently, and he'd been feeling bad about it. And, most importantly, she knew about what went on at school, because Will had spelt it out. Marcus hadn't been able to spell it out, because he'd never been able to see the whole word before, but it didn't really matter who'd done it; the point was that Fiona understood.

'You're not going round there again,' she said on the way home.

Marcus knew she'd say it, and he also knew that he'd take no notice, but he argued anyway.

'Why not?'

'If you've got anything to say, you say it to me. If you want new clothes, I'll get them.'

'But you don't know what I need.'

'So tell me.'

'I don't know what I need. Only Will knows what I need.'

'Don't be ridiculous.'

'It's true. He knows what things kids wear.'

'Kids wear what they put on in the mornings.'

'You know what I mean.'

‘You mean that he thinks he’s trendy, and that even though he’s God knows how old he knows which trainers are fashionable, even though he doesn’t know the first thing about anything else.’

That was exactly what he meant. That was what Will was good at, and Marcus thought he was lucky to have found him.

‘We don’t need that kind of person. We’re doing all right our way.’

Marcus looked out of the bus window and thought about whether this was true, and decided it wasn’t, that neither of them was doing all right, whichever way you looked at it.

‘If you are having trouble it’s nothing to do with what shoes you wear, I can tell you that for nothing.’

‘No, I know, but—’

‘Marcus, trust me, OK? I’ve been your mother for twelve years. I haven’t made too bad a job of it. I do think about it. I know what I’m doing.’

Marcus had never thought of his mother in that way before, as someone who knew what she was doing. He had never thought that she didn’t have a clue either; it was just that what she did with him (for him? to him?) didn’t appear to be anything like that. He had always looked on being a mother as straightforward, something like, say, driving: most people could do it, and you could mess it up by doing something really obvious, by driving your car into a bus, or not telling your kid to say please and thank you and sorry (there were loads of kids at school, he reckoned, kids who stole and swore too much and bullied other kids, whose mums and dads had a lot to answer for). If you looked at it that way, there wasn’t an awful lot to think about. But his mum seemed to be saying that there was more to it than that. She was telling him she had a plan.

If she had a plan, then he had a choice. He could trust her, believe her when she said she knew what she was doing; that meant putting up with things at school because they’d turn out all right in the end and she could see things he couldn’t. Or he could decide that, actually, she was off her head, someone who took drug overdoses and then apparently forgot all about them afterwards. Either way it was scary. He didn’t want to put up with things as they were, but the other choice meant that he’d have to be his own mother, and how could you be your own mother when you were only twelve? He could tell himself to say sorry and please and thank you, that was easy, but he didn’t know where to start with the rest of it. He didn't even know what the rest of it was. He hadn't even known until today that there was a rest of it.

Every time he thought about this, it came back to the same problem: there were only two of them, and at least – *at least* – one of them was nuts.

In the next few days he began to notice more things about the way Fiona talked to him. Everything she said about what he could and should watch or listen to or read or eat made him curious: was this part of the plan, or was she just making it up as she went along? It never occurred to him to ask her until she told him to go to the shops to get some eggs for their dinner: it struck him that he was a vegetarian only because she was too.

'Did you always know I was going to be a vegetarian?'

She laughed. 'Of course I did. I didn't decide on the spur of the moment because we'd run out of sausages.'

'And do you think that's fair?'

'How do you mean?'

'Shouldn't I have been allowed to make up my own mind?'

'You can when you're older.'

'Why aren't I old enough now?'

'Because you don't do your own cooking. I don't want to cook meat, so you have to eat what I eat.'

'But you don't let me go to McDonald's either.'

'Is this premature teenage rebellion? I can't stop you going to McDonald's.'

'Really?'

'How can I? I'd just be disappointed if you did.'

Disappointed. Disappointment. That was how she did it. That was how she did a lot of things.

'Why?'

'I thought you were vegetarian because you believed in it.'

'I do.'

'Well, you can't go to McDonald's then, can you?'

She'd done him again. She always told him he could do what he wanted, and then argued with him until what he wanted was what she wanted anyway. It was beginning to make him angry.

'That's not fair.'

She laughed. 'That's what life is, Marcus. You have to work out what you believe in, and then you have to stick to it. It's hard, but it's not unfair. And at least it's easy to understand.'

There was something wrong with this, but he didn't know what. All he knew was that not everyone thought like this. When they talked in class about things like smoking, everyone agreed it was bad, but then loads of kids smoked; when they talked about violent films, everyone said they disapproved of them, but they still watched them. They thought one thing and did another. In Marcus's house it was different. They decided what was bad and then they never touched it or did it again. He could see how that made sense: he thought stealing was wrong and killing was wrong, and he didn't steal things or kill people. So was that all there was to it? He wasn't sure.

But of all the things that made him different, he could see this was the most important. It was why he wore clothes that other kids laughed at – because they'd had this talk about fashion, and they'd agreed that fashion was stupid – and why he listened to music that was old-fashioned, or that no one else had ever heard of – because they'd had this talk about modern pop music, and they'd agreed it was just a way for record companies to make a lot of money. It was why he wasn't allowed to play violent computer games, or eat hamburgers, or do this or that or the other. And he'd agreed with her about all of it, except he hadn't agreed really; he'd just lost the arguments.

'Why don't you just tell me what to do? Why do we always have to talk about it?'

'Because I want to teach you to think for yourself.'

'Was that your plan?'

'What plan?'

'When you said the other day that you knew what you were doing.'

'About what?'

'About being a mum.'

'Did I say that?'

'Yeah.'

'Oh. OK. Well, of course I want you to think for yourself. All parents want that.'

'But all that happens is we have an argument and I lose, and I do what you want me to do. We might as well save time. Just tell me what I'm not allowed, and leave it at that.'

'So what's brought all this on?'

'I've been thinking for myself.'

'Good for you.'

'I've been thinking for myself, and I want to go round to Will's house after school.'

'You've already lost that argument.'

'I need to see someone else who's not you.'

'What about Suzie?'

'She's like you. Will's not like you.'

'No. He's a liar, and he doesn't do anything, and—'

'He bought me those trainers.'

'Yes. He's a rich liar who doesn't do anything.'

'He understands about school and that. He knows things.'

'He knows things! Marcus, he doesn't even know he's born.'

'You see what I mean?' He was getting really frustrated now. 'I'm thinking for myself and you just . . . it just doesn't work. You win anyway.'

'Because you're not backing it up. It's not enough to tell me that you're thinking for yourself. You've got to show me, too.'

'How do I show you?'

'Give me a good reason.'

He could give her a reason. It wouldn't be the right reason, and he'd feel bad saying it, and he was pretty sure it would make her cry. But it was a good reason, a reason that would shut her up, and if that was how you had to win arguments, then he'd use it.

'Because I need a father.'

It shut her up, and it made her cry. It did the job.

EIGHTEEN

November the nineteenth. November the fucking nineteenth. That was definitely a new record, Will noted darkly. Last year it had been November the fucking twenty-sixth. He hadn't made it through into December for years now; he could see that when he was fifty or sixty he'd be hearing his first rendition of 'Santa's Super Sleigh' in July or August. This year it was a busker at the bottom of the escalator at the Angel station, a cheerful, attractive young woman with a violin who was obviously trying to supplement her music scholarship. Will scowled at her with all the hatred he could muster, a look intended to convey not only that he wouldn't be giving her any money, but that he would like to smash up her instrument and then staple her head to the escalator steps.

Will hated Christmas, for the obvious reason: people knocked on his door, singing the song he hated more than any song in the world and expected him to give them money. It had been worse when he was a kid, because his dad hated Christmas too, for the obvious reason (although Will hadn't realized it was the obvious reason until he was much older – back then, he just thought that his dad was as sick of the song as everybody else): it was a terrible reminder of how badly he had failed in his life. Quite often people wanted to interview his father about 'Santa's Super Sleigh', and they always used to ask what else he had written, and he would tell them, sometimes even play them things, or show them records which featured another of his songs. They would look embarrassed, cluck sympathetically and tell him how hard it was for everyone who was famous for only one thing, a long time ago, and ask him whether the song had ruined his life, or made him wish he'd never written it. He would get angry, and tell them not to be so stupid and patronizing and insensitive, and when they had gone, he would complain bitterly that the song had ruined his life, and say he wished he'd never written it. One radio journalist even went away and made a series called *One-Hit Wonders* inspired completely by his interview with Charles Freeman, all about people who'd written one great book, or appeared in one film, or written one famous song; the journalist had

had the cheek to ask him for another interview and, perhaps understandably, Will's father had refused.

So Christmas was the season of anger and bitterness and regret and recrimination, of drinking binges, of frantic and laughably inadequate industry (one Christmas Day his father wrote an entire, and entirely useless, musical, in a doomed attempt to prove that his talent was durable). It was a season of presents by the chimney too, but even when he was nine Will would gladly have swapped his Spirographs and his Batmobiles for a little peace and goodwill.

But things changed. His father died, and then his mother, and he lost touch with his stepbrother and stepsister, who were old and dull anyway, and Christmas was usually spent with friends, or girlfriends' families, and all that was left was 'Santa's Super Sleigh' and the cheques it carried to him through the snow. But that was more than enough. Will had often wondered whether there was any other stupid song which contained, somewhere deep within it, as much pain and despair and regret. He doubted it. Bob Dylan's ex-wife probably didn't listen to *Blood On The Tracks* too often, but *Blood On The Tracks* was different – it was about misery and damage. 'Santa's Super Sleigh' wasn't supposed to be like that at all, but he still felt he needed a stiff drink, or counselling, or a good cry, when he heard it in a department-store lift or through a supermarket tannoy in the weeks leading up to 25 December. Maybe there were others like him somewhere; maybe he should form a Successful Novelty Song support group, where rich, bitter men and women would sit around in expensive restaurants and talk about doggies and birdies and bikinis and milkmen and horrible dances.

He had no plans for this Christmas whatsoever. There was no girlfriend, and so there were no girlfriend's parents, and though he had friends on whom he could inflict himself, he didn't feel like it. He would sit at home and watch millions of films and get drunk and stoned. Why not? He was as entitled to a break as anyone else, even if there was nothing to break from.

If the first thing he had thought of when he heard the busker at the tube station was his father, the unexorcizable ghost of Christmas past, the second was Marcus. He didn't know why. He hadn't thought about him much since the trainers incident, and he'd had no contact with him since Fiona dragged him out of the flat the previous week. Maybe it was because Marcus was the only child he really knew, although Will doubted whether he was soppy enough to swallow the repulsive notion that Christmas was a time for children; the more likely explanation was that he had made some kind of link between Marcus's childhood and his own. It wasn't as if Will had been a nerdy kid with the wrong trainers; on the contrary, he had worn the right shoes and the right socks and the right trousers and the right shirts, and he had gone to the right hairdresser for the right haircut. That was the point of fashion, as far as Will was concerned; it meant that you were with the cool and the powerful, and against the alienated and the weak, just where Will wanted to be, and he'd successfully avoided being bullied by bullying furiously and enthusiastically.

But there was more than a whiff of the Freeman household in Fiona's flat: you got that same sense of hopelessness and defeat and bewilderment and straightforward lunacy. Of course, Will had grown up with money and Marcus had none, but you didn't need dosh to be dysfunctional. So what if Charles Freeman had killed himself with expensive malt whisky, and Fiona had tried to kill herself with National Health tranquillizers? The two of them would still have found plenty to talk about at parties.

Will didn't like the connection he had made very much, because it meant that if he had any decency in him at all he would have to take Marcus under his wing, use his own experience of growing up with a batty parent to guide the boy through to a place of safety. He didn't want to do that, though. It was too much work, and involved too much contact with people he didn't understand and didn't like, and he preferred watching *Countdown* on his own anyway.

But he had forgotten that he seemed to have no control over his relationship with Marcus and Fiona. On November the fucking twentieth, the day after November the fucking nineteenth, when he had more or less decided that Marcus would have to get by without his help, Fiona rang and started saying mad things down the phone.

'Marcus doesn't need a father, and he certainly doesn't need a father like you,' she said. Will was lost even before they'd started. At this point in the conversation he had contributed an admittedly guarded but otherwise entirely unprovocative, 'Hello, how are you?'

'I'm sorry?'

'Marcus seems to think he needs adult male company. A father figure. And somehow your name came up.'

'Well, I can tell you, Fiona, I didn't put him up to it. I don't need junior male company, and I definitely don't need a son figure. So, fine. You and I are in complete agreement.'

'So you won't see him even if he wants to see you?'

'Why doesn't he use his father as a father figure? Isn't that the easiest solution, or am I being dim?'

'His father lives in Cambridge.'

'What, Cambridge, Australia? Cambridge, California? Presumably we're not talking about the Cambridge just up the M11?'

'Marcus can't drive up the M11. He's twelve.'

'Hold on, hold on. You phoned up to tell me to keep out of Marcus's way. I told you that I had no intention of getting in Marcus's way. And now you're telling me . . . What? I missed a bit somewhere.'

'You just seem very keen to be shot of him.'

'So you're *not* telling me to leave him alone. You're telling me to apply for custody.'

'Are you incapable of conducting a conversation without resorting to sarcasm?'

'Just explain to me clearly and simply, without changing your mind halfway through, what you want me to do.'

She sighed. 'Some things are a little more complicated than that, Will.'

'Is that what you phoned me up to tell me? Because I got the wrong end of the stick early on, I think, during the bit about how I was the most unsuitable man in the world.'

'You're really not very easy to deal with.'

'So don't deal with me!' He was nearly shouting now. He was certainly angry. They had been talking for less than three minutes, yet he was beginning to feel as though this telephone conversation was going to be his life's work; that once every few hours he would put the receiver down to eat and sleep and go to the toilet, and the rest of the time Fiona would be telling him one thing and then its opposite over and over again. 'Just put the phone down! Hang up on me! I really won't be offended!'

'I think we need to talk about this properly, don't you?'

'What? What do we need to talk about properly?'

'This whole thing.'

'There isn't a whole thing. There isn't even a half thing!'

'Are you free for a drink tomorrow night? Maybe it would be better to talk face to face. We're not getting anywhere here.'

There was no point in fighting her. There wasn't even any point in not fighting her. They made arrangements to meet for a drink, and it was a mark of Will's frustration and confusion that he was able to look on the agreement of a time and a place as a resounding triumph.

Will had never been alone with Fiona; up until now Marcus had always been there, telling them when to talk, and what to talk about – apart from the trainers day, when he was kind of telling them what to talk about, even though he wasn't saying anything. But when Will had got the drinks in – they went to a quiet pub off the Liverpool Road where they knew they would get a seat and be able to talk without competing against a juke-box, or a grunge band, or an alternative comedian – and sat down opposite Fiona, and ascertained, once again, without even meaning to, that he did not find her in the least attractive, he realized something else: he had been drinking in pubs for nearly twenty years and not once had he been to a pub with a woman in whom he had no sexual interest whatsoever. He thought again. Could that be right? OK, he'd carried on seeing Jessica, the ex, who always insisted he was missing out, after they had split up. But there had been sexual interest once upon a time, and he knew that if Jessica were ever to announce that she was looking for a discreet extra-marital affair, he would certainly apply for the job, put his name forward for consideration.

No, this was certainly a first for him, and he had no idea whether different rules applied in these situations. Obviously it would be neither appropriate nor sensible to take her by the hand and look into her eyes, or move the subject gently on to sex so that he could introduce a more flirtatious note into the proceedings. If he had no desire to sleep with Fiona, then of course there was no necessity to pretend that every single thing she said was interesting. But a strange thing happened: he was interested, mostly. Not in a well-I-never-knew-that kind of way, because even though Fiona probably knew a lot of things that Will didn't, he was almost sure that all of them would be very dull . . . It was just that he was absorbed in the conversation. He listened to what she said, he thought about it, he answered. He couldn't remember the last time that had happened, so why was it happening now? Was it just sod's law – you don't fancy someone, so they're bound to be endlessly fascinating – or was something happening here that he should think about?

She was different today. She didn't want to tell him what a useless human being he was, and she didn't want to accuse him of molesting her son; it was almost as if she had decided that this was a relationship she was stuck with. Will didn't like the implications of that.

'I'm sorry about yesterday,' she said.

'That's OK.'

Will lit a cigarette, and Fiona made a face and wafted the smoke away. Will hated people who did that in places where they had no right to do so. He wasn't going to apologize for smoking in a pub; in fact, what he was going to do was single-handedly create a fug so thick that they would be unable to see each other.

'I was very upset when I called. When Marcus said he felt he needed some male input, I felt as though I'd been slapped round the face.'

'I can imagine.'

He didn't have a clue what she was talking about. Why would anyone take the blindest bit of notice of anything Marcus said?

'You know, it's the first thing you think of when you split up with the father of your son, that he's going to need a man around and so on. And then good feminist common sense takes over. But ever since Marcus has been old enough to understand we've talked about it, and every time he's assured me that it doesn't matter. And then yesterday it came right out of the blue . . . He's always known how worried I am about that.'

Will didn't want to get involved in any of this. He didn't care whether Marcus needed a man in his life or not. Why should he? It wasn't his business, even though he seemed to be the man in question. He hadn't asked to be and, anyway, he was pretty sure that if Marcus did need a man, it wasn't his sort. But listening to Fiona now, he realized that in some respects at least he understood Marcus better than she did – possibly, he conceded reluctantly, because he was a man and Fiona wasn't, and possibly because Marcus was, in his own junior and eccentric way, a devious man. Will understood devious men.

'Well there you are then,' he said flatly.

'Where am I?'

'That's why he said it. Because he knew it would do the job.'

'What job?'

'Whatever job he wanted it to do at the time. I expect he's been saving it. That was his nuclear option. What were you arguing about?'

'I'd just reiterated my opposition to his relationship with you.'

'Oh.' That was very bad news. If Marcus was willing to go nuclear on his account, then he was in even deeper than he'd feared.

'Are you saying what I think you're saying? That he was attacking me in my most vulnerable spot just so he could win an argument?'

'Yeah. Course he was.'

'Marcus isn't capable of that.'

Will snorted. 'Whatever.'

'Do you really think so?'

'He's not daft.'

'It's not his intelligence I'm worried about. It's his ... emotional honesty.'

Will snorted again. He had intended to keep his thoughts to himself throughout this conversation, but they kept escaping through his nose. What planet did this woman live on? She was so unworldly that she seemed to him to be an unlikely suicidal depressive, even though she sang with her eyes closed: surely anyone who floated that high above everything was protected in some way? But of course that was part of the problem. They were sitting here because a twelve-year-old's craftiness had brought her crashing down to earth, and if Marcus could do it, any boyfriend or boss or landlord – any adult who didn't love her – could do it. There was no protection in that. Why did these people want to make things so hard for themselves? It was *easy*, life, easy-peasy, a matter of simple arithmetic: loving people, and allowing yourself to be loved, was only worth the risk if the odds were in your favour, but they quite clearly weren't. There were about seventy-nine squillion people in the world, and if you were very lucky, you would end up being loved by fifteen or twenty of them. So how smart did you have to be to work out that it just wasn't worth the risk? OK, Fiona had made the mistake of having a child, but it wasn't the end of the world. In her position, Will wouldn't let the little sod drag him under.

Fiona was looking at him. 'Why does everything I say make you do that?'

'What?'

'Make that snorting noise?'

'I'm sorry. It's just that . . . I don't know anything about, you know, stages of development and what kids should do when and all that. But

I do know that it's around now you shouldn't trust anything a human male says about what he feels.'

Fiona looked bleakly at her Guinness.

'And when does that stop, in your expert opinion?' The last two words had a rusty serrated edge on them, but Will ignored it.

'When he's around seventy or eighty, and then he can use the truth at highly inappropriate moments to shock people.'

'I'll be dead then.'

'Yup.'

She went to the bar to get him a drink, and then sat back down heavily in her seat. 'But why you?'

'I just told you. He doesn't really need a male influence. He just said it to get his own way.'

'I know, I know. I understand that. But why does he want to see you so much he'd do that to me?'

'I don't know.'

'Do you really not know?'

'Really.'

'Maybe it is best if he doesn't see you.'

Will said nothing. He had learnt something from the previous day's conversation, anyway.

'What do you think?'

'I don't.'

'What?'

'I don't think. I don't think anything. You're his mother. You make the decisions.'

'But you're involved now. He keeps coming round to your house. You take him out to buy shoes. He's living this whole life I can't control, which means you have to.'

'I'm not going to control anything.'

'In which case, it's best that he doesn't see you.'

'We've been here before. What do you want me to do if he rings on the bell?'

'Don't let him in.'

'Fine.'

'I mean, if you're not prepared to think about how to help me, then keep out.'

'Right.'

'God, you're a selfish bastard.'

'But I'm on my own. There's just me. I'm not putting myself first, because there isn't anybody else.'

'Well, he's there too now. You can't just shut life out, you know.'

She was wrong, he was almost positive. You could shut life out. If you didn't answer the door to it, how was it going to get in?

NINETEEN

Marcus didn't like the idea of his mum talking to Will. A while ago he would have got excited about it, but he no longer thought that he and his mum and Will and Ned and another baby perhaps were going to live together in Will's flat. For a start, Ned didn't exist, and for another start, if you could have two starts, Fiona and Will didn't like each other very much, and anyway Will's flat was nowhere near big enough for them all, even though there weren't as many of them as he had originally thought.

But now everyone knew too much, and there were too many things that he didn't want the two of them to talk about without him. He didn't want Will to talk to his mum about the hospital, in case it made her go funny again; and he didn't want Will to tell her about how he'd tried to blackmail Will into going out with her; and he didn't want his mum to talk about how much telly he was allowed to watch, in case Will started turning it off when he went round . . . As far as he could tell, every possible topic of conversation meant trouble of some sort.

She was only gone for a couple of hours after tea time, so they didn't have to find a babysitter; he put the chain on the door, did his homework, watched a bit of TV, played on the computer and waited. At five-past nine she buzzed the special buzz on the doorbell. He let her in, and stared at her face to try to work out just how angry or depressed she was, but she seemed OK.

'Did you have a good time?'

'It was OK.'

'What does that mean?'

'He's not a very nice man, is he?'

'I think he is. He bought me those trainers.'

'Well, you're not to go round any more.'

'You can't stop me.'

'No, but he's not going to answer the door, so it's a waste of time.'

'How do you know he's not going to answer the door?'

'Because he told me he wouldn't.'

Marcus could just hear Will saying that, but it didn't worry him. He knew how loud the buzzer was inside the flat, and he had the time to ring it and ring it and ring it.

Marcus had to go and see the headmistress about his trainers. His mum had made a complaint to the school, even though Marcus had told her, *begged* her, not to. They'd spent so long arguing about it that he ended up having to go days after the event. So now he had a choice: he could lie to the headmistress, tell her that he had no idea who had stolen his shoes, and make himself look stupid; or he could tell her and lose his shoes, jacket, shirt, trousers, underpants and probably an eye or a piece of ear on the way home. He couldn't see that he'd lose much sleep worrying about what to do.

He went at the beginning of lunch break, the time his form teacher had told him to go, but Mrs Morrison wasn't ready for him; he could hear her through the door, shouting at someone. He was on his own at first, but then Ellie McCrae, this sulky, scruffy girl from year ten who hacked off her own hair and wore black lipstick, sat down on the far end of the row of chairs outside the office. Ellie was famous. She was always in trouble for something or other, usually something quite bad.

They sat in silence for a bit, and then Marcus thought he'd try to talk to her; his mum was always on at him to talk to people at school.

'Hello, Ellie,' he said. She looked at him and laughed once under her breath, shook her head bitterly and then turned her face away. Marcus didn't mind. In fact, he almost laughed. He wished he had a video camera. He'd love to show his mum what happened when you tried to talk to another kid at school, especially an older kid, especially a girl. He wouldn't bother trying again.

'How come every squitty little shitty snotty bastard knows my name?'

Marcus couldn't believe she was talking to him, and when he looked at her it seemed as though he was right to be doubtful, because she was still looking the other way. He decided to ignore her.

'Oi, I'm talking to you. Don't be so fucking rude.'

'Sorry. I didn't think you were talking to me.'

'I don't see any other squitty little shitty bastards here, do you?'

'No,' Marcus admitted.

'So. How come you know my name? I haven't got a bloody clue who you are.'

'You're famous.' He knew that was a mistake as soon as he had said it.

'What am I famous for?'

'Dunno.'

'Yes you do. I'm famous because I'm always in trouble.'

'Yes.'

'Fucking hell.'

They sat there for a while longer. Marcus didn't feel like breaking the silence; if saying 'Hello, Ellie' caused that much trouble, then he wasn't about to ask her whether she'd had a nice weekend.

'I'm always in trouble, and I've never done anything wrong,' she said eventually.

'No.'

'How do you know?'

'Because you just said so.' Marcus thought that was a good answer. If Ellie McCrae said she hadn't done anything wrong, then she hadn't.

'If you're being cheeky, you'll get a slap.'

Marcus wished Mrs Morrison would hurry up. Even though he was prepared to believe that Ellie had never done anything wrong, ever, he could see why some people might think she had.

'Do you know what I've done wrong this time?'

'Nothing,' Marcus said firmly.

'OK, do you know what I'm supposed to have done wrong?'

'Nothing.' This was his line, and he was sticking to it.

'Well, they must think I've done something wrong, or I wouldn't be sitting here, would I?'

'No.'

'It's this sweatshirt. They don't want me to wear it, and I'm not going to take it off. So there's going to be a row.'

He looked at it. They were all supposed to wear sweatshirts with the school logo on them, but Ellie's showed a bloke with scraggy hair and half a beard. He had big eyes and looked a little bit like Jesus, except more modern and with bleached hair.

'Who's that?' he asked politely.

'You must know.'

'Ummm . . . Oh, yes.'

'So who is it?'

'Ummm . . . Forgotten.'

'You never knew it.'

'No.'

'That's incredible. That's like not knowing the name of the prime minister or something.'

'Yeah.' Marcus gave a little laugh, to show her that at least he knew how stupid he was, even if he didn't know anything else. 'Who is it, then?'

'Kirk O'Bane.'

'Oh, yes.'

He'd never heard of Kirk O'Bane, but he'd never heard of anybody.

'What does he do?'

'He plays for Manchester United.'

Marcus looked at the picture on the sweatshirt again, even though that meant sort of looking at Ellie's tits. He hoped she understood that he wasn't interested in her tits, only in the picture.

'Does he?' He looked much more like a singer than a footballer. Footballers weren't sad, usually, and this man looked sad. He wouldn't have thought that Ellie would be the sort of person who liked football, anyway.

'Yeah. He scored five goals for them last Saturday.'

'Wow,' said Marcus.

Mrs Morrison's door opened and two white-faced year sevens came out. 'Come in, Marcus,' said Mrs Morrison.

'Bye, Ellie,' said Marcus. Ellie went through her head-shaking routine again, still apparently bitter that her reputation had gone before her. Marcus wasn't looking forward to seeing Mrs Morrison, but if the alternative was sitting out in the corridor with Ellie, then he'd take the head's office any day of the week.

He lost his temper with Mrs Morrison. Bad idea, he could see afterwards, losing your temper with the headmistress of your new school, but he couldn't help it. She was being so thick that in the end he just had to shout. They started off OK: no, he'd never had any trouble from the shoe-stealers before, no, he didn't know who they were and no, he wasn't very happy at school (only one lie there). But then she started talking about what she called 'survival strategies', and that was when he got cross.

'I mean, I'm sure you've thought of this, but couldn't you just try keeping out of their way?'

Did they all think he was thick? Did they reckon that he woke up every morning thinking, I must find the people who call me names and give me shit and want to steal my trainers, so that they can do more things to me?

'I have tried.' That was all he could say for the moment. He was too frustrated to say any more.

'Maybe you haven't tried hard enough.'

That did it. She had said this not because she wanted to be helpful, but because she didn't like him. Nobody at this school liked him and he didn't understand why. He'd had enough, and he stood up to go.

'Sit down, Marcus. I haven't finished with you yet.'

'I've finished with you.'

He didn't know he was going to say that, and he was amazed when he had. He had never been cheeky to a teacher before, mostly because there hadn't been a need for it. Now he could see that he hadn't started in a great place. If you were going to get yourself into trouble, maybe it was best to work up to it slowly, get some practice in first. He had started right at the top, which was probably a mistake.

'SIT down.'

But he didn't. He just walked out the way he had come in, and kept on walking.

As soon as he left Mrs Morrison's office he felt different, better, as if he'd let go and he was now falling through space. It was an exciting feeling, really, and it was much better than the feeling of hanging on that he'd had before. He wouldn't have been able to describe it as 'hanging on' until just now, but that was definitely what it was. He'd been pretending that everything was normal – difficult, yes, but normal – but now he'd let go he could see it had been everything but normal. You don't get your shoes stolen *normally.* Your English teacher doesn't make out you're a nutter *normally*. You don't get boiled sweets thrown at your head *normally.* And that was just the school stuff.

And now he was a truant. He was walking down Holloway Road while everyone else at school was . . . actually, they were eating their lunch, but he wasn't going back. Soon he'd be walking down Holloway Road (well, not Holloway Road, probably, because he was almost at the end of it already, and lunch would go on for another thirty minutes yet) during history, and then he'd be a proper truant. He wondered whether all truants started like that, whether there was always a Mrs Morrison moment which made them blow their top and leave. He supposed there had to be. He'd always presumed that truants were different sort of people entirely, not like him at all, that they'd been born truants, sort of thing, but he was obviously wrong. In May, before they moved to London, when he was in his last term at his old school, he wasn't a truant kind of person in any way whatsoever. He turned up at school, listened to what people said, did his homework, took part. But six months later that had all changed, bit by bit.

It was probably like that for tramps, too, he realized. They walked out of their house one evening and thought, I'll sleep in this shop doorway tonight, and when you'd done it once, something changed in you, and you became a tramp, rather than someone who didn't have anywhere to sleep for one night. And the same with criminals! And drug addicts! And . . . He decided to stop thinking about it all then. If he carried on, walking out of Mrs Morrison's office might begin to look like the moment his whole life changed, and he wasn't sure he was ready for that. He wasn't someone who wanted to become a truant or a tramp or a murderer or a drug addict. He was just someone who was fed up with Mrs Morrison. There had to be a difference.

TWENTY

Will loved driving around London. He loved the traffic, which allowed him to believe he was a man in a hurry and offered him rare opportunities for frustration and anger (other people did things to let off steam, but Will had to do things to build it up); he loved knowing his way around; he loved being swallowed up in the flow of the city's life. You didn't need a job or a family to drive around London; you only needed a car, and Will had a car. Sometimes he just drove for the hell of it, and sometimes he drove because he liked to hear music played at a volume that would not be possible in the flat without a furious knock on the door or the wall or the ceiling.

Today he had convinced himself that he had to drive to Waitrose, but if he was honest the real reason for the trip was that he wanted to sing along to *Nevermind* at the top of his voice, and he couldn't do that at home. He loved Nirvana, but at his age they were kind of a guilty pleasure. All that rage and pain and self-hatred! Will got a bit . . . *fed up* sometimes, but he couldn't pretend it was anything stronger than that. So now he used loud angry rock music as a replacement for real feelings, rather than as an expression of them, and he didn't even mind very much. What good were real feelings anyway?

The cassette had just turned itself over when he saw Marcus ambling down Upper Street. He hadn't seen him since the day of the trainers, nor had he wanted to see him particularly, but he suddenly felt a little surge of affection for him. Marcus was so locked into himself, so oblivious to everyone and everything, that affection seemed to be the only possible response: the boy somehow seemed to be asking for absolutely nothing and absolutely everything all at the same time.

The affection that Will felt was not acute enough to make him want to stop the car, or even toot: he had discovered that it was much easier to sustain one's fondness for Marcus if one just kept one's foot down, literally and metaphorically. But it was funny, seeing him out in the street in broad daylight, wandering aimlessly . . . Something nagged at him. Why was it funny? Because Will had never really seen Marcus in broad daylight before. He had only previously seen him in the gloom of a winter afternoon. And why had he only seen him in the gloom of a winter afternoon? Because Marcus only came round after school. But it was just after two o'clock. Marcus should be in school now. Bollocks.

Will wrestled with his conscience, grappled it to the ground and sat on it until he couldn't hear a squeak out of it. Why should he care if Marcus went to school or not? OK, wrong question. He knew very well why he should care whether Marcus went to school. Try a different question: *how much* did he care whether Marcus went to school or not? Answer: not a lot. That was better. He drove home.

At exactly 4.15, right in the middle of *Countdown*, the buzzer went. If Will hadn't seen Marcus bunking off this afternoon, the precision of the timing would have escaped his notice, but now it just seemed transparently obvious: Marcus had clearly decided that arriving at the flat before 4.15 would arouse suspicion, so he'd timed it to the second. It didn't matter, however; he wasn't going to answer the door.

Marcus buzzed again; Will ignored him again. On the third buzz he turned *Countdown* off and put *In Utero* on, in the hope that Nirvana might block out the sound more effectively than Carol Vorderman. By the time he got to 'Pennyroyal Tea', the eighth or ninth track, he'd had enough of listening to Kurt Cobain and Marcus: Marcus could obviously hear the music through the door, and was providing his own accompaniment by buzzing in time. Will gave up.

'You're not supposed to be here.'

'I came to ask you a favour.' Nothing in Marcus's face or voice suggested that he had been the least bit inconvenienced or bored during his thirty-odd minutes of buzzing.

They had a brief bout of leg-wrestling: Will was standing in Marcus's way, but Marcus managed to force his way into the flat regardless.

'Oh no, *Countdown*'s finished. Did that fat bloke get knocked out?'

'What favour do you want to ask me?'

'I want you to take me and a friend to football.'

'Your mum can take you.'

'She doesn't like football.'

'Neither do you.'

'I do now. I like Manchester United.'

'Why?'

'I like O'Bane.'

'Who the hell's O'Bane?'

'He scored five goals for them last Saturday.'

'They drew nil–nil at Leeds.'

'It was probably the Saturday before, then.'

'Marcus, there isn't a player called O'Bane.'

'I might have got it wrong. Something that sounds like that. He's got bleached hair and a beard and he looks like Jesus. Can I have a Coke?'

'No. There's nobody who plays for Man United with bleached hair and a beard who looks like Jesus.'

'Tell me some of their names.'

'Hughes? Cantona? Giggs? Sharpe? Robson?'

'No. O'Bane.'

'O'Kane?'

Marcus's face lit up. 'That must be it!'

'Used to play for Nottingham Forest about twenty-five years ago. Didn't look like Jesus. Didn't bleach his hair. Never scored five goals. How was school today?'

'OK.'

'How was the afternoon?'

Marcus looked at him, trying to work out why he might have asked the question.

'OK.'

'What did you have?'

'History, and then . . . ummm . . .'

Will had intended to store the skiving up, just as Marcus had stored the Ned thing up, but now he had him wriggling on the hook he couldn't resist taking him off and making him swim round and round in the bucket.

'It's Wednesday today, isn't it?'

'Er . . . Yes.'

'Don't you have double walking up and down Upper Street on Wednesday afternoons?'

He could see Marcus beginning the slow descent towards panic.

'What do you mean?'

'I saw you this afternoon.'

'What, in school?'

'Well, I couldn't have seen you in school, Marcus, could I? Because you weren't there.'

'This afternoon?'

'Yes, this afternoon.'

'Oh, right. I had to nip out and get something.'

'You had to nip out? And they're all right about nipping out, are they?'

'Where did you see me?'

'I drove past you on Upper Street. I have to say, it didn't look as though you were nipping. It looked like you were skiving.'

'It was Mrs Morrison's fault.'

'Her fault that you had to nip out? Or her fault that you had to skive?'

'She told me to keep out of their way again.'

'You're losing me, Marcus. Who is Mrs Morrison?'

'The head. You know they always say when I get in trouble that I should keep out of their way? She said that about the training-shoe kids.' His voice rose an octave, and he started to speak more quickly. 'They followed me! How can I keep out of their way if they follow me?'

'OK, OK, keep your hair on. Did you tell her that?'

'Course I did. She just didn't take any notice.'

'Right. So you go home and tell your mum this. It's no good telling me. And you've got to tell her that you bunked off as well.'

'I'm not telling her that. She's got enough problems without me.'

'Marcus, you're already a problem.'

'Why can't you go and see her? Mrs Morrison?'

'You're joking. Why should she take any notice of me?'

'She would. She—'

'Marcus, listen. I'm not your father, or your uncle, or your stepfather, or anybody at all. I'm nothing to do with you. No headmistress is going to take any notice of what I say, and nor should she, either. You've got to stop thinking I know the answer to anything, because I don't.'

'You know about things. You knew about the trainers.'

'Yeah, and what a triumph they were. I mean, they were a source of endless happiness, weren't they? You'd have been in school this afternoon if I hadn't bought you the trainers.'

'And you knew about Kirk O'Bane.'

'Who?'

'Kirk O'Bane.'

'The footballer?'

'Except I don't think he can be a footballer. Ellie was making one of those jokes that you make.'

'But his first name's Kirk?'

'I think so.'

'Kurt Cobain, you jerk.'

'Who's Kurt Cobain?'

'The singer with Nirvana.'

'I thought he must be a singer. Bleached hair? Looks a bit like Jesus?'

'I suppose so.'

'There you are, then,' said Marcus triumphantly. 'You knew about him, too.'

'Everyone knows about him.'

'I didn't.'

'No, you didn't. But you're different, Marcus.'

'And my mum wouldn't.'

'No, she wouldn't either.'

'You see, you know things. You can help.'

It was then, for the first time, that Will saw the kind of help Marcus needed. Fiona had given him the idea that Marcus was after a father figure, someone to guide him gently towards male adulthood, but that wasn't it at all: Marcus needed help to be a kid, not an adult. And, unhappily for Will, that was exactly the kind of assistance he was qualified to provide. He wasn't able to tell Marcus how to grow up, or how to cope with a suicidal mother, or anything like that, but he could certainly tell him that Kurt Cobain didn't play for Manchester United, and for a twelve-year-old boy attending a comprehensive school at the end of 1993, that was maybe the most important information of all.

TWENTY-ONE

Marcus went back to school the following morning. Nobody seemed to have noticed that he hadn't been around the previous afternoon: his form teacher knew he'd had to go to see Mrs Morrison during afternoon registration, and Mr Sandford the history teacher never noticed him even when he was there. The other kids in the class might have worked out that he was bunking off, but as they never spoke to him anyway, how would he ever know?

He bumped into Ellie at breaktime at the vending machine. She was wearing her Kurt Cobain sweatshirt and standing with a friend from her class.

'Kurt Cobain doesn't play for Manchester United,' he told her. The girl from her class burst into hysterical laughter.

'Oh, no!' said Ellie, mock-horrified. 'Have they got rid of him?'

Marcus was confused for a moment – maybe Ellie really did think he was a footballer? But then he realized she was making one of those jokes he never got.

'Ha, ha,' he said, without laughing at all. That was what you were supposed to do, and he felt the thrill of having done something right for a change. 'No, he plays . . . he *sings* for Nirvana.'

'Thanks for telling me.'

'That's OK. A friend of mine has got one of their records. *Nevermind*.'

'Everybody's got that one. I'll bet he hasn't got the new one.'

'He might have. He's got lots of stuff.'

'What year's he in? I didn't think anyone in this school liked Nirvana.'

'He's left school. He's quite old. It's grunge, isn't it, Nirvana? I don't know what I think of grunge.' He didn't, either. Will had played him some Nirvana the previous evening, and he'd never heard anything quite like it. At first he hadn't been able to hear anything apart from noise and shouting, but there were some quiet bits, too, and in the end he had been able to make out a tune. He didn't think he'd ever like it as much as he liked Joni or Bob or Mozart, but he could sort of see why someone like Ellie might like it.

The two girls looked at each other and laughed louder than they had done the first time.

'And what do you think you might think of it?' asked Ellie's friend.

'Well,' said Marcus. 'It's a bit of a racket, but it's got a good beat, and the picture on the cover is very interesting.' It was a picture of a baby underwater, swimming after a dollar bill. Will had said something about the picture, but he couldn't remember what it was. 'I think the cover has a meaning. Something about society.'

The girls looked at him, looked at each other and laughed.

'You're very funny,' said Ellie's friend. 'Who are you?'

'Marcus.'

'Marcus. Cool name.'

'Do you think so?' Marcus hadn't thought about his name that much, but he'd never thought it was cool.

'No,' said Ellie's friend, and they laughed again. 'See you around, Marcus.'

'See you.'

It was the longest conversation he'd had with anyone at school for weeks.

'So we've scored,' said Will when Marcus told him about Ellie and her friend. 'I don't fancy yours much, though.'

Sometimes he didn't understand one word Will said, and when that happened Marcus just ignored him completely.

'They said I was funny.'

'You are funny. You're hilarious. But I don't know if it's much to build a whole relationship on.'

'Can I invite Ellie round?'

'I'm not sure she'd come, Marcus.'

'Why not?'

'Well . . . I'm not sure that . . . How old is she?'

'I dunno. Fifteen?'

'I'm not sure that fifteen-year-olds hang out with twelve-year-olds. I'll bet you her boyfriend is twenty-five, drives a Harley Davidson and works as a roadie for some band. He'd beat you up. He'd squash you like a bug, man.'

Marcus hadn't thought of that.

'I don't want to go out with her. I know she'd never go for someone like me. But we can come round here and listen to your Nirvana records, can't we?'

'She's probably heard them already.'

Marcus was getting frustrated with Will. Why didn't he want him to make friends?

'OK, forget it, then.'

'I'm sorry, Marcus. I'm glad you spoke to Ellie today, I really am. But a two-minute conversation with someone who's taking the piss out of you . . . I can't see that working out long term, you know?'

Marcus wasn't really listening. Ellie and her friend had said he was funny, and if he could be funny once, he could be funny again.

He saw them by the vending machine the next day. They were leaning against it and saying things about anyone who had the nerve to come up and put money in. Marcus watched them for a little while before he went up to them.

'Hello, Ellie.'

'Marcus! My man!'

Marcus didn't want to think about what that might mean, so he didn't take any notice.

'Ellie, how old is your boyfriend?'

He'd only asked one question, and already he had made the girls laugh. He knew he could do it.

'A hundred and two.'

'Ha, ha.' He'd done it right again.

'Nine.'

'Ha, ha.'

'Why do you want to know? How do you even know I've got a boyfriend?'

'My friend Will said he was probably about twenty-five and drove a Harley Davidson and he'd squash me like a bug.'

'Aaaah, Marcus.' Ellie grabbed him round the neck and ruffled his hair. 'I wouldn't let him.'

'Good. Thank you. I have to admit I was a bit worried when he said that.'

More laughter. Ellie's friend was staring at him as if he was the most interesting person she'd ever met.

'How old is your girlfriend, anyway? She probably wants to kill me, doesn't she?' They were laughing all the time now. You couldn't tell where one laugh ended and the next one began.

'No, because I haven't got one.'

'I don't believe that. A good-looking boy like you? We'll have to fix you up.'

'It's OK, thanks. I don't really want one at the moment. I don't feel ready yet.'

'Very sensible.'

Mrs Morrison suddenly appeared beside them.

'In my office now, Ellie.'

'I'm not changing the sweatshirt.'

'We'll talk about it in my office.'

'There's nothing to talk about.'

'Do you want to argue in front of everyone?'

Ellie shrugged. 'I don't mind if you don't.'

Ellie genuinely didn't care, Marcus could see that. Loads of kids acted as if they weren't scared, but dropped the act the moment a teacher said anything to them. Ellie could keep going for ever, though, and there was nothing Mrs Morrison could do. There was a load of stuff she could do to him, though, and Ellie's friend didn't look like she wanted to pick a fight with Mrs Morrison either. Ellie had something that they didn't have – or they had something Ellie didn't have, he didn't know which.

'Zoe, Marcus, I want to talk to Ellie in private. And Marcus, you and I have some unfinished business to attend to, don't we?'

'Yes, Mrs Morrison.' Ellie caught his eye and smiled, and for a moment he really felt as if the three of them were a trio. Or maybe a triangle, with Ellie at the top and him and Zoe at the bottom.

'Off you go.'

And off they went.

Ellie and Zoe came looking for him at lunchtime. He was sitting at his desk eating his sandwiches, listening to Frankie Ball and Juliet Lawrence talk about some bloke in year nine, when they just turned up.

'Here he is, look!'

'Oooeee! Marcus!'

Just about every kid in the room stopped what they were doing and turned round. You could see what they were thinking: Ellie and *Marcus????????* Even Nicky and Mark, who hadn't spoken to him for weeks and liked to pretend that they had never known him, looked up from their Gameboy; Marcus hoped that one of them had lost a life. He felt great. If Kurt Cobain himself had walked through the form-room door looking for him, the mouths of his classmates couldn't have opened any wider.

'What are you lot staring at? Marcus is our friend, aren't you, Marcus?'

'Yes,' said Marcus. Whatever his relationship with Ellie and Zoe was, 'yes' was definitely the right answer here.

'Come on, then, let's go. You don't want to hang around here all lunchtime, do you? Come to our form room. It's a waste of time hanging out with this lot. Boring fuckers.'

Marcus could see some of them start to blush but nobody said anything. They couldn't, unless they were prepared to argue with Ellie, which clearly none of them were. What would be the point? Even Mrs Morrison couldn't argue with Ellie, so what chance did Frankie Ball and the rest of them have?

'OK,' said Marcus. 'Hang on a minute.' He wanted them to wait simply because he wanted the moment to last longer: he didn't know whether Ellie and Zoe would come looking for him ever again and, even if they did, he doubted whether they'd announce to the world, or the part of the world eating sandwiches in his classroom, that he was their friend and that everyone else was a boring fucker. That would be too much to ask. But now he'd asked them to hang on, he had no idea what they might be hanging on for.

'Shall I . . . Do you want me to bring anything?'

'Like what?' said Zoe. 'A bottle?'

'No, but, like . . .'

'Or condoms?' said Ellie. 'Is that what you mean? We can't have sex in our room, Marcus, even though I'd like to, of course. There are too many people in there.' Zoe was laughing so hard that Marcus thought she might be sick. Her eyes were closed and she was sort of choking.

'No, I know, I . . .' Maybe asking them to hang on had been a mistake. He was turning his moment of triumph into what seemed like a year of horrible awfulness.

'Just bring your sweet self, Marcus. But get a move on, eh?'

He knew he was red in the face, and the condom bit had been bad. But he still got to walk from his desk to where Ellie and Zoe were standing while everyone else watched, and when he got there Ellie gave him a kiss. OK, she was making fun of him, but it didn't matter, there weren't many people in his class that Ellie would bother to spit on, let alone kiss. 'There's no such thing as bad publicity,' his dad had said once, ages ago, when Marcus had asked him why some actor was letting Noel Edmonds pour stuff over his head, and now he could see what he meant. Ellie had kind of poured stuff over his head, but it was really, really worth it.

Ellie's form room was upstairs and the walk made the good bit, the fucking-hell-Marcus-and-Ellie bit, last longer. One of the teachers even stopped him to ask if he was OK, as if anyone hanging around with Ellie must have been kidnapped or brainwashed.

'We're adopting him, sir,' said Ellie.

'I wasn't asking you, Ellie. I was asking him.'

'They're adopting me, sir,' said Marcus. He didn't mean it as a joke – he just thought that saying what Ellie said was sensible – but they all laughed anyway.

'And you couldn't hope for more responsible parents,' said the teacher.

'Ha, ha,' said Marcus, although he wasn't sure he should have done this time.

'We'll take that as a compliment,' said Ellie. 'Thank you. We'll look after him. Have him home by midnight and all that.'

'Make sure you do,' said the teacher. 'In one piece.'

Ellie made him wait outside her form room while she announced him. He could hear her shouting.

'OK, listen everybody, I want you to meet Marcus. The only other Kurt Cobain fan in the whole fucking school. Come in, Marcus.'

He walked into the room. There weren't many people in there, but those that were all laughed when they saw him.

'I didn't say I was a fan as such,' he said. 'I just think they have a good beat and their cover means something.'

Everyone laughed again. Ellie and Zoe stood beside him proudly, as if he had just done a magic trick that they had told everyone he could do even though nobody believed them. They were right; he did feel he'd been adopted.

TWENTY-TWO

Will had been trying not to think about Christmas, but as it got nearer he was beginning to go off the idea of watching a few hundred videos and smoking a few thousand joints. It didn't seem very festive, somehow, and even though festivities invariably entailed The Song somewhere along the line, he didn't want to ignore them completely. It struck him that how you spent Christmas was a message to the world about where you were at in life, some indication of how deep a hole you had managed to burrow for yourself, and therefore spending three days bombed out of your head on your own said things about you that you might not want saying.

So he would spend Christmas in the bosom of a family – not his family, because he didn't have one, but *a* family. There was one family he wanted to avoid at all costs: no way did he want to spend Christmas eating nut fucking roast, not watching TV, and singing carols with his eyes closed. He had to be careful, though, because if he just let himself drift along he'd be carried right over the weir; he had to start swimming in the opposite direction fast.

Having decided with such unshakeable firmness that he would absolutely definitely not be celebrating 25 December with Fiona and Marcus, it came as something of a surprise to him to find himself accepting an invitation from Marcus the following afternoon to do exactly that.

'Do you want to spend Christmas round ours?' Marcus asked, even before he had stepped into the flat.

'Ummm,' said Will. 'That's, ah, very kind of you.'

'Good,' said Marcus.

'I only said that's very kind of you,' said Will.

'But you're coming.'

'I don't know.'

'Why not?'

'Because— '

'Don't you want to come?'

'Yes, of course I do, but . . . What about your mum?'

'She'll be there too.'

'Yes, I'd sort of presumed that. But she wouldn't want me there.'

'I've already spoken to her about it. I said I wanted to invite a friend, and she said OK.'

'So you didn't tell her it was me?'

'No, but I think she guessed.'

'How?'

'I haven't got any other friends, have I?'

'Does she know you still come round here?'

'Sort of. She's stopped asking me, so I think she's given up worrying about it.'

'And there really isn't anyone else you'd rather ask?'

'No, course not. And if there was, they wouldn't be allowed to come to my house for Christmas lunch. They'd be going to their own houses. Except they live in their own houses, so they wouldn't be going anywhere, would they?'

Will was finding the conversation depressing. What Marcus was saying, in his artful, skewed way, was that he didn't want Will to be alone on Christmas Day.

'I'm not sure what I'm doing yet.'

'Where might you be going instead?'

'Nowhere, but . . .'

Any conversational holes that needed filling were usually filled by Marcus. His concentration was such that any ums and ers and buts he looked on as cues to change the subject entirely. For some reason, though, he suddenly abandoned his usual technique and stared at Will intently.

'What are you staring at?' Will said eventually.

'I wasn't staring. I was waiting for you to answer the question.'

'I answered it. "Nowhere," I said.'

'You said "Nowhere, but . . .". I was waiting for what came after the but.'

'Well, nothing. I'm not going anywhere for Christmas.'

'So you can come to us.'

'Yes, but—'

'But what?'

'Stop asking me "But what?" all the time.'

'Why?'

'Because . . . it's not polite.'

'Why not?'

'Because . . . I clearly have reservations, Marcus. That's why I keep saying "But". I'm obviously not one hundred per cent convinced that I want to come to your house for Christmas.'

'Why not?'

'Are you being funny?'

'No.'

It was true, of course: Marcus was never deliberately funny. One look at Marcus's face was enough to convince Will that the boy was merely curious, and that his curiosity showed no signs of abating. The conversation had already been extended way beyond Will's comfort point, and now he was beginning to worry that he would eventually be forced to articulate the cruellest of truths: that Marcus's mother was, like her son, a lunatic; that even disregarding the sanity aspect of things they were both a pair of losers anyway; that he couldn't imagine a gloomier Christmas; that he would much, much rather revert to his original plan for oblivion and the entire output of the Marx Brothers than pull wishbones with either of them; that any sane person would feel the same way. If the kid couldn't take a hint, what option did he have? Unless . . .

'I'm sorry, Marcus, I was being rude. I'd love to spend Christmas with you.'

That was the other option. It wasn't his chosen option, but it was the other option.

As it turned out it wasn't just the three of them, which helped him no end when he showed up. He was expecting one of Fiona's logic-free lectures, but all he got was a look; she clearly didn't want to resume hostilities in front of her other guests. There was Marcus's dad Clive, and his girlfriend Lindsey, and his girlfriend's mum, six of them altogether, all squashed round the fold-out dining table in the flat. Will didn't know that the world was like this. As the product of a 1960s second marriage, he was labouring under the misapprehension that when families broke up some of the constituent parts stopped speaking to each other, but the set-up here was different: Fiona and her ex seemed to look back on their relationship as the thing that had brought them together in the first place, rather than something that had gone horribly wrong and driven them apart. It was as if sharing a home and a bed and having a child together was like staying in adjacent rooms in the same hotel, or being in the same class at school – a happy coincidence that had given them the opportunity for an occasional friendship.

This couldn't happen all the time, Will thought, otherwise SPAT would have been full of happy but estranged couples, all introducing their exes and their nexts and their kids from here, there and everywhere; but it hadn't been like that at all – it had been full of justified and righteous anger, and a very great deal of unhappiness. From what he had seen that evening he didn't think too many SPAT families would be reconvening for a game of Twister and a sing-song round the tree today.

But even if it didn't happen very often, it was happening here, today, which at first Will found rather sickening: if people couldn't live together, he reckoned, they should at least have the decency to loathe each other. But actually, as the day wore on and he had a little more to drink, Will could dimly see that to strive for pleasantness and harmony once a year wasn't an entirely contemptible ambition. A room full of people trying to get on made Marcus happy, for a start, and even Will was not cynical enough to wish Marcus anything but happiness on Christmas Day. On New Year's Eve he would make a resolution to recover some of his previous scepticism, but until then he would do as the Romans do, and smile at people even if he disapproved of them. Smiling at people didn't mean that you had to be friends with them for ever, surely? Much later in the day, when common sense prevailed and everyone started squabbling, he learnt that smiling at people didn't even mean that you had to be friends for a day, but for a few hours he was happy to believe in an inverted universe.

He had bought presents for Fiona and Marcus. He gave Marcus a vinyl copy of *Nevermind*, because they didn't own a CD player, and a Kurt Cobain T-shirt, so he could keep in with Ellie; he gave Fiona a pretty groovy and pretty expensive plain glass vase, because she'd complained after the hospital business that she didn't know what to do with the flowers. Marcus gave him a crossword-solver's book to help him with *Countdown*, and Fiona gave him *The Single Parent's Handbook* as a joke.

'What's the joke?' Lindsey asked him.

'Nothing,' said Will quickly and, he could see as soon as he'd said it, feebly.

'Will pretended to have a kid so's he could join this single parent group,' said Marcus.

'Oh,' said Lindsey. The strangers in the room, Lindsey and her mum and Clive, looked at him with some interest, but he declined to elucidate. He just smiled at them, as if it were something anyone would do in the circumstances. He wouldn't like to have to explain what those circumstances were, however.

The present-giving part of the day didn't take that long, and for the most part it was the usual stuff – alarmingly so, given the complicated web of relationships in the room. Penis-shaped chocolate was all very well, Will thought (actually he didn't think that at all, but never mind – he was trying to live and let live) but was penis-shaped chocolate an appropriate gift for your boyfriend's currently boyfriendless and celibate ex-lover? He really didn't know, but it seemed a little tasteless, somehow – surely the whole subject of penises was best left alone on occasions like this? – and anyway Fiona had never struck Will as a penis-shaped-chocolate kind of woman, but she laughed anyway.

As the pile of discarded wrapping paper grew bigger, it struck Will that just about any present given in these circumstances could be deemed inappropriate or darkly meaningful. Fiona gave Lindsey some silk underwear, as if to say, 'Hey, it doesn't matter to me what you two get up to at nights,' and she gave Clive a new book called *The Secret History*, as if to say something rather different. Clive gave Fiona a Nick Drake cassette, and though Clive did not know about the hospital business, as far as Will was aware, there still seemed to be something weird about him forcing a possibly suicidal depressive's music on a possibly suicidal depressive.

Clive's presents for Marcus were in themselves uncontroversial, computer games and sweatshirts and a baseball cap and the Mr Blobby record and so on, but what made them seem pointed was their contrast with the joyless little pile that Fiona had given Marcus earlier in the day: a jumper that wouldn't do him any favours at school (it was baggy and hairy and arty), a couple of books and some piano music – a gentle and very dull maternal reminder, it transpired, that Marcus had given up on his lessons some time ago. Marcus showed him this miserable haul with a pride and enthusiasm that almost broke Will's heart . . . 'And a really nice jumper, and these books look really interesting, and this music because one day when I . . . when I get a bit more time I'm going to really give it a go . . .' Will had never properly given Marcus credit for being a good kid – up until now he'd only noticed his eccentric, troublesome side, probably because there hadn't been much else to notice. But he was good, Will could see that now. Not good as in obedient and uncomplaining; it was more of a mindset kind of good, where you looked at something like a pile of crap presents and recognized that they were given with love and chosen with care, and that was enough. It wasn't even that he was choosing to see the glass as half-full, either – Marcus's glass was full to overflowing, and he would have been amazed and mystified if anyone had attempted to tell him there were kids who would have hurled the hairy jumper and the sheet music back in the parental face and demanded a Nintendo.

Will knew he would never be good in that way. He would never look at a hairy jumper and work out why it was precisely right for him, and why he should wear it at all hours of the day and night. He would look at it and conclude that the person who bought it for him was a pillock. He did that all the time: he'd look at some twenty-five-year-old guy on roller-skates, sashaying his way down Upper Street with his wraparound shades on, and he'd think one of three things: 1) What a prat; or 2) Who the fuck do you think you are?; or 3) How old are you? Fourteen?

Everyone in England was like that, he reckoned. Nobody looked at a roller-skating bloke with wraparound shades on and thought, hey, he looks cool, or, wow, that looks like a fun way of getting some exercise. They just thought: wanker. But Marcus wouldn't. Marcus would either fail to notice the guy at all, or he would stand there with his mouth open, lost in admiration and wonder. This wasn't simply a function of being a child, because, as Marcus knew to his cost, all his classmates belonged to the what-a-prat school of thought; it was simply a function of being Marcus, son of Fiona. In twenty years' time he'd be singing with his eyes closed and swallowing bottles of pills, probably, but at least he was gracious about his Christmas presents. It wasn't much of a compensation for the long years ahead.

TWENTY-THREE

It was good having a mum and dad who didn't decide things together, Marcus thought; that way you got the best of both worlds at Christmas. You got things like jumpers and sheet music, which you had to have, but then you got things like computer games and fun stuff as well. And if his mum and dad had still been together, what would Christmas have been like now, with just the three of them? Pretty boring, probably. This way it was more like a party, what with Will and Lindsey and, well, he wasn't really bothered about Lindsey's mum, if he were honest, but she sort of helped to fill the room up.

After presents they had lunch, which was a big ring doughnut-type thing made of pastry rather than doughnut, with a lovely cream and mushroom sauce in the hole in the middle, and then they had Christmas pudding with five-pence pieces hidden in it (Marcus had two in his portion), and then they pulled crackers and put the hats on, except Will wouldn't wear his for very long. He said it made his head itch.

After they'd watched the queen on TV (nobody wanted to, apart from Lindsey's mum, but whatever old people wanted they got, in Marcus's experience), Clive rolled a joint, and there was a bit of a row. Lindsey was angry with Clive because of her mum, who had no idea what he was doing until people started shouting about it, and Fiona was angry with Clive because of Marcus, who had seen him roll a joint about one thousand million times before.

'He's seen me do it hundreds of times before,' said Clive. It was the wrong thing to say, as it turned out, so Marcus was glad *he* hadn't said it.

'I wish you hadn't told me,' said Fiona. 'I really didn't want to know.'

'What, you thought I'd given up dope the day we separated? Why would I do that?'

'Marcus was younger then. He was always in bed before you started rolling up.'

'I never smoke any, Mum. Dad won't let me.'

'Oh, well that's all right then. As long as you're not smoking any, I have no objection to your father indulging his drug habit in front of you.'

'Ha, ha,' said Marcus. Everyone in the room looked at him, and then they continued the argument.

'I'd hardly describe the occasional spliff as a drug habit, would you?'

'Well obviously I would, because I just have.'

'Can we talk about this another time?' Lindsey asked. Her mother hadn't said anything so far, but she certainly seemed interested in what was going on.

'Why? Because your mother is here?' Marcus had never seen Fiona get cross with Lindsey before, but she was getting cross with her now. 'Unfortunately I can never have a conversation with Marcus's father without your mother being present, for reasons I have yet to fathom. So you'll just have to bloody well put up with it.'

'Look, I'll put the dope away, OK? Then we'll all calm down and watch *International Velvet* and forget about it.'

'*International Velvet* isn't on,' said Marcus. 'It's *Indiana Jones and the Temple of Doom*.'

'That wasn't the point I was making, Marcus.'

Marcus didn't say anything, but inwardly he disagreed: it hadn't been the only point, but it had certainly been one of them.

'I know he takes drugs,' said Lindsey's mum suddenly. 'I'm not daft.'

'I don't . . . *take drugs*,' said Clive.

'Well, what do you call it then?' said Lindsey's mum.

'It's not drug-taking. It's . . . just normal. Drug-taking is something different.'

'Do you think he takes them on his own?' Fiona said to Lindsey's mum. 'Do you think your daughter just sits there watching him?'

'What do you mean?'

'She doesn't mean anything, Mum. I think Clive's idea is an excellent one. Let's put it all away and play charades or something.'

'I didn't say anything about charades. I suggested watching *International Velvet*.'

'It's not *International*—' Marcus begun.

'Shut up, Marcus,' said everybody, and then they all laughed.

The row changed the atmosphere, though. Clive and Fiona agreed to have a proper conversation about the dope thing some other time, Fiona and Lindsey snapped at each other a couple of times, and even Will seemed different, although none of it had had anything to do with him. Marcus reckoned Will had been having a good time up until then, but afterwards he seemed apart from it all, whereas before he'd been one of the family. It was almost like he was laughing at them for rowing, for reasons Marcus couldn't understand. And then, after they'd had supper (there were cold meats for the meat-eaters, and Marcus had some, just to see the look on his mum's face), Suzie came round with her little girl and it was their turn to laugh at Will.

Marcus didn't know that Will hadn't seen Suzie since his mum had told her about Ned and SPAT and all that. Nobody had said anything, but that didn't mean much – Marcus had always presumed that after he had gone to school or to bed adults did all sorts of things they didn't tell him about, but now he was beginning to suspect this wasn't true, and that the adults he knew didn't have any sort of a secret life at all. It was obvious when Suzie walked into the room that this was an awkward moment, especially for Will: he stood up, and then he sat down, and then he stood up again, and then he went red, and then he said he ought to be going, and then Fiona told him not to be pathetic, so he sat down again. The only spare chair was in Will's corner, so Suzie had to sit next to him.

'Have you had a nice day, Suze?' Fiona asked her.

'OK, yeah. We're just on the way home from Grandma's.'

'And how's Grandma?' asked Will. Suzie turned to look at him, opened her mouth to reply, but changed her mind and ignored him completely. It was one of the most exciting things Marcus had ever seen in real life, and easily the most exciting thing he had ever seen in his own living room. (His mum and the sick on the Dead Duck Day didn't count. That wasn't exciting. It was just horrible.) Suzie was snubbing, he reckoned. He'd heard a lot about snubbing, but he had never watched anyone do it. It was great, if a bit frightening.

Will stood up and sat down again. If he really wanted to leave, Marcus thought, nobody could stop him. Or rather, they *could* stop him – if everyone in the room grabbed him and sat on him he wouldn't get very far. (Marcus smiled to himself at the thought of Lindsey's mum sitting on Will's head.) But they *wouldn't* stop him. So why didn't he just stand up, stay stood up and start walking? Why did he keep on bobbing up and down? Maybe there was something about snubbing that Marcus didn't know. Maybe there were snubbing rules, and you just had to sit there and be snubbed, even if you didn't feel like it.

Megan wriggled out of her mother's lap and went over to the Christmas tree.

'There might be a present for you under there, Megan,' said Fiona.

'Oooh, Megan, presents,' said Suzie. Fiona went over to the tree, picked up one of the last two or three parcels and gave it to her. Megan stood there clutching it and looked around the room.

'She's wondering who to give it to,' said Suzie. 'She's had as much fun giving them out as opening them today.'

'How sweet,' said Lindsey's mum. Everyone watched and waited while Megan made her decision; it was almost as if the little girl had understood the snubbing business and wanted to make mischief, because she toddled over to Will and thrust the present at him.

Will didn't move. 'Well, take it from her then, you fool,' said Suzie.

'It's not my bloody present,' said Will. Good for you, Marcus thought. Do some snubbing of your own. The only trouble was that as things stood Will was snubbing Megan, not Suzie, and Marcus didn't think you should snub anyone under the age of three. What was the point? Megan didn't seem to mind, though, because she continued to hold the present out to him until he reached for it.

'Now what?' said Will crossly.

'Open it with her,' said Suzie. She was more patient this time; Will's anger seemed to have calmed her down a little. If she wanted a row with Will, she clearly didn't want it here, in front of all these people.

Will and Megan tore off the paper to reveal some sort of plastic toy that played tunes. Megan looked at it and waved it at Will.

'What now?' said Will.

'Play with her,' said Suzie. 'God, spot the childless person here.'

'Tell you what,' said Will. 'You play with her.' He tossed Suzie the toy. 'As I'm so bloody clueless.'

'Maybe you could learn to be less clueless,' said Suzie.

'What for?'

'I would have thought that in your line of work it might be handy to know how to play with kids.'

'What's your line of work?' Lindsey asked politely, as if this were a normal conversation amongst a normal group of people.

'He doesn't do anything,' Marcus said. 'His dad wrote "Santa's Super Sleigh" and he earns a million pounds a minute.'

'He pretends he has a child so he can join single parent groups and chat up single mothers,' said Suzie.

'Yeah, but he doesn't get paid for that,' said Marcus.

Will stood up again, but this time he didn't sit down.

'Thanks for the lunch and everything,' he said. 'I'm off.'

'Suzie has a right to express her anger, Will,' said Fiona.

'Yes, and she's expressed it, and now I have a right to go home.' He started to weave his way through the presents and glasses and people towards the door.

'He's my friend,' Marcus said suddenly. 'I invited him. I should be able to tell him when he goes home.'

'I'm not sure that's how the whole hospitality thing works,' said Will.

'But I don't want him to go yet,' said Marcus. 'It's not fair. How come Lindsey's mum's still here, and no one invited her, and the one person I invited is leaving because everyone's being horrible to him?'

'First of all,' said Fiona, 'I invited Lindsey's mum, and it's my house too. And we haven't been horrible to Will. Suzie's angry with Will, as she has every right to be, and she's telling him so.'

Marcus felt as though he were in a play. He was standing up, and Will was standing up, and then Fiona stood up; but Lindsey and her mum and Clive were sat on the sofa watching, in a line, with their mouths open.

'All he did was make up a kid for a couple of weeks. God. That's nothing. So what? Who cares? Kids at school do worse than that every day.'

'The point is, Marcus, that Will left school a long time ago. He should have grown out of making people up by now.'

'Yeah, but he's behaved better since, hasn't he?'

'Can I go yet?' said Will, but nobody took any notice.

'Why? What's he done?' asked Suzie.

'He never wanted me round his flat every day. I just went. And he bought me those shoes, and at least he listens when I say I'm having a hard time at school. You just tell me to get used to it. And he knew who Kirk O'Bane was.'

'Kurt Cobain,' said Will.

'And it's not like you lot never do anything wrong ever, is it?' said

Marcus. 'I mean . . .' He had to be careful here. He knew he couldn't say too much, or even anything at all, about the hospital stuff. 'I mean, how come I got to know Will in the first place?'

'Because you threw a bloody great baguette at a duck's head and killed it, basically,' said Will.

Marcus couldn't believe Will was bringing that up now. It was supposed to be all about how everyone else did things wrong, not about how he had killed the duck. But then Suzie and Fiona started laughing, and Marcus could see that Will knew what he was doing.

'Is that true, Marcus?' said his father.

'There was something wrong with it,' said Marcus. 'I think it was going to die anyway.'

Suzie and Fiona laughed even harder. The audience on the sofa looked appalled. Will sat down again.

TWENTY-FOUR

Will fell in love on New Year's Eve, and the experience took him completely by surprise. She was called Rachel, she illustrated children's books, and she looked a little bit like Laura Nyro on the cover of *Gonna Take A Miracle* – nervy, glamorous, Bohemian, clever, lots of long, unruly dark hair.

Will had never wanted to fall in love. When it had happened to friends it had always struck him as a peculiarly unpleasant-seeming experience, what with all the loss of sleep and weight, and the unhappiness when it was unreciprocated, and the suspect, dippy happiness when it was working out. These were people who could not control themselves, or protect themselves, people who, if only temporarily, were no longer content to occupy their own space, people who could no longer rely on a new jacket, a bag of grass and an afternoon rerun of *The Rockford Files* to make them complete.

Lots of people, of course, would be thrilled to take their seats next to their computer-generated ideal life-partner, but Will was a realist, and he could see immediately that there was only cause for panic. He was almost sure that Rachel was about to make him very miserable indeed, mostly because he couldn't see anything he might have which could possibly interest her.

If there was a disadvantage to the life he had chosen for himself, a life without work and care and difficulty and detail, a life without context and texture, then he had finally found it: when he met an intelligent, cultured, ambitious, beautiful, witty and single woman at a New Year's Eve party, he felt like a blank twit, a cypher, someone who had done nothing with his whole life apart from watch *Countdown* and drive around listening to Nirvana records. That had to be a bad thing, he reckoned. If you were falling in love with someone beautiful and intelligent and all the rest of it, then feeling like a blank twit put you at something of a disadvantage.

One of his problems, he reflected as he was trying to dredge his memory for a single tiny scrap of experience that this woman might regard as worth her momentary contemplation, was that he was reasonably good-looking and reasonably articulate. It gave people the wrong impression. It gave him admission to a party from which he should be barred by ferocious bouncers with thick necks and tattoos. He may have been good-looking and articulate, but that was just a quirk of genetics, environment and education; at his core he was ugly and monosyllabic. Maybe he should undergo some sort of reverse plastic surgery – something that would rearrange his features so that they were less even, and push his eyes closer together or further apart. Or maybe he should put on an enormous amount of weight, sprout a few extra chins, grow so fat that he sweated profusely all the time. And, of course, he should start grunting like an ape.

Because the thing was that when this Rachel woman sat down next to him at dinner she was interested, for the first five minutes, before she'd worked him out, and in that five minutes he got a glimpse of what life could be like if he were in any way interesting. On balance, he thought, he'd prefer not to have that glimpse. What good did it do him, after all? He wasn't going to get to sleep with Rachel. He wasn't going to go to a restaurant with her, or see what her sitting room looked like, or get to understand how her father's affair with her mother's best friend had affected her views on having children. He hated the five-minute window of opportunity. In the end, he thought, he would be far happier if she turned round to look at him, just about managed not to vomit, and turned her back on him for the rest of the evening.

He missed Ned. Ned had given him an extra something, a little *il ne sait quoi*, that would have come in handy on an evening like this. He wasn't going to bring him back to life, though, poor little sod. Let him rest in peace.

'How do you know Robert?' Rachel was asking him.

'Oh, just . . .' Robert produced television programmes. He hung out with actors and writers and directors. People who knew Robert were arty movers and shakers, and were almost obliged to be glamorous. Will wanted to say that he had written the music for Robert's last film, or given him his big break, or that they met for lunch to talk about the godawful mess that was this government's arts policy. He wanted to say that, but he couldn't.

'Just . . . I used to buy my dope off him years ago.' That, unhappily, was the truth. Before Robert became a television producer, he was a dope dealer. Not a dope dealer with a baseball bat and a pit-bull, just someone who bought a bit extra to sell on to his mates, who at the time included Will, because Will was going out with a friend of Robert's . . . Anyway, it didn't matter why he was knocking around with Robert in the mid-eighties. The point was that he was the only person in the room who neither moved nor shook, and now Rachel knew it.

'Oh, right,' she said. 'But you've kept in touch.'

Maybe he could make up some story about why he still saw Robert, a story that might cast him in a more flattering light, make him seem a little more complicated.

'Yeah. Dunno why, really.' No story, then, obviously. Oh well. The truth was that he didn't know why they'd kept in touch. They got on reasonably well, but Robert had got on reasonably well with most of that crowd, and Will had never been entirely sure why he had been the one who survived the inevitable career-change cull. Maybe – and this sounded paranoid, but he was sure there was a grain of truth in here somewhere – he was enough of a deadbeat to demonstrate to the people here that Robert had pre-media roots, while at the same time he was presentable enough not to scare them all away.

He'd lost Rachel, for now at least. She was talking to the person sitting on her other side. What could he reel her back with? He must have had some talent or other which he could exaggerate and dramatize somehow. Cooking? He could cook a bit, but who couldn't? Maybe he was writing a novel and had forgotten about it. What had he been good at when he was at school? Spelling. 'Hey, Rachel, how many 'c's in necessary?' She probably knew anyway. It was hopeless. The most interesting thing about his life, he realized, was Marcus. That was something which set him apart. 'Sorry to butt in, Rachel, but I have this weird relationship with a twelve-year-old boy. Is that any good to you?' OK, the material needed some work, but it was there, definitely. It just needed shaping. He vowed to bring up Marcus at the first available opportunity.

Rachel had noticed he wasn't talking to anyone, and wheeled round so that he could be included in a conversation about whether there was anything new under the sun, with particular reference to contemporary popular music. Rachel said that to her Nirvana sounded just like Led Zeppelin.

'I know a twelve-year-old who'd kill you for saying that,' said Will. It wasn't true, of course. A couple of weeks ago, Marcus had thought that the lead singer of Nirvana played for Manchester United, so he was probably not yet at the stage where he wanted to annihilate people who accused the band of being derivative.

'So do I, come to that,' said Rachel. 'Maybe they should meet. What's yours called?'

He's not mine, exactly, he thought. 'Marcus,' he said.

'Mine's Ali. Alistair.'

'Right.'

'And is Marcus into skateboards and rap and *The Simpsons* and so on?'

Will raised his eyes skywards and chuckled fondly, and the misapprehension was cast in concrete. It wasn't his fault, this conversation. He hadn't lied once in the entire minute and a half. OK, he had been speaking more figuratively than the expression usually implied when he had said that Marcus would kill her. And OK, the rolling eyes and the fond chuckle did suggest a certain amount of parental indulgence. But he hadn't actually said that Marcus was his son. That was one hundred per cent her interpretation. Certainly over fifty per cent, anyway. But it definitely wasn't the SPAT thing, when he'd lied through his teeth for the entire duration of the evening.

'And is Marcus's mother here tonight?'

'Ummm . . .' Will looked up and down the dinner table as if to remind himself one way or the other. 'No.' Not a lie! Not a lie! Marcus's mother was not there!

'You're not spending New Year's Eve with her?' Rachel was narrowing her eyes and looking down her nose to indicate that she knew this was a leading question.

'No. We, er, we don't live together.' He'd really got the hang of this truth-telling business now, he felt. If anything, he'd moved right away from lying and towards understatement, because not only was he not living with Fiona at the moment, but he had never lived with her, and never intended to live with her in the future.

'I'm sorry.'

'It's OK. How about Ali's dad?'

'Not at this table. Not in this city. Not in this country. He gives me his phone number when he moves.'

'Right.'

Will had at least managed to introduce some friction into the conversation. Until he'd played the Marcus card he'd kept slipping off before he'd even started. Now he felt as though he were climbing a mountain, rather than a glacier. He imagined himself right at the bottom of the cliff-face, looking up and around for footholds.

'Which country is he in, then?'

'The States. California. I'd prefer Australia, but there you are. At least it's the west coast.'

Will reckoned he'd now heard fifty-seven varieties of this conversation, but this gave him an advantage: he knew how it went, and go it did. He might not have done anything in the last decade and a half, but he could cluck sympathetically when a woman told him how badly her ex-husband had behaved. Clucking was something he had got really good at. But it worked, as clucking often did – no one, he decided, ever did themselves any harm by listening attentively to other people's woes. Rachel's story was, by SPAT standards, run-of-the-mill, and it turned out that she hated her ex because of who he was, rather than what he had done to her.

'So why the fuck did you have a child with him?' He was drunk. It was New Year's Eve. He was feeling cheeky.

She laughed. 'Good question. No answer. You change your mind about people. What's Marcus's mother's name?'

'Fiona.' Which, of course, it was.

'Did you change your mind about her?'

'Not really.'

'So what happened?'

'I dunno.' He shrugged, and somehow managed to give a rather convincing impression of a man who was still baffled, shell-shocked even. The words and the gesture were born of desperation; it was ironic, then, that they somehow managed to make a connection.

Rachel smiled, and picked up the knife she hadn't used, and examined it. 'In the end, "I dunno" is the only honest answer anyone can give, isn't it? Because I dunno either, and I'd be kidding myself, and you, if I pretended any different.'

At midnight they sought each other out and kissed, a kiss that was somewhere between cheek and lip, the embarrassed ambiguity hopefully significant. And at half-past midnight, just before Rachel left, they arranged to get their lads together to compare skateboards and baseball caps and the Christmas edition of *The Simpsons*.

TWENTY-FIVE

Ellie was at Suzie's New Year's Eve party. For a moment, Marcus thought it was just someone who looked like Ellie, and wore the same Kurt Cobain sweatshirt as Ellie, but then the Ellie lookalike saw him and shouted 'Marcus!' and came over and hugged him and kissed him on the head, which kind of cleared up the confusion.

'What are you doing here?' he asked her.

'We always come here on New Year's Eve,' she said. 'My mum's really good friends with Suzie.'

'I've never seen you here.'

'You've never been here on New Year's Eve, you twit.'

It was true. He'd been to Suzie's flat loads of times, but he'd never come to the parties. This was the first year he'd been allowed to go. Why was it that even in the simplest, most straightforward conversations with Ellie he found something stupid to say?

'Which one's your mum?'

'Don't ask,' said Ellie. 'Not now.'

'Why not?'

'Because she's dancing.'

Marcus looked over at the very small group dancing in the corner where the TV usually was. There were four people, three women and a man, and only one of them seemed to be having a good time: she was sort of punching the air with her fists and shaking her hair. Marcus guessed that this had to be Ellie's mum – not because she looked like her (no adult looked like Ellie, because no adult would chop her hair up with kitchen scissors and wear black lipstick, and that was all you saw), but because Ellie was clearly embarrassed, and this was the only dancer who would embarrass anyone. The other dancers were embarrassed themselves, which meant that they weren't actually embarrassing; they weren't doing much more than tapping their feet, and the only way you could tell they were dancing at all was that they were facing each other but not looking at each other and not talking.

'I wish I could dance like that,' said Marcus.

Ellie made a face. 'Anyone can dance like that. All you need is no brain and crap music.'

'I think she looks great. She's enjoying herself.'

'Who cares whether she's enjoying herself? The point is she looks like a total cretin.'

'Don't you like your mum, then?'

'She's all right.'

'What about your dad?'

'He's all right. They don't live together.'

'Do you mind?'

'No. Sometimes. Don't want to talk about it. So, Marcus, have you had a good nineteen ninety-three?'

Marcus thought for a moment about 1993, and a moment was all it took to decide that 1993 hadn't been a very good year at all. He only had ten or eleven others to compare it with, and three or four of them he couldn't remember much about, but as far as he could see nobody would have enjoyed the twelve months he'd had. Moving schools, the hospital stuff, the other kids at school . . . It had been totally useless.

'No.'

'You need a drink,' said Ellie. 'What do you want? I'll get you a drink and you can tell me all about it. I might get bored and wander off, though. I do that.'

'OK.'

'So, what are you drinking?'

'Coke.'

'You've got to have a proper drink.'

'I'm not allowed.'

'You're allowed by me. In fact, if you're going to be my date for the evening, I insist that you have a proper drink. I'll put something in the Coke, OK?'

'OK.'

Ellie disappeared, and Marcus looked round for his mum: she was talking to a man he didn't know and laughing a lot. He was pleased, because he had been worried about tonight. Will had told him to watch out for his mum on New Year's Eve, and though he didn't explain why, Marcus could guess: a lot of people who weren't happy killed themselves then. He had seen it somewhere, *Casualty*, maybe, and as a consequence the night had been hanging over him. He thought he'd be watching her all evening, looking for something in her eyes or her voice or her words that would tell him she was thinking about trying it again, but it wasn't like that: she was getting drunk and laughing, like everyone else. Had anyone ever killed themselves a couple of hours after laughing a lot? Probably not, he reckoned. You were miles away, if you were laughing, and he did now think of it all in terms of distance. Ever since the Dead Duck Day he had imagined his mother's suicide to be something like the edge of a cliff: sometimes, on days when she seemed sad or distracted, he felt as though they were a little too close for comfort, and other days, like Christmas Day or today, they seemed to be a long way away, in the middle lane of a motorway and cruising. On the Dead Duck Day it had been way too close, two wheels over the edge and lots of terrible skidding noises.

Ellie came back with a plastic beaker containing something which looked like Coke but smelt like trifle.

'What's in it?'

'Sherry.'

'Is that what people drink? Coke and sherry?' He took a cautious sip. It was nice, sweet and thick and warming.

'So why has it been such a shit year?' Ellie asked. 'You can tell me. Auntie Ellie will understand.'

'Just . . . I dunno. Horrible things happened.' He didn't really want to tell Ellie what they were, because he didn't know whether they were friends or not. It could go either way with her: he might go into her form room one morning and she'd shout it all out to anyone who would listen, or she might be really nice. It wasn't worth taking the risk.

'Your mum tried to kill herself, didn't she?'

Marcus looked at her, took a big gulp of Coke and trifle, and was nearly sick all over her feet.

'No,' he said quickly, when he had finished coughing and swallowed the sick back down.

'Are you sure?'

'Well,' he said. 'Not positive.' He knew how stupid that sounded and he started to blush, but then Ellie burst into peals of laughter. He had forgotten that he made Ellie laugh so much and he was grateful.

'I'm sorry, Marcus. I know it's serious, but you are funny.'

He started to laugh too, then, little uncontrollable giggles that tasted of puke and sherry.

Marcus had never had a proper talk with someone of his own age before. He had had proper talks with his mum, of course, and his dad, and Will, kind of, but you expected to have proper talks with people like that and, anyway, you still had to watch what you said. It was different, much easier, with Ellie, even though she was a) a girl, b) older than him, and c) scary.

It turned out she'd known for ages: she'd overheard a conversation between her mum and Suzie just after it happened, but didn't make the connection until much later.

'And do you know what I thought? I feel terrible about it now, but I was like, why shouldn't she kill herself if she wants to?'

'But she's got me.'

'I didn't know you then.'

'No, but I mean, how would you like it if your mum killed herself?'

Ellie smiled. 'How would I like it? I wouldn't like it. Because I like my mum. But, you know. It's her life.'

Marcus thought about that. He didn't know whether it was his mum's life or not.

'What about if you have kids? Then it's not your life any more, is it?'

'Your dad's around, isn't he? He would've looked after you.'

'Yeah, but . . .' Something wasn't right with what Ellie was saying. She was talking as if his mum might go down with flu, so his dad would have to take him swimming.

'See, if your dad killed himself, nobody would say, you know, oh, he's got a son to look after. But when women do it, people get all upset. It's not fair.'

'That's because I'm living with my mum. If I was living with my dad, I'd think it wasn't his life either.'

'But you aren't living with your dad, are you? How many of us are? At our school, there's about a million kids whose parents have split. And none of them are living with their dads.'

'Stephen Wood is.'

'Yeah, right, Stephen Wood. You win.'

Even though what they were talking about was miserable, Marcus was enjoying the conversation. It seemed big, as though you could walk round it and see different things, and that never happened when you talked to kids normally. 'Did you see *Top of the Pops* last night?' There wasn't much to think about in that, was there? You said yes or no and it was over. He could see now why his mum *chose* friends, instead of just putting up with anyone she happened to bump into, or sticking with people who supported the same football team, or wore the same clothes, which was pretty much what happened at school; his mum must have conversations like this with Suzie, conversations which moved, conversations where each thing the other person said seemed to lead you on somewhere.

He wanted to keep it going but he didn't know how, because Ellie was the one who said the things that got them started. He was OK at coming up with the answers, he reckoned, but he doubted if he'd ever be clever enough to make Ellie think in the way she made him think, and that panicked him a little: he wished they were equally clever, but they weren't, and they probably never would be, because Ellie would always be older than him. Maybe when he was thirty-two and she was thirty-five it wouldn't matter so much, but it felt to him that unless he said something really smart in the next few minutes, then she wouldn't hang around for the rest of the evening, let alone for the next twenty years. Suddenly he remembered the thing boys were supposed to ask girls at parties. He didn't want to ask, because he knew he was hopeless at it, but the alternative – to let Ellie wander away and talk to somebody else – was just too horrible.

'Would you like to dance, Ellie?'

Ellie stared at him, her eyes wide with surprise.

'Marcus!' She started laughing again, really hard. 'You're so funny. Of course I wouldn't like to dance! I couldn't think of anything worse!'

He knew then that he should have thought of another proper question, something about Kurt Cobain or politics, because Ellie disappeared off somewhere for a smoke, and he had to go and find his mum. But Ellie came looking for him at midnight and gave him a hug, so he knew that even though he'd been stupid, he hadn't been unforgivably stupid.

'Happy New Year, darling,' she said, and he blushed.

'Thank you. Happy New Year to you.'

'And I hope nineteen ninety-four is better for all of us than nineteen ninety-three was. Hey, do you want to see something really disgusting?'

Marcus wasn't at all sure that he did, but he was given no choice in the matter. Ellie grabbed his arm and took him through the back door to the garden. He tried to ask her where they were going, but she shushed him.

'Look,' she whispered. Marcus peered into the darkness. He could just make out two human shapes kissing with frantic energy; the man was pressing the woman against the garden shed and his hands were all over her.

'Who is it?' Marcus asked Ellie.

'My mum. My mum and a guy called Tim Porter. She's drunk. They do this every year, and I don't know why they bother. Every New Year's Day she wakes up and says, "My God, I think I went outside with Tim Porter last night." Pathetic. PATHETIC!' She shouted out the last word so that she'd be heard, and Marcus saw Ellie's mum push the man away and look in their direction.

'Ellie? Is that you?'

'You said you weren't going to do that this year.'

'It's none of your business what I do. Go back inside.'

'No.'

'Do as you're told.'

'No. You're disgusting. Forty-three years old and you're snogging against a garden shed.'

'One night of the year I get to behave nearly as badly as you do on the other three hundred and sixty-four, and you stand there giving me a hard time. Go away.'

'Come on, Marcus. Let's leave the SAD OLD TART to get on with it.'

Marcus followed Ellie back into the house. He hadn't seen his mum do anything like that, and he couldn't imagine that she ever would, but he could see how it might happen to other people's mums.

'Doesn't that bother you?' he asked Ellie when they were inside.

'Nah. It doesn't mean anything, does it? It's just her having some fun. She doesn't get much, really.'

Even though it didn't seem to bother Ellie, it bothered Marcus. It was just too odd for words. It wouldn't have happened in Cambridge, he didn't think, but what he couldn't work out was whether Cambridge was different because it wasn't London, or because it was where his parents had lived together, and where, therefore, life was simpler – no snogging with strange people in front of your kid, and no yelling rude words at your mum. There were no rules here, and he was old enough to know that when you went to a place, or a time, with no rules then things were bound to be more complicated.

TWENTY-SIX

'I don't get it,' said Marcus. He and Will had walked down to an amusement arcade at the Angel to play on the video machines, and the Angel Funhouse, with its epileptic lights and sirens and explosions and tramps, turned out to be a suitably nightmarish setting for the difficult conversation Will knew they were going to have. It was, in a way, a grotesque version of popping the question. He had chosen the setting, somewhere that would soften Marcus up and make him more likely to say yes, and all he had to do was spit it out.

'There's nothing to get,' said Will blithely. It wasn't true, of course. There was a lot to get, from Marcus's point of view, and Will could quite see why he wasn't getting it.

'But why did you tell her you were my dad?'

'I didn't tell her. She just sort of got the wrong end of the stick.'

'So why didn't you just say, you know, "Sorry, you've got the wrong end of the stick"? She probably wouldn't have minded. Why would she care whether you were my dad or not?'

'Don't you ever have conversations where someone took a wrong turn at some point, and then it goes on and on and it becomes too late to put things right? Say someone thought your name was Mark, not Marcus, and every time they saw you they said, "Hello, Mark", and you're going to yourself, Oh, no, I can't tell him now, 'cos he'll be really embarrassed that he's been calling me Mark for the last six months.'

'Six months!'

'Or however long it is.'

'I'd just tell him the first time he got it wrong.'

'It's not always possible to do that.'

'How can it not be possible to tell someone they've got your name wrong?'

'Because . . .' Will knew that sometimes it was not possible through personal experience. One of his neighbours opposite, a nice old guy with a stoop and a horrible little Yorkshire terrier, called him Bill – always had done and presumably always would, right up till the day he died. It actually irritated Will, who was not, he felt, by any stretch of the imagination, a Bill. Bill wouldn't smoke spliffs and listen to Nirvana. So why had he allowed this misapprehension to continue? Why hadn't he just said, four years ago, 'Actually my name's Will'? Marcus was right, of course, but being right was no use if the rest of the world was wrong.

'Anyway,' he continued, in a brisk let's-cut-the-crap tone. 'The point is, this woman thinks you're my son.'

'So tell her I'm not.'

'No.'

'Why not?'

'We're going round and round in circles here, Marcus. Why can't you just accept the facts?'

'I'll tell her, if you like. I don't mind.'

'That's very kind of you, Marcus, but that wouldn't help.'

'Why not?'

'Oh, for Christ's sake! Because she has this rare disease, and if she believes something that's not right and you tell her the truth, her brain will boil in her head and she'll die.'

'How old do you think I am? Shit. You've made me lose a life now.'

Will was beginning to come to the conclusion that he was not, as he had always previously thought, a good liar. He was an enthusiastic liar, certainly, but enthusiasm was not the same thing as efficacy, and he was now constantly finding himself in a situation whereby, having lied through his teeth for minutes or days or weeks, he was obliged to articulate the humiliating truth. Good liars would never do that. Good liars would have persuaded Marcus ages ago that there were hundreds of good reasons why he should pretend to be Will's son, but Will could only think of one.

'Marcus, listen. I'm really interested in this woman, and the only thing I could think of that might make her interested in me was to let her believe you were my son. So I did. I'm sorry. And I'm sorry I didn't tell you straight out.'

Marcus stared at the video screen – he'd just been exploded by a cross between Robocop and Godzilla – and took a long pull on his can of Coke.

'I don't get it,' he said, and burped ostentatiously.

'Oh, come on, Marcus. We've been here before.'

'What do you mean, you're really interested in her? Why is she so interesting?'

'I mean . . .' He groaned with despair. 'Leave me with just one scrap of dignity, Marcus. That's all I'm asking. Just a little tiny, tatty piece.'

Marcus looked at him as if he had suddenly started speaking in Urdu.

'What's dignity got to do with her being interesting?'

'OK. Forget dignity. I don't deserve any. I fancy this woman, Marcus. I want to go out with her. I'd like her to be my girlfriend.'

Finally, Marcus swivelled his eyes away from the TV screen, and Will could see they were shining with fascination and pleasure.

'Really?'

'Yes, really.' Really, really. He had thought of almost nothing else since New Year's Eve (not that he had much to think about, apart from the word Rachel, a vague recollection of lots of long dark hair and a lot of foolish fantasies involving picnics and babies and tearfully devoted mothers-in-law and huge hotel beds) and it was a relief to be able to bring Rachel out into the light, even though it was only Marcus who was up there to inspect her, and even though the words he had had to use did not, he felt, do her justice. He wanted Rachel to be his wife, his lover, the centre of his whole world; a girlfriend implied that he would see her from time to time, that she would have some kind of independent existence away from him, and he didn't want that at all.

'How do you know?'

'How do I know?'

'Yeah. How do you know you want her to be your girlfriend?'

'I don't know. I just feel it in my guts.' That was exactly where he felt it. He wasn't feeling it in his heart, or his head, or even his groin; it was his guts, which had immediately tensed up and allowed for the ingestion of nothing more calorific than cigarette smoke. If he went on ingesting only cigarette smoke he might lose some weight.

'You just met her the once? On New Year's Eve?'

'Yeah.'

'And that was enough? You knew you wanted her to be your girlfriend straight away? Can I have another fifty pence?'

Will gave him a pound coin abstractedly. It was true that something had happened in him immediately, but what had pushed him over the edge into the land of permanent daydream was a remark Robert had made a couple of days later, when Will had phoned to thank him for the party. 'Rachel liked you,' he said, and though it wasn't much to build a whole future on, it was all Will had needed. Reciprocation was a pretty powerful stimulant to the imagination.

'What is this? How long should I have known her for, according to you?'

'Well, I wouldn't really describe myself as an expert.' Will laughed at Marcus's turn of phrase, and the furrowed brow which both accompanied it and seemed to contradict it: anyone who could look that professional while talking about the minutiae of dating was clearly a twelve-year-old Doctor Love. 'But I didn't know when I met Ellie the first time that I wanted her to be my girlfriend. It took a while to develop.'

'Well, that's a sign of maturity, I guess.' The Ellie business was news to Will, and suddenly he could see this was where they had been heading right from the beginning. 'You want Ellie to be your girlfriend?'

'Yeah. Course.'

'Not just your friend?'

'Well.' He inserted the pound coin into the slot and pressed the one-player button. 'I was going to ask you about that. What would you say are the main differences?'

'You're funny, Marcus.'

'I know. People keep telling me. I don't care. I just want you to answer the question.'

'OK. Do you want to touch her? That's got to be the first thing.'

Marcus carried on blasting away at the monster on the screen, apparently oblivious to Will's profundities.

'Well?'

'I don't know. I'm thinking about it. Go on.'

'That's it.'

'That's it? There's only one difference?'

'Yeah. Marcus. You have heard of sex, haven't you? It's kind of a big deal.'

'I know, I'm not stupid. But I can't believe there's nothing more to it. Oh, piss.' Marcus had lost another life. ''Cos I'm not sure if I want to touch Ellie or not. But I still know that I want her to be my girlfriend.'

'OK, so what things do you want to be different?'

'I want to be with her more. I want to be with her all the time, instead of just when I bump into her. And I want to get rid of Zoe, even though I like Zoe, because I want Ellie to myself. And I want to tell her things first, before I tell anyone, even you or Mum. And I don't want her to have another boyfriend. If I could have all those things, I wouldn't mind if I touched her or not.'

Will shook his head, a gesture that Marcus missed because his eyes were still glued to the video screen. 'I tell you, Marcus, you'll learn. You won't feel like that for ever.'

But later that night, when he was home on his own and listening to the sort of music he needed to listen to when he felt like this, music that seemed to find the sore spot in him and press up hard against it, he remembered the deal Marcus was prepared to strike. And yes, he wanted to touch Rachel (the fantasies which involved enormous hotel beds definitely involved touching as well), but right now, he thought, if he had the choice, he'd settle for the less and the more that Marcus wanted.

The conversation in the video games arcade at least had the virtue of creating a mutuality between them: they had both confessed to something they wanted, and those somethings were, when all was said and done, not entirely dissimilar, even though the someones connected with the somethings evidently were. Will couldn't get a very clear sense of Ellie from Marcus's descriptions – he always ended up with the impression of an angry ball of black-lipsticked motion, an unimaginable cross between Siouxsie of the Banshees and the Roadrunner – but he could picture her well enough to see that Ellie and Rachel would not pass as twins. This mutuality, however, seemed more than enough to persuade Marcus that it would be disloyal of him, and some kind of curse on his own desire, not to act as Will's son for an afternoon. So Will made the call, heart thumping, and wangled a Saturday lunch invitation for the pair of them. Marcus came round just after midday, in the hairy jumper Fiona had given him for Christmas and a disastrous pair of canary-yellow cords that might have looked cute on a four-year-old. Will was wearing his favourite Paul Smith shirt and a black leather jacket that he liked to think made him look a little like Matt Dillon in *Drugstore Cowboy*. What was going on here, Will reckoned, was that Marcus was showing a refreshingly rebellious disregard for his dad's dandyism, so he tried to inculcate a feeling of pride, and to ignore the urge to take him out shopping.

'What did you tell your mum?' Will asked him in the car on the way over to Rachel's place.

'I told her you wanted me to meet your new girlfriend.'

'And she was all right about that?'

'No. She thinks you're mad.'

'I'm not surprised. Why would I take you to meet my new girlfriend?'

'Why would you tell your new girlfriend I was your son? You can think up your own explanations next time, if mine are no good. Listen, I've got some questions. How much did I weigh at birth?'

'I dunno. It was your birth.'

'Yeah, but you should know, shouldn't you? If you're my dad, I mean.'

'Surely at this stage in our relationship we're a bit beyond birth weights, aren't we? If you were twelve weeks old it might come up, but twelve *years* old . . .'

'OK, so when's my birthday?'

'Marcus, she doesn't suspect we're not father and son. She's not going to be trying to catch us out.'

'But suppose it came up. Suppose I said, you know, Dad's promised me a new Nintendo for my birthday, and she said to you, when's his birthday?'

'Why is she asking me? Why isn't she asking you?'

'Just suppose.'

'OK, when's your birthday?'

'August the nineteenth.'

'I'll remember, I promise. August the nineteenth.'

'And what's my favourite food?'

'Tell me,' Will said wearily.

'Pasta with the mushroom and tomato sauce my mum makes.'

'Right.'

'And where did I go the first time I went abroad?'

'I don't know. Grenoble.'

'Doh,' said Marcus scornfully. 'Why would I want to go there? Barcelona.'

'OK. Got it. Barcelona.'

'And who's my mum?'

'Sorry?'

'Who's my mum?'

The question was so basic and yet so pertinent that for a moment Will was completely thrown.

'Your mum's your mum.'

'So you were married to my mum and you've split up.'

'Yeah. Whatever.'

'And does that bother you? Or me?'

Suddenly the absurdity of the questions got to both of them. Marcus began to giggle, a peculiar high-pitched miaow that sounded nothing like himself or any other human but proved to be extraordinarily infectious. Will launched into his own version of a giggling fit.

'It doesn't bother me. Does it bother you?' he said eventually.

But Marcus was unable to reply. He was still miaowing.

One sentence, the first sentence she said, was all it took to bring the whole thing, the elaborate past, present and future he had created for the two of them, crashing to the floor.

'Hi. It's Will and . . . Mark, is that right?'

'Marcus,' said Marcus, and nudged Will meaningfully.

'Come in, both of you. Come and meet Ali.'

Will had remembered every single tiny detail that Rachel had offered him that first night. He knew the names of the books she had illustrated, although he wasn't absolutely sure whether the first one was called *The Way* to *the Woods* or *The Way* Through *the Woods* – he would have to check – and her ex's name, and where he lived, and what he did, and . . . It was unimaginable that he could have forgotten Ali's name. That was one of his principal facts. That would be like forgetting when England had won the World Cup, or the name of Luke Skywalker's real father – it just couldn't be done, no matter how hard you tried. But she had forgotten Marcus's name – Mark, Marcus, it was all the same to her – and it was thus perfectly clear that she hadn't spent the last ten days in a sleepless fever of imagining and remembering and wondering. He felt crushed. He might as well give up now. These feelings were exactly what he had been so afraid of, and this was why he had been so sure that falling in love was rubbish, and, surprise surprise, it was rubbish, and . . . and it was too late.

Rachel lived just up the road from Camden Lock, in a tall, thin house full of books and old furniture and sepia photographs of dramatic, romantic Eastern European relatives, and for a moment Will was grateful that his flat and her house would never get a chance to meet, current north London seismological conditions prevailing. Her house would be warm and welcoming, and his would be cocky and cool, and he'd be ashamed of it.

She shouted up the stairs: 'Ali!' Nothing. 'ALI!' Still nothing. She looked at Will and shrugged. 'He's got his headphones on. Shall we go up?'

'He won't mind?' Will would have minded, when he was twelve years old, for reasons he didn't necessarily want to remember.

Ali's bedroom door was indistinguishable from all the other bedroom doors: no skull and crossbones, no 'Keep Out' signs, no hip-hop graffiti; once inside, however, there was no question but that the room belonged to a boy stuck between the equally wretched states of childhood and adolescence in early 1994. Everything was there – the Ryan Giggs poster and the Michael Jordan poster and the Pamela Anderson poster and the Super Mario stickers . . . A social historian of the future would probably be able to date the room to within a twenty-four-hour period. Will glanced at Marcus, who was looking bewildered. Standing Marcus in front of posters of Ryan Giggs and Michael Jordan was like taking an average twelve-year-old to look at the Tudors in the National Portrait Gallery. Ali himself was slumped in front of his computer, headphones still on, oblivious to his guests. His mother went over and tapped him on the shoulder, and he jumped.

'Oh, hi. Sorry.' Ali stood up, and Will immediately saw that this wasn't going to work. Ali was cool – basketball boots, baggy skatepunk trousers, shaggy grunge hair, even an earring – and his face seemed to darken when he took in Marcus's yellow cords and hairy jumper.

'Marcus Ali, Ali Marcus,' said Rachel. Marcus offered his hand, and Ali took it almost satirically. 'Ali Will, Will Ali.' Will raised his eyebrows in Ali's direction. He thought Ali might appreciate the understatement.

'Do you guys want to hang out up here for a while?' Rachel asked them.

Marcus glanced at Will and Will nodded once, while Rachel's back was turned towards him.

'Yeah,' Marcus shrugged, and for a moment Will loved him, really loved him.

'OK,' said Ali, with even less enthusiasm.

Rachel and Will went downstairs; ten minutes later – time enough for Will to have dreamed up a whole scenario whereby the four of them took a house in Spain for the summer – they heard a door slam. Rachel went to investigate and came flying back into the sitting room seconds afterwards.

'I'm afraid Marcus has gone home,' she said.

TWENTY-SEVEN

Marcus had meant to try. He knew the lunch with Rachel was a big thing for Will, and he knew too that if he did well today, acted out his part, then Will might feel that he had to help him out with Ellie somehow. But this Ali kid never gave him a chance. Will and Rachel went downstairs, Ali stared at him for a few seconds and then started on him.

'There's no fucking way,' was the first thing he said.

'No?' said Marcus, in an attempt to buy himself some time. He had obviously missed something already, although he wasn't quite sure what.

'I'll tell you, if your dad goes out with my mum you're fucking dead. Really. Dead.'

'Oh, he's all right,' said Marcus.

Ali looked at him as though he were mad.

'I don't care if he's all right. I don't want him going out with my mum. So I don't want to see him or you round here ever again, OK?'

'Well,' said Marcus. 'I'm not sure it's really up to me.'

'It better be. Or you're dead.'

'Can I have a go on the computer? What games have you got?' Marcus knew that a change of subject wouldn't necessarily work. It worked sometimes, but maybe not when someone was threatening to kill you.

'Are you listening to me?'

'Yes, but . . . I'm not sure there's very much I can do at the moment. We've come for lunch, and Will . . . that's my dad, I call him Will, because, anyway . . . he's talking to Rachel, that's your mum—'

'I fucking know it's my mum.'

'—downstairs, and to be honest he's really pretty keen, and who knows? She might be keen on him, so—'

'SHE'S NOT KEEN ON HIM!' Ali suddenly shouted. 'SHE'S ONLY KEEN ON ME!'

Marcus was beginning to realize that Ali was nuts, and he wasn't sure what to do about it. He wondered whether this had ever happened before and, if it had, whether the kid who had been in his position was still here somewhere – either in pieces under the carpet, or tied up in a cupboard, where he was fed once a day on leftover bits of Ali's supper. This kid probably weighed three stone and only talked his own language that nobody else could understand, not that anyone ever listened anyway, not even his mum and dad, who he would never see again.

Marcus considered his options carefully. The least attractive, he felt, and also the most unlikely, was to stay here and pass the time of day with Ali, chat about this and that, have a laugh and a couple of games on the computer; that simply wasn't going to happen. He could go downstairs and join in with Will and Rachel, but Will had as good as told him to stay upstairs, and if he went downstairs he'd have to explain that Ali was a psycho who was on the point of cutting off his arms and legs, and that would be really embarrassing. No, Marcus's choice would simply be to dash downstairs without anyone noticing, sneak out of the front door and get a bus home; after a very brief moment's thought, that is exactly what he did.

He was standing at a bus stop near the Lock when Will found him. His sense of direction wasn't brilliant and he was actually standing on the wrong side of the road, waiting for a bus that would have taken him to the West End, so it was probably just as well that Will drew up alongside him and told him to get into the car.

'What are you playing at?' Will asked him angrily.

'Have I messed it up?' And then, although he shouldn't have said it, even though, or probably because, it was the first thing he thought of: 'Will you still help me out with Ellie?'

'What happened upstairs?'

'He's off his head. He said he'd kill me if you went out with her. And I believed him, too. Anyone would have. He's really scary. Where are we going?' It was raining now, and Camden was choked with traffic and market shoppers. Everywhere Marcus looked there were men and women with long wet straggly hair who looked like they probably played in Nirvana or one of the other bands Ellie liked.

'Back to Rachel's.'

'I don't want to go back there.'

'Tough.'

'She'll think I'm stupid.'

'She won't.'

'Why not?'

'Because she thought something like this might happen. She said Ali could be difficult sometimes.'

That made Marcus laugh, 'Ha!', the kind of laugh you did when there was nothing much to laugh at. 'Difficult? He was going to tie me up and lock me in a cupboard and only feed me once a day.'

'Is that what he said?'

'Not in so many words.'

'Anyway, he's crying his eyes out now.'

'Really?'

'Really. Blubbing like a three-year-old.'

This cheered Marcus up no end; he was perfectly happy to go back to Rachel's, he decided.

As it turned out, running away from the house was the best thing Marcus could possibly have done. If he'd known it was all going to end so well, he wouldn't have been so panicky when Will found him at the bus stop. He would have just winked at Will like a wise old owl, and said, 'Wait and see.' When they got back, everything had changed: it was like everyone knew why they were there, instead of pretending that the whole lunch thing was a way of Ali and Marcus getting together to play computer games.

'Ali has got something to say to you, Marcus,' Rachel said, when they walked in.

'Sorry, Marcus,' Ali snivelled. 'I didn't mean to say those things.'

Marcus couldn't see how you could threaten to kill someone by mistake, but he didn't want to make a thing of it; the sight of Ali snivelling away made him feel generous.

'That's OK, Ali,' he said.

'OK, shake hands, guys,' said Rachel, and they did, although it was a rather peculiar and embarrassing handshake. They went up and down much too far three times, and Will and Rachel laughed, which annoyed Marcus. He knew how to shake hands. It was the other idiot who was doing all the up-and-down business.

'Ali finds this very difficult.'

'So does Marcus. Marcus feels just the same, don't you?'

'About what?' He had drifted off temporarily. He was wondering whether there was any connection between Ali's tears and his ability to hurt: did it follow that because he cried so easily he wasn't hard? Or could it be that he was a psycho, and he would pull your head off with his bare hands, blubbing all the time? Maybe the crying had been a bit of a red herring, and Marcus was in even more danger than he had feared.

'About . . . you know . . . this sort of thing.'

'Yes,' Marcus said. 'I do. Exactly the same.' He was sure he would find out soon enough what he felt exactly the same about.

'Because you get into a pattern, and then each new person who comes along seems to represent some kind of a threat.'

'Exactly. And the last guy I—' Rachel broke off. 'I'm sorry, I'm not comparing you to him. And I'm not saying that, you know, we're—' She broke off hopelessly.

Will smiled. 'It's OK,' he said gently, and Rachel looked at him and smiled back. Suddenly Marcus could see why people like Rachel and Suzie – nice, attractive women who you thought wouldn't give someone like that the time of day – might like Will. He had gone into this way of looking that he never used on Marcus: there was something in his eyes, a kind of softness that Marcus could see would really work. While he was listening to the conversation, he practised with his own eyes – you had to sort of narrow them, and then make them focus exactly on the other person's face. Would Ellie like that? She'd probably thump him.

'Anyway,' Rachel went on. 'The last guy I went out with . . . He wasn't one hundred per cent good news, and he certainly couldn't work out how Ali fitted in, and they ended up . . . not on good terms.'

'He was a weirdo,' said Ali.

'Look, I'm sorry that everything's become quite so . . . unsubtle,' Rachel said. 'I have no idea whether . . . I mean, I don't know, I just got the impression that on New Year's Eve . . .' She made a face. 'Oh, God, this is so embarrassing. And it's all your fault, Ali. We shouldn't have to talk about this now.'

'It's OK,' said Marcus brightly. 'He really fancies you. He told me.'

'Are you going cross-eyed?' Ellie said after school on Monday.

'I might be,' Marcus said, because it was easier than saying he was practising a trick he'd learnt from Will.

'Maybe you need new glasses.'

'Yeah.'

'Can you get glasses that are stronger than that?' Zoe asked. She wasn't being nasty, he didn't think, just curious.

The problem was that they were walking to the newsagent's between school and home, and they weren't talking about anything in particular. Will and Rachel had been sitting down, facing one another, and basically talking about how much they liked each other. Walking along the street meant that Marcus kept having to twist his neck to do the eye thing, and he could see that this would make him look a little peculiar, but the trouble was that he and Ellie never did any sitting down and facing each other. They hung out at the vending machine, and sometimes, like today, they met up after school and just mooched around for a while. So what was he supposed to do? How could you gaze into someone's eyes if all you ever saw was their ears?

The newsagent's was full of kids from school, and the guy who owned the place was shouting at some of them to go outside. He wasn't like Mr Patel, who never shouted and never told kids to clear off.

'I'm not going,' said Ellie. 'I'm a customer, not a kid.' She carried on browsing over the sweet display, her hand poised to strike when she saw something she liked.

'You, then,' said the owner to Marcus. 'Outside, please.'

'Don't listen to him, Marcus,' said Ellie. 'It's a breach of human rights. Just because you're young he's calling you a thief. I might take him to court.'

'It's OK,' said Marcus. 'I don't want anything.'

He stepped outside and read the postcards in the window. 'YOUNG DISCIPLINARIAN – UNIFORMS AVAILABLE' . . . 'PUMA STRIKER BOOTS, SIZE 5, STILL IN BOX'.

'You're a pervert, Marcus.'

It was Lee Hartley and a couple of his mates; Marcus hadn't had much trouble from them so far this term, probably because he hung around with Ellie and Zoe.

'What?'

'I bet you don't even know what those cards are all about, do you?'

Marcus couldn't see how the first sentence and the second went together: if he was a pervert, then of course he would understand what the cards were all about, but he let it pass, as he let everything pass at times like this. One of Lee Hartley's mates reached out, removed Marcus's glasses and put them on.

'Fucking hell,' he said. 'No wonder he doesn't know what's going on.' He reeled around for a moment, his arms stretched out in front of him, making grunting noises meant to show that Marcus was in some way mentally deficient.

'Can I have those back now, please? I can't see much without them.'

'Fuck *off*,' said Lee Hartley's mate.

Ellie and Zoe suddenly emerged from the shop.

'You pathetic little shitbags,' said Ellie. 'Give him those back or you'll get such a slap.'

Lee Hartley's mate handed Marcus the glasses, but she hit him anyway, hard, somewhere between his nose and his eye.

'Tricked you,' she said, and Zoe laughed. 'Now run along, all of you, before I get really cross.'

'Slags,' said Lee Hartley, but he said it quietly as he was walking away.

'Now why does hitting someone make me a slag, I wonder?' said Ellie. 'Boys are peculiar creatures. Not you, though, Marcus. Well, you're peculiar, but in a different way.'

But Marcus wasn't really listening. He was too overcome by Ellie – by her style, and her beauty, and her ability to beat people up – to pay any attention to what she was saying.

TWENTY-EIGHT

Twenty-four hours later Marcus was still buzzing, and Will was finding it difficult to adopt the right tone. It would be a mistake, he felt, for the boy to regard Ellie's assault on Lee Somebody's mate as evidence of an uncontrollable passion: surely it proved something like the opposite – that while he relied on teenage girls to defend him in the street, he was unlikely to be much of a catch for anybody. But then, maybe Will was being too traditional in his thinking. Maybe that's how things worked now, and until a girl had smacked someone in the eye for you she wasn't worth a second look. Either way, Marcus was even more smitten than he had been before, and Will feared for him.

'You should have seen her,' Marcus enthused.

'I feel as though I did.'

'Wham!' said Marcus.

'Yes. Wham. You said.'

'She's fantastic.'

'Yes, but . . .' Will knew he would have to outline his theory that Marcus's current status as victim did nothing for him sexually or romantically, even though it would be a rocky conversational road. 'What do you think *she* thinks about having to get you out of trouble?'

'How do you mean?'

'It's just . . . It's not what normally happens.'

'No. That's why it's so great.'

'I'm not so sure. See, I think it'll be hard for Ellie to think of you as a boyfriend if every time she buys a Mars Bar someone steals your glasses and she has to turn herself into Jean-Claude Van Damme.'

'Who's Jean-Claude Van Damme?'

'Never mind. D'you see what I'm getting at?'

'What am I supposed to do about it then? Take karate lessons or something?'

'All I'm saying is, it might not turn out to be the sort of relationship you want it to be. In my experience romances don't develop in this way. This looks more like pet and owner rather than boyfriend and girlfriend.'

'That's OK,' said Marcus cheerfully.

'You don't mind being treated like a . . . like a *gerbil*?'

'No. Course not. That'd do me. I just want to be with her.' And he said it with such sincerity, and with such a complete absence of self-pity, that for the first time ever Will was tempted to hug him.

Will had no intention of adopting the Ellie/Marcus/gerbil model with Rachel, and though he could recognize the simplicity and decency of Marcus's desire, his own was neither simple nor, frankly, decent, and it was with this knowledge he intended to proceed. At least Ellie knew who and what Marcus was, though, not that Marcus had any choice in the matter: that weird little speccy guy being tormented outside the news-agent's, that was Marcus, and nobody was pretending any different. The guy who turned up for lunch with his twelve-year-old son, that wasn't really Will, and somebody – namely Will himself – was certainly pretending different. One day, he thought, he might learn the lesson that lying about one's very identity was a purely short-term strategy, useful only in relationships that had a limited life-span. You could tell a bus-conductor or a taxi driver all sorts of rubbish, provided the journey was brief, but if you intended to spend the rest of your life with somebody, then it was kind of inevitable that she would find out a few things sooner or later.

Will decided he would correct any erroneous impressions he might have given slowly and patiently, but halfway through their first time out alone together, he was reminded of the old April Fool's Day joke about Britain changing over to driving on the right, and making the changeover gradually. Either you lied or you told the truth, it appeared, and that in-between state was pretty tricky to achieve.

'Oh,' was all Rachel said at first, when he told her he wasn't Marcus's natural father. She was trying and failing to pick up a clump of seaweed with her chopsticks.

'It's not really seaweed, you know,' said Will in a misguided attempt to make out that what he was telling her wasn't any kind of big deal – not to him, anyway. 'It's lettuce or something. They shred it and fry it and put sugar and—'

'So who is his natural father?'

'Well,' said Will. Why hadn't it occurred to him that if he wasn't Marcus's father, then someone else would have to be? Why did these things never occur to him? 'It's a guy called Clive who lives in Cambridge.'

'Right. And you get on OK with him?'

'Yeah. We spent Christmas together, actually.'

'So – sorry, I'm being a bit thick here – if you're not Marcus's natural father, and you don't live with him, then, you know, how is he your son?'

'Yes. Ha ha. I see what you mean. It must look very confusing from the outside.'

'Tell me how it is on the inside.'

'It's just that sort of relationship. I'm old enough to be his father. He's young enough to be my son. So—'

'You're old enough to be the father of just about anyone under twenty. Why this particular boy?'

'I don't know. Just one of those things. Would you like to move on to wine now, or do you want to stick with the Chinese beer? Anyway, tell me about your relationship with Ali. Is it as complicated as mine and Marcus's?'

'No. I slept with his father and nine months later I gave birth, and that's about it. Pretty straightforward, but these things usually are.'

'Yes. I envy you.'

'I'm sorry to harp on about this, but I still haven't got it all worked out. You're Marcus's stepfather, but you don't live with him or his mother.'

'I suppose you could look at it that way, yes.'

'How else could you look at it?'

'Ha. I see what you mean,' he said thoughtfully, as if he had just that second worked out that there was only one way of looking at it.

'Did you ever live with Marcus's mother?'

'Define "live with".'

'Did you ever have a spare pair of socks at her house? Or a toothbrush?'

Say that Fiona had given him a pair of socks for Christmas. And say that he had left them at her house, and hadn't got around to picking them up yet. Then he could point out, with a clear conscience, that not only had he once kept a spare pair of socks at Fiona's house, *but they were still there*! Unfortunately, however, she hadn't given him socks, she had given him that stupid book. And he hadn't even left the book there anyway. So the dream sock scenario was just that – a dream.

'No.'

'Just . . . no?'

'Yes.'

He picked up the last little spring roll, dunked it in the chilli sauce, put it in his mouth, and behaved as though it were way too big, so he wouldn't be able to speak for several minutes. Rachel would have to do the talking, and she would probably want to talk about something else eventually. He wanted her to tell him about the book she was currently illustrating, or her ambition to exhibit her work, or how much she had been looking forward to seeing him. Those were the kinds of conversations he had envisaged; he was fed up with talking about imaginary children, and even more fed up with talking about why he had imagined them in the first place.

But Rachel simply sat there and waited for him to finish his mouthful, and however much he chewed and grimaced and swallowed and choked he couldn't make a mini spring roll last for ever. So he told her the truth, as he knew he would, and she was appalled, as she had every right to be.

'I never actually said he was my son. The words "I have a son called Marcus" never passed my lips. That's what you chose to believe.'

'Yeah, right. It's me who's the fantasist. I wanted to believe you had a son, so I let my imagination run riot.'

'You know, that's a very interesting theory. I read this thing in the paper once about this guy who'd taken all these middle-aged women for a ride, cleaned them out of their life savings because they were convinced he was rich. And, the thing was, he didn't even have to do anything to prove it. They just believed him.'

'So he told them he was rich. He lied. That's different.'

'Ah. Yes. I see what you mean. That's sort of where the comparison breaks down, doesn't it?'

'Because you didn't lie. I just made it up. I thought, Cute guy, if only he had a kid, a geeky son, pre-teenage if possible, and then you turned up at my house with Marcus, and bingo! I made this crazy link because of some deep psychological need in me.'

It wasn't turning out as badly as Will feared it might. She was definitely seeing some kind of funny side, even though she clearly thought he was a weirdo.

'You shouldn't beat yourself up about it. Could have happened to anyone.'

'Hey, don't push your luck. If I want to be amused and tolerant, that's my business. I'm not yet at a stage where you can make jokes too.'

'Sorry.'

'But where does Marcus come in? I mean, you obviously hadn't hired him for the afternoon. There's some kind of relationship there.'

She was right, of course, and he rescued a potentially disastrous evening by telling her everything there was to tell. Nearly everything, anyway: he didn't tell her the reason he had come across Marcus in the first place was because he had joined SPAT. He didn't tell her that because he thought it might sound bad coming on top of a similar revelation. He didn't want her to think he had a problem.

Rachel invited him back for coffee after the meal, but Will knew that sex wasn't in the air. Or rather, there was a little, the merest whiff, but it was emanating from him, so it didn't count. He found Rachel so attractive that there would always be sex in the air when he was with her. All that seemed to be coming from her was a quiet amusement and a sort of baffled tolerance, and though he was grateful for these small mercies, they were very rarely, he would imagine, precursors to any kind of physical intimacy beyond a quick hair-ruffle.

Rachel made coffee in great big blue designer cups and they sat opposite each other, Rachel spread out on the sofa, Will bolt upright in an old armchair covered with some kind of Asian throw.

'Why did you think Marcus would make you more interesting?' she asked him after they had poured and stirred and blown and done everything else they could think of doing to a cup of coffee.

'Was I more interesting?'

'Yes, I suppose you were.'

'Why?'

'Because . . . You really want to know the truth?'

'Yes.'

'Because I thought you were a sort of blank – you didn't do anything, you weren't passionate about anything, you didn't seem to have much to say – and then when you said you had a kid—'

'I didn't actually say—'

'Yeah, whatever . . . I thought, I've got this guy all wrong.'

'So there you are then. You've answered your own question.'

'But I *had* got you wrong.'

'How d'you work that out?'

'Because there is something there. You didn't make it all up about Marcus. You're involved, and you care, and you understand him, and you worry about him . . . So you're not the guy I thought you were before you brought him up.'

Will knew this was supposed to make him feel better about everything, but it didn't. For a start, he'd only known Marcus for a few months, so Rachel had raised some interesting questions about the thirty-six years he had let slip through his fingers. And he didn't want to be defined by Marcus. He wanted his own life, and his own identity; he wanted to be interesting in his own right. Where had he heard that complaint before? At SPAT, that's where. He had somehow managed to turn himself into a single parent without even going to the trouble of fathering a child.

There was hardly any point in moaning though. It was too late for that; he had chosen to ignore his own advice, advice that had served him well for his entire adult life. The way Will saw it, the reason that some of the people at SPAT were in a state wasn't because they had kids – their problems had started earlier than that, when they first fell for someone and made themselves vulnerable. Now Will had done the same and, as far as he was concerned, he deserved all he got. He'd be singing with his eyes closed soon, and there was nothing he could do about it.

TWENTY-NINE

For three or four weeks – it couldn't have been any longer than that, but later on, when Marcus looked back on that time, it seemed like months, or years – nothing happened. He saw Will, he saw Ellie (and Zoe) at school, Will bought him some new glasses and took him to have his hair cut, he discovered through Will a couple of singers he liked who weren't Joni Mitchell or Bob Marley, singers that Ellie had heard of and didn't hate. It felt as though he were changing, in his own body and in his head, and then his mum started the crying thing again.

Just like before, there didn't seem to be any reason for it. And just like before, it began slowly, with the odd snuffle after dinner, which one night turned into a long, frightening burst of sobbing, a burst that Marcus could do nothing about, no matter how many questions he asked or hugs he gave her; and then, finally, there was the breakfast crying again, and he knew for sure that things were serious and they were in trouble.

But one thing had changed. Back in the first breakfast crying time, hundreds of years ago, he was on his own; now, there were loads of people. He had Will, he had Ellie, he had . . . Anyway, he had two people, two friends, and that was some kind of improvement on before. He could just go up to either of them and say, 'My mum's at it again,' and they'd know what he meant, and they'd be able to say something that might make some kind of sense.

'My mum's at it again,' he said to Will on the second breakfast crying day. (He hadn't said anything on day one, just in case it turned out to be merely a temporary depression, but when she started up again the next morning he could see he'd just been stupidly hopeful.)

'At what?'

Marcus was disappointed for a moment, but he hadn't really given Will very much to go on. She could have been at anything, which was weird if you thought about it: no one could say his mum was predictable. She could have been moaning about Marcus coming round to Will's flat again, or she could have been on about him taking up the piano, or she could have found a boyfriend that Marcus didn't like very much (Marcus had told Will about some of the peculiar men she'd been out with since his parents had split) . . . It was nice, in a way, contemplating all the things he could have meant when he'd said she was at it again. He thought it made his mum seem interesting and complicated, which of course she was.

'The crying.'

'Oh.' They were in Will's kitchen, toasting crumpets under the grill; it was a Thursday afternoon routine they'd got into. 'Are you worried about her?'

'Course. She's just the same now as she was before. Worse.' That wasn't true. Nothing could be worse than before, because before it had gone on for ages and it had all come to a head on the Dead Duck Day, but he wanted to make sure that Will knew it was serious.

'So what are you going to do?'

It hadn't occurred to Marcus that he would have to do anything – partly because he hadn't done anything before (but then, before hadn't worked out so brilliantly, so maybe he shouldn't use before as any kind of example), and partly because he thought Will might take over. That's what he wanted. That was the whole point of having friends, he thought. 'What am *I* going to do? What are *you* going to do?'

'What am *I* going to do?' Will laughed, and then remembered that what they were talking about wasn't supposed to be funny. 'Marcus, I can't do anything.'

'You could talk to her.'

'Why should she listen to me? Who am I? Nobody.'

'You're not nobody. You're— '

'Just because you come round here for a cup of tea after school doesn't mean I can stop your mum from . . . doesn't mean I can cheer your mum up. In fact, I know I can't.'

'I thought we were friends.'

'Ow. Fuck. Sorry.' In attempting to remove a crumpet, Will had burnt his fingers. 'Is that what we are, d'you reckon? Friends?' He seemed to find this funny too; at any rate, he was smiling.

'Yeah. So what would you say we are?'

'Well. Friends is fine.'

'Why are you smiling?'

'It's a bit funny, isn't it? You and me?'

'I suppose so.' Marcus thought about it for a little while longer. 'Why?'

'Because we're such different heights.'

'Oh. I see.'

'Joke.'

'Ha ha.'

Will let Marcus butter the crumpets because he loved doing it. It was much better than buttering toast, because with toast you had that thing where if the butter was too cold and hard all you could do was scrape off the brown that made toast what it was, and he hated that. With crumpets it was effortless: you just put a lump of butter on top, waited for a few seconds, then messed it about until it started to disappear into the holes. It was one of the few occasions in life where things seemed to go right every time.

'D'you want anything on it?'

'Yeah.' He reached for the honey, put his knife in the jar and began twirling it about.

'Listen,' Will said. 'That's right. We're friends. That's why I can't do anything about your mum.'

'How d'you work that out?'

'I said it was a joke that we're different heights, but maybe it's not. Maybe that's how you should look at it. I'm your mate and I'm about a foot taller than you, and that's it.'

'I'm sorry,' Marcus said. 'I'm not getting you.'

'I had a mate at school who was about a foot taller than me. He was enormous. He was six foot one when we were in the second year.'

'We don't have second years.'

'Year whatever it is. Year eight.'

'So what?'

'I'd never have asked him to help if my mum was depressed. We used to talk about football and *Mission: Impossible* and that was it. Say we were talking about whether, I don't know, Peter Osgood should be playing for England, and then I said, "Oi, Phil, will you talk to my mum because she's in tears all the time," he'd have looked at me as if I were nuts. He was twelve. What's he going to say to my mum? "Hello, Mrs Freeman, have you thought of tranquillizers?"'

'I don't know who Peter Osgood is. I don't know about football.'

'Oh, Marcus, stop being so bloody obtuse. What I'm saying is, OK, I'm your friend. I'm not your uncle, I'm not your dad, I'm not your big brother. I can tell you who Kurt Cobain is and what trainers to get, and that's it. Understood?'

'Yes.'

'Good.'

But on the way home Marcus remembered the end of the conversation, the way Will had said 'Understood?' in a way that was supposed to tell him that the conversation was over, and he wondered whether friends did that. He didn't think they did. He knew teachers who said that, and parents who said that, but he didn't know any friends who said that, no matter how tall they were.

Marcus wasn't surprised about Will, not really. If he had been asked to say who his best friend was, he'd have gone for Ellie – not just because he loved her and wanted to go out with her, but because she was nice to him, and always had been, not counting the first time he'd met her, when she'd called him a squitty little shitty snotty bastard. She hadn't been all that nice then. It wouldn't be fair to say that Will hadn't ever been nice to him, what with the trainers and the crumpets and the two video games and so on, but it would be fair to say that sometimes Will didn't look thrilled to see him, especially if he called round four or five days in a row. Ellie, on the other hand, always threw her arms around him and made a fuss of him, and that, Marcus thought, had to mean something.

Today, however, she didn't seem terribly pleased to see him. She looked down and distracted, and she didn't say anything, let alone do anything, when he went to see her in her classroom at breaktime. Zoe was sitting next to her, looking at her and holding her hand.

'What's happened?'

'Haven't you heard?' said Zoe.

Marcus hated it when people said that to him, because he never had.

'I don't think so.'

'Kurt Cobain.'

'What about him?'

'He tried to kill himself. Took an overdose.'

'Is he all right?'

'We think so. They pumped his stomach.'

'Good.'

'Nothing's good,' said Ellie.

'No,' said Marcus. 'But—'

'He'll do it, you know,' said Ellie. 'In the end. They always do. He wants to die. It wasn't a cry for help. He hates this world.'

Marcus suddenly felt sick. The moment he'd walked out of Will's flat the previous evening he'd been imagining this conversation with Ellie, and how she would cheer him up in a way that Will never could, and it wasn't like that at all; instead, the room was beginning to turn round slowly, and all the colour was draining out of it.

'How do you know? How do you know he wasn't just messing about? I'll bet you he never does anything like it again.'

'You don't know him,' Ellie said.

'Neither do you,' Marcus shouted at her. 'He's not even a real person. He's just a singer. He's just someone on a sweatshirt. It's not like he's anyone's mum.'

'No, he's someone's dad, you little prat,' said Ellie. 'He's Frances Bean's dad. He's got a beautiful little girl and he still wants to die. So, you know.'

Marcus did know, he thought. He turned around and ran out.

He decided to skip the next couple of lessons. If he went to the maths class, he would sit and dream and get picked on and laughed at when he attempted to answer a question that had been asked an hour or a month before, or that hadn't been asked at all; he wanted to be on his own to think properly, without irrelevant interruptions, so he went to the boys' toilets near the gym and shut himself in the right-hand cubicle, because it had comforting hot pipes running along the wall which you could sort of squat down on. After a few minutes someone came in and started kicking on the door.

'Are you in there, Marcus? I'm sorry. I'd forgotten about your mum. It's OK. She's not like Kurt.'

He paused for a moment, then unbolted the door and peered round it.

'How do you know?'

'Because you're right. He's not a real person.'

'You're only saying that to make me feel better.'

'OK, he's a real person. But he's a different sort of real person.'

'In what way?'

'I don't know. He just is. He's like James Dean and Marilyn Monroe and Jimi Hendrix and all those people. You know that he's going to die, and it'll be OK.'

'OK for who? Not for . . . what's her name?'

'Frances Bean?'

'Yeah. Why is it OK for her? It's not OK for her. It's just OK for you.'

A boy from Ellie's year came in to use the toilet. 'Go *away*,' said Ellie, as if she had said it a hundred times before, and as if the kid had no right to be wanting a pee in the first place. 'We're talking.' He opened his mouth to argue, realized who he was about to argue with, and went out again. 'Can I come in?' Ellie said when he'd gone.

'If there's room.'

They squashed up next to each other on the hot pipes, and Ellie pulled the door towards her and bolted it.

'You think I know things, but I don't,' said Ellie. 'Not really. I don't know anything about this stuff. I don't know why he feels like he does, or why your mum feels like she does. And I don't know what it feels like to be you. Pretty scary, I should think.'

'Yeah.' He started to cry, then. It wasn't noisy crying – his eyes just filled with tears and they started to stream down his cheeks – but it was still embarrassing. He'd never thought he'd cry in front of Ellie.

She put her arm around him. 'What I mean is, don't listen to me. You know more than I do. You should be telling me things about it.'

'I don't know what to say about it.'

'Let's talk about something else, then.'

But they didn't talk about anything for a while. They just sat on the pipes together, moving their bottoms when they got too hot, and waited until they felt like going back out into the world.

THIRTY

Will had vertigo, so he didn't like looking down. But sometimes it couldn't be helped. Sometimes someone said something, and he did look down, and he was left with an irresistible urge to jump. He could remember the last time it had happened: it was when he had split up with Jessica, and she had phoned him late at night and told him he was useless, worthless, that he would never be or do anything, that he had had the chance with her to – there was some peculiar, incomprehensible phrase she had used – *sprinkle some salt on the ice*, that was it, by having a relationship that meant something, and maybe a family. And while she was saying it he had started to get panicky, clammy, dizzy, because he knew that some people might think she was right, but he also knew that there was nothing in the world he could do about it.

He'd had just the same feeling when Marcus was asking him to do something about Fiona. Of course he should do something about Fiona; all that stuff about being the same but taller was bollocks, obviously. He was older than Marcus, he knew more . . . Every way you looked at it there was an argument that said, get involved, help the kid out, look after him.

He wanted to help him out, and he had done in some ways. But this depression thing, there was no way he wanted to get involved in that. He could write the whole conversation in his head, he could hear it like a radio play, and he didn't like what he heard. There were two words in particular that made him want to cover his ears with his hands; they always had done, and they always would, as long as his life revolved around *Countdown* and *Home and Away* and new Marks and Spencer sandwich combinations, and he could see no way in which he could avoid them in any conversation with Fiona about her depression. Those two words were 'the point'. As in, 'What's the point?'; 'I don't see the point'; 'There's just no point' (a phrase which omits the 'the', but one that counts anyway, because the 'the' wasn't the point of 'the point', really) . . . You couldn't have a talk about life, and especially about the possibility of ending it, without bringing up the fucking point, and Will just couldn't see one. Sometimes that was OK; sometimes you could be bombed out of your head on magic mushrooms at two in the morning, and some arsehole lying on the floor with his head jammed up against the speakers would want to talk about the point, and you could simply say, 'There isn't one, so shut up.' But you couldn't say that to someone who was so unhappy and lost that they wanted to empty a whole bottle of pills down themselves and go to sleep for as long as it took. Telling someone like Fiona that there was no point was more or less the same as killing her off, and though Will hadn't always seen eye-to-eye with her, he could honestly say he had no desire to murder her.

People like Fiona really pissed him off. They ruined it for everyone. It wasn't easy, floating on the surface of everything: it took skill and nerve, and when people told you that they were thinking of taking their own life, you could feel yourself being dragged under with them. Keeping your head above water was what it was all about, Will reckoned. That was what it was all about for everyone, but those who had reasons for living, jobs and relationships and pets, their heads were a long way from the surface anyway. They were wading in the shallow end, and only a bizarre accident, a freak wave from the wave machine, was going to sink them. But Will was struggling. He was way out of his depth, and he had cramp, probably because he'd gone in too soon after his lunch, and there were all sorts of ways he could see himself being dragged up to the surface by some smoothy life-guard with blond hair and a washboard stomach, long after his lungs had filled with chlorinated water. He needed someone buoyant to hang on to; he certainly didn't need a dead weight like Fiona. He was very sorry, but that was the way things were. And that was the thing about Rachel: she was buoyant. She could keep him afloat. He went to see Rachel.

His relationship with Rachel was weird, or what Will considered weird, which was, he supposed, very different from what David Cronenberg or that guy who wrote *The Wasp Factory* considered weird. The weird thing was that they still hadn't had sex, even though they'd been seeing each other for a few weeks. The subject just never came up. He was almost sure that she liked him, as in she seemed to enjoy seeing him and they never seemed to run out of things to talk about; he was more than sure that he liked her, as in he enjoyed seeing her, he wanted to be with her all the time for the rest of his life, and he couldn't look at her without being conscious of his pupils dilating to an enormous and possibly comical size. It was fair to say that they liked each other in different ways.

(On top of which he had developed an almost irresistible urge to kiss her when she was saying something interesting, which he regarded as a healthy sign – he had never before wanted to kiss someone simply because she was stimulating – but which she was beginning to view with some distrust, even though she didn't, as far as he knew, know what was going on. What happened was, she would be talking with humour and passion and a quirky, animated intelligence about Ali, or music, or her painting, and he would drift off into some kind of possibly sexual but certainly romantic reverie, and she would ask him whether he was listening, and he would feel embarrassed and protest too much in a way that suggested he hadn't been paying attention because she was boring him stupid. It was something of a double paradox, really: you were enjoying someone's conversation so much that a) you appeared to glaze over, and b) you wanted to stop her talking by covering her mouth with yours. It was no good and something had to be done about it, but he had no idea what: he had never been in this situation before.)

He didn't mind having a female friend; his realization during his drink with Fiona that he had never had any kind of relationship with someone he hadn't wanted to sleep with still unsettled him. The problem was that he did want to sleep with Rachel, very much, and he didn't know whether he could bear to sit there on her sofa with his eyes dilating wildly for the next ten or twenty years, or however long female friends lasted (how would he know?), listening to her being unintentionally sexy on the subject of drawing mice. He didn't know whether his pupils could bear it, more to the point. Wouldn't they start hurting after a while? He was almost sure it wouldn't do them much good, all that expanding and contracting, but he would only mention the pupil-pain to Rachel as a last resort; there was a remote possibility that she might want to sleep with him to save his eyesight, but he'd prefer to find another, more conventionally romantic route to her bed. Or his bed. He wasn't bothered about which bed they did it in. The point was that it just wasn't happening.

And then it happened, that evening, for no reason that he could fathom at the time – although later, when he thought about it, he came up with one or two ideas that made sense but the implications of which he found somewhat disturbing. One moment they were talking, the next moment they were kissing, and the moment after that she was leading him upstairs with one hand and unbuttoning her denim shirt with the other. And the weird thing was that sex hadn't been in the air, as far as he could tell; he'd simply come round to see a friend because he was feeling low. So here was the first of the disturbing implications: if he ended up having sex when he had been unable to detect sex in the air, he was obviously a pretty hopeless sex detective. If, in the immediate aftermath of an apparently sex-free conversation, a beautiful woman started to lead you to the bedroom while unbuttoning her shirt, you were clearly missing something somewhere.

It began with a stroke of luck that passed him by at the time: Ali was away for the night, sleeping over at a schoolfriend's house. If Rachel had told him at any other stage of their relationship that she was unencumbered by her psychotically Oedipal son, he would have taken it as a sign from Almighty God that he was about to get laid, but today it didn't even register. They went into the kitchen, she made them coffee and he found himself launching into the whole thing about Fiona and Marcus and the point even before the kettle had boiled.

'What's the *point*?' Rachel echoed. 'Jesus.'

'And don't say Ali. I haven't got an Ali.'

'You've got a Marcus.'

'It's hard to think of Marcus as the point of anything. I know that's a terrible thing to say, but it's true. You've met him.'

'He's just a bit messed up. But he adores you.'

It had never occurred to Will that Marcus actually had any real feelings towards him, especially feelings that were visible to a third party. He knew that Marcus liked hanging out at his place, and he knew that Marcus described him as a friend, but all this he had taken merely as evidence of the boy's eccentricity and loneliness. Rachel's observation that there were real feelings involved kind of changed things, just as they sometimes did when you found out that a woman you hadn't noticed was attracted to you, so that you ended up reassessing the situation and finding her much more interesting than you ever had done before.

'You reckon?'

'Of course he does.'

'He's still not the point, though. If I were about to stick my head in the gas oven, and then you told me Marcus adored me, I wouldn't necessarily take it out again.'

Rachel laughed.

'What's so funny?'

'I don't know. Just the idea that I'd be there in that situation. If you ended up sticking your head in a gas oven at the end of an evening, we'd have to come to the conclusion that the evening hadn't been a raging success.'

'I . . .' Will stopped, and started, and then ploughed on anyway, with as much sincerity as he could muster, and with much more sincerity than the line could bear. 'I would never stick my head in a gas oven at the end of an evening with you.'

He knew the moment he'd said it that it was a big mistake. He'd meant it, but that was precisely what provoked the hilarity: Rachel laughed and laughed until her eyes filled with tears. 'That', she said in between great gulps of air, 'is . . . the . . . most . . . romantic . . . thing . . . anyone's ever said to me.'

Will sat there helplessly, feeling like the most stupid man in the world, but when things calmed down again they seemed to be in a different place, somewhere where they were able to be warmer and less nervous with each other. Rachel made the coffee, found some stale custard creams and sat down with him at the kitchen table.

'You don't need a point.'

'Don't I? That's not what it feels like.'

'No. See, I was thinking about you. About how you have to be fairly tough in your head to do what you do.'

'What?' For a moment Will was completely bewildered. 'Tough in your head', 'do what you do' . . . These were not phrases that anyone used about him too often. What the fuck was it he'd told Rachel he did? Work in a coalmine? Teach young offenders? But then he remembered he'd never actually told Rachel any lies, and his bewilderment took a different shape. 'What do I do?'

'Nothing.'

That's what Will thought he did. 'So how come I have to be tough to do that?'

'Because . . . most of us think that the point is something to do with work, or kids, or family, or whatever. But you don't have any of that. There's nothing between you and despair, and you don't seem a very desperate person.'

'Too stupid.'

'You're not stupid. So why don't you ever put your head in the oven?'

'I don't know. There's always a new Nirvana album to look forward to, or something happening in *NYPD Blue* to make you want to watch the next episode.'

'Exactly.'

'That's the point? *NYPD Blue*? Jesus.' It was worse than he thought.

'No, no. The point is you keep going. You want to. So all the things that make you want to are the point. I don't know if you even realize it, but on the quiet you don't think life's too bad. You love things. Telly. Music. Food.' She looked at him. 'Women, probably. Which I guess means you like sex too.'

'Yeah.' He said it sort of grumpily, as if she had caught him out somehow, and she smiled.

'I don't mind. People who like sex are usually pretty good at it. Anyway. I'm the same. I mean, I love things, and they're mostly different things from you. Poetry. Paintings. My work. Men, and sex. My friends. Ali. I want to see what Ali gets up to tomorrow.' She started fiddling with the biscuit, breaking off the ends in an attempt to expose the cream, but the biscuit was too soft and it crumbled.

'See, a few years ago, I was really, really down, and I did think about . . . you know, what you imagine Fiona's thinking about. And I really felt guilty about it, because of Ali, and I knew I shouldn't be that way but I was, and . . . Anyway, it was always, you know, not today. Maybe tomorrow, but not today. And after a few weeks of that I knew I was never going to do it, and the reason I was never going to do it was because I didn't want to miss out. I don't mean that life was great and I didn't want not to participate. I just mean there were always one or two things that seemed unfinished, things I wanted to follow through. Like you want to see the next episode of *NYPD Blue*. If I'd just finished stuff for a book, I wanted to see it come out. If I was seeing a guy, I wanted one more date. If Ali had a parents' evening coming up, I wanted to talk to his form teacher. Little things like that, but there was always something. And in the end I realized there would always be something, and that those somethings would be enough.' She looked up from the remnants of her biscuit and laughed, embarrassed. 'That's what I think, anyway.'

'Fiona must have things like that.'

'Yeah, well. I don't know. It doesn't sound like Fiona's getting the breaks. You need them too.'

Was that really all there was to it? Probably not, Will thought, on balance. There were probably all sorts of things missing – stuff about how depression made you tired of everything, tired of everything no matter how much you loved it; and stuff about loneliness, and panic, and plain bewilderment. But Rachel's simple positivity was something to be going on with and, in any case, the conversation about the point created a point of its own, because there was this pause, and Rachel looked at him, and that was when they started kissing.

'Why don't I talk to her?' said Rachel. They were the first words spoken afterwards, although there had been a bit of talking during, and for a moment Will didn't understand what she meant at all: he was trying to trace it back to something that had taken place in the previous thirty minutes, a half-hour that had left him feeling a bit shaky and almost tearful, and had led him to question his previous conviction that sex was some sort of fantastic carnal alternative to drink, drugs and a great night out, but nothing much more than that.

'You? She doesn't know you.'

'I don't see why that would matter. Might even help. And maybe you'd get the hang of it, if I showed you how. It's not so bad.'

'OK.' There was something in Rachel's voice that Will couldn't quite isolate, but he didn't want to think about Fiona just at that moment, so he didn't try very hard. He couldn't ever remember feeling so happy.

THIRTY-ONE

Marcus was finding it hard to get used to the idea that winter was over. Pretty much everything Marcus had experienced in London had taken place in the dark and the wet (there must have been a few light evenings right at the beginning of the school year, but so much had happened since that he no longer had any recollection of them), and now he was able to walk home from Will's place in the late afternoon sunshine. It was hard not to feel that everything was OK the first week after the clocks had gone forward; it was ridiculously easy to believe that his mum would get better, that he'd suddenly age three years and suddenly get cool so that Ellie would like him, that he'd score the winning goal for the school football team and become the most popular person in school.

But that was stupid, in the same way that star signs were stupid, in his opinion. The clocks had gone forward for everybody, not just him, and there was no way that every depressed mother was going to cheer up, there was no way that every kid in Britain was going to score the winning goal for the school football team – especially every kid in Britain who hated football and didn't know which end of a ball to kick – and there was certainly no way that every single twelve-year-old was going to become fifteen overnight. The chances of it happening to even one of them were pretty slim, and even if it did, it wouldn't be Marcus, knowing his luck. It would be some other twelve-year-old at some other school who wasn't in love with someone three years older than him, and who therefore wouldn't even care very much. The injustice of the scene that Marcus had just pictured made him angry, and he marked his return home by slamming the door in a temper.

'Have you been round to Will's?' his mum asked. She looked OK. Maybe one of the clocks-forward wishes had come true.

'Yeah. I wanted to . . .' He still felt he should come up with reasons for why he went round, and he still couldn't think of anything to say.

'I don't care. Your dad's hurt himself. You've got to go up and see him. He fell off a window-ledge.'

'I'm not going while you're like this.'

'Like what?'

'Like crying all the time.'

'I'm OK. Well, I'm not OK, but I'm not going to do anything. Promise.'

'Is he really bad?'

'He's broken his collar bone. And he's a bit concussed.'

He fell off a window-ledge. No wonder his mum had cheered up.

'What was he doing on a window-ledge?'

'Some sort of DIY thing. Painting, or grouting, or one of those Scrabble words. For the first time ever. That'll teach him a lesson.'

'And why do I have to go up?'

'He was asking for you. I think he's a bit doolally at the moment.'

'Thanks.'

'Oh, Marcus, I'm sorry, that isn't why he's been asking for you. I just meant . . . I think he's feeling a bit pathetic. Lindsey said he was quite lucky it wasn't worse, so maybe he's having this big think about his life.'

'He can piss off.'

'Marcus!'

But Marcus didn't want an argument about where and why he had learnt to swear; he wanted to sit in his room and sulk, and that's exactly what he did.

He's having this big think about his life . . . That had made Marcus so angry, when his mum had told him, and now he was trying to work out why. He was quite good at working things out when he wanted to: he had an old bean bag in his room, and he sat on it and stared at the wall where he had stuck up some interesting stories out of the newspaper. 'MAN FALLS FIVE THOUSAND FEET AND LIVES'; 'DINOSAURS MAY HAVE BEEN WIPED OUT BY METEOR.' Those were the sorts of things that made you have a big think about your life, not falling off a window-ledge while you were pretending to be a proper dad. Why had he never had a big think before, when he wasn't falling off a window-ledge? Over the last year or so it seemed like everyone had been having big thinks, apart from his father. His mum, for example, never did anything else other than have big thinks, which was probably why everyone had to worry about her all the time. And why did he only want to see his son when he'd broken his collar bone? Marcus couldn't remember ever having come home before and his mum telling him to get on the train to Cambridge because his dad was desperate. All those hundreds and hundreds of days when his collar bone was all right, Marcus had heard nothing.

He went downstairs to see his mother.

'I'm not going,' he said to her. 'He makes me sick.'

It wasn't until the next day, when he was talking to Ellie about the window-ledge, that he began to change his mind about going to see his dad. They were in an empty classroom during the morning break, although it hadn't been empty at first: when Marcus had told her he wanted a chat, she'd taken his hand, led him inside, and scared off the half-dozen kids messing about in there, kids she didn't know but who seemed perfectly prepared to believe that Ellie would follow through with the terrible threats she was making. (Why did that happen? he wondered. She wasn't much taller than him, so how did she get away with this stuff? Maybe if he started to wear that sort of eye make-up and cut his own hair he'd be able to make people scared of him, too, but there would still be something missing.)

'You should go and see him. Tell him what you think of him. I would. Jerk. I'll come with you, if you like. Give him what for.' She laughed, and though Marcus heard her he had already drifted off by then. He was thinking about how nice it would be to have a whole hour on a train with Ellie, just the two of them; and then he was thinking how great it would be if he let Ellie loose on his dad. Ellie was like a guided missile in school, and sometimes it felt as though she were his personal guided missile. Whenever he was with her he could point her at targets and she destroyed them, and he loved her for it. She had beaten up Lee Hartley's mate, and she stopped people laughing at him quite so much . . . And if it worked so well in school, why wouldn't it work away from school? There was no reason he could think of. He was going to point Ellie at his dad and see what happened.

'Will you come with me really, Ellie?'

'Yeah, of course. If you want me to. It'd be a laugh.' Marcus knew she would say yes, if he asked her. Ellie would say yes to just about anything, apart from a dance at a party. 'Anyway, you don't want to go up there on your own, do you?'

He always did things on his own, so he had never bothered even thinking about whether there was a choice. That was the trouble with Ellie: he was frightened that when and if he didn't see her any more, he'd still be aware that there were choices, but it wouldn't do him any good because he wouldn't be able to get at them, and his whole life would be ruined.

'Not really. Would Zoe come?'

'No. She wouldn't know what to say to him, and I will. Just us.'

'OK then. Brilliant.' Marcus didn't want to think about what Ellie might have to say. He'd worry about that later.

'Have you got any money? 'Cos I haven't got the train fare.'

'I can get it.' He didn't spend very much; he reckoned he had at least twenty pounds saved up, and his mum would give him what he needed for the trip anyway.

'So shall we go next week, then?' It was nearly Easter, and they were on holiday next week, so they could stay overnight if they wanted. And Marcus would have to ring Ellie at home to make arrangements – it would be like a proper date.

'Yeah. Cool. We'll have a great time.'

Marcus wondered for a moment whether his idea of a great time would be the same as Ellie's idea of a great time, and then he decided not to worry about that until later.

Fiona wanted to come to King's Cross with Marcus, but he managed to talk her out of it.

'It'd be too sad,' he told her.

'You're only going for a night.'

'But I'll miss you.'

'You'll still be missing me if we say goodbye at the underground station. In fact, you'll have to miss me for longer.'

'It'll seem more normal to say goodbye at the underground, though.'

He knew he was overdoing it, and he knew what he was saying didn't make much sense anyway, but he wasn't going to risk a meeting between Ellie and his mum at the station. She'd stop him from going if she knew he was taking Ellie along to Cambridge to blow up his dad.

The two of them walked from the flat to Holloway Road station, and said goodbye in the tube entrance.

'You'll be OK,' she said to him.

'Yeah.'

'And it'll be over before you know it.'

'It's only for a night,' he said. By the time they reached the underground he'd forgotten he'd told her how much he would miss her. 'It's only for a night, but it seems like for ever.' He was hoping his mum wouldn't remember this when he came back. If she did, he probably wouldn't be allowed down to the shops on his own.

'I shouldn't be making you go. You've had such a rough time lately.'

'I'll be fine. Really.'

Because he was going to miss her so much, she gave him an enormous hug that went on for ever, while everyone walking past watched.

The tube wasn't crowded. It was mid-afternoon – his dad had worked out the train times so that Lindsey could pick him up from Cambridge on her way home from work – and there was only one other person in his carriage, an old guy reading the evening paper. He was looking at the back page, so Marcus could see some of the stuff on the front; the first thing he noticed was the photo. It seemed so familiar that for a moment he thought it was a picture of someone he knew, a member of the family, and maybe they had it at home, in a frame on the piano, or pinned on to the cork board in the kitchen. But there was no family friend or relative who had bleached hair and half a beard and looked like a sort of modern Jesus . . .

He knew who it was now. He saw the same picture every single day of the week on Ellie's chest. He felt hot all over; he didn't even need to read the old guy's paper, but he did anyway. 'ROCK STAR COBAIN DEAD', was the headline, and underneath, in smaller writing 'Nirvana singer, 27, shoots himself'. Marcus thought and felt a lot of things all at once: he wondered whether Ellie had seen the paper yet, and if she hadn't then how she'd be when she found out; and he wondered if his mum was OK, even though he knew there was no connection between his mum and Kurt Cobain because his mum was a real person and Kurt Cobain wasn't; and then he felt confused, because the newspaper headline had turned Kurt Cobain into a real person somehow; and then he just felt very sad – sad for Ellie, sad for Kurt Cobain's wife and little girl, sad for his mum, sad for himself. And then he was at King's Cross and he had to get off the train.

He found Ellie underneath the departure board, which was where they had arranged to meet. She seemed normal. 'Platform ten b,' she said. 'It's in another part of the station, I think.'

Everyone was carrying an evening paper, so Kurt Cobain was everywhere. And because the photo in the paper was exactly the same picture that Ellie had on her sweatshirt, it took Marcus a while to get used to the idea that all these people were holding something that he had always thought of as a part of her. Every time he saw it he wanted to nudge her and point at it, but he said nothing. He didn't know what to do.

'Right. Follow me,' Ellie shouted in a pretend-bossy voice that would have made Marcus giggle at any other time. Today, however, he could only manage a weak little smile; he was too worried to respond to her in the way he usually did, and he could only listen to what she was saying, not the way she was saying it. He didn't want to follow her, because if she was out in front she was bound to notice the army of Kurt Cobains marching towards her.

'Why should I follow you? Why don't you follow me for a change?'

'Ooh, Marcus. You're so masterful,' said Ellie. 'I love that in a man.'

'Where are we going?'

Ellie laughed. 'Ten b. Over there.'

'Right.' He stood directly in front of her and began to walk very slowly towards the platform.

'What are you doing?'

'Leading you.'

She pushed him in the back. 'Don't be an idiot. Get a move on.'

He suddenly remembered something that he'd seen in one of the Open University programmes his mum used to have to watch for her course. He'd watched it with her because it was funny: there were all these people in a room, and half of them were wearing blindfolds, and the other half had to lead the blindfolded half around and not let them bump into each other. It was something to do with trust, his mum had said. If someone could guide you around safely when you were feeling vulnerable, then you learnt to trust them, and that was important. The best bit of the programme was when this woman walked an old man straight into a door and he smashed his head, and they started having a row.

'Ellie, do you trust me?'

'What are you on about?'

'Do you trust me, yes or no?'

'Yes. As far as I can throw you.'

'Ha, ha.'

'Of course I trust you.'

'OK, then. Close your eyes and hang on to my jacket.'

'Eh?'

'Close your eyes and hang on to my jacket. You're not allowed to peek.'

A young guy with long, straggly bleached hair looked at Ellie, at her sweatshirt and then her face. For a moment it looked as though he was going to say something to her, and Marcus began to panic; he stood in between her and the guy and grabbed her.

'Come on.'

'Marcus, have you gone mad?'

'I'm going to guide you through all these people and I'm going to get you on the train, and then you'll trust me for ever.'

'If I trust you for ever, it won't be because I spent five minutes wandering around King's Cross station with my eyes closed.'

'No. OK. But it'll help.'

'Oh, fucking hell. Come on, then.'

'Ready?'

'Ready.'

'Eyes closed, no peeking?'

'Marcus!'

They set off. To get to the Cambridge train you had to go out of the main part of the station and into another, smaller part tucked away at the side; most people were walking in their direction to get the train home from work, but there were enough people coming at them holding newspapers to make the game worthwhile.

'Are you OK?' he said over his shoulder.

'Yes. You'll tell me if we have to go upstairs or anything?'

'Course.'

Marcus was almost enjoying it all now. They were going through a narrow passageway, and you had to concentrate, because you couldn't just stop dead or sidestep, and you had to remember that you'd sort of doubled in size, so you had to think about what sort of spaces you could fit into. This must be what it was like if you started driving a coach when you were used to a Fiat Uno or something. The best thing about it was that he really did have to look after Ellie, and he liked the feeling that brought with it. He'd never looked after anything or anybody in his whole life – he'd never had a pet, because he wasn't bothered about animals, even though he and his mum had agreed not to eat them (why hadn't he just told her he wasn't bothered about animals, instead of getting into an argument about factory farming and so on?) – and as he loved Ellie more than he would ever have loved a goldfish or a hamster, it felt real.

'Are we nearly there?'

'Yeah.'

'The light's different.'

'We're out of the big station and now we're going into the little one. The train's there waiting for us.'

'I know why you're doing this, Marcus,' she suddenly said in a small, quiet voice that didn't sound like her. He stopped, but she didn't let go of him. 'You think I haven't seen the paper, but I have.'

He turned round to look at her, but she wouldn't open her eyes.

'Are you OK?'

'Yeah. Well. Not really.' She rummaged around in her bag and produced a bottle of vodka. 'I'm going to get drunk.'

Suddenly Marcus could see a problem with his guided missile plan: the problem was that Ellie wasn't actually a guided missile. You couldn't guide her. That didn't matter so much in school, because school was full of walls and rules and she could just bounce off them; but out in the world, where there were no walls and rules, she was scary. She could just blow up in his face any time.

THIRTY-TWO

There was absolutely nothing wrong with the idea – it wasn't even particularly risky. On the contrary, it was just a mundane social arrangement, the sort that people make all the time, all over the place. If these people were ever to realize the possible consequences, Will reflected later, all the tears and embarrassment and panic that could ensue in the event of these arrangements going just slightly wrong, they would never arrange to meet for a drink again.

The plan was for Rachel, Will and Fiona to go to a pub in Islington while Marcus was up in Cambridge visiting his father. They would have a drink and a chat, then Will would absent himself and Rachel and Fiona would have a drink and a chat, as a result of which Fiona would cheer up, feel better about things and lose the urge to top herself. What could possibly go wrong?

Will arrived at the pub first, got himself a drink, sat down, lit a cigarette. Fiona arrived shortly afterwards; she was distracted and slightly manic. She asked for a large gin and ice, no mixer, and sipped at it nervously and quickly. Will started to feel a little uncomfortable.

'Have you heard from the boy?'

'Which boy?'

'Marcus?'

'Oh, him!' She laughed. 'I'd forgotten all about him. No. He'll leave a message while I'm out, I should think. Who's your friend?'

Will looked round, just to check that the seat beside him was as empty as he remembered it to be, and then back at Fiona. Maybe she was imagining people; maybe that's why she got down and cried a lot. Maybe the people she imagined were horrible, or as depressed as she was.

'Which friend?'

'Rachel?'

'Who's my friend Rachel?' Now he didn't understand the question. If she knew his friend Rachel was Rachel, what exactly was the information she required?

'Who is she? Where does she come from? How does she fit in? Why do you want me to meet her?'

'Oh. I see. I just thought, you know.'

'No.'

'I just thought you might find her interesting.'

'Will this happen every time you meet somebody? I have to see them for a drink, even though I don't really know you, let alone them?'

'Oh, no. Not every time, anyway. I'll weed out the rubbish.'

'Thank you.'

And still no Rachel. She was now fifteen minutes late. After a peculiar and pointless conversation about John Major's shirts (Fiona's choice of conversational topic, not his), and several lengthy silences, Rachel was thirty minutes late.

'She does exist?'

'Oh, she definitely exists.'

'Right.'

'I'll go and phone her.' He went to the payphone, got the answerphone, waited for a human interruption that never came, and went back to his seat without leaving a message. The only excuse he would accept, he decided, would involve Ali and a large articulated vehicle . . . Unless she had never intended to come. He suddenly realized with terrible clarity that he'd been set up, that when Rachel had said that he would get the hang of it if she showed him how, this is what she had meant. He wanted to hate her, but he couldn't: instead he felt a rising panic.

Another silence, and then Fiona started crying. Her eyes filled up and started to leak down her face and on to her pullover, and she just sat there quietly, like a kid oblivious to a runny nose. For a while Will thought he could just ignore it, and it would go away, but he knew deep down that ignoring her was simply not an option, not if he were worth anything at all.

'What's the matter?' He tried to say it as if he knew it were a big question, but it came out all wrong: the gravity sounded, to him at least, like tetchiness, as if there were a 'now' missing from the end.

'Nothing.'

'That's not true, is it?' It still wouldn't be too late. If Rachel arrived breathless and apologetic at this second, he could stand up, make the introductions, tell Rachel that Fiona was just about to explain the root cause of her misery, and then shove off. He looked towards the door hopefully and, as if by magic, it opened: two guys in Man United away shirts walked in.

'It is true. Nothing's the matter. No thing. I'm just like this.'

'Existential despair, right?'

'Yeah. Right.'

Again, he hadn't got the tone of it. He'd used the phrase to prove that he knew it (he wondered whether Fiona thought he was dim), but quickly realized that if you knew it, these were precisely the circumstances in which you would give it an enormous body-swerve; it sounded flip and pseud and shallow. He wasn't cut out for chats about existential despair. It just wasn't *him*. And what was wrong with that? There was no shame in it, surely? Leather trousers weren't him. (He'd tried some on once, just for a laugh, in a shop called Leather-Time in Covent Garden, and he'd looked like a . . . Anyway.) The colour green wasn't him. Antique furniture wasn't him. And depressive hippy-liberal women weren't him. Big deal. It didn't make him a bad person.

'I don't know if there's a lot of point in talking about this with you,' she said.

'No,' he said, more cheerfully than was appropriate. 'I know what you mean. Shall we finish this and go, then? I don't think Rachel's going to show up.'

Fiona smiled sadly and shook her head. 'You could try persuading me that I'm wrong.'

'Could I?'

'I think I probably need to talk to somebody, and you're the only one here.'

'I'm the only one here that you know. But I'd be useless. You could throw that slice of lemon across the pub and hit somebody who was better than me. As long as you aimed away from that guy who's singing on his own over there.'

She laughed. Maybe his lemon joke had done the trick. Maybe she'd look back on those few seconds as a turning point in her life. But then she shook her head, and said, 'Oh, shit,' and began to cry again, and he could see that he had overrated the power of the throwaway one-liner.

'Do you want to go and get something to eat?' he said wearily. He was going to have to look a long way down now.

They went to Pizza Express on Upper Street. He hadn't been there since the last time he had had lunch with Jessica, the ex-girlfriend who was determined to make him as unhappy and sleepless and out of touch and burdened by parenthood as she had become. That was a long, long time ago, before SPAT and Marcus and Suzie and Fiona and Rachel and everything. He'd been an idiot then, but at least he'd been an idiot with an idea, some kind of belief system; now he was hundreds of years older, one or two IQ points wiser, and absolutely all over the place. He'd rather be an idiot again. He'd had his whole life set up so that nobody's problem was his problem, and now everybody's problem was his problem, and he had no solutions for any of them. So how, precisely, was he, or anybody else he was involved with, better off?

They looked at the menu in silence.

'I'm not really hungry,' said Fiona.

'Please eat,' said Will, too quickly and too desperately, and Fiona smiled.

'You think a pizza will help?' she said.

'Yes. Veneziana. 'Cos then you'll stop Venice sinking into the sea and you'll feel better.'

'OK. If I can have extra mushrooms on it.'

'Good call.'

The waitress came to take their order; Will asked for a beer, a bottle of house red, and a Four Seasons with extra everything he could think of, including pine nuts. If he was lucky, he would be able to induce a heart attack, or find that he was suddenly fatally allergic to something.

'I'm sorry,' said Fiona.

'What for?'

'Being like this. And being like this with you.'

'I'm used to women being like this with me. This is how I spend most evenings.' Fiona smiled politely, but suddenly Will felt sick of himself. He wanted to find a way into the conversation that they had to have, but there didn't seem to be one, and there never would be while he was stuck with his brain and his vocabulary and his personality. He kept feeling as though he were on the verge of saying something proper and serious and useful; but then he ended up thinking, Oh, fuck it, say something stupid instead.

'I'm the one who should apologize,' he said. 'I want to help, but I know I won't be able to. I haven't got the answers to anything.'

'That's what men think, isn't it?'

'What?'

'That unless you've got some answer, unless you can say, "Oh, I know this bloke in Essex Road who can fix that for you", then it's not worth bothering.'

Will shifted in his seat and didn't say anything. That was precisely what he thought; in fact, he had spent half the evening trying to think of the name of the bloke in Essex Road, metaphorically speaking.

'That's not what I want. I know there's nothing you can do. I'm depressed. It's an illness. It just started. Well, that's not true, there were things happening that helped it along, but . . .'

And they were away. It was easier than he could possibly have anticipated: all he had to do was listen and nod and ask pertinent questions. He had done it before, loads of times, with Angie and Suzie and Rachel, but that was for a reason. There was no ulterior motive here. He didn't want to sleep with Fiona, but he did want her to feel better, and he hadn't realized that in order to make her feel better he had to act in exactly the same way as if he did want to sleep with her. He didn't want to think about what that meant.

He learnt a lot of things about Fiona. He learnt that she hadn't really wanted to be a mother, and that sometimes she hated Marcus with a passion that worried her; he learnt that she worried about her inability to hold down a relationship (Will restrained a desire to leap in at this point and tell her that an inability to hold down a relationship was indicative of an undervalued kind of moral courage, that only cool people screwed up); he learnt that her last birthday had scared her to bits, because she hadn't been anywhere, done anything, all the usual malarkey. None of it amounted to anything enormous, but the sum of her depression was much greater than its parts, and now she had to live with something that tired her and made her see everything through a greeny-brown gauze. And he learnt that if someone were to ask her where this thing lived (Will found it hard to imagine a more unlikely question, but that was just one of the many differences between them), she would say that it was in her throat, because it stopped her from eating, and made her feel as though she were constantly on the verge of tears – when she wasn't actually crying.

And that was it, more or less. What Will had been most frightened of – apart from Fiona asking him about the point (a subject that never even came close to showing its face, probably because it was clear in *his* face and even in his life that he didn't have a clue) – was that there was going to be a cause of all this misery, some dark secret, or some terrible lack, and he was one of the only people in the world who could deal with it, and he wouldn't want to, even though he would have to anyway. But it wasn't like that at all; there was nothing – if life, with its attendant disappointments and compromises and bitter little defeats, counted as nothing. Which it probably didn't.

They got a taxi back to Fiona's place. The cabbie was listening to GLR, and the disc jockey was talking about Kurt Cobain; it took Will a while to understand the strange, muted tone in the DJ's voice.

'What's happened to him?' Will asked the cabbie.

'Who?'

'Kurt Cobain.'

'Is he the Nirvana geezer? He shot himself in the head. Boom.'

'Dead?'

'No. Just a headache. Yeah, course he's dead.'

Will wasn't surprised, particularly, and he was too old to be shocked. He hadn't been shocked by the death of a pop star since Marvin Gaye died. He had been . . . how old? He thought back. The first of April 1984 . . . Jesus, ten years ago, nearly to the day. So he had been twenty-six, and still of an age when things like that meant something: he probably sang Marvin Gaye songs with his eyes closed when he was twenty-six. Now he knew that pop stars committing suicide were all grist to the mill, and the only consequence of Kurt Cobain's death as far as he was concerned was that *Nevermind* would sound a lot cooler. Ellie and Marcus weren't old enough to understand that, though. They would think it all meant something, and that worried him.

'Isn't he the singer Marcus liked?' Fiona asked him.

'Yeah.'

'Oh, dear.'

Suddenly Will was fearful. He had never had any kind of intuition or empathy or connection in his life before, but he had it now. Typical, he thought, that it should be Marcus, rather than Rachel or someone who looked like Uma Thurman, who brought it on. 'I'm not being funny, but can I come in with you to listen to Marcus's answerphone message? I just want to hear that he's OK.'

But he wasn't, really. He was calling from a police station in a place called Royston, and he sounded little and frightened and lonely.

THIRTY-THREE

They didn't talk on the train at first; every now and again Ellie would give a small sob, or threaten to press the emergency stop button, or threaten to do things to the people who looked at her when she swore or swigged from her bottle of vodka. Marcus felt exhausted. It was now perfectly clear to him that, even though he thought Ellie was great, and even though he was always pleased to see her at school, and even though she was funny and pretty and clever, he didn't want her to be his girlfriend. She just wasn't the right sort of person for him. He really needed to be with someone quieter, someone who liked reading and computer games, and Ellie needed to be with someone who liked drinking vodka and swearing in front of people and threatening to stop trains.

His mum had explained to him once (perhaps when she was going out with Roger, who wasn't like her at all) that sometimes people needed opposites, and Marcus could see how that might work: if you thought about it, right at this moment Ellie needed someone who was going to stop her from pressing the button more than she needed someone who loved pressing buttons, because if she was with someone who loved pressing buttons, they would have pressed it by now and they'd be on their way to prison. The trouble with this theory, though, was that actually it wasn't an awful lot of fun being the opposite of Ellie. It *had* been fun sometimes – at school, where Ellie's . . . *Ellieness* could be contained. But out in the world it was no fun at all. It was frightening and embarrassing.

'Why does it matter so much?' he asked her quietly. 'I mean, I know you like his records and everything, and I know it's sad because of Frances Bean, but—'

'I loved him.'

'You didn't know him.'

'Of course I knew him. I listened to him sing every single day. I wear him every single day. The things he sings about, that's him. I know him better than I know you. He understood me.'

'He *understood* you?' How did that work? How did someone you had never met understand you?

'He knew what I felt, and he sang about it.'

Marcus tried to remember some of the words to the songs on the Nirvana record that Will had given him for Christmas. He had only ever been able to hear little bits: 'I feel stupid and contagious.' 'A mosquito.' 'I don't have a gun.' None of it meant anything to him.

'So what were you feeling?'

'Angry.'

'What about?'

'Nothing. Just . . . life.'

'What about life?'

'It's shit.'

Marcus thought about that. He thought about whether life was shit, and whether Ellie's life in particular was shit, and then he realized that Ellie spent her whole time wanting life to be shit, and then making life shit by making things difficult for herself. School was shit because she wore her sweatshirt every day, which she wasn't allowed to do, and because she shouted at teachers and got into fights, which upset people. But what if she didn't wear her sweatshirt and stopped shouting at people? How shit would life be then? Not very, he thought. Life was really shit for him, what with his mum and the other kids at school and all that, and he'd give anything to be Ellie; but Ellie seemed determined to turn herself into him, and why would anyone want to do that?

Somehow it reminded him of Will and his pictures of dead drug-takers; maybe Ellie was like Will. If either of them had real trouble in their lives, they wouldn't want or need to invent it for themselves, or put pictures of it on the walls.

'Is that really true, Ellie? Do you really think life is shit?'

'Course.'

'Why?'

'Because . . . because the world is sexist and racist and full of injustice.'

Marcus knew this was true – his mum and dad had told him so often enough – but he wasn't convinced that this was what made Ellie angry.

'And is that what Kurt Cobain thought?'

'I don't know. Probably.'

'So you're not sure that he felt the same way as you.'

'He sounded as though he did.'

'Do you feel like shooting yourself?'

'Of course. Sometimes, anyway.'

Marcus looked at her. 'That's not true, Ellie.'

'How do you know?'

'Because I know how my mum feels. And you don't feel like that. You'd like to think you do, but you don't. You have too good a time.'

'I have a shit time.'

'No. I have a shit time. Apart from the time I spend with you. And my mum has a shit time. But you . . . I don't think so.'

'You don't know anything.'

'I know some things. I know about that. I'll tell you, Ellie, you don't feel anything like my mum, or Kurt Cobain. You shouldn't say that you feel like killing yourself when you don't. It's not right.'

Ellie shook her head and laughed her low nobody-understands-me laugh, a noise that Marcus hadn't heard since the day they met outside Mrs Morrison's office. She was right, he hadn't understood her then; he understood her much better now.

They sat in silence for a couple of stops. Marcus looked out of the window and tried to work out how to explain Ellie to his dad. He hardly noticed when the train pulled in at Royston station, and he wasn't even completely alert when Ellie suddenly stood up and jumped off the train. He hesitated for a moment, then, with a horrible sick feeling, he jumped off after her.

'What are you doing?'

'I don't want to go to Cambridge. I don't know your dad.'

'You didn't know him before, and you wanted to come then.'

'That was before. Everything's different now.'

He followed her; he wasn't going to let her out of his sight. They walked out of the station, up a side road and then on to the High Street. They walked past a chemist and a greengrocer's and a Tesco, and then they came to a record shop which had a big cardboard cut-out of Kurt Cobain in the window.

'Look at that,' said Ellie. 'Bastards. They're trying to make money out of him already.'

She took off one of her boots, and threw it at the glass as hard as she could. She cracked it first time, and Marcus found himself thinking about how shop windows in Royston were much weedier than shop windows in London before he realized what was going on.

'Shit, Ellie!'

She picked up the boot and used it as a hammer, carefully smashing a hole big enough to lean through without hurting herself, and rescued Kurt Cobain from his record-shop prison.

'There. He's out.' She sat down on the kerb outside the shop, holding Kurt to her as if he were a ventriloquist's dummy, and smiling this weird little smile to herself; meanwhile Marcus panicked. He charged up the road, intending to run all the way back to London or on to Cambridge, whichever direction he was heading. After a few yards, however, his legs went all shaky, and he stopped, took a few deep breaths, and went back to sit with her.

'What did you do that for?'

'I dunno. It just didn't seem right, him being in there on his own.'

'Oh, Ellie.' Once again, Marcus was left with the feeling that Ellie didn't have to do what she had just done, and that she had brought the trouble she was in upon herself. He was tired of it. It wasn't real, and there was enough real trouble in the world without having to invent things.

The street had been quiet when Ellie broke the window, but the noise of breaking glass had woken Royston up, and a couple of people closing up their shops had run down to see what was going on.

'Right, you two. Stay there,' said a guy with long hair and a suntan. Marcus reckoned he had to be a hairdresser or someone who worked in a boutique. He wouldn't have been able to work something like that out a while ago, but if you hung around with Will long enough you picked stuff up.

'We're not going anywhere, are we, Marcus?' said Ellie sweetly.

When they were sitting in the police car Marcus remembered the day he had walked out of school, and the future he had predicted for himself that afternoon. He'd been right, in a way. His whole life had changed, just as he thought it would, and he was almost certain now that he would become a tramp or a drug addict. He was already a criminal. And it was all his mum's fault! If his mum hadn't complained to Mrs Morrison about the shoes, then he would never have got cross with Mrs Morrison for suggesting that he should keep out of the way of the kids who were giving him a hard time. And then he wouldn't have walked out, and . . . and he would never have met Ellie that morning. Ellie had something to answer for here. It was Ellie, after all, who had just chucked a boot at a plate-glass window. The point was that once you had become a truant, you started hanging out with people like Ellie, and getting into trouble, and being arrested and taken to Royston police station. Now there was nothing he could do about it.

The policemen were nice, really. Ellie had explained to them that she wasn't a hooligan or on drugs; she was simply making a protest, which was her right as a citizen, about the commercial exploitation of Kurt Cobain's death. The policemen thought this was funny, which Marcus took as a good sign, although it made Ellie very angry indeed: she told them they were patronizing, and they looked at each other and laughed a bit more.

When they got to the station, they were shown into a little room, and a policewoman came in and started talking to them. She asked them their ages and addresses, and what they were doing in Royston. Marcus tried to explain about his dad and the window-ledge and the big think and Kurt Cobain and the vodka, but he could see that it was all a bit of a muddle, and that the policewoman couldn't understand what his dad's accident had to do with Ellie and the shop window, so he gave up.

'He didn't do anything,' Ellie suddenly said. She didn't say it in a nice way, either; she said it as if he should have done something but didn't. 'I got off the train and he followed me. I broke the window. Let him go.'

'Let him go where?' the policewoman asked her. It was a very good question, Marcus thought, and he was glad that she'd asked it. He didn't especially want to be let go in Royston. 'We've got to phone one of his parents. We've got to phone yours too.'

Ellie glared at her and the policewoman glared back. There didn't seem much else to say. They knew the crime and the identity of the criminal; the said criminal had been apprehended and was in the police station, so they sat and waited in silence.

His dad and Lindsey were the first to turn up. Lindsey had had to drive, because of the broken collar bone, and she hated driving, so they were both in a bit of a state: Lindsey was tired and nervy, and his dad was grumpy and in pain. He didn't look like a man who'd had a big think, and he certainly didn't look like a man who until very recently had been desperate to see his only son.

The policewoman left them alone. Clive slumped on a bench that ran along one side of the room, and Lindsey sat down next to him, looking at him with concern.

'That was just what I needed. Thank you, Marcus.'

Marcus looked at his dad unhappily.

'He didn't *do* anything,' said Ellie impatiently. 'He was trying to help me.'

'And who exactly are you?'

'*Who exactly?*' Ellie was taking the piss out of his dad. Marcus didn't think that was a particularly good idea, but he was tired of wrestling with Ellie. 'Who *exactly*? I'm Eleanor Toyah Gray, aged fifteen years seven months. I live at twenty-three . . .'

'What are you doing messing around with Marcus?'

'I'm not messing around with him. He's my friend.' This was news to Marcus. He hadn't felt Ellie was his friend since they got on the train. 'He asked me to come with him to Cambridge, because he wasn't looking forward to a heart-to-heart with a father he feels doesn't understand him and who has abandoned him at a time when he needed him most. Great, aren't they, men? You've got a mother who wants to top herself and they're not interested. But they fall off a fucking window-sill and suddenly you're summoned for a talk about the meaning of life.'

Marcus slumped on the table and put his head in his hands. He was suddenly very, very tired; he didn't want to be with any of these people. Life was hard enough without Ellie shooting her mouth off.

'Whose mum wants to top herself?' Clive asked.

'Ellie's,' said Marcus firmly.

Clive looked at Ellie with interest.

'Sorry to hear that,' he said, without sounding either sorry or even particularly interested.

'That's OK,' said Ellie. She took the hint and said nothing for a while.

'I suppose you blame me for all this,' said his father. 'I suppose you think that if I'd stayed with your mother you wouldn't have gone off the rails. And you're probably right.' He sighed, and Lindsey took his hand and stroked it sympathetically.

Marcus sat bolt upright. 'What are you talking about?'

'I've messed you up.'

'All I did was get off a train,' said Marcus. His tiredness had vanished now. It had been replaced by the kind of anger which he didn't feel very often, an anger that gave him the strength to argue with anyone of any age. He wished you could buy this stuff in bottles, so he could keep it in his desk at school and sip from it throughout the day. 'What's going off the rails about getting off a train? Ellie's off the rails. She's nuts. She just broke a window with her boot because it had a photo of a pop star in it. But I haven't done anything. And I don't care if you left home or not. It doesn't make any difference to me. I'd have got off the train if you were still with Mum because I wanted to try and look after my friend.' That wasn't quite right, actually, because if his mum and dad were still together, he wouldn't have been on the train in the first place, unless he'd been going to Cambridge with Ellie for some other reason that he couldn't imagine. 'I suppose you are a useless father, and that doesn't help a kid very much, but you'd have been a useless father wherever you were living, so I don't see what difference it makes.'

Ellie laughed. 'Yay, Marcus! Cool speech!'

'Thank you. I rather enjoyed making it.'

'You poor kid,' said Lindsey.

'And you can shut up,' said Marcus. Ellie laughed even harder. It was the anger juice talking – poor Lindsey had never done anything wrong, particularly – but it still felt good.

'Can we go now?' Ellie asked.

'We have to wait for your mother,' said Clive. 'She's coming with Fiona. Will's driving them up.'

'Oh, no,' said Marcus.

'Fucking hell,' said Ellie, and Marcus groaned. The four of them sat there staring at each other, waiting for the next scene in what was beginning to feel like a never-ending play.

THIRTY-FOUR

Life was, after all, like air. Will could have no doubt about that any more. There seemed to be no way of keeping it out, or at a distance, and all he could do for the moment was live it and breathe it. How people managed to draw it down into their lungs without choking was a mystery to him: it was full of bits. This was air you could almost chew.

He rang Rachel from Fiona's flat while Fiona was in the bathroom, and this time she answered the phone.

'You were never going to come, were you?'

'Well—'

'Were you?'

'No. I thought . . . I thought it might do you some good. Did I do a terrible thing?'

'I guess not. I guess it did me some good.'

'So there you are.'

'But as a general rule—'

'As a general rule, I'll turn up when I say I'm going to.'

'Thank you.'

He told Rachel about Marcus and Ellie, and promised to keep her informed. The moment he'd put the phone down Ellie's mother Katrina called and spoke to Fiona, and then Fiona spoke to Clive, and then she called Katrina back to offer her a lift to Royston with them, and then Will went home to get his car, and they drove off to look for Ellie's house.

While Fiona was collecting Ellie's mum, Will sat in the car listening to Nirvana and thinking about the Dead Duck Day. Something about now was reminding him of then; there was that same sense of unpredictability and absorption and chaos. The main difference was that today wasn't as . . . well, as enjoyable. It wasn't that Fiona's attempted suicide had been a riot of fun and laughter; it was just that he neither knew nor cared about any of them then, and it had been possible for him to observe, with a terrible but neutral fascination, the kind of mess that people can make if they are wilful or unlucky or both. But the neutrality had gone now, and he was more worried about poor Marcus sitting with some deranged teenager in a small-town police station, an experience that Marcus would probably have forgotten all about by the weekend, than about the same boy's mother attempting to take her own life, the memory of which he was almost certain to carry with him to his grave. It seemed that whether you felt something, or whether you felt nothing, it didn't matter: your responses were off either way.

Ellie's mum was an attractive woman in her early forties, youthful-looking enough to get away with the tatty, faded blue jeans and leather biker jacket she was wearing. She had a shock of curly hennaed hair and nice crinkles around her eyes and mouth, and she seemed to have given up on her daughter a long time ago.

'She's mad,' Katrina said with a shrug as soon as she got into the car. 'I don't know how or why, but she is. Not *mad* mad, but, you know. Out of control. Do you mind if I smoke, if I open the window?' She fiddled around in her bag, failed to find her lighter, and then forgot about smoking altogether. 'It's funny, because when Ellie was born I really hoped she'd turn out like this, feisty and rebellious and loud and bright. That's why I called her Eleanor Toyah.'

'Is that something classical?' Fiona asked.

'No, it's pop,' said Will. Fiona laughed, although Will couldn't see why.

'Toyah Wilcox.'

'And now it's happened, and she *is* feisty and rebellious and what have you, I'd give anything for her to be mousy and home every night. She's killing me.'

Will winced at Katrina's turn of phrase, and glanced at Fiona alongside him, but she gave no indication of being aware that the expression had anything but a figurative meaning.

'This is the last straw, though,' Katrina said.

'Ditto,' said Fiona.

'Until the next last straw, anyway.'

They both laughed, but it was true, Will thought. There would always be one more last straw. Ellie was killing Katrina, and Marcus was killing Fiona, and they would go on killing them for years and years. They were the Undead. They couldn't live, not properly, and they couldn't die; all they could do was sit in a stranger's car and laugh about it. And people like Jessica had the nerve to tell him that he was missing out? He didn't think he'd ever understand what that was supposed to mean.

They stopped to get petrol, cans of drink, crisps and chocolate bars, and when they got back into the car the atmosphere between them had changed: somewhere among the popping cans and the rustling crisp packets they seemed to have become a trio. It was almost as if they had forgotten why they were travelling in the first place; the journey had become the point of the trip. Will remembered from school coach trips that it was something to do with getting out and getting back in again, although he wasn't sure exactly what. Perhaps you didn't notice that you had created a feeling until you left it and went back to it, but there was a feeling now – a heady mix of despair, shared concern, suppressed hysteria, and straightforward team spirit – and Will could feel that he was inside it, rather than looking at it through a window. This couldn't possibly be what he was missing out on, because he wasn't missing out, but it still involved kids. You had to hand it to Marcus, he thought: the boy was awkward and weird and the rest of it, but he had this knack of creating bridges wherever he went, and very few adults could do that. Will would never have imagined that he would have been able to walk across to Fiona, but he could now; his relationship with Rachel had been entirely underpinned by Marcus. And here was a third person, someone he had never met before tonight, and they were swapping fingers of Kit-Kat and swigs of Diet Lilt as if they had already exchanged bodily fluids. It was kind of ironic that this strange and lonely child could somehow make all these connections, and yet remain so unconnected himself.

'Why did that guy shoot himself?' Fiona suddenly asked.

'Kurt Cobain?' said Will and Katrina together.

'If that was his name.'

'He was unhappy, I suppose,' said Katrina.

'Well, I gathered that much. What about?'

'Oh, I can't remember now. Ellie did tell me, but I switched off after a while. Drugs? A bad childhood? Pressure? That sort of thing, anyway.'

'I'd never heard of him before Christmas,' said Fiona, 'but he was quite a big deal, wasn't he?'

'Did you see the news tonight? There were all these heartbroken young people hugging each other and crying. It was very sad to watch. None of them seemed to be trying to break shop windows, though. Only my daughter wanted to express her grief like that, apparently.'

Will wondered whether Marcus had ever sat in his room listening to *Nevermind* in the same way that Will had sat in his room listening to the first Clash album. He couldn't imagine that he had. Marcus couldn't possibly have understood that kind of rage and pain, even though he probably had his own version of those feelings swilling around in there somewhere. And yet here he was, banged up in jail – well, sitting in a police station waiting room – because he had been accomplice to a crime that was somehow meant to avenge Kurt Cobain's death. It was hard to imagine two less kindred spirits than Marcus and Kurt Cobain, and yet they had both managed to pull off the same trick: Marcus forced unlikely connections in cars and police stations and Kurt Cobain did the same thing on international television. It was proof that things weren't as bad as they thought they were. Will wished he was able to show this proof to Marcus, and to anybody else who might be in need of it.

They were nearly there now. Katrina was still chatting away, apparently completely reconciled to the idea that her daughter was in trouble again (the only route open to you, Will presumed, if you had the misfortune to have Ellie as a daughter), but Fiona had gone terribly quiet.

'He'll be OK, you know,' he said to her.

'I know he will,' she said, but there was something in her voice that he didn't like.

Will was not surprised to find that the vibes in the police station were bad – like most habitual users of soft drugs he was no fan of the police – but he was surprised to find these vibes were coming not from the front desk, where they encountered only a slightly strained civility, but from the interview room, where there was a frosty silence and a lot of angry glares. Lindsey and Clive were glaring angrily at Marcus, who was glaring angrily at the wall. A furious teenage girl (who looked, Will was gratified to see, not unlike a cross between Siouxsie and Roadrunner, except with the haircut of someone who had recently been released into the community) was glaring angrily at anyone brave enough to catch her eye.

'You took your time,' said Ellie, when her mother walked in.

'I took as long as it takes to make a phone call and drive here,' said Katrina, 'so don't start.'

'Your daughter', said Clive, with a pomposity that didn't really suit a man wearing a University of Life sweatshirt and a plaster cast, 'has been insulting and aggressive. And your son', he went on, nodding at Fiona, 'has clearly been mixing with the wrong crowd.'

'*Your* son,' hooted Ellie, but Fiona was still grim and silent.

'He told me to shut up,' said Lindsey.

'Diddums,' said Ellie.

The policewoman who had shown them in was beginning to let her enjoyment of their disharmony show in her face. 'Are we allowed to go?' Will asked her.

'Not yet. We're waiting for the shop owner to come down.'

'Good,' said Ellie. 'I want to give him a piece of my mind.'

'It's a her, actually,' said the policewoman.

Ellie blushed. 'Him or her, doesn't matter. She's sick.'

'Why is she sick, Ellie?' asked Katrina, in a tone which managed brilliantly to combine sarcasm and world-weariness, and which had clearly taken a very long time and a lot of practice to perfect.

'Because she's exploiting a tragic event for her own gain,' said Ellie. 'She has no idea what today means. She just thinks there's a few quid in it.'

'Why is she coming, anyway?' Will asked the policewoman.

'It's something we're trying here. You know, criminals face-to-face with victims of crime, so they get to see the consequences of their actions.'

'Who's the criminal and who's the victim?' asked Ellie meaningfully.

'Oh, Ellie, do shut up,' said her mother.

A nervous-looking young woman in her late twenties was shown into the room. She was wearing a Kurt Cobain sweatshirt and lots of black eye make-up and if she wasn't Ellie's older sister, genetic scientists would want to know why not.

'This is Ruth, who owns the shop. This is the young lady who broke your window,' said the policewoman. Ellie looked at the shop owner, bewildered.

'Did they tell you to do that?'

'What?'

'Look like me.'

'Do I look like you?'

Everyone in the room, including the police officers, laughed.

'You put that picture in the window to exploit people,' said Ellie, with noticeably less confidence than she had been exhibiting previously.

'Which picture? The picture of Kurt? That's always been there. I'm his biggest fan. His biggest fan in Hertfordshire, anyway.'

'You didn't just stick it in today to make some money?'

'Make some money out of all the grieving Nirvana fans in Royston, you mean? That would only work if it was a picture of Julio Iglesias.'

Ellie looked embarrassed.

'Is that why you broke the window?' Ruth asked. 'Because you thought I was exploiting people?'

'Yeah.'

'Today has been the saddest day of my life. And then some little idiot comes up and breaks my window because she thinks I'm trying to rip people off. Just . . . grow up.'

Will doubted very much whether Ellie was lost for words too often, but it was clear that if you wished to reduce her to a gaping, red-faced mess, all you had to do was find a twenty-something *doppelgänger* whose commitment to Kurt Cobain was even more devout than her own.

'I'm sorry,' she whispered.

'Yeah, well,' said Ruth. 'Come here.' And while the assembled and for the most part unsympathetic occupants of the police interview room watched, Ruth opened her arms, and Ellie stood up, walked over to her and hugged her.

It seemed to have escaped Fiona's notice that this embrace should have marked the end of the whole sorry cardboard-cut-out affair, but then Will had been aware for some time that more or less everything had passed her by since they stopped for petrol. It soon became clear, however, that she had been steeling herself for action, rather than day-dreaming, and for reasons best known to herself she had decided that the time for action was now. She stood up, walked around the table, put her arms around Marcus from behind and, with an embarrassingly emotional intensity, addressed the policewoman who had been looking after them.

'I haven't been a good mother to him,' she declared. 'I've let things slide, and I haven't been noticing properly, and . . . I'm not surprised things have come to this.'

'They haven't come to anything, Mum,' said Marcus. 'How many more times? I haven't done anything.' Fiona ignored him; she didn't seem even to have heard.

'I know I don't deserve a chance, but I'm asking for one now, and . . . I don't know whether you're a mother or not?'

'Me?' asked the policewoman. 'Yeah. I've got a little boy. Jack.'

'I'm appealing to you as a mother . . . If you give us another chance, you won't regret it.'

'We don't need a chance, Mum. I haven't done anything wrong. I only got off a train.'

Still no reaction. Will had to hand it to her: once she had decided to fight for her child she was unstoppable, however wrong-headed the decision, and however inappropriate the weapons. What she was saying was barmy – she might even have been aware that it was barmy – but at least it was coming from a part of her that knew she had to do something for her son. It was a turning point, of sorts. You could imagine this woman saying all kinds of inappropriate things at peculiar times; but it was getting much harder to imagine finding her sprawled off a sofa covered in sick, and Will was beginning to learn that sometimes good news came in unpromising shapes and sizes.

'We're willing to cut a deal,' said Fiona. Was Royston law the same as *LA Law*? Will wondered. It seemed unlikely, but one never knew. 'Marcus will testify against Ellie, if you let him go. I'm sorry, Katrina, but it's too late for her. Let Marcus start again with a clean sheet.' She buried her face in the back of Marcus's neck, but Marcus shook her off and moved away from her and towards Will. Katrina, who had spent much of Fiona's speech trying not to laugh, went over to comfort her.

'Shut up, Mum. You're mad. Bloody hell, I can't believe how crap my parents are,' said Marcus with real feeling.

Will looked at this strange little group, his gang for the day, and tried to make some sense of it. All these ripples and connections! He couldn't get his head round them. He was not a man given to mystical moments, even under the influence of narcotics, but he was very worried that he was having one now, for some reason: maybe it was something to do with Marcus walking away from his mother and over to him? Whatever the explanation, it was making him feel very peculiar. Some of these people he hadn't known until today; some of them he had only known for a little while, and even then he couldn't say that he knew them well. But here they were anyway, one of them clutching a cardboard cut-out Kurt Cobain, one of them in a plaster cast, one of them crying, all of them bound to each other in ways that it would be almost impossible to explain to anyone who had just wandered in. Will couldn't recall ever having been caught up in this sort of messy, sprawling, chaotic web before; it was almost as if he had been given a glimpse of what it was like to be human. It wasn't too bad, really; he wouldn't even mind being human on a full-time basis.

They all went to the nearest burger bar for supper. Ruth and Ellie sat apart and ate chips and smoked and whispered; Marcus and his relatives carried on the sniping they had embarked on with such enthusiasm in the police station. Clive wanted Marcus to complete his journey to Cambridge, but Fiona felt he should return to London, while Marcus seemed too confused by his afternoon to feel anything very much.

'Why was Ellie with you in the first place?' Will asked him.

'I can't remember now,' said Marcus. 'She just wanted to come.'

'Was she going to stay with us?' asked Clive.

'Dunno. S'pose so.'

'Thanks for asking us first.'

'Ellie's not right for me,' said Marcus firmly.

'You've worked that out, have you?' said Will.

'I'm not sure who she is right for,' said Katrina.

'I think we'll always be friends,' Marcus continued. 'But I don't know. I think I ought to look for someone less—'

'Less rude and mad? Less violent? Less bloody stupid? There are any number of lesses I can think of.' This contribution was from Ellie's mother.

'Less different from me,' said Marcus diplomatically.

'Well, good luck,' said Katrina. 'There are a lot of us who've spent half our lives looking for someone less different from us, and we haven't found them so far.'

'Is it that hard?' asked Marcus.

'It's the hardest thing in the world,' said Fiona, with more feeling than Will wanted to contemplate.

'Why do you think we're all single?' said Katrina.

Was that really it? Will wondered. Was that what they were all doing, looking for someone less different? Was that what he was doing? Rachel was dynamic and thoughtful and focused and caring and different in more ways than he could count, but the whole point of Rachel, as far as Will was concerned, was that she wasn't him. There was a flaw in Katrina's logic, then. This thing about looking for someone less different . . . It only really worked, he realized, if you were convinced that being you wasn't so bad in the first place.

THIRTY-FIVE

Marcus did end up going to stay with his dad and Lindsey. He felt sorry for them, in a funny sort of way: at the police station they had seemed really out of it, as if they weren't able to cope. Marcus hadn't thought about it before, but that evening you could really tell who lived in London and who didn't, and the ones who didn't just seemed more scared of everything. Clive and Lindsey had been scared of Ellie, for a start, but they'd been scared of Ellie's mum, and the police, and they'd moaned a lot, and looked nervous . . . Maybe it wasn't anything to do with London; maybe it was more to do with the kind of people he knew now, or maybe he'd just got a lot older in the last couple of months. But he couldn't really see what his dad could offer him any more, which was why he felt sorry for him, which was why he agreed to go back to Cambridge with him.

Clive carried on moaning in the car. Why did Marcus want to get involved with someone like that? Why hadn't he tried to stop her? Why had he been rude to Lindsey? What had she ever done to him? Marcus didn't answer. He just let his father go on and on until eventually he seemed to run out of moans like you run out of petrol: they started to slow up and get quieter, and then they just disappeared altogether. The thing was, he couldn't be that kind of dad any more. He'd missed his moment. It was like if God suddenly decided to be God again a zillion years after creating the world: He couldn't suddenly come down from heaven and say, oh, you shouldn't have put the Empire State Building there, and you shouldn't have organized it so that African people get less money, and you shouldn't have let them build nuclear weapons. Because you could say to Him, well, it's a bit late now, isn't it? Where were You when we were thinking about these things?

It wasn't as though he thought his dad should have been around, but he couldn't have it both ways. If he wanted to be up in Cambridge with Lindsey, smoking pot and falling off window-ledges, fine, but he couldn't then start picking up on the little things – and Ellie was a little thing now really, even though when they'd been sitting on the kerb waiting for the police car to come, she'd seemed like the biggest thing ever. He'd have to find another job for himself. Will could do the little things, and his mum, but his dad was out of it.

They arrived back at his dad's place around ten-thirty, which meant it had taken him six hours to get to Cambridge – not bad, really, seeing as he'd been arrested halfway there. (Arrested! He'd been arrested! Taken to a police station in a police car, at least. He'd already stopped thinking of the broken window as something that had come out of playing truant, and that would lead on to being a tramp and a drug addict. Now he was free he could see he had overreacted. Instead, he took the Royston incident as a measure of how far he'd come in the last few months. He'd never have been able to get arrested when he'd first arrived in London. He wouldn't have known the right sort of people.)

Lindsey made them a cup of tea and they sat around the kitchen table for a while. Then Clive sort of nodded at Lindsey, and she said she was tired and she was going to bed, leaving the two of them alone.

'Do you mind if I roll a joint?' his dad asked him.

'No,' said Marcus. 'You do what you want. I'm not smoking any, though.'

'Too right you're not. Would you mind getting my tin down for me? It hurts me to stretch.'

Marcus moved his chair over towards the shelves, climbed up on it and started fumbling around behind the cereal packets on the top shelf. It was funny how you could still know tiny little things about people, like where they kept their tin, even though you didn't know what they were thinking from one week to the next.

He got down, handed the tin over and moved his chair back to the table. His dad started to roll himself a joint, mumbling into his cigarette papers as he did so.

'I've had a big think since, you know. Since my accident.'

'Since you fell off the window-ledge?' Marcus loved saying that. It sounded so daft.

'Yeah. Since my accident.'

'Mum said you'd been having a big think.'

'And?'

'And what?'

'I dunno. What do you think?'

'What do I think of you having a think?'

'Well.' His dad looked up from his Rizlas. 'Yeah. I suppose.'

'It depends, really, doesn't it? On what you've been thinking about.'

'OK. What I was thinking about was . . . It frightened me, my accident.'

'When you fell off the window-ledge?'

'Yeah. My accident. Why do you always have to say what it was? Anyway, it frightened me.'

'You didn't fall very far. You only broke your collar bone. I know loads of people who've done that.'

'It doesn't matter how far you fall if it makes you think, does it?'

'I suppose not.'

'Did you mean what you said in the police station? About me being a useless father?'

'Oh, I dunno. Not really.'

'Because I know I haven't been great.'

'No. Not great.'

'And . . . you need a father, don't you? I can see that now. I couldn't see it before.'

'I don't know what I need.'

'Well, you know you need a father.'

'Why?'

'Because everyone does.'

Marcus thought about that. 'Everyone does, you know, to get them going. And after that, I'm not sure. Why do you think I need one now? I'm doing OK without.'

'It doesn't look like it.'

'What, because someone else broke a window? No, really, I am doing OK without. Maybe I'm doing better. I mean, it's hard with Mum, but this year at school . . . I can't explain it, but I feel safer than before, because I know more people. I was really scared because I didn't think two was enough, and now there aren't two any more. There are loads. And you're better off that way.'

'Who are these loads? Ellie and Will and people like that?'

'Yeah, people like that.'

'They won't be around for ever.'

'Some of them will, some of them won't. But, see, I didn't know before that anyone else could do that job, and they can. You can find people. It's like those acrobatic displays.'

'What acrobatic displays?'

'Those ones when you stand on top of loads of people in a pyramid. It doesn't really matter who they are, does it, as long as they're there and you don't let them go away without finding someone else.'

'You really think that? It doesn't matter who's underneath you?'

'I do now, yeah. I didn't, but now I do. Because you can't stand on top of your mum and dad if they're going to mess around and wander off and get depressed.'

His dad had finished rolling the joint. He lit it and took a big lungful of smoke. 'That's what my big think was about. I shouldn't have wandered off.'

'It doesn't matter, Dad. Really. I know where you are if things get bad.'

'Gee, thanks.'

'Sorry. But . . . I'm OK. Really. I can find people. I'll be all right.'

And he would be, he knew it. He didn't know whether Ellie would be, because she didn't think about things that hard, even though she was clever and knew about politics and so on; and he didn't know whether his mum would be, because she wasn't very strong a lot of the time. But he was sure that he would be able to cope in ways that they couldn't. He could cope at school, because he knew what to do, and he had worked out who you could trust and who you couldn't, and he had worked that out down there, in London, where people came at each other from all sorts of odd angles. You could create little patterns of people that wouldn't have been possible if his mum and dad hadn't split up and the three of them had stayed in Cambridge. It didn't work for everyone. It didn't work for mad people and people who didn't know anybody, or for people who were sick, or who drank too much. But it was going to work for him, he'd make sure of that, and because it was going to work for him he had decided that this was a much better way of doing things than the way that his dad wanted him to try.

They talked a little bit longer, about Lindsey and how she wanted a baby, and how his dad couldn't decide, and whether Marcus would mind if they did have one; and Marcus said that he'd like it, that he liked babies. He didn't really; but he knew the value of extra people around him, and Lindsey's baby would grow up to be an extra person one day. And then he went to bed. His dad gave him a hug and got a bit teary, but he was stoned by then, so Marcus didn't take any notice.

In the morning his dad and Lindsey gave him a lift to the station, and enough money for a taxi from King's Cross to the flat. He sat on the train looking out of the window. He was sure he was right about the acrobatics display; but even if it was all rubbish he was still going to carry on believing it. If it helped get him through to the time when he was completely free to make the mistakes that they were all making, then what was the harm?

THIRTY-SIX

Wanting Rachel so much still frightened Will. At any time, it seemed to him, she might decide that he was too much trouble, or worthless, or no good in bed. She might meet someone else; she might come to the conclusion that she didn't want a relationship with anybody at all. She might die, suddenly, without warning, in a car crash on the way back from dropping Ali off at school. He felt as if he were a chick whose egg had been cracked open, and he was outside in the world shivering and unsteady on his feet (if chicks were unsteady on their feet – maybe that was foals, or calves, or some other animal), without so much as a Paul Smith suit or a pair of Ray-Bans to protect him. He wasn't even sure what all this fear was *for*. What good was it doing him? None whatsoever, as far as he could see, but it was much too late to ask that now. All he knew was that there was no going back; that part of his life was over.

Most Saturdays now, Will took Ali and Marcus out somewhere. It had begun because he wanted to give their mothers a break . . . No, that wasn't true. It had begun because he wanted to wriggle his way into Rachel's life, and he wanted to make her believe that there was some kind of substance to him. And it wasn't as if it was the worst job in the world; the first couple of outings had been difficult, because for some reason he'd tried to do the education thing, and he'd taken them to the British Museum and the National Gallery, and all three of them had been bored and tetchy, but that was mostly because Will hated doing those things himself. (Was there a more boring place in the world than the British Museum? If there was, Will wouldn't want to know about it. Pots. Coins. Jugs. Whole rooms full of plates. There had to be a point of exhibiting things, Will decided. Just because they were old, it didn't mean they were necessarily interesting. Just because they'd survived didn't mean you wanted to look at them.)

But right when he was on the verge of abandoning the whole idea he had taken them to the cinema, to one of those dumb summer movies that were pitched at kids, and all three of them had had a great time. So now it was a regular thing: lunch at McDonald's or Burger King, film, shake at Burger King or McDonald's, whichever they hadn't been in at lunchtime, home. He'd taken them to Arsenal a couple of times, too, and that was OK, but Ali would still snipe at Marcus, given half a chance, and there was more than half a chance in a long afternoon in the family enclosure at Highbury, so football was kept for those rare times when they had run out of films that would not only insult their intelligence but the rest of them as well.

Marcus was older than Ali now. The first time they had met, when Marcus had been Will's son for the afternoon, Ali had appeared to be Marcus's senior by many years, but his explosion that day had blown his cover a little bit, and in any case Marcus had moved on in the intervening months. He dressed better – he had won the argument with his mother over whether he should be allowed to go shopping with Will – and he had his hair cut regularly, and he tried very hard not to sing out loud, and his friendship with Ellie and Zoe (which, much to everyone's surprise, had endured and deepened) meant that he was more teenage in his attitude: even though the girls prized and cherished his occasional eccentricities, Marcus was beginning to tire of their whoops of delight every time he said something daft, and he had – sadly, in a way, but inevitably and healthily – become more circumspect when he spoke.

It was strange; Will missed him. Since the egg had cracked Will had found himself wanting to talk to Marcus about what it was like to wander about with nothing on, feeling scared of everything and everybody, because Marcus was the only person in the world who might be able to offer him advice; but Marcus – the old Marcus, anyway – was disappearing.

'Are you going to marry my mum?' Ali asked out of the blue, during one of their pre-cinema fast-food meals. Marcus looked up from his chips with interest.

'I dunno,' Will mumbled. He had thought about it a lot, but could never quite make himself believe that he was entitled to ask her; every time he stayed over at her house he felt impossibly blessed, and he didn't want to do anything that would endanger his sense of privilege. Sometimes he hardly even dared ask her when he could see her again; asking her whether she was willing to spend the rest of her life with him seemed to be pushing it.

'I used to want him to marry my mum,' Marcus said cheerfully. Will was suddenly seized with the desire to pour his boiling-point fast-food coffee down the front of Marcus's shirt.

'Did you?' said Ali.

'Yeah. For some reason I thought it would sort everything out. Your mum's different, though. She's more together than mine.'

'Do you still want him to marry your mum?'

'Don't I get a say in this?' Will asked.

'Naah,' said Marcus, ignoring Will's interruption. 'See, I don't think that's the right way.'

'Why not?'

'Because . . . You know when they do those human pyramids? That's the sort of model for living I'm looking at now.'

'What *are* you talking about, Marcus?' Will asked him. It wasn't a rhetorical question.

'You're safer as a kid if everyone's friends. When people pair off . . . I don't know. It's more insecure. Look at it now. Your mum and my mum get on OK.' It was true. Fiona and Rachel saw each other regularly now, to Will's agonizing discomfort. 'And Will sees her, and I see you, and Ellie and Zoe, and Lindsey and my dad. I've got it sorted now. If your mum and Will get together, you think you're safe, but you're not, because they'll split up, or Will will go mad or something.'

Ali nodded sagely. Will's urge to scald had been replaced by an urge to shoot Marcus and then turn the gun on himself.

'What if Rachel and I don't split up? What if we stay together for ever?'

'Fine. Great. Prove it. I just don't think couples are the future.'

'Oh, well, thank you . . . Einstein.' Will had wanted his comeback to be sharper than that. He wanted to think of some sort of socio-cultural marriage expert whose name two twelve-year-olds would instantly recognize, but Einstein was all he could come up with. He knew it wasn't right.

'What's he got to do with it?'

'Nothing,' Will mumbled. Marcus looked at him pityingly. 'And don't patronize me.'

'What does patronize mean?' Marcus asked, in all seriousness. So there it was. Will was being patronized by someone who wasn't even old enough to understand what the word meant.

'It means, don't treat me like an idiot.'

Marcus looked at him as if to say, well, how else *can* I treat you? and Will had every sympathy. He was really struggling to maintain the age gap now: Marcus's air of authority, the been-there-done-that tone in his voice, was so convincing that Will didn't know how to argue with him. He didn't want to either. He hadn't lost all face yet; there was still a tiny patch left, about the size of a small scab, and he wanted to keep it.

'He just seems so much older,' Fiona said one afternoon, after Will had dropped him off, and he had disappeared into his bedroom with a cursory thank you and a brusque hello to his mother.

'Where did we go wrong, eh?' Will asked plaintively. 'We've given that boy everything, and this is how he repays us.'

'I feel as though I'm losing him,' said Fiona. Will still hadn't got the hang of joking with her. What left his mouth with the weight and substance of froth on a cappuccino seemed to enter her ear like suet pudding. 'It's all Smashing Pumpkins and Ellie and Zoe and . . . I think he's been smoking.'

Will laughed.

'It's not funny.'

'It is, kind of. How much would you have given for Marcus to be caught smoking with his mates a few months ago?'

'Nothing. I abhor smoking.'

'Yes, but . . .' He gave up. Fiona was determined not to see the point he was trying to make. 'Does it bother you that you're losing him?'

'Why do you ask that? Of course it bothers me.'

'It's just that you've seemed . . . I don't want to be crude about it, but you've seemed better recently.'

'I think I am. I don't know what it is, but I just feel less worn down by everything.'

'That's great.'

'I think I'm just on top of things more. I don't know why.'

Will thought he knew one of the reasons why, but he also knew that it would be neither wise nor kind to elaborate. The truth was that this version of Marcus really wasn't so hard to cope with. He had friends, he could look after himself, he had developed a skin – the kind of skin Will had just shed. He had flattened out, and become as robust and as unremarkable as every other twelve-year-old kid. But all three of them had had to lose things in order to gain other things. Will had lost his shell and his cool and his distance, and he felt scared and vulnerable, but he got to be with Rachel; and Fiona had lost a big chunk of Marcus, and she got to stay away from the casualty ward; and Marcus had lost himself, and got to walk home from school with his shoes on.

Marcus came out of his room scowling.

'I'm bored. Can I go and get a video?'

Will couldn't resist it: he had a theory he wanted to test out. 'Hey, Fiona. Why don't you get your sheet music out, and we can murder "Both Sides Now"?'

'Would you like to?'

'Yeah. Sure.' But he was watching Marcus, whose expression was that of a boy who had been asked to dance naked before a mixed audience of supermodels and cousins.

'Please, Mum. Don't.'

'Don't be silly. You love singing. You love Joni Mitchell.'

'I don't. Not any more. I bloody hate Joni Mitchell.'

Will knew then, beyond any shadow of a doubt, that Marcus would be OK.